A2
LEVEL

GEOGRAPHY
FOR CCEA AS LEVEL

2nd
EDITION

COLOURPOINT EDUCATIONAL

Rewarding Learning

Martin Thom and Eileen Armstrong

with Stephen Royle

© Martin Thom, Eileen Armstrong,
Stephen Royle and Colourpoint
Creative Limited 2017

ISBN: 978 1 78073 119 3

Second Edition
First Impression

Layout and design: April Sky Design
Printed by: GPS Colour Graphics Ltd, Belfast

**COLOURPOINT
EDUCATIONAL**

Colourpoint Educational
An imprint of Colourpoint Creative Ltd
Colourpoint House
Jubilee Business Park
21 Jubilee Road
Newtownards
County Down
Northern Ireland
BT23 4YH

Tel: 028 9182 0505
Fax: 028 9182 1900
E-mail: sales@colourpoint.co.uk
Web site: www.colourpointeducational.com

The Authors

Martin Thom is a teacher of geography, an Examiner
for an awarding body and a writer of articles and
textbooks. He would like to thank the Carcassonne crew
and his colleagues and pupils at Sullivan Upper, both
past and present, for helping him to communicate how
geography uniquely links people to both their everyday
world and the extraordinary.

Eileen Armstrong has a BA (Hons) from Queen's
University Belfast and has taught in a number of leading
Grammar schools in the greater Belfast area. She has
worked as a Senior Examiner for an awarding body for
over 20 years. She is co-author of a number of endorsed
A level Geography text books published by Colourpoint.

The author acknowledges her husband's contribution to
the research, data collection and photographic material
used in this book. She also acknowledges the help and
support of the editorial and design staff in Colourpoint,
Newtownards.

Stephen Royle studied geography at St John's College,
Cambridge and took a PhD at the University of
Leicester. He taught geography for 40 years at Queen's
University Belfast before retiring as Professor of Island
Geography. He has written 17 books and over 200 other
publications. He first worked for an awarding body in
1977 and has been Chief Examiner for over 25 years. He
is a Member of the Royal Irish Academy.

Rewarding Learning

Endorsed by CCEA on 1 October 2017. If in any doubt about the
continuing currency of CCEA endorsement, please contact Margaret
McMullan (Principal Officer) by telephone 028 9026 1200 or email
mmcmullan@ccea.org.uk

Whilst the publisher has taken all reasonable care in the preparation
of this book CCEA makes no representation, express or implied, with
regard to the accuracy of the information contained in this book.
CCEA does not accept any legal responsibility or liability for any
errors or omissions from the book or the consequences thereof.

Contents

A2 1: PHYSICAL PROCESSES, LANDFORMS AND MANAGEMENT

Option A: Plate Tectonics – Theory and Outcomes

Option B: Tropical Ecosystems – Nature and Sustainability

Option C: Dynamic Coastal Environments

Option D: Climate Change – Past and Present

Contents

A2 2: PROCESSES AND ISSUES IN HUMAN GEOGRAPHY

Option A: Cultural Geography

Option B: Planning For Sustainable Settlements

Option C: Ethnic Diversity

Option D: Tourism

Glossary

Unit A2 1:
Physical Processes, Landforms and Management

Plate Tectonics – Theory and Outcomes

1. PLATE TECTONICS: MARGINS AND LANDFORMS

Case studies

General reference to places for illustration purposes

Students should be able to:

(i) demonstrate knowledge and understanding of the evidence for and the theory of plate tectonics

(ii) demonstrate knowledge and understanding of plate and sub-plate processes at constructive, conservative, destructive and collision plate margins

(iii) demonstrate knowledge and understanding of resultant landforms – ocean ridges, rift valleys, deep sea trenches, island arcs and fold mountains

Figure A1: Model of the Earth's internal structure

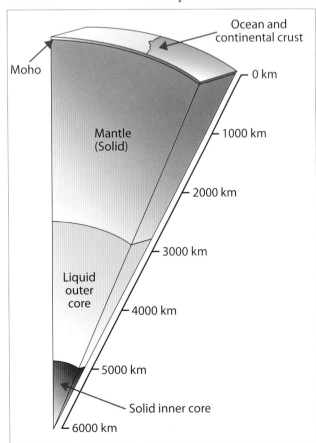

Modern research and current theory suggests that the Earth has layers. Despite the fact that the deepest hole drilled into the Earth so far is only 13 km, a mere scratch of 0.2% of the planet's radius, scientists have built a picture of the Earth's internal structure. In essence a basic three layer model of the planet has emerged – a central core, surrounded by a mantle, with a thin outer crust comprising of the rocks of the continents and ocean floors.

The evidence for this structure comes mainly from the interpretation of how energy released by earthquakes and nuclear weapons testing travels through the Earth. These events release energy as waves that can help identify changes in the Earth's composition, deep beneath the surface. The speed at which compression and shear waves travel will vary with the density of material, and shear waves will not pass through liquids at all. As early as 1909, a Yugoslavian pioneer seismologist used such techniques to identify a line of change, or discontinuity, where the rocks of the crust meet those of the mantle. This line, named after its discoverer – the Mohorovivic discontinuity – is thankfully usually known as the Moho.

The technique of using variation in earthquake wave velocity to construct 3D images of the Earth's interior is known as seismic tomography. This reveals structural, thermal and chemical variations found deep beneath the surface. Geoscientists use these

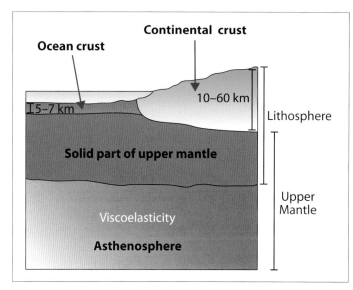

Figure A2: Model of the first 100 km below the surface

images to study the core, mantle and plate tectonic processes, helping to produce a model view of the Earth's internal structure (Figure A1).

The Earth's core has a diameter of around 7000 km, making it larger than the planet Mars. It has two distinct sections: an inner solid core surrounded by an outer liquid core. The inner core is largely made of iron and, along with the outer core, it creates the planet's magnetic field. The composition of the core is known from calculation of densities, melting points and clues provided by meteorites that have fallen to Earth from space.

Surrounding the core is the mantle, a 2900 km thick layer that contains 80% of the Earth's volume. The mantle is solid rock but near its outer edge, beneath the crust, it can flow or deform (viscoelasticity). This layer of the upper mantle is termed the asthenosphere and its existence is crucial to the theory of plate tectonics. Above this layer, part of the upper mantle and the thin crust form a final shell of solid rock termed the lithosphere (Figure A2). Molten rock or magma reaches the Earth's surface at volcanoes, where it is known as lava once it is erupted. This material originates no more than 1000 km below the surface and so it reveals more about the nature of the upper mantle than any of the Earth's deeper layers.

The crust itself is the thinnest element of the model, averaging only 20 km in thickness, and ranging from 60 km in the continents to a mere 5 km beneath the oceans. Other differences between continental and oceanic crust concern their relative density and composition. Oceanic crust is composed of denser basaltic rocks, while continental crustal rocks are lighter and more granitic in nature. If the Earth were scaled down to the size of an ordinary balloon, the relative thickness of the balloon's skin would over-represent that of the crust (Figure A3).

Figure A3: Two contrasting types of crustal rocks

	Oceanic Crust	Continental Crust
Thickness	Thin 5–7 km	Thick 10–60 km
Rock density	Denser 3–3.3 (gm/m³)	Less dense 2.7 (gm/m³)
Rock type	Basaltic SIMA (Silica and magnesium)	Granitic SIAL (Silica and alumina)
Rock age	Less than 250 million years	From 1000 to 3,5000 million years

Plate tectonics and resulting landforms

Plate tectonics

For centuries observers and scientists have been fascinated by the night sky. They often describe the beauty of 'the Great Dance' of the planets, stars and galaxies. Study of the Earth over the past 100 years has revealed another Great Dance, much more earth bound, beneath our feet. The theory of plate tectonics suggests that our current world map is but a point along a continuum of change. It appears while the rocks of the continents are often ancient, even billions of years old, the floor of the deep oceans that form most of the Earth's outer skin are in fact relatively young.

The huge jigsaw pieces that carry these oceans and continents jostle and move in three common patterns, in opposing directions: towards, away or past each other.

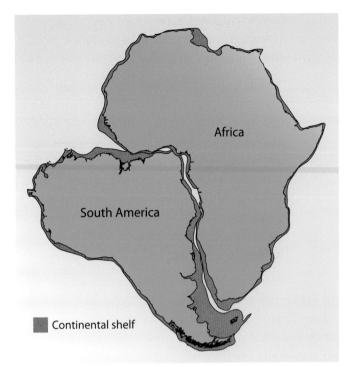

Figure A4: Parallel coastlines

The idea of continent drift

It was during the great era of European discovery – when the Spanish, Portuguese, Dutch and British fleets ruled the waves – that the gaps in our knowledge of the world map were gradually filled in. In 1620, Francis Bacon, the eminent British scientist, noted that the coastlines of western Africa and eastern South America run parallel to each other. Their coastlines, and in particular, the edge of their off-shore continental shelves, would form a neat junction if the South Atlantic Ocean basin did not exist (Figure A4).

Not until just over 100 years ago did any scientist take such an idea any further. In 1915, Alfred Wegener proposed that the world's continents had formerly been a single land mass. He called this Pangaea ('all lands'), which he said had gradually broken up over the past 200 million years to form today's familiar outline. Wegener spent 25 years and all his energy in the search for evidence of continent drift and a process capable of explaining it. In the first part he largely succeeded but never convinced the scientific world before his death, aged 50, on yet another research trip to Greenland in 1930.

The evidence he gathered included the parallel nature of some continental coastlines, along with other rock, fossil and past climate evidence.

Figure A5: Original Caledonian mountain chain (left) and the mountain chain separated by a new ocean (right)

- The distribution pattern of both rock types and the mountain chains they often form made more sense when the separate landmasses of the continents were placed together. Past periods of mountain building, including the ancient Caledonian epoch, created long fold mountain chains across the world, many of which now exist as weathered fragments on the opposite shores of the world's ocean basins (Figure A5).

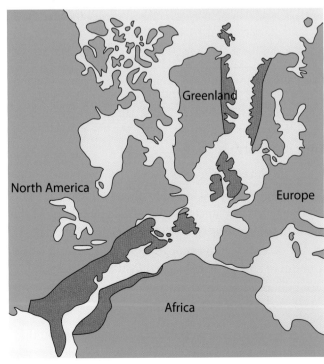

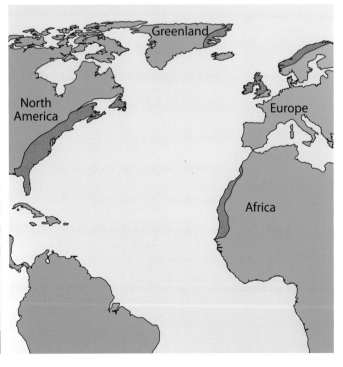

- Within these rocks, fossil evidence included the remains of ancient Mesosaur reptiles and gigantic Glossopteris ferns. These were found in similar aged rocks in South America, Africa, India and Antarctica, places now separated by thousands of miles of ocean water in which these animals and plants could not survive (Figure A6).

Figure A6: Fossil evidence of continental drift

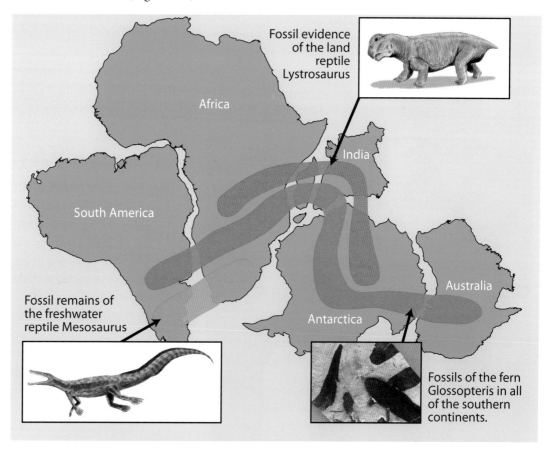

- It was also clear from the landforms on their surface that these continents, including tropical hot desert regions, had in the distant past been covered and carved by huge ice sheets, similar to those found in Greenland today. Again, the location and direction of flow of such sheets seemed to make sense only when these continents were placed together, as a huge southern landmass Wegener named Gondwanaland (Figure A7).

Despite building this array of evidence, one British geologist, when talking of Wegener's theory of continental drift, stated that anyone that, "valued his reputation for scientific sanity" would never dare support such a theory.

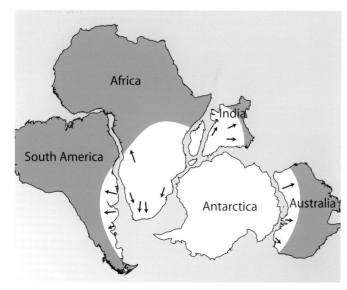

Figure A7: Fossil glaciation and Gondwanaland

Alfred Wegener did not live to see the final proofs of his theory and the discovery of the possible mechanism for continent drift. These emerged after 1945 and continue to be refined today. This is the theory of plate tectonics.

Plate tectonic theory

Figure A8: The exploration of the ocean floor

This modern theory describes a mechanism that explains the moving continents. The evidence for it is almost entirely derived from study of the ocean floor that has only been technically possible for the last 60 years (Figure A8).

The first piece of evidence that the rocks of the ocean floors differ from those of the continents was that waves from earthquakes moved more quickly through ocean floor material. Later the development of sonar, initially to detect enemy submarines in war, allowed the depth of the ocean to be plotted. In the 1950s, using magnetometers, ships crossed the oceans, uncovering patterns of change in the direction of magnetism from the rocks deep below. Finally, robotic and later manned submarines collected samples of ocean bed rock. All these sources of data meant a radical new comprehension of the ocean floor developed.

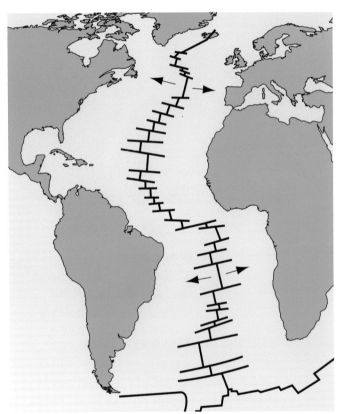

The evidence for the theory of plate tectonics

1. The topography of the oceans

The first accurate maps of the ocean basins were created using sonar techniques developed during World War II. These showed that rather than being deepest far from land, the ocean floor had huge, linear mountain ranges, with deep central valleys running down the centre. These submarine mountain chains stretched in a continuous line for 50,000 km around the Earth, making them the largest single feature on its surface. These are known as the mid-ocean ridges and the North and South Atlantic Ocean basins provide perfect examples (Figure A9).

The island of Iceland is in fact the summit of a mid-ocean ridge which unusually has extended above sea-level. Here we can find the evidence for processes that have created the underwater mountain chains and rift valleys (Figure A10).

Figure A9: The mid-Atlantic ridge

Figure A10: Surface rifts at a constructive plate margin in Iceland. The arrows show tensional forces between the North American and Eurasian plates.

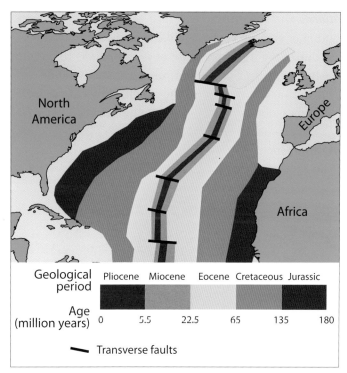

Figure A11: The mid-Atlantic ridge and rock age

2. The age and pattern of ocean basin geology

One early and puzzling discovery was that the amount of material lying on the ocean floor was much less than expected. If the ocean floors were, like the continents, billions of years old, then they should be buried under thick layers of deposited sediment. But in fact there was little or no sediment found. Later scientists developed a method of dating ancient rocks using a technique involving the radio-active decay of potassium-argon. When samples of ocean rocks were dated, their age was numbered in millions or tens of millions of years and not billions. In fact the world's ocean floors, which form 70% of the surface, are young, recently formed within the last 260 million years. This fact alone sent shockwaves through the scientific community but a related finding was even more astonishing. The mountains of the mid-ocean ridges were made of the very youngest rocks and the age of rocks on the ocean floor increased away from the mid-ocean ridges in a mirror-like pattern (Figure A11). Iceland provides a rare insight into the rock age pattern commonly found on the ocean floor around constructive margins (Figure A19, page 16).

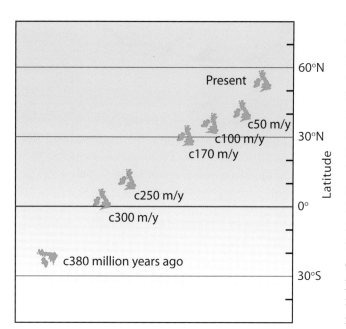

Figure A12: The changing location of the British Isles

3. Paleomagnetism and magnetic striping

Scientists studying ancient or palaeomagnetism knew that when molten rock solidifies, iron particles in the rock would line up with the Earth's magnetic field. They had also seen that over periods of about 250,000 years the Earth's magnetic field reverses or flips, so that conventional compasses would then point south rather than north. The reasons for these reversals are not fully understood but they have allowed researchers to identify where crustal rocks were originally formed compared to where they lie at present (Figure A12). Using magnetometers in ships crossing the Atlantic they revealed a banded and symmetrical pattern in the ocean floor rocks across the mid-ocean ridge (Figure A19, page 16).

4. The distribution of earthquakes and volcanoes

Mapping of the global distribution of active volcanoes and earthquake activity has continuously improved, largely due to the widespread use of seismometers to monitor and record nuclear weapons testing between rival superpowers. Distinctive and repeated patterns have emerged: both volcanic and seismic activity tends to occur in long, narrow, linear bands, sometimes along coastlines or through oceans (Figure A13).

Figure A13: World earthquake distribution
Earthquakes magnitude 3.5 and greater for the period 1963–1998
Source: NASA

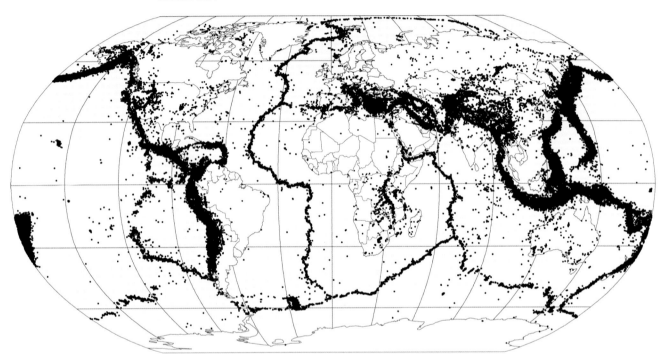

Perhaps the most noted distribution is the so called 'ring of fire', a line of volcanoes that marked the circumference of the Pacific basin, including the volcanoes of Washington State, USA and the island volcanoes of Japan and New Zealand. Identifying these active zones also highlights huge regions of the surface that have little or no such activity today.

Plate tectonic theory – Harry Hess, sea floor spreading and subduction

In the 1960s, Harry Hess and others suggested that mid-ocean ridges are weak zones in the crust where the ocean floor is being pulled apart along the ridge crest. New magma from deep in the mantle rises easily through these weaker zones and eventually erupts along the crest of the ridges, creating new oceanic crust. This process, later named sea floor spreading, has operated over many millions of years creating the basaltic rocks of the ocean basin floor. This sea floor spreading hypothesis made good sense of the newly uncovered evidence:

- The existence of the great submarine mountain chains and rift valleys at the ocean centres.
- At the mid-ocean ridges the rocks are very young and become progressively older away from the ridge.
- Bands of rock parallel to the ridge have alternating magnetic polarity, reflecting the repeated reversal of the Earth's magnetic field.

- The patterns of submarine volcanoes along the ridges revealed active processes at work. In 1963 one such volcano rose above the surface of the Atlantic near Iceland to form the new island of Surtsey.

Harry Hess further reasoned that if the Earth's crust was growing at oceanic ridges but the Earth was not expanding, then somewhere the crust must be shrinking. As new ocean crust forms and spreads away from mid-ocean ridges like a conveyor belt, millions of years later it is destroyed at deep ocean trenches. These features were another finding of sea floor mapping along the edge of the Pacific – long narrow deep trenches on the sea floor with associated volcano and earthquake activity (Figure A14). In effect, the rocks of the ocean floors are continuously recycled, with new lithosphere plate material created at ridges and old oceanic plate melted and destroyed at destructive boundaries. The theory then neatly explains why:

- the earth does not get bigger despite sea floor spreading.
- there is so little sediment accumulation on the ocean floor.
- the rocks forming the floor of the ocean basins are much younger than continental rocks.

While debate continues about the precise nature of the forces operating within the mantle, the evidence that continents are mobile is now conclusive. Measurements using radio signals from 21 GPS satellites orbiting the Earth show that while the North Atlantic Ocean expands at an average rate of 2 cm per year, sea floor spreading in the Pacific basin averages 6 cm and even 10 cm per year near Easter Island. Wegener's theory, dismissed in 1924 by some as lunacy, had 50 years later become accepted fact.

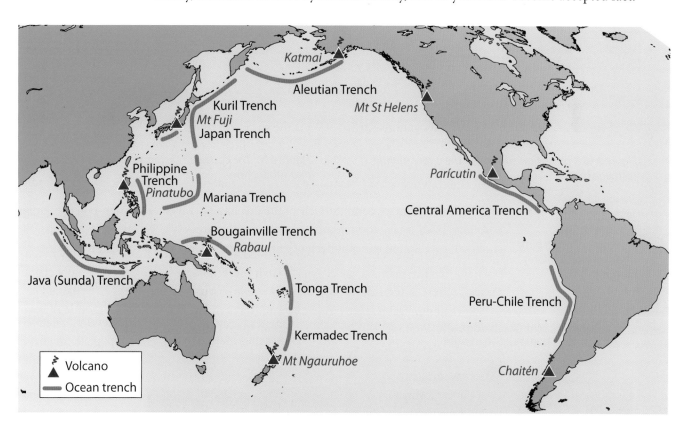

Figure A14: The Pacific 'ring of fire' volcanoes and related deep ocean trenches

When plates meet – plate margins

Today, the precise nature of the sub-plate processes that cause the plates to move is debated. The older view is that the plates forming the lithosphere are driven by slow flows of molten magma in the asthenosphere beneath them. These movements are termed convection currents (Figure A15) and represent material rising in the mantle driven by heat originating from radioactive decay processes in the core, in much the same way as warm air rises in the atmosphere. In this model these currents reach the underside of the solid lithosphere, about 80 km below the surface, where they slowly migrate sideways, dragging the plates above along by friction. At mid-ocean ridges the rising part of these convection currents break through into the crust or even through it onto the surface as volcanic activity (Figure A16).

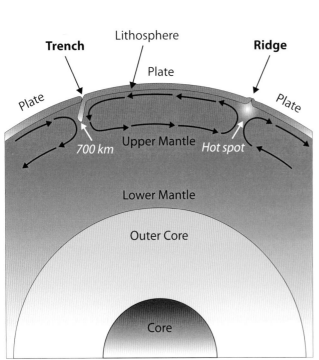

Figure A15: Convection currents in the upper mantle (asthenosphere)

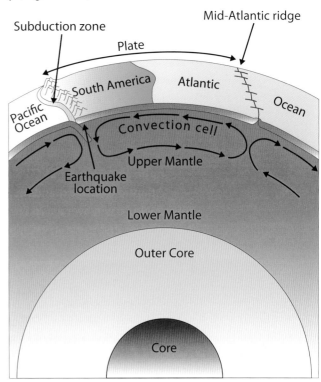

Figure A16: The conveyor system linking sea floor spreading and subduction

Figure A17: The processes of ridge-push and slab-pull at plate margins

The modern and more complex view of the mechanism involves the slab-pull (dragging) and ridge-push (gravitational sliding) processes (Figure A17). Slab-pull is based on studies of subduction zones at deep ocean trenches where oceanic plates are moving down into the mantle. The concept is that the weight of the descending relatively 'cold' plate drags itself downwards, deep into the mantle and this is what pulls the plate away from the constructive ridges. At the same time rising plumes of heat energy from the

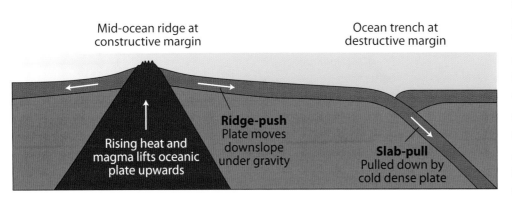

boundary of the mantle and core stretch plates upwards. At this ocean ridge new oceanic crust is formed and the plates move under gravity away from the raised ridge – this is ridge-push.

In reality, elements of all three processes (convection, ridge-push and slab-pull) may act together or be present at different plate margins. The outcome is that three distinct types of margin or boundary form where the continuously jostling plates meet:

- **Constructive margin** – Pulling or tension forces plates apart allowing new material to be formed, most commonly at the ocean ridges.
- **Conservative margin** – Plates slide past each other without either forming or destroying plate material.
- **Destructive margin** – Compression forces drive plates towards each other, causing either one to be gradually subducted and destroyed (oceanic plate) or both to crumple (a collision margin).

Figure A18: Stages in the development of a constructive plate margin

Constructive plate margins

As we have seen, the sub-marine mountain chains of the central Atlantic, Indian and Pacific oceans are the products of the process of sea floor spreading. The sequence of events that has created the world's ocean basins is as follows. Hot spots deep in the mantle cause magma to rise, forcing the solid plates above to warp upwards, stretching the crust and breaking along fault lines. This zone of weakness is marked by tensional cracks, with uplifted and slumping blocks giving mountain ridges and rift valleys, and rising magma solidifying to create new oceanic plate material (Figure A18).

As this creative process continues, the stretched plate may allow a nearby ocean to spill in and water to flood the rift valley, starting the formation of a new ocean basin. The North Atlantic is one of the most recent of these formations, as Europe and North America were firstly separated and then slowly forced apart. This process continues today with Iceland as a summit of the vast mid-Atlantic mountain ridge that runs the entire length of the ocean. Along this line, which includes the central valley of Iceland itself, fresh eruptions pour out lava, forming new plate material and crustal rocks. Shallow earthquakes are also associated with constructive margins, caused by the movement of magma rising towards the surface.

Warping, stretching of continental plate

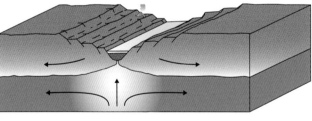

Formation of rift valley

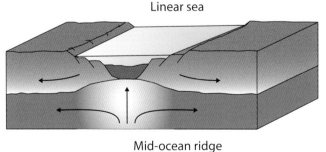

Linear sea

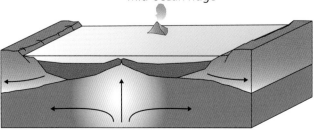

Mid-ocean ridge

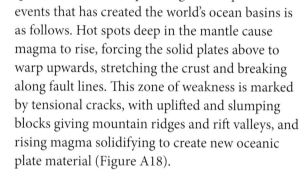

Plate movement

Convection currents

Continental crust

Oceanic crust

Asthenosphere

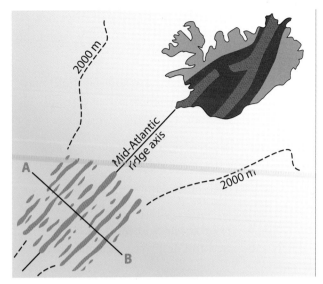

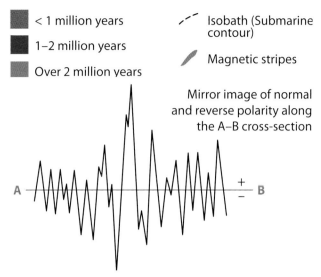

< 1 million years

1–2 million years

Over 2 million years

Isobath (Submarine contour)

Magnetic stripes

Mirror image of normal and reverse polarity along the A–B cross-section

Figure A19: Rock age and magnetic stripes across Iceland and the Mid-Atlantic ridge

Figure A20: The East African Rift Valley

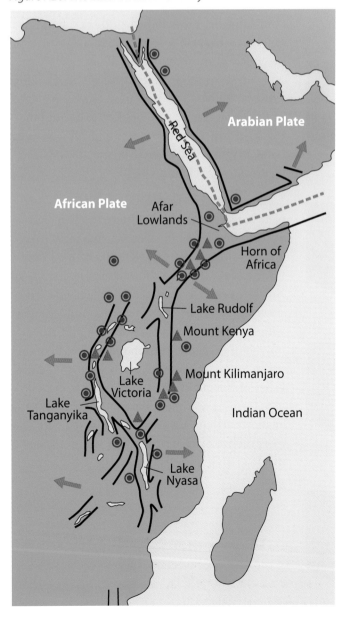

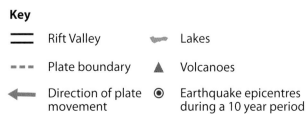

Key

— — Rift Valley

- - - Plate boundary

⟵ Direction of plate movement

⟍ Lakes

▲ Volcanoes

⊙ Earthquake epicentres during a 10 year period

As Figure A19 shows, the mirror image of rock age and magnetic polarity around the central ridge reveals the sea floor spreading process.

There is one other location on land where a constructive margin may be studied. The Great Rift Valley of East Africa is at the initial stage in the formation of a new ocean, as the land stretches under the rising convection currents of magma from the mantle below (Figure A20). Such processes have already pulled the Arabian Plate away from the African Plate to form the Red Sea. In East Africa, the continental crust has been stretched and the slumping crust formed the Rift Valley which is occupied by many elongated lakes. Meanwhile, magma rises through the widening cracks, sometimes to erupt and build volcanoes such as Mt Kenya and Kilimanjaro. This could be the site of the Earth's next major ocean and these features provide scientists with the chance to study, at first hand, the processes that started the birth of the Atlantic Ocean 200 million years ago. Geologists suggest that if the spreading continues for another 10 million years, the plates will separate completely, allowing the Indian Ocean to flood the Rift Valley through the Afar Lowlands, linking the lakes into a linear sea and leaving the region known as the Horn of Africa as a large island.

Destructive plate margins

This type of margin, where two plates are forced towards each other in convergence, produces two possible variations:

A – the meeting of an ocean plate with a continental plate

B – the meeting of two ocean plates

Figure A21: The destructive margin of Western South America

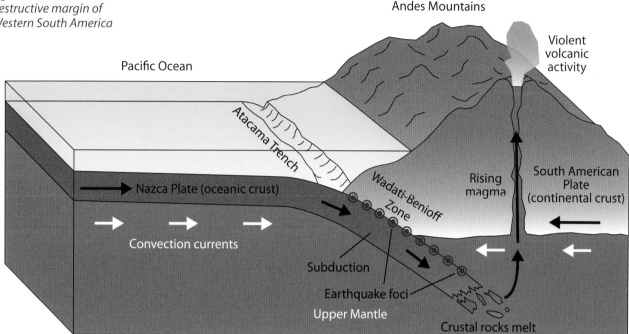

A – Ocean and continental

The best known example of this lies in the Eastern Pacific Ocean Basin, where the relatively small Nazca Plate, formed at the constructive margin of the East Pacific Rise, moves westward to meet the South American Plate (Figures A16 and A21).

The South American Plate not only carries the continent of South America but also the floor of the western section of the South Atlantic Ocean. The eastern edge of the plate is at the Mid-Atlantic Ridge, a constructive margin, but the western edge of the plate marks a destructive boundary. Distinctive landforms and patterns of tectonic activity mark where these two plates meet. On the ocean floor, close to and parallel with the western coast of South America, lies a long, narrow, deep ocean feature – the Atacama Trench. This marks the point at which the denser Nazca Plate, pushing eastwards, meets the South American Plate and is dragged downwards into the asthenosphere beneath. This process is termed subduction. At the trench the leading edge of the continental plate is pulled down towards the sea floor. As the ocean plate subducts, ocean bed sediments are carried down or scraped up against the continent's edge helping form the adjacent Andes mountain range. Beneath the surface, as the huge plates slowly grind past each other, earthquakes are frequent. Seismologists can plot each earthquake's focus with precision and in these regions a clear pattern of shallow to deeper foci is recorded. This gives a clear picture of where the contact plane between the two plates is located as the ocean plate subducts down into the mantle. The region of these seismic events is known as the Wadati-Benioff Zone, after two scientists who identified its significance (Figures A21 and A23). Around 200–300 km down in the mantle, the water-laden ocean floor sediment and some rocks of the plate itself start to melt, releasing magma. This new molten material starts to move upwards towards the

Figure A22: Fold mountain ridges in the Andes, Peru

underside of the continental South American Plate. This magma may force its way through lines of weakness into the plate or indeed right through it to erupt, forming volcanoes on the surface. The western coastline of South America is dominated by the high Andes Mountains, composed partly of folded sedimentary rocks pushed upwards by the collision of the two plates. They also contain dozens of active volcanoes, including many of the highest in the world such as Chaitén (Chile) and Nevado del Ruiz (Colombia).

Ocean trenches

If the world's ocean basins were drained, the topography revealed would more than rival the variation seen on land. Along with 9 km high mountains rising from the ocean floor, as at Big Island Hawaii, and the 50,000 km long mountain chains of the mid-ocean ridges, there are also narrow chasms plunging down 10 km – the deep ocean trenches. The deepest of all lies in the Mariana Trench, south of Japan and is nearly 11 km deep. Known as the Challenger Deep, the deepest point was named after the British research vessel that first mapped it in 1951. While 12 people have walked on the surface of the moon, only three have seen the deepest ocean floor.

Ocean trenches are clear evidence of the subduction of an ocean plate at a destructive margin. They are commonly associated with earthquake patterns, increasing in depth with lateral distance from the trench and with parallel lines of volcanic activity often hundreds of kilometres away.

B – Ocean to ocean plates

Where convection forces in the mantle cause oceanic plates to collide, a line or arc of volcanoes (submarine or as islands) is often found parallel to a deep ocean trench (Figure A23). These features, along with a Wadati-Benioff pattern of earthquakes, indicate subduction. Similar to the previous destructive margin, the denser of the two oceanic plates is dragged down into the upper mantle, creating friction earthquakes

Figure A23: The pattern of earthquake foci at Wadati-Benioff zone

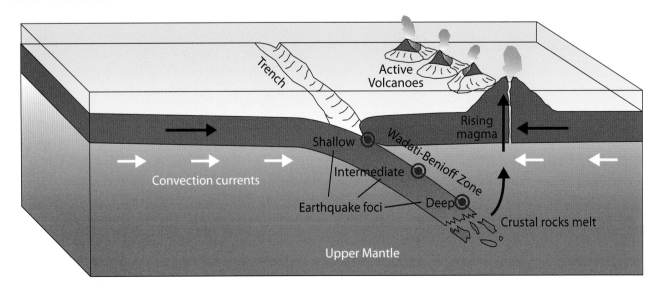

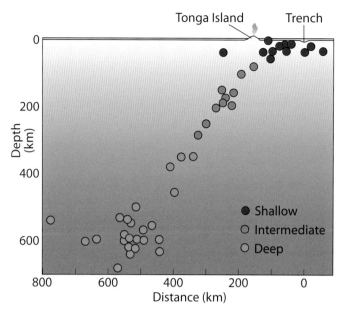

Figure A24: Tonga island arc and related earthquakes marking the subduction zone

and eventually melting at depths of up to 600 km. Such margins are common in the western region of the Pacific basin. These include the islands of New Zealand in the south, through those of Tonga, Mariana, Indonesia, the Philippines and Japan, to the Aleutians in the north. Long curving ocean trenches are paralleled by similarly shaped arcs of volcanic islands, known as island arcs. Figure A24 illustrates the Tongan island arc and the associated Tonga Trench. This cross-section shows the location of earthquake foci beneath the region. Shallow earthquakes occur near the Tonga Trench itself and with increasing distance away the earthquake foci are deeper. The line formed is interpreted as the contact zone of the two plates along the subduction area, the Wadati-Benioff zone. The islands themselves are the result of ocean crust material melting around 100 km down and erupting onto the ocean floor, eventually building to reach the ocean surface. As the diagram shows, the plate itself continues to plunge deep into the mantle to depths of over 600 km – slab-pull in action. Over a longer time period, the growth and reworking of rock material can produce more substantial landmasses and islands, such as those of Japan and the Philippines. These are then termed mature island arc systems.

Collision plate margins

Similar to destructive boundaries, collision margins form where plates are moved towards each other by processes in the asthenosphere. However, in this case both plates carry continents.

Where two continental plates meet there is no subduction of plate material, rather the edges of the plates and any sediments deposited between them are crushed upwards into a mountain belt of folded and faulted mountains (Figure A25). The Himalayas are one example, resulting from the collision of the Indian Sub-continent Plate into the huge Eurasian Plate. In reality, as the plate carrying the Indian sub-continent sped across what is now the Indian Ocean, towards Eurasia, its leading edge was oceanic and subduction occurred. As the two continents drew near, the ocean drained as the sediments on its floor were forced upwards. These sediments continue to rise today as the series of huge ridges that form the mountain kingdom of Nepal and the vast high plateau of Tibet. The summit of Mt Everest (Sagarmatha), at 8850 m, is made of limestone, a rock formed under shallow tropical seas. Another example of a collision boundary, where mountain building, earthquake and volcanic activity continue, is located along the Mediterranean Sea of Southern Europe.

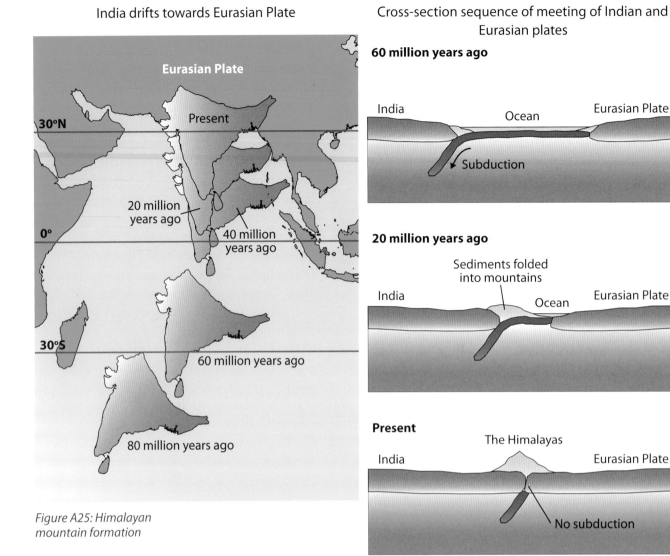

Figure A25: Himalayan mountain formation

Africa meets Europe

The Alps are merely one part of a long and complex fold mountain chain that runs across the region. It includes numerous mountain ranges such as the Atlas (north-west Africa); the Pyrenees, Apennines, Carpathian (in Europe); and the Taurus and Zagros Mountains (in Asia) (Figure A26).

A cross-section of the Alps reveals that tremendous tectonic forces have squeezed, contorted and broken the rocks into a series of huge waves (folds) and fractures (faults). Older rocks are often overturned on top of younger ones, a reversal of the normal pattern. Only the clash of tectonic plates has the power to so comprehensively rewrite the geological landscape. The suggested sequence of events in this region is:

- As the two continents approached each other there was subduction of the oceanic plate, releasing volcanic material into the region.
- The continents crushed the sedimentary rocks of the sea bed upwards, forming mountains belts. At this stage subduction no longer took place.

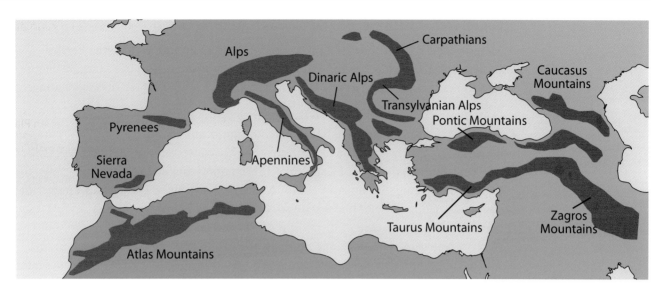

Figure A26: Fold mountains in Southern Europe, North Africa and Near East

- Finally, today there are volcanoes and shallow earthquakes in the Mediterranean Sea region but no deep ocean trench or deep earthquakes that would suggest an active subduction zone.

Regular activity of volcanoes, such as Mt Vesuvius (Naples) and Mt Etna (Sicily), and the on-going threat of earthquakes, such as the three events during 2016 in central Italy, in which over 300 people died, provide evidence for the continuation of plate movement at this margin.

The term used for such a margin is a collision zone, an appropriate name given the degree of change to the sediments, the rocks and landscape of the continental masses.

Fold mountains

During mountain building phases, compression forces horizontal beds of sedimentary and volcanic rock to bend into a series of wavelike forms or folds. Rock folds may be microscopically small or they may involve thousands of metres of rock. Folds may be simple symmetrical waves or, as in the Alps, they may be overturned or recumbent. From the distant geological past there is evidence of several global mountain building periods (orogeny). One, named after the ancient mountains of Scotland, is the Caledonian. It is believed that Ben Nevis, at 1344 m the highest mountain on these islands, is the remnant stump of its 9000 m original height. In the current geological era, across the globe the formation of fold mountains continues. This is the Alpine-Himalayan orogeny and it includes the development of the Rockies and Andes chains, as well as those of Europe and Asia. The formation of fold mountains is closely related to the location of converging destructive and collision plate margins.

Figure A27: Cross-section through the Alps showing the extreme folding and faulting of rock strata as the result of the collision margin between the African and Eurasian plates

Rock ages: Youngest ▢▢▨▨■ Oldest

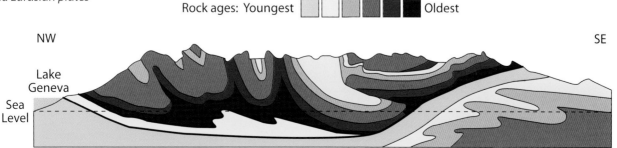

Conservative plate margins (known as transform faults)

Margins where plates slide past each other are extremely common on the Earth's surface. Most are under the sea and run at angles across constructive margins. Figure A28 shows that this is necessary to allow an even spread during sea floor spreading.

Conservative margins are so called because they do not involve the creation or destruction of plate material and therefore no significant volcanic activity. They are, however, frequently the cause of earthquakes. One conservative margin that appears on land runs through the state of California. This margin is marked by a series of faults, the most famous being the San Andreas (St Andrews) fault. Since 1906, when a powerful earthquake along the fault line destroyed the city of San Francisco, the San Andreas has been the focus of intensive study into the causes and possible prediction of earthquakes. At conservative margins plates are normally moving in opposite directions but in this case the plates are both moving in the same north-west direction but at different speeds. The two plates involved are the North America Plate and the Pacific Plate. The first is moving at an average rate of 6 cm per year, the second at 2 cm per year, giving a relative difference of 4 cm per year (Figure A29). In the short-term, the people of California, especially around San Francisco, fear the 'Big One', a quake of the scale experienced in 1906 (8.3 on the Richter scale). It is estimated that this would cause in the region of 10,000 deaths and over 50,000 injuries. In the longer term, if the plates continue on their present course, Los Angeles will move past San Francisco and south California will become an island off the west coast, in around 8 million years!

Figure A28:
Transform fault

Problem of uneven spreading at ridge

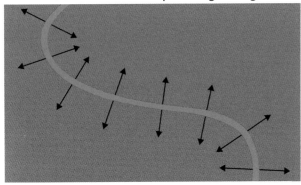

Transform faults allow even spreading

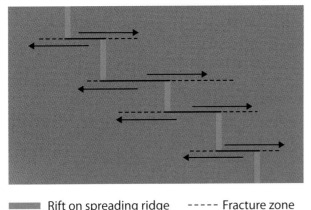

▬▬ Rift on spreading ridge   ----- Fracture zone

──▶ Direction of spreading   ─── Transform fault

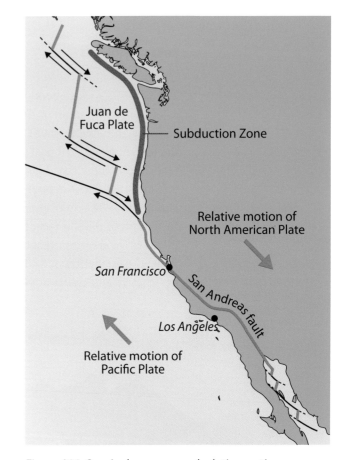

Figure A29: San Andreas map and relative motion

The distribution of tectonic activity

The mapping of the worldwide distribution of earthquakes and volcanoes played a key role in the development of plate tectonic theory. By identifying the linear zones of these activities, the boundaries of the lithosphere's plates were marked out. The presence of both earthquakes and volcanic activity at both destructive and constructive zones, though different in nature, helped shape the concepts. At conservative margins, the tension that caused earthquakes but not volcanic action confirmed their nature. Plate margins and related fault lines account for the vast majority of tectonic activity but there are some processes found well away from these boundaries. Among these are the highly active and huge volcanoes of the Hawaiian Islands. Located in the centre of the Pacific Ocean these islands are about as far from an active plate boundary as it is possible to be – so why all the activity?

Hot spots

Sub-lithosphere thermal anomalies or hot spots are seen as a driving force behind plate tectonic movement and the creation of lines of construction and destruction at plate margins, but isolated hot spots beneath unbroken plates may also cause local volcanic and earthquake activity. A common picture used is the idea of a piece of paper being moved across the tip of a Bunsen burner flame. The paper would show a scorched or burn line. The paper represents an oceanic plate being pushed across a fixed plume of heat and magma, rising from a hot spot originating deep in the mantle near the edge of the outer core. Some magma rises through the plate to form a submarine volcano that might just grow to reach the surface as a volcanic island. The outcome is a conveyor-belt sequence of volcanoes that pass from active (over the hot spot) to dormant and eventually extinct as they move away (Figure A30).

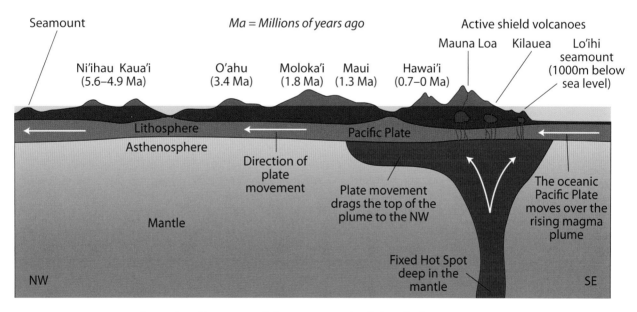

Figure A30: Formation of the Hawaiian Island chain by hot spot activity

The Hawaiian Islands/Emperor Seamounts

In the central Pacific, a chain of 50 volcanic islands, coral atolls and submarine mountains (seamounts) stretches over 6,000 km from Hawaii to the Aleutian Trench (Figure A31). Starting with the Hawaiian Island Chain itself, this merges with a series of atolls (coral reefs on the remains of islands), including Midway and then a string of mountains on the ocean floor – the Emperor Seamounts. It is believed that all these features are the result of magma rising to the ocean floor above a fixed hot spot beneath the Pacific Plate. Figure A32 is a graph showing the strong, direct relationship between the ages of the rocks in these features against distance from Hawaii.

As the volcanic islands are moved away from the rising magma plume they become extinct. Weathering and erosion gradually reduces their size until they are worn down to below sea level, firstly forming platforms for coral reefs to grow on and finally becoming mere stumps of their former size on the sea floor. The only active volcanoes today are found on the main and most southerly island of Hawaii. Although offshore, there is already evidence of volcanic activity starting to build a new Hawaiian island (Lo'ihi).

It appears that the Pacific Plate has moved at an average rate of 8.2 cm per year for the past 70 million years. About 43 million years ago, the direction of plate movement changed from northerly to north-westerly, as shown by the dog-leg in the line near the Yuryaku seamount. If you trace the map in Figure A31, then place the Meiji Seamount over the hot spot at Hawaii, you can re-create the pattern of movement of the Pacific Plate over the past 70 million years.

Figure A31: Map of the Hawaii–Emperor chain

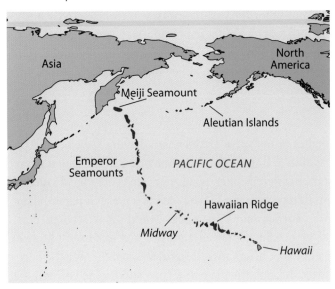

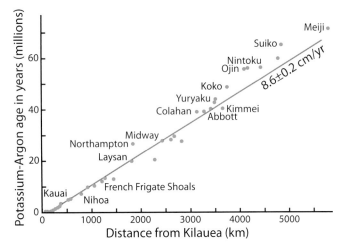

Figure A32: Graph of age of Hawaii–Emperor islands and sea-mounts against distance from active volcano (Kilauea)

Source: Data from USGS Paper 1350, Volcanism in Hawaii, Vol 1

Exam Questions

1. Describe and explain **two** types of evidence for plate movement based on knowledge of oceanic crust material. [8]

2. With the aid of a diagram, explain the processes and landforms associated with a collision plate margin. [9]

3. Study Resource A which describes the tectonic situation in Northern Turkey. Identify the type of plate margin found at the North Antolian Fault and explain the processes that result in earthquakes without volcanic activity along this margin. [9]

Question from CCEA A2 1 Physical Processes, Landforms and Management, Specimen Assessment Materials © CCEA 2017

Resource A: Tectonic instability in Turkey

The North Anatolian Fault is a major fracture that runs across the northern part of Turkey, marking the boundary between the Anatolian plate and the larger Eurasian plate. The area is considered as one of the most seismically active zones of the world. Turkey is being squeezed sideways to the west as the Arabian plate pushes into the Eurasian plate. The North Anatolian Fault forms the edge of the Anatolian plate and earthquakes happen regularly along it as different sections break. The map illustrates how, within the last one hundred years, a series of significant earthquakes has rocked northern Turkey along the line of the fault.

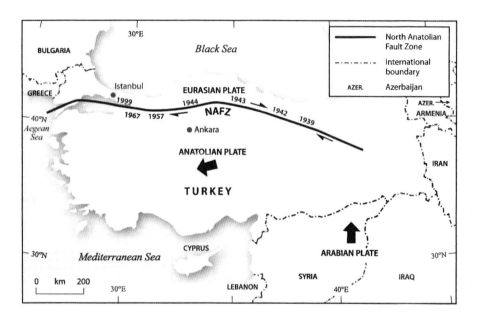

References

Geofile articles:
'Ocean ridges and rift valleys', *Geofile* 638, series 29, 2010–2011
'Two Plate Boundaries: The Himalayas and Pacific USA', *Geofile* 554, series 26, 2007–2008

Geo Factsheet:
'Volcanic Activity and landforms of the Hawaiian Hot Spot', *Geo Factsheet* 319, Curriculum Press

Plate margins:
https://www.geolsoc.org.uk/Plate-Tectonics/Chap3-Plate-Margins

Plate tectonics (including videos of past and future change):
http://www.acegeography.com/plate-tectonic-theory.html

2. VOLCANIC ACTIVITY AND ITS MANAGEMENT

Case studies

Small-scale case study of volcanic activity: Iceland, Eyjafjallajökull (2010)

Students should be able to:

(i) demonstrate knowledge and understanding of volcanic activity at constructive and destructive plate margins and at hot spots

(ii) demonstrate knowledge and understanding of the socio-economic and environmental hazards and benefits of volcanic activity

(iii) evaluate how a country prepares for and responds to volcanic activity

The term volcanic is used to describe all the activity associated with the extrusion of magma onto the Earth's surface. This includes a range of material from huge boulders through lava flows to emissions of steam and gases. Specifically a volcano is where molten rock (lava) and gas erupts and solidifies through a rift or vent in the crust. Volcanoes come in many shapes and sizes and the type of eruption is equally varied. Eruptions may come from a central single vent or along a line of weakness known as a fissure. Volcanoes are normally classified as being active, dormant or extinct. Dormant suggests that while there is no historic record of eruption the volcano cannot yet be regarded as extinct. Each year about 50 of the world's active volcanoes actually erupt. For some this is for the first time in many centuries (Mt Pinatubo in 1991) while for others it is a regular event (Mt Etna on Sicily has some crater or vent activity most years). Some volcanoes are in almost continual activity such as Kilauea in Hawaii.

Plate margins and hot spots

As noted earlier, volcanic activity is associated with three distinct locations: constructive margins, destructive margins and at individual hot spots.

While 75% of volcanic material is created at constructive margins, in general eruptions are less violent and extrude very hot, freely flowing basaltic (low silica content) lavas to form volcanoes with gentle slopes. Most constructive margin volcanic activity is hidden beneath the sea where magma forms the mountains of the mid-ocean ridges. As magma extrudes onto the ocean floor it cools rapidly forming bulbous shapes known as pillow lavas, composed of fine textured igneous basalt or gabbro rocks. This is where and how the ocean plates are created and so over 65% of the Earth's crust is the result of this volcanic action. On land the basalt rocks of the Antrim plateau, including those eroded by the sea at the Giant's Causeway, are the produce of constructive margin activity some 55 million years ago. Today, the island of Iceland gives us easier access to

Figure A33: Geyser at sunset (left) and lava flows (right) in South-West Iceland

these processes and landforms. Along with frequent eruptions from central volcanoes and fissures creating wide lava flows, thermal lakes and geysers are also common.

At destructive margins, including the Pacific 'Ring of Fire', eruptions tend to be more violent and the less fluid, acidic, silica rich lavas form steeper, cone shaped volcanoes. The magma produced by former ocean plate and ocean floor sediment material melting deep in subduction zones rises to penetrate and move through the plate above, leading to violent volcanic activity in the mountains or along island arcs. Around 80% of the world's active volcanoes are at destructive margins. The eruption of Mt Pinatubo (Luzon, Philippines) in 1991 was an example of the violent volcanic activity associated with destructive plate margins. This eruption sent a vast cloud of debris, 16 km wide, more than 30 km up into the atmosphere. Volcanic ash, 10 cm deep, covered the landscape for a 60 km radius. The event released more material (a total of over 20 million tonnes) into the atmosphere than any other eruption in the last 100 years. The sheer weight of debris caused thousands of buildings to collapse, including schools, hospitals, children's homes and thousands of houses in the city of Olongapo, 56 km south-west of Pinatubo. Much more damage was caused by rivers of water mixed with hot volcanic ash, known as lahars, which inundated the low-lying farms and villages. The final death toll was around 900 people and but for a well co-ordinated prediction and evacuation plan, would have been thousands more. The damage and costs due to the eruption were estimated at over £10 billion.

Figure A34: Impact map and photograph of the Mt Pinatubo eruption 1991

Source: (right) D Harlow, U.S. Geological Survey

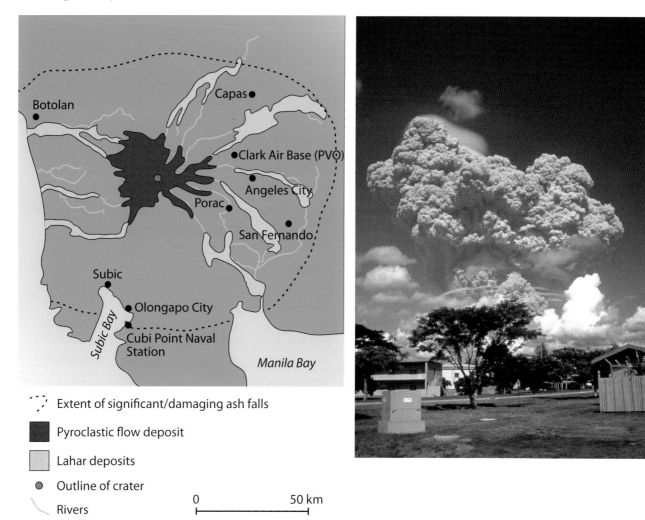

Extent of significant/damaging ash falls

Pyroclastic flow deposit

Lahar deposits

Outline of crater

Rivers

0   50 km

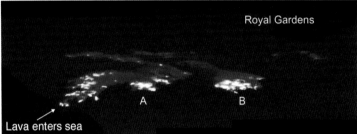

Figure A35: Visual and thermal images of a shield volcano lava flow, Hawaii 2009

Source: U.S. Geological Survey/Hawaiian Volcano Observatory

Hot spot volcanoes are among the most active and predictable. In Hawaii they produce lava capable of flowing rapidly and for long distances. Aa is a blocky lava while pahoehoe lava is a liquid lava with a surface skin that resembles coiled rope. Kilauea on Big Island, Hawaii has been erupting lava for decades and tourists can routinely view the material flow across the island surface eventually reaching the sea. Such fluid lava means the volcanoes have very wide gentle slopes. The dormant volcano of Mauna Kea in Hawaii stretches over 6 km up from the floor of the Pacific Ocean and 4 km above sea level, making it higher than Everest and the island is the largest single volume of volcanic material in the world (Figure A35).

The hazards created by volcanic activity

The variety of potential hazards following a volcanic eruption is illustrated in Figures A36 and A37. Some hazards are confined to the immediate area, including lava flows. Others, such as lahars, may travel many kilometres from the source, while ash falls can settle over hundreds of square kilometres or enter the upper troposphere and circle the globe.

Figure A36: Potential hazards of volcanic activity

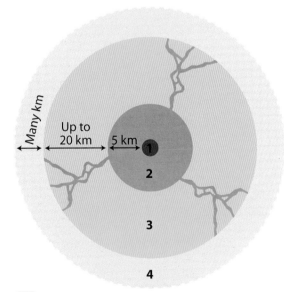

Crater: Lava lake, explosion

Adjacent: Explosion, lava flows, ash falls, fire, volcanic bombs, pyroclastic flows

Intermediate: Volcanic mud flows (lahars), ash falls, nuée ardente

Distant: Ash falls, earthquakes, upper atmosphere impacts

Explosion

Some volcanoes erupt without significant violence, such as the volcanoes of Hawaii, but elsewhere the force of a volcanic eruption can be enormous. When the Indonesian volcanic island of Krakatoa (Figure A38) erupted in 1883, the explosion was heard 4000 km away in Australia. The blast destroyed the island itself and 36,000 people drowned in the 40 m tsunami that swept the coasts of the neighbouring islands. On one island a ship was washed 20 km inland along a river valley. Tsunamis are huge waves generated by either volcanic eruptions or earthquakes, which can travel across oceans at great speed resulting in the devastation of coastal regions. The scale of volcanic eruptions can be measured in a similar way to earthquakes and the Richter scale. The Volcanic Explosivity Index (VEI), while open-ended, varies from 0 (a non-explosive eruption), through 4 (a cataclysmic event) to the very rare 8 (a mega-colossal eruption), such as the Yellowstone supervolcano event of two million years ago.

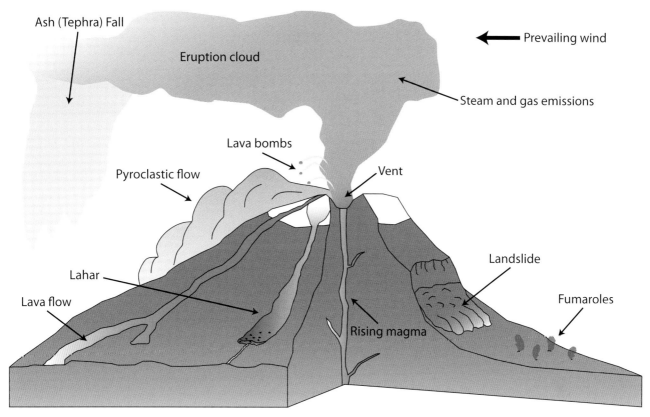

Figure A37: Types of hazard from volcanic explosion

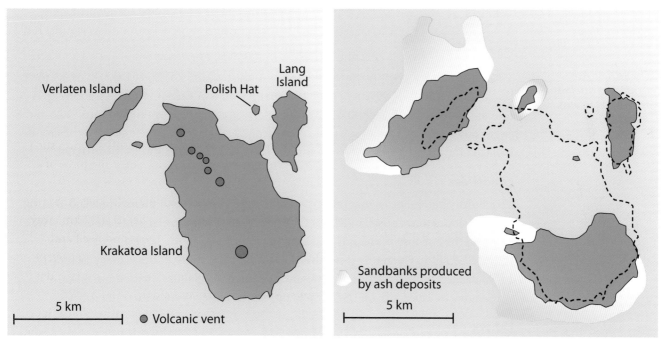

Figure A38: Krakatoa before and after the eruption of 1883   Dotted lines show the pre-eruption islands

Materials

Numerous types of material are ejected by volcanoes such as lava, pyroclastic material and gases (Figures A37 and A39).

Lava rarely threatens life as its flow is relatively predictable but it does destroy property by swamping buildings or starting fires. The frequent flows of lava down the slopes of

Figure A39: Materials ejected by volcanic activity

Mt Etna (Italy) in recent decades have destroyed cable car stations and overwhelmed houses, hotels and restaurants. These also buried rich farmland, burning vines and orchards.

LAVA (erupted magma)	PYROCLASTIC MATERIALS (ejected fragments)	GASES
Acid (viscous, silica rich) eg Andesitic Basic (free flowing) eg Aa (Ah Ah) or Blocky lava Pahoehoe or Ropy lava	Volcanic bombs Stones (lapilli) Hot ash and fine dust Pumice Cinders Nuée ardente (glowing avalanche)	Steam Sulphur dioxide Carbon dioxide Cyanide (These are often issued from small vents called fumaroles)

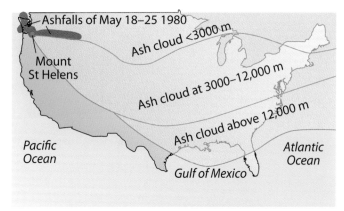

Pyroclastic material is the term used to describe a wide variety of solid material ejected by volcanic activity other than lava. Nuée ardentes, (literally 'glowing cloud') are spectacular, potentially lethal mixtures of superheated gases, hot ash and rock fragments that flow at enormous speed down the side of some volcanoes. Over the USA volcanic ash from the Mt St Helens eruption of 1980 entered the upper atmosphere and circled the globe helping create spectacular sunsets for months (Figures A40 and A41).

Figure A40: Ash cloud and ash falls from Mt St Helens, May 1980

Volcanic gases are often hot and toxic. One August night in 1986 at Lake Nyos, a crater lake in Cameroon, West Africa over 1700 people died of carbon dioxide poisoning. A heavier than air cloud, rich in carbon dioxide, was expelled from the volcanic lake and swept down adjacent valleys. Up to 23 km away people died in their sleep as the cloud replaced the air. Farmers' livestock and the local wildlife were similarly impacted.

Landslides

Volcanoes often bulge as magmatic pressure builds up beneath them. This deformation of steep slopes may cause landslides. The devastating eruption of Mt St Helens in 1980 followed the collapse of the north side of the mountain, in the largest landslide ever recorded on film. Currently it is feared that volcanic activity in the Canary Islands might cause a huge landslide to generate an enormous tsunami, with devastating consequences especially on the densely populated eastern seaboard of the USA.

Lahars

These are volcanic mud flows. When hot ash mixes with river water or with heavy rain, which can be triggered by eruptions, it can flow as a thick hot mixture at great speed, flooding valleys, burying the environment and drowning people. In 1985, the eruption of Nevado del Ruiz in Colombia resulted in a lahar flowing at 100 km per hour through the town of Armero, some 50 km from the volcano. In one night over 20,000 of the town's 23,000 inhabitants perished, buried by hot mud. At both Mt St Helens (1980) and Mt Pinatubo (1991) volcanic lahars extended the area of impact and deaths tens of kilometres from the eruption crater (Figure A34 and A41).

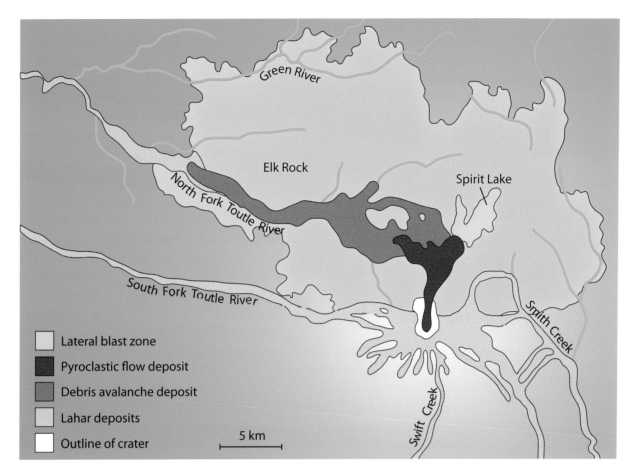

Figure A41: Map of the impact zone of the 18 May 1980 eruption of Mt St Helens

Jokulhlaups (glacial outburst floods)

These are floods caused by volcanic eruptions beneath ice sheets or glaciers. Small events happen almost every year in Iceland, where over 20 volcanoes lie beneath the ice. Large-scale events threaten farmland and transport networks, in particular the island's vital coastal highway. Despite its propensity for regular earthquakes and volcanic eruptions, Iceland has not had a death caused directly by such events in over 100 years.

The socio-economic and environmental hazards of volcanic activity

Socio-economic

Volcanic hazards affect both individuals and communities, causing costly damage to infrastructure, agriculture, industry and governments.

Volcanic eruptions are often fatal but the estimated total of 200,000 deaths in the last 500 years is much lower than other natural (earthquakes and floods) or human (wars and traffic accidents) disasters. Sometimes signs or precursor events allow prediction and evacuation of an area but this is not always the case. It has been possible to divert or steer some small lava flows but more often the red hot lava will destroy anything in its path regardless of planning. The preceding section identifies a number of examples of fatal volcanic hazards: lahars, gas emissions, tsunamis, pyroclastic flows and floods. Fatalities may be caused by secondary impacts such as the Icelandic famine after the Skaftar Fires eruption of 1783, in which one quarter of the island's population died. Other social impacts include homelessness and refugee movements. The 1991 Mt Pinatubo eruption displaced over 100,000 people, many of whom could not return to their homes for years, if at all. This was the result of a huge ashfall that collapsed their houses and buried their farmland. Repeated lahars swept the region's river valleys in the months and years after the eruption had died away. The aboriginal, Aeta tribal people had to abandon their mountain forest homes on the slopes of Pinatubo and in lowland refugee camps hundreds of their young children and elderly died of illness. This was a result of overcrowding and inadequate supplies of water and medicine. Any traumatic event caused by volcanic activity will have a huge psychological impact on the communities involved and people may simply refuse to return to the region, even when it is possible to do so.

Closely linked to social impacts are the negative effects on a region's economy. Lava flows can destroy any built structure, such as houses, factories, roads, bridges or farms. Lahars, ash falls and jokulhlaups can extend this destruction over a much wider area. The damage caused to farmland, commercial forestry or tourist amenity may take decades of restoration to re-establish the economy. The blast of the 1980 Mt St Helens eruption flattened several million trees over an area of 600 km². Between 1995 and 1997, the Caribbean island of Montserrat, a British dependency, suffered because of an erupting volcano called Soufriere Hills. The net outcome was that most of the island was uninhabitable and over 7000 of its 11,000 population had be to be evacuated and resettled for several years at least. Dealing with the impacts and this mass relocation program cost the British government over £100 million. Even in cases where the nature of the activity is less destructive, any disruption to people and their employment will be expensive in economic terms.

Figure A42: Table of selected historical eruptions including the top six in total deaths

LOCATION	DATE	DEATHS	MAIN CAUSE OF DEATH
Tambora, Indonesia	1815	92,000	Starvation
Krakatau, Indonesia	1883	36,417	Tsunami
Mt Pelee, Martinique	1902	29,025	Ash flow, nuée ardente
Nevado de Ruiz, Colombia	1985	25,000	Lahars – mudflows
Unzen, Japan	1792	14,300	Volcano collapse, tsunami
Laki, Iceland	1783	9350	Starvation
Vesuvius, Italy	79	3360	Ash falls, pyroclastic flows
Pinatubo, Philippines	1991	900	Disease, lahars, ash fall

Environmental

The impacts of volcanic hazards on the landscape, the ecosystem and the climate.

Volcanoes are capable of re-writing landscapes. People frequently describe the scene of recent eruptions as lunar – barren and desolate. In 1883, the enormous eruption on the island of Krakatoa replaced a 300 m high mountain with a 300 m deep submarine crater (Figure A38). At Mt St Helens the landslide and explosive eruption on its northern flank eventually reduced the near 3000 m summit by 400 m. Such explosions and movements of lava and ash often kill all vegetation and animal life in the region. We know, for example, that over one million farm animals died at Pinatubo in 1991 but no accurate figure is known for its impact of the natural ecosystem (Figure A34).

Major volcanic events, or a series of them, can impact the global climate. In 1815, the cold summer and consequent worldwide crop failures and famine, in which millions died, has been linked to the eruption of Mt Tambora in Indonesia. Scientists speculate that worldwide mass extinction of species in the past may be the outcome of a series of volcanic eruptions. These could fill the upper atmosphere with dust and reduce the level of insolation entering the Earth's energy system.

The socio-economic and environmental benefits of volcanic activity

Despite their destructive image, volcanic activity is not only hazardous, it can prove beneficial to both people and the environment. In fact, volcanoes may have been the seed bed of all life on planet Earth, as the one location where the necessary physical and chemical conditions existed.

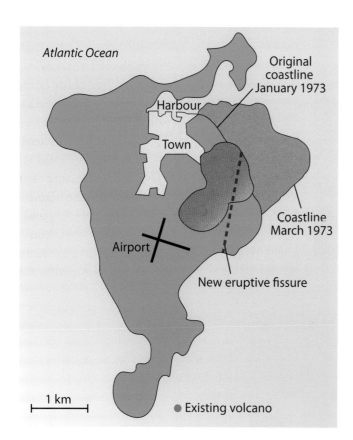

Figure A43: Impacts of the Heimaey eruption in 1973

Figure A44: Recent ash falls in the foreground contrast with the lush forests that have grown of older volcanic deposits on the upper slopes of Mt Etna. In the distance vineyards and citrus groves surround the local rural towns.

Land creation

While ash and lava may bury useful land, the same activity can create new land. In 1963, a small fishing fleet off the south coast of Iceland saw a column of smoke rise from the sea. They immediately shipped their nets and made way to what they assumed was another boat in distress. On arrival at the scene, they witnessed the summit of an underwater volcano breach the surface to form a new island, later named Surtsey. The new island has provided a golden opportunity for scientists to study not only volcanic processes but also the development of a prisere and ecological succession. On another Icelandic island, Heimaey, the eruption of Eldfell destroyed hundreds of houses buried by ash fall or burnt by lava. However, the lava flows that had threatened to block off the harbour entrance were stopped and actually enhanced the shelter provided for the local fishing fleet (Figure A43).

Fertile soils

Benefits from volcanic activity include the fact that some, but not all, lava flows and ash falls can be weathered into rich, fertile soils. Soils based on basic lavas or ash deposits rich in potassium or phosphorus are highly valued. It is no coincidence that over 20% of the population of Sicily lives and depends on the fertile slopes of Mt Etna, an active volcano. Here the high yield from olive and orange groves, and wine produced from local vineyards supports a thriving agricultural community. This is at once both an economic and a social benefit (Figure A44). The natural environment benefits in a similar way. In the three years following an eruption of Katmai, Alaska, in 1912, the ash fall resulted in the tallest grass and largest berry production ever known.

Mineral deposits – industrial resources

Volcanic deposits provide a wide variety of industrial materials and chemicals including sulphur, pumice, arsenic and boric acid. Beneath the surface in active volcanic areas, mineral-rich gas from lava cools, forming veins of minerals and metal ores. The oldest written reference to our islands off Western Europe is from Greek sources, naming them the 'Tin islands' due to the copper and tin deposits in old volcanic rocks of Cornwall and southern Ireland. Today in Indonesia, at the Ijen volcano, local workers climb into the 200 m deep crater at the top of the mountain to mine and carry out blocks of sulphur that is deposited around the perimeter of the crater lake. They undertake this back-breaking task on alternate days, as the conditions within the crater are hazardous to their respiration (Figure A45). Diamonds are formed deep in volcanic zones along narrow channels called kimberlite pipes.

Figure A45: Miners carrying sulphur blocks from Ijen volcano in Indonesia

Energy

In Iceland, New Zealand, Italy and the USA naturally produced volcanic steam is harnessed to generate electricity (Figure A46). The largest such plant is The Geysers in California, generating 1000 MW of electricity, said to be enough energy to supply the needs of San Francisco, a city of 800,000 people.

Reykjavik, Iceland's capital also gets most of its heating from geothermal water derived from volcanic springs.

Figure A46: Krafla geothermal power station in Iceland
Source: Wesley Johnston

Over 50,000 homes receive water heated naturally to 87°C from this environmentally friendly system. As a natural and renewable energy source, geothermal energy is both economically and environmentally beneficial.

Tourism

Volcanoes, especially those that are currently or recently active, are strong magnets for adventurers and tourists alike. The 2001 eruption of Mt Etna in Sicily coincided with the holiday season and companies flew, coached and sailed thousands of visitors in to witness the event, which was particularly spectacular at night. The mud pools and geysers of Yellowstone National Park, Wyoming USA, are the key attraction for tens of thousands of visitors annually. The most famous feature being Old Faithful, a geyser that regularly (around every 95 minutes) sends a column of hot water and steam into the air. In the Canary Islands or the volcanic islands in the Caribbean, a volcanic barbeque is often part of the tourist itinerary. The sheer beauty of volcanoes such as Mt Fuji in Japan is a priceless asset and Crater Lake in Oregon is regarded as

Figure A47: Tourists wait to photograph the water and steam eruption of Strokkur Geyser, Iceland

one of the world's most beautiful landscapes. Even ancient volcanic activity can be of economic benefit. Northern Ireland's leading tourist attraction is the remnant of the outpouring of millions of tonnes of lava during the Tertiary era, which solidified into the regularly shaped columns of the Giant's Causeway. The economic spin-off from volcanic attractions is common to all tourism: jobs and income from guides, accommodation, catering, transport, ancillary services and the selling of souvenirs (Figure A49).

Figure A48: Tourists explore the preserved Roman city of Pompeii beneath the summit of Mt Vesuvius the volcano that buried it in 79AD, Napoli, Italy

Figure A49: Cooking instructions at the Sankampaeng natural hot springs tourist resort, Northern Thailand

The management of volcanic activity

In common with many other natural hazards, the management of volcanic activity involves three areas:

1. Prediction: when, where and exactly what is going to happen.
2. Protection: developing physical structures to improve safety.
3. Preparation: raising awareness and educating people in how to be ready for, and react to, the event.

In addition, because volcanic activity does create potential socio-economic benefits, such as fertile soils and tourist attractions, there is an important positive aspect to its management.

Prediction of volcanic activity

Some volcanoes are highly predictable, such as the huge crater of Hawaii's Mauna Loa or Mt Etna in Sicily – currently Europe's most active volcano. Others are much less readily anticipated. Of the 700 active (as opposed to dormant or extinct) volcanoes, only around 70 are continuously surveyed. Not surprisingly, volcanoes in the developed nations of Japan, New Zealand, Iceland and the USA are studied more intensely and prediction has improved. Prediction has several aspects; in the case of volcanic activity it is necessary to predict not only the time and length of an eruption but also its scale and the nature of its impacts. Inaccuracy on any one of these factors could prove even more disastrous than no prediction at all. Technological advance means that volcanic activity can now be monitored from the air and also from space by satellite.

Monitoring the warning signs

The obvious way to predict volcanic activity is to monitor the likely precursors or warning signs of eruptions. These include local seismic events, the deformation of the ground surface and any steam or gas release. Other observations that might be made are the melting of snow caps, changes in levels in crater lakes or the death of local vegetation. Volcanoes by definition involve the release of magma or gas, so beneath them material must be moving upwards, causing earth tremors and bulging of the surface. Seismic activity does not guarantee eruption. For example, Vesuvius in south Italy has shown strong activity several times without a subsequent volcanic event. It is not uncommon for prediction to be accurate in terms of timing but inaccurate in terms of scale and even direction. The 1980, Mt St Helens' eruption was closely monitored and, with respect to timing, well predicted. A 5 km wide exclusion zone was set up and if the volcano had erupted vertically then it is possible no lives would have been lost. In the event, the bulging northern slope of Mt St Helens collapsed in a huge landslide, creating an outlet for the pressure from which an enormous blast of ash, debris and superheated gas erupted laterally, devastating the landscape well beyond the 5 km zone in that direction (Figure A41).

Sometimes it all goes wrong. In 1985, a Colombian volcano, Nevado del Ruiz, was monitored by scientists following signs of activity. After several weeks they declared that a major eruption was not imminent. The next day it erupted and as mentioned earlier, a lahar swept down an adjacent valley burying the town of Armero. It was of little comfort to the scientists that they had accurately predicted the path of such lahars – only their timing was wrong. By contrast, in 1980, scientists did evacuate many people from a threatening volcano at Mammoth Lake in California. No eruption occurred and the scientists faced the anger of residents over the inconvenience and their economic losses.

Bernard Chouet of the United States Geological Service (USGS) believes that the identification of a seismic pattern known as a long-period event is a reliable indicator of volcanic activity. A long-period event is a particular frequency of movement that he suggests links to magma rising towards the surface. Models are now being designed to test these theories under laboratory conditions. Confidence in volcanic prediction based on seismic patterns was undermined when, in September 2014, the Japanese volcano, Mt Ontake erupted without any significant earthquake events being detected.

Tiltmeters are used on the volcano slopes and on craters to monitor rises, falls or bulges in surface levels due to magmatic movement underground. Other physical changes that have been monitored to aid prediction are the temperature of crater lakes and springs, gravity and magnetism. The latter two are based on the idea that new magma moving below a volcano will subtlety alter these values. Satellites routinely use thermal infrared imaging to study the invisible energy radiated by volcanoes and monitor the heat flow patterns of the world's volcanoes.

Volcanologists also study gas emitted by volcanoes using the geo-chemical profile to inform their predictions. Gas sampling correlation spectrometers and laser monitoring are used to detect small changes in gases across the surface or crater of a volcano. Any changes in the chemical nature or quantity of these may help to forecast the timing,

Figure A50: Methods of monitoring volcanic activity

1. Measuring ground deformation using tiltmeters and satellite imaging.

2. Recording location and strength of seismic activity.

3. Geological observation by fly past or sampling.

4. Lasers used to monitor level of gas emission.

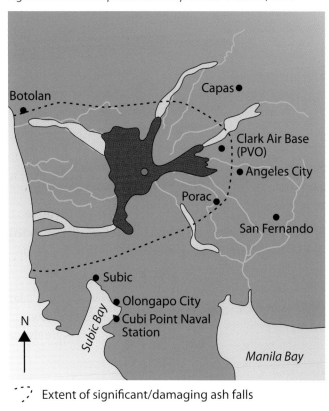

Figure A51: Hazard prediction map of Mt Pinatubo, 1991

Capas●

Botolan

Clark Air Base (PVO)

● Angeles City

Porac ●

San Fernando

● Subic

● Olongapo City

Cubi Point Naval Station

Subic Bay

N

Manila Bay

‾ ‾ ‾ ⁄ Extent of significant/damaging ash falls

▮ Pyroclastic flow deposit   ● Outline of crater

▯ Lahar deposits   ⟍ Rivers

scale or nature of future events (Figure A50). Since 1995, the volcano of Soufriere Hills, on the island of Montserrat, has kept scientists busy assessing the nature and the future of its on-going activity. In this case, remote sensing from satellites has been used to plot lava flows and gas emissions using ultra violet filters on camera shots.

An important aspect of prediction is the production of accurate hazard mapping. These maps are often based on information from historical eruption, if available, or from survey work on the surrounding landscape. It was this approach by the USGS that produced a hazard map of the potential impact of an eruption of Mt Pinatubo weeks before it happened in 1991. Comparison of Figures A34 and A51 shows that the map accurately predicted the three main impacts (ash fall, lahars and pyroclastic flows), even though the aerial extent of the ash fall was underestimated (Figure A51). In the longer term, the identification of areas at risk means land-use planning can ensure that vital structures such as transport routes, hospitals and emergency service stations avoid such areas or are, at least, appropriately designed.

Protection and preparation

Active intervention during a volcanic eruption is rare but as mentioned earlier, when a lava flow threatened the sheltered fishing port on Heimaey, off Iceland's south coast, fishing trawlers and coast guard boats turned sea water hoses on the flowing lava in an attempt to cool and solidify it. In Sicily, the regular lava flows on the slopes of Mt Etna provide opportunities for attempts to divert and redirect lava away from settlements and valuable property. In 1991–1993, when the settlement of Zafferena was threatened by such a flow, quickly erected earth barriers failed to stop the lava but explosives detonated closer to the flow's source successfully forced the lava into a new artificial channel that avoided the town.

Preparation concerns people who live with the risk, the emergency services and local government. These agencies act to ensure that information about possible events is communicated accurately and quickly in order for the most significant response to take place – evacuation. Getting out of the way of volcanic activity, whether primary impacts of explosive eruptions, ash fall and lava flows or

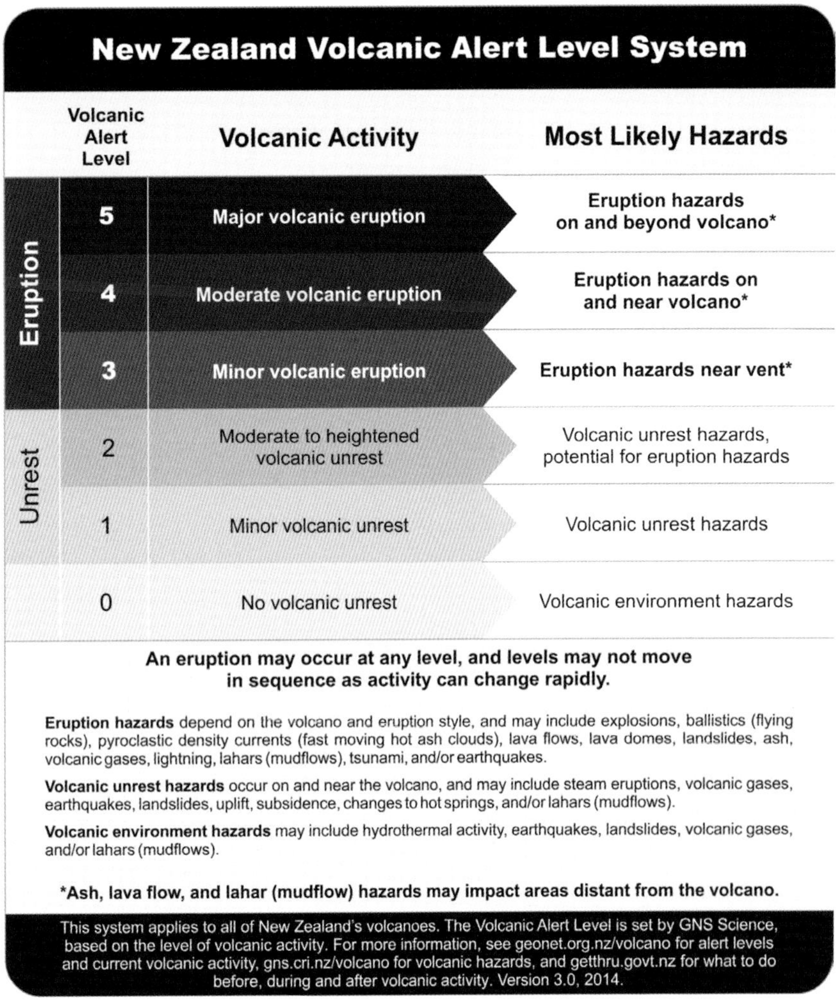

New Zealand Volcanic Alert Level System

	Volcanic Alert Level	Volcanic Activity	Most Likely Hazards
Eruption	5	Major volcanic eruption	Eruption hazards on and beyond volcano*
	4	Moderate volcanic eruption	Eruption hazards on and near volcano*
	3	Minor volcanic eruption	Eruption hazards near vent*
Unrest	2	Moderate to heightened volcanic unrest	Volcanic unrest hazards, potential for eruption hazards
	1	Minor volcanic unrest	Volcanic unrest hazards
	0	No volcanic unrest	Volcanic environment hazards

An eruption may occur at any level, and levels may not move in sequence as activity can change rapidly.

Eruption hazards depend on the volcano and eruption style, and may include explosions, ballistics (flying rocks), pyroclastic density currents (fast moving hot ash clouds), lava flows, lava domes, landslides, ash, volcanic gases, lightning, lahars (mudflows), tsunami, and/or earthquakes.

Volcanic unrest hazards occur on and near the volcano, and may include steam eruptions, volcanic gases, earthquakes, landslides, uplift, subsidence, changes to hot springs, and/or lahars (mudflows).

Volcanic environment hazards may include hydrothermal activity, earthquakes, landslides, volcanic gases, and/or lahars (mudflows).

*Ash, lava flow, and lahar (mudflow) hazards may impact areas distant from the volcano.

This system applies to all of New Zealand's volcanoes. The Volcanic Alert Level is set by GNS Science, based on the level of volcanic activity. For more information, see geonet.org.nz/volcano for alert levels and current volcanic activity, gns.cri.nz/volcano for volcanic hazards, and getthru.govt.nz for what to do before, during and after volcanic activity. Version 3.0, 2014.

Figure A52: The New Zealand Volcanic activity alert system (2014)
Source: courtesy of GNS Science, New Zealand

secondary impacts such as lahars and building collapse, is often the only real response. It takes good pre-planning to move large numbers of people rapidly and to a safe distance and environment. In the 1991 Mt Pinatubo eruption, the world's largest in the last 100 years, the figure of 900 fatalities is only 5% of the probable total deaths had ample warning not been given. Alert systems are used for communicating the likelihood of volcanic activity. The detail and style of these vary between countries but they usually have four to six stages and are either numbered or colour coded. Figure A52 is an example from New Zealand.

Short and long-term responses

The immediate response to hazardous volcanic activity is evacuation. The scale, distance and length of time involved will depend on the magnitude and duration of the event. On the Caribbean Island of Montserrat, the volcano that helped create the island, Soufriere, started to show signs of activity in 1995. In preparation, 11,000 people were moved to neighbouring islands. In 1997 the main eruption killed 19 people, destroyed the capital of Plymouth and the southern half of the island was abandoned. Over 20 years on, periodic eruptive activity and a lack of consistent economic development mean that Montserratians have yet to return to their former social and economic life. On the other hand, in the villages on Mt Etna, periodic ash that falls onto the tiled roofs and tarmacked streets may be swept up, washed down or given as tourist souvenirs within days of the event.

Each event that is studied helps to improve both our understanding of, and our ability to deal with, volcanic activity. In the long-term, improved preparedness includes the drawing up and use of hazard maps. It also requires developing evacuation strategies, with designated shelter zones and emergency evacuation camps constructed for local people, along with stored emergency food and water supplies. People are drawn to volcanically active areas for all the potential benefits they bring and part of management is to ensure that developing these resources does not increase the risk. Any injury or fatalities to tourists due to volcanic activity is likely to profoundly undermine that industry in a local area. Consequently, visits to recently active craters or other sites are normally confined to researchers and scientists only.

CASE STUDY: Eyjafjallajökull (2010), a small-scale study of how Iceland prepares for and responds to volcanic activity

Iceland is one of the most volcanically active regions on Earth and in recent decades it has used this to develop its economy in a number of ways. The nation perceives the hazards posed by volcanism but is also aware of the opportunities it provides. Spouting geysers and thermally heated lakes and pools are continuous evidence of the island's volcanism but other significant, recent volcanic events include eruptions by Eyjafjallajökull in 2010, Grimsvötn in 2011, Holuhraun in 2013–2014 and on-going activity at Katla and Krafla volcanoes (Figure A53).

In the management of environmental hazards, such as volcanic activity, four options can be identified. These and their potential consequences are outlined in Figure A54.

In Iceland, the high level of volcanic activity means the first option is unrealistic. The second might involve strengthening structures such as reinforced roofs on houses or diverting lava flows but again the scale of events in Iceland makes this option unlikely. There is scope in the third option to avoid development adjacent to active volcanoes but on an island with widespread volcanic activity and given that ash falls, lava flows and flooding can cover large areas, again it has limited relevance. In conclusion, if Icelanders are to best manage the hazards of their volcanically active home, while also using its potential benefits for their social and economic advantage, the fourth option is the logical choice.

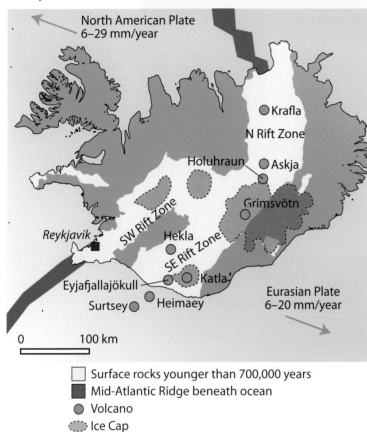

Figure A53: Volcanic activity in Iceland

Figure A54: The management options and their consequences in areas with natural hazards

Management option	Consequences
1. Do nothing	Disasters may occur
2. Protect people from hazards	May not be possible and may reduce risk perception
3. Avoid the hazard	May not be possible and may limit development
4. Live with the hazards	Socio-economic life integrated with the threats and opportunities

The Icelandic government (the nation only became independent in 1944) has overall responsibility for monitoring the dynamic nature of the island's environment. Apart from volcanic activity, seismic events, Atlantic storms, glacial processes and flooding all require preparation and management. The role of monitoring volcanic activity falls to the Icelandic Volcanic Observatory (IVO), based at the University of Iceland and this is closely linked to the Icelandic Meteorological Office (IMO). From the early 1990s, a network of 30–40 seismographs distributed across the active belt, south-west and central Iceland to the central north coast, has recorded the sub-surface seismic activity. The devices were made locally and mostly operated by local people – only a few could be remotely accessed from Reykjavik centrally. The IMO communicated with government as and when patterns of seismicity suggested a potential threat. Icelandic volcanicity, because of its association with a constructive plate margin, is normally not explosive in nature but on an island it has the potential for harm. Most of the island's 333,000 people, a population total similar to Belfast, live within a few kilometres of the capital, leaving the rest of the island with a very low population density of less than 2 people per km². Historically, the eruption in 1783 along the Laki fissure cost the lives of over 9300 people in Iceland, then about one in four of the nation's total. Proportionally this was the worst single national volcanic event in modern times. However, it was a smaller event in the spring of 2010 that really alerted the international community to the threat of Icelandic volcanic activity.

The 2010 eruption of Eyjafjallajökull (*pronounced Ayer fee-atler-yurkutl*)

After almost 200 years of dormancy, one of Iceland's more minor volcanoes began to show life in March 2010. Eyjafjoll, a 1666 m peak lies beneath a 150 m thick ice sheet, named Eyjafjallajökull, a fact that initially disguised its activity and later enhanced its impact. Eyjafjallajökull is Icelandic for 'mountain island glacier'. At first it erupted slowly from some small vents and a 500 m long fissure but in April a central vent erupted with more violence, registering 4 on the VEI scale. Magma erupting under ice will not flow as lava but rather react explosively to form mass clouds of ash and pyroclastic material. At Eyjafjallajökull, two centuries of rising magma pressure beneath the ice was released in clouds of volcanic particles, reaching 11,000 m into the atmosphere. The larger particles fell locally across the fertile and productive southern coast of Iceland. Its acidity temporarily reduced the land's fertility and made local water undrinkable. The volcanic heat melted the ice sheet and floods (jokulhlaups) swept south towards the coast, washing away landforms and effectively reforming the landscape. The swollen rivers then flooded farmland, destroying 20 farms along with sections of Route 1, the island's main ring-road.

The immediate response

The potential event had been carefully monitored by the IVO and the IMO, and the warning allowed 700 people to be safely evacuated in April before the ash fall and flooding occurred. The evacuation was arranged by the Icelandic Civil Protection and Emergency Management department using fire and ambulance workers. A number needed to be moved by helicopter as they were cut off by flooding but most people were able to return home within two days. Some of the damage to the ring-road had been deliberate, as engineers removed four sections of embanked highway to release the flood water and to prevent bridges and junctions being lost. It is cheaper to replace a section of road than such key transport links. An ash fall emergency was declared on 14 April when local and international flights were stopped in Iceland itself. The government used text messages to warn citizens and distributed face masks, although the wind direction ensured that little ash fell on Reykjavik. Local flights around the island resumed almost immediately.

Impacts local and international

The acidic ash and soil erosion due to floods meant that harvest yields were significantly reduced over the following two years and some farmers were bankrupted. This and the loss of greenhouses meant food supplies had to be imported, with a resulting increase in costs. In addition, the fishing ports along the south coast were closed and the negative publicity produced a dip in tourist visitor numbers. These economic impacts in turn led to an increase in the country's national debt and to a three year recession.

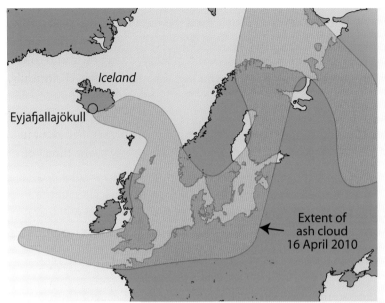

Figure A55: The 2010 ash cloud over the North Atlantic and European airspace

The 2010 event is more memorable for its disruption internationally. The ash cloud rose over 10 km into the air and directly into the upper westerly air flows and the jet stream. Not only did this spread the ash over a wide area of Western Europe, it also produced a hazard for planes flying through that air space. The North Atlantic routes between Europe and North America are both busy and commercially important. The potential risk presented by this ash cloud to aircraft was three-fold: poor visibility, scratched windscreens and serious damage to jet engine performance. European airlines and airports could not risk a disaster and all flights were grounded for six days. 95,000 flights were cancelled and millions of passengers were left unable to travel. Airlines said the event cost them $200 million each day. Business was badly hit and between this and multiple insurance compensation claims, billions of pounds were lost to Europe's economy. The grounded European and North American flights had a knock-on impact in that trade with South America, Asia and Africa was disrupted. Perishable goods such as food and flowers could not be transported, with the horticultural industry stating that $3 million was lost each day by the cut flower trade alone.

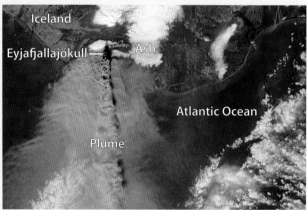

Figure 56: The 2010 eruption of Eyjafjallajökull, Southern Iceland
Source: (left) U.S. Geological Survey and (right) Boaworm

Long-term response

The awareness raised by the 2010 event across Europe has helped to highlight Iceland's need to predict and prepare for volcanic activity. This has spurred the European Union (EU) to fund a three year project involving 26 member states but focusing on Iceland. The FutureVolc project aims to reduce future impacts of ash clouds on flights across European airspace through more accurate prediction. FutureVolc targeted greater integration and co-operation between national meteorological and geological organisations, sharing information and expertise. Iceland was provided with the latest equipment and data relaying systems, such as gas emission detectors, GPS heat sensors and seismometers. In 2016 the project included a full scale test exercise based on Katla, one of the Island's largest and potentially most dangerous volcanoes. Experts from outside the FutureVolc team created a three day scenario of a large-scale eruption that the team had to monitor and manage. The IMO, the University of Iceland and the Icelandic Civil Protection and Emergency Management department formed the Scientific Advisory Board to discuss the unfolding scenario. Their response, which included the set up and use of ash sampling equipment and real-time data streaming, was then assessed by the external team. Any weaknesses identified in the system became the focus for FutureVolc work for the rest of the project.

Managing the Katla volcano

Katla, like Eyjafjallajökull, lies beneath an ice cap but it has the potential to produce much larger volcanic and flooding events. Nine large-scale eruptions have occurred at intervals of between 13 and 102 years over the last 500 years. It is now 100 years since this 10 km wide caldera (a very large crater) erupted.

As eruptions cannot be prevented or reduced, the only approach is to monitor and prepare for response. Scientists suggest that a glacier burst flood (jokulhlaup) could happen in as little as 90 minutes but that evacuation of the people at risk would take at least 2–4 hours. Consequently, seismic activity is carefully monitored for changes and five 'tilt stations' are located around the area, constantly recording any changes in the level or shape of the land. The precautions include 'Katla Information Day', which happens on the 18 October, the date of the last major event in 1918. Eruption drills take place in local workplaces and schools, and all residents and holiday accommodation centres are contacted by radio and by text. Flares would be used in a real emergency to warn any visitors or locals that cannot be contacted. Emergency evacuation centres are designated in 'safer' (higher) areas and printed advice is sent to every home and made available to all campers and hikers that visit the region.

How successful is Iceland's preparation and response to volcanic activity?

Although two people were reported missing, believed drowned after the 2010 jokulhlaup event, the records show that no lives have been lost in over 100 years due to direct volcanic activity. This in part reflects the remote location of many of the volcanoes and the very low population density but it is also testament to the work applied to monitoring, predicting and responding to these threats. Iceland's long experience of volcanic activity has helped both scientists and practical management teams to develop expertise in both preparation for and response to these events. The nation's wealth, its well educated workforce, along with the strong tradition of communities working together in a challenging environment mean Icelanders are able to react effectively to the threats posed by volcanic activity. As the breadth and depth of volcanic monitoring improves, the level of preparedness gets similarly better over time. Only a year after the Eyjafjallajökull eruption, Grimsvötn, an even larger Icelandic volcano erupted. The accurate prediction of the Grimsvötn event allowed earlier evacuation of people at risk and a more effective breaching of the ring-road to protect it from glacial meltwater flooding.

The downturn in the island's economy immediately after 2010 has been reversed and some of the recovery can be attributed directly to the management of the benefits of volcanic activity. The short-term loss of soil fertility due to acidic ash fall along the southern coast is gradually improving, as the ash breaks down and enhances the soil nutrition. The dramatic international story of the week long disruption to air traffic seems to have encouraged and invigorated the tourist industry, with record numbers of people travelling to visit the island. The thermally heated pools such as the Blue Lagoon, the geysers, the volcanoes, lava flows and even the volcanic black sand beaches form a key attraction for people from around the world. The relative wealth of the nation has ensured that the recovery has been rapid, with infrastructure restored effectively. In particular the vital Route 1 ring-road was rebuilt and upgraded within months of both the 2010 and 2011 events. The investment from the EU, specifically in FutureVolc, has allowed the national government to maintain a better equipped and trained volcano and seismic monitoring service.

Exam Questions

1. With reference to a small-scale case study, evaluate how a country prepared for and responded to volcanic activity. [18]

2. Study Resource A which concerns the Blue Lagoon, a geothermal tourist attraction in Iceland.

   Use the resource **to help you** describe and explain the potential socio-economic benefits of volcanic activity. (Reference should be made to places for illustration purposes). [9]

   Resource A: The Blue Lagoon, Iceland

   The Blue Lagoon is one of Iceland's most popular tourist destinations. Situated a few minutes from the nation's international airport, it is often the first or last stop on the holiday itinerary. The lagoon is man-made and was originally designed, in 1976, as the overflow for the nearby geothermal power plant at Svartsengi (seen in the centre background of the photograph). Local people started to bathe in the water and some claimed it helped with skin ailments. By 1992 the lagoon was developed as a commercial business and a luxury hotel was completed in 2017 when the number of annual visitors passed 600,000.

Naturally heated water is raised from 2000 m down and used to run turbines to generate electricity. After creating the electricity the steam and hot water passes through a heat exchanger to provide heat for local housing, then the water is fed into the lagoon for recreational and medicinal users to bathe in. In Iceland between 2010 and 2015, tourism increased its contribution to national wealth (GDP) from 18% to 31% and tourist related employment grew from 16,000 to 22,000 jobs. The Blue Lagoon Company now employs hundreds of local people in a range of positions from security to head chefs.

References

Geofile articles:
'Impacts and management of Iceland's 2010 volcanic eruption', *Geofile* 755, series 35, 2016–2017
'Geothermal Power in Iceland', *Geofile* 747, series 34, 2015–2016
'Living on a plate margin: Economic opportunities & reducing risk', *Geofile* 694, series 32, 2013–2014

Geo Factsheet:
'The Canary Islands – volcanic landscape and hazards', *Geo Factsheet* 329, Curriculum Press
'Tectonic hazards in New Zealand', *Geo Factsheet* 275, Curriculum Press
'An inconvenient plume – the eruption of Eyjafjalljokull, Iceland', *Geo Factsheet* 264, Curriculum Press

Other useful sources:
YouTube 'BBC – Volcano live, Iceland Erupts: A volcano live special'
YouTube 'Eyjafjallajökull 2010 eruption (HD)' for footage of the event

3. SEISMIC ACTIVITY AND ITS MANAGEMENT

Case studies

Small-scale case study of seismic activity: Japan, Tohoku (2011)

Students should be able to:

(i) demonstrate knowledge and understanding of the nature of seismic events and their impact – p, s and l waves, seismic shaking, liquefaction and tsunamis

(ii) demonstrate knowledge and understanding of the attempts to predict seismic events – seismic gap theory and dilation

(iii) evaluate how a country prepares for and responds to seismic activity

Contrary to most people's experience, Earth is not an inactive planet. Seismic events are continuous, occurring every few minutes, with frequent significant hazardous quakes. On average, earthquakes are responsible for up to 10,000 deaths a year. When rocks in the crust are placed under increased stress they deform. Eventually the pressure, tensional (pulled apart) or compressional (pushed together), is released in a sudden movement along a line of weakness or fault. The energy released is an earthquake, a series of

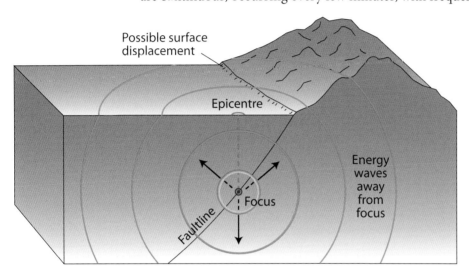

Figure A57: Relationship between faultline, focus and epicentre

vibrations or shock waves. The location where the earthquake occurs is termed its focus and seismic waves radiate away from here. The point on the Earth's surface immediately above the focus is called the epicentre (Figure A57).

Most earthquakes (75%) are shallow, less than 70 km from the Earth's surface. Intermediate earthquakes are found from 70–300 km below the surface with the focus of deep earthquakes lying 300–700 km down within the upper mantle. The depth of the focus is one important consideration in the impact of earthquakes, as deeper quakes are less damaging. The two common causes of earthquakes are:

1. The release of stress between rocks moving at plate boundaries.
2. The movement of magma within the crust beneath active volcanoes.

Around 95% of all earthquakes are located at plate boundaries and their global distribution is largely confined to the linear zones of destructive, constructive and conservative margins (Figure A13).

Seismic wave types

An earthquake releases energy through the surrounding rocks in a number of different forms. There are two sets of body waves that travel through the Earth's interior: P waves (the primary, pressure waves) and S waves (the secondary, transverse waves).

P waves are compressional in nature with a forward motion of compression and expansion, like the pulse along a slinky toy. These waves are readily transferred by rocks, gas and liquid material, and are the first to arrive as they move faster, 5.5 km per second. S waves involve a side-to-side motion at right angles to the direction of travel. Unlike P waves these can only be transferred by rock and not by gas or liquid material, and move at 3 km per second.

On reaching the Earth's surface, both P and S body waves transfer energy as L waves (surface waves). These are slower moving waves and include the side-to-side movement of Love waves and the up and down (rolling) motion of Rayleigh waves.

Figure A58: Types of seismic wave

Seismic wave	Abbreviation	Description	Ground motion
Primary wave	P	• Type of body wave • First to arrive (fastest wave type) • Ground stretches and squeezes in the direction of wave travel • Travels through solids, liquids and gases	Direction of motion
Secondary wave	S	• Type of body wave • Second to arrive (slower wave) • Ground motion is at right angles to the direction of wave travel • Travels through solids but not liquids	Direction of motion
Surface wave	L	• Travels along the surface of the Earth • Last to arrive (slowest) • Ground motion is a rolling action, like waves on a pond	Direction of motion

These waves, moving with different speeds and through different materials have helped scientists to create the picture of the Earth's internal structure that we use today. They also allow the precise location of an earthquake's focus to be calculated within minutes of an event. In relation to the impact of earthquakes, the geology is important. Unconsolidated sediment, such as sand or clay layers, tends to amplify seismic waves, increasing the motion much as a jelly does. This means structures built on such material are prone to greater levels of damage and destruction in an earthquake than those constructed on solid rock.

The magnitude of earthquakes is commonly recorded by two different scales: the first is the Modified Mercalli scale, a 12 level system based on the impact upon built structures (Figure A59). The second is the Richter scale, which records the energy release and wave size (Figure A60). The Richter scale is open ended and logarithmic in nature. On the Richter scale a magnitude 7 event will have a 10-fold increase in wave size, compared to a magnitude 6 and a 30-fold increase in energy release. In turn, compared to a magnitude 5 event, the 7 has 100 times the wave motion and 900 times the energy! The 2004 Indian Ocean tsunami was the result of an earthquake registered at 9.1 on the Richter scale. This is one of the highest values ever recorded and in energy terms equivalent to 23,000 Hiroshima atomic bombs and enough to move the Earth on its axis so changing the length of a day. Earthquakes normally last for seconds or minutes at most and the main event is often followed by aftershocks, which can cause additional damage to already weakened structures.

Figure A59: The Modified Mercalli scale based on observed impacts

Level	Nature of structure damage
I	Felt by very few under special circumstances.
II	Felt by some at rest, especially on upper floors of buildings.
III	Felt noticeably indoors but not often recognised as an earthquake.
IV	During the day most indoors will feel it, like a vehicle striking the building.
V	Felt by nearly all, many wakened. Tall objects moved – trees, poles.
VI	Felt by all, some run outside, furniture moved but slight damage.
VII	Everyone runs out. Damage to ordinary buildings, little to those specially designed.
VIII	Considerable damage and collapse of structures – chimneys, some walls.
IX	Damage even to well designed buildings – some ground cracking.
X	Most masonry and frame buildings destroyed – badly cracked ground.
XI	Few masonry structures standing – bridges collapse. Wide fissures in ground.
XII	Damage total. Objects thrown up – waves seen on ground surface.

Figure A60: The Richter scale based on amplitude

Richter magnitude	Effects of earthquake	Expected annual frequency
Less than 2.5	Recorded but not felt	900,000
2.5–5.4	Felt but only minor damage	30,000
5.5–6.0	Slight structural damage	500
6.1–6.9	Can be destructive in populous area	100
7.0–7.9	Major event – serious damage	20
8.0 and above	Total destruction to local region	One every 5–10 years

The impacts of seismic activity

Apart from the climatic hazards of tropical cyclones, floods and droughts, earthquakes are responsible for more death and destruction than any other natural hazard. They are also a dramatic event that can modify the landscape in seconds, whereas the slow processes of weathering and erosion may take millennia. There are several direct and indirect consequences of an earthquake. Ground deformation is the only direct impact of earthquakes on the surface. Ground deformation is when the ground surface above an earthquake is distorted or displaced. The ground can be moved vertically, horizontally or a combination of these elements. Earthquakes along the transform San Andreas Fault in California often cause lateral deformation, as seen by the offsetting of roads, walls, fences and even furrows in ploughed fields (Figures A61 and A62). In other cases, vertical movements can leave cliff-like steps running across the countryside from a few centimetres to several metres in height. The major Alaskan earthquake of 1964 vertically lifted the land surface by an average of 2 m, and in some places up to 12 m, over a 400,000 km² area. In many cases earthquakes do not leave any visible evidence of displacement at the surface. This may be because the surface line of the fault is covered by sediment or other rock material.

Other earthquake impacts are a consequence of the energy radiating from the focus of an earthquake in the form of seismic waves.

Figure A61: Fence moved by fault displacement – 1906 San Francisco earthquake

Source: U.S. Geological Survey/photo by GK Gilbert

Figure A62: Driveway destroyed by fault displacement – 1989 Loma Prieta earthquake

Source: U.S. Geological Survey/photo by JK Nakata

Figure A63: Earthquake proofing for buildings

Identification number visible to helicopters assessing damage after earthquake

Automatic shutters over windows to prevent pedestrians below being showered with glass

Rolling weights on roof to counteract shockwaves

Panels of glass flexibly anchored to steel super-structure

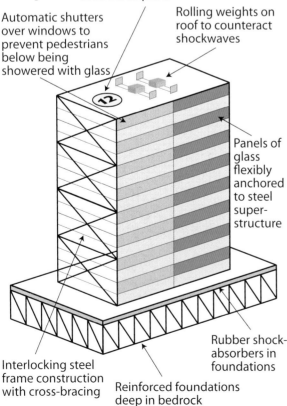

Interlocking steel frame construction with cross-bracing

Reinforced foundations deep in bedrock

Rubber shock-absorbers in foundations

Seismic shaking

The energy released by an earthquake radiates out from its focus in all directions, like ripples on a pond. These waves shake the crust as they pass through it, and when they reach the Earth's surface they shake the ground and anything built on it. Most waves produce a lateral, side-to-side motion. This is known as a shear motion, bending structures at right angles. This is why building designs based on triangles are more earthquake resistant than rectangular forms (Figure 63).

Shaking of only 20–30 cm is potentially devastating for buildings made from weak materials and the longer the shaking persists the greater the damage caused. Design is another factor; in the 1995 earthquake in Kobe, Japan, many traditional homes collapsed as they had heavy tiled roofs supported by vertical wooden columns. On the other hand, ancient pagoda buildings have survived many earthquakes as they appear to flex with the seismic motion. A number of high-rise buildings in Kobe were subject to a phenomenon known as 'pancaking'. In this case, shaking causes one floor of a building to crumble bringing the structure above that point collapsing down. Often the missing floor was structurally different and had less support, such as the ground floor shopping area in an office block.

Figure A64: Retrofitting of the Golden Gate Bridge, San Francisco

As well as horizontal shaking, earthquakes may also cause violent vertical motion. It has been reported that during some earthquakes, objects and people have been thrown repeatedly into the air. In one case a three tonne Californian fire truck parked in its garage bounced and damaged a wall over a metre above its position.

Walls made of weak material, such as mud brick (adobe) or poorly mortared brickwork, offer little resistance to shaking and such structures are often the cause of a large proportion of the deaths and injuries sustained. Even in well-constructed buildings, they may have a natural resonance which matches that of the earthquake and this increases the impact of shaking. In 1985, seismic waves from a distant earthquake shook Mexico City and several medium sized tower blocks collapsed with great loss of life. Later scientists showed that the tremors matched the natural resonance of these buildings, causing their destruction, meanwhile nearby smaller and taller buildings survived without significant damage. Action taken to improve earthquake resistance on existing structures is known as retrofitting (Figure A64).

Shaking buildings do not have to fall to create hazards. Glass from skyscrapers, overhanging balconies, parapets and even advertising hoardings may fall onto people and property nearby. Even inside buildings seismic shaking creates hazards; fixtures such as machinery in factories, filing cabinets in offices and large fridges in homes become potential threats to life and limb.

Structures other than buildings, including bridges and flyovers, may also suffer damage from shaking. The 1989 Loma Prieta earthquake, near San Francisco, lasted only 15 seconds but in that time dozens of concrete columns supporting a 1 km long section of the upper tier of the Interstate 880 highway (known as the Nimitz structure) sheared away, causing it to fall onto the roadway below (Figure A65). Dozens of vehicles were crushed and around 50 lives were lost at this site alone.

Figure A65: Collapse of Interstate 880 elevated highway in Oakland, San Francisco, 1989

Source: U.S. Geological Survey/photo by HG Wilshire

Seismic shaking also leads to secondary impacts such as landslides, fires and floods. The term landslide covers the movement of material down slopes and includes rock falls, avalanches and earth slumps. In many cases earthquakes act as the trigger mechanism starting the movement down steep slopes. A disastrous earthquake in central China in 1976 is known to have killed at least 250,000 people. In the mountainous region near the epicentre, most deaths were caused by hundreds of landslides that carried away or buried rural settlements. One of the best documented cases of an earthquake induced avalanche was in 1970, in the mountains of Peru. A quake measuring 7.8 on the Richter scale triggered the movement of 50 million cubic metres of ice, rock and mud. Within minutes the debris fell over 3000 m and travelled 11 km, burying two towns including Yungay, and killing 18,000 residents.

Seismic shaking can also cause flooding in several indirect ways. The earth or concrete walls of dams may be weakened or destroyed, releasing the water in the related reservoir to sweep downstream. River levées are another feature that may collapse during violent earthquake shaking, with the risk that rivers spill onto the adjacent floodplains. Landslides may block river channels causing water to back-up and flood the valleys. Later such a natural dam may itself break or overflow creating another flood risk downstream.

The citizens of California and in particular those in San Francisco live in fear of what they term 'The Big One', an earthquake event to rival that of 1906. In that year, the city contained mainly wooden structures and unreinforced brick buildings. While many of these were badly damaged by seismic shaking, the greatest single cause of destruction was fire. Initiated by broken gas pipelines and severed electrical cables, the fire raged out of control for three days, burning down 500 city blocks. The problem was compounded by the fact that the earthquake had also destroyed the city's underground water supply network, leaving fire fighters without their key weapon in the fight. In Japan too, the city of Tokyo awaits the next great seismic event to match the Great Kanto earthquake of 1923. Numerous fires started when traditional wooden homes collapsed and were set ablaze by cooking stoves and open fires. These many fires combined to produce a phenomenon known as a fire storm. This engulfed city parks where 50,000 survivors of the initial event had taken refuge only to be burnt to death. All this initiated by a few minutes of ground shaking.

Liquefaction

This is the process by which soft or unconsolidated sediments amplify the effect of shaking ground. The effect can occur with either dry or wet sediments but is most clearly seen where there is significant water content. Liquefaction is similar to the effect of standing on sand and wiggling your toes. The sand that supported your weight when standing still, allows you to sink down into it when you move and water rises to the surface. Liquefaction occurs when sediment is shaken loose and starts to act as a liquid, often causing building foundations to sink or subside (Figure A66).

Water-saturated sediment

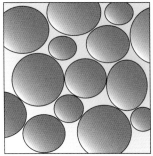

Water fills in the pore space between grains. Friction between grains holds sediment together.

Figure A66: Liquefaction effects in saturated sediment

Liquefaction

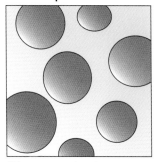

Water completely surrounds all grains and eliminates all grain to grain contact. Sediment flows like a fluid.

Beach or lake bed sediments, along with reclaimed land, are highly susceptible to liquefaction and it is wisest not to build on such material in seismically active areas. Not only will liquefaction cause land to fail to support buildings but underground service pipes may bend and fracture. Studies of the major earthquake that helped destroy San Francisco in 1906 showed that the buildings on loose, often reclaimed land were subject to four times as much damage as those founded on bedrock (Figure A67). In 1989, in the same Marina District, the Loma Prieta earthquake induced liquefaction that caused the collapse of buildings and ruptured gas and water pipelines (Figure A68). The resultant fires were eventually brought under control by pumping saltwater from the nearby bay.

Liquefaction may also cause land and anything built upon it to spread laterally so that roads or airport runways can crack open. In 1995, the Japanese port city of Kobe was struck by a magnitude 7.2 quake. The authorities had recently completed building the world's largest container port terminal on two artificially reclaimed

■ Alluvium, sands, clays and mud	■ Severe impact Level VII and above	The correlation between areas of more severe earthquake impact and those with weak unconsolidated deposits
□ Solid rock	□ Impact less than Level VII	

Figure A67: The relationship between geology and impact of the 1906 earthquake in San Francisco

islands in the bay. The loose infill material was water saturated, and during the 20 second quake it suffered widespread liquefaction and lateral settlement. Most of the port was damaged beyond use for many months and Japanese trade was significantly disrupted (Figure A69).

Figure A68: Damage from liquefaction in the Marina District in San Francisco, 1989

Source: U.S. Geological Survey/photo by JK Nakata

Figure A69: Earthquake damage at Kobe's port, 1995

Source: U.S. Geological Survey

Another phenomenon associated with liquefaction is that water and sand can rise to the surface as sand boils. While not particularly hazardous, they indicate the presence of liquefaction and the risk it poses. In this era of almost universal availability of camera phones, footage of these events is readily available after many contemporary earthquake events.

Tsunamis

It is probably true to say that as a result of the events of 26 December 2004 (Indian Ocean) and 11 March 2011 (Japan), the knowledge of the Japanese word 'tsunami' and the perception of its potential threat have become global. Technically known as seismic sea waves, tsunamis are fast moving high waves that radiate away from some large undersea earthquakes. When a section of oceanic crust rises or falls, a major earthquake follows, displacing a large amount of water and transferring a huge amount of energy. Tsunamis travel across the oceans at an amazing rate of 500–950 km/hr. At the surface, tsunamis spread out like ripples from a splash in a pond. In deep water, the transfer of energy is as a very long, low wave, often less than 1 m high and with a wavelength of 100–700 km. Far from the shore these may go undetected and unnoticed by shipping. However, a tsunami changes its nature when entering shallower water. As waves feel the seabed,

Figure A70: The Boxing Day tsunami 2004 on the coast of Thailand
Source: David Rydevik

friction slows them down and causes water to pile up. Some can reach heights of 30 m, as high as a 10 storey building. Perhaps surprisingly, the first sign of an approaching tsunami may be the withdrawal of water from the shore, at which point people should quickly move to higher ground. Between 5 and 30 minutes later the first great wave arrives as a surge of water, which may extend hundreds of metres inland, depending on the nature of the shoreline. Several waves may arrive, sometimes with many minutes between. Such events are relatively common in the Pacific, where a good tsunami warning system, based in Honolulu (Hawaiian Islands, USA) has existed for many years. The Indian Ocean did not have such a warning system and many of the people who lived along its coastline had little or no experience of the phenomenon (Figure A70).

The 2004 Boxing Day tsunami was the direct consequence of one of the largest earthquakes ever recorded. Off the north coast of the island of Sumatra, Indonesia, a 9.1 magnitude earthquake caused a section of seabed over 1500 km long to fall by 15 m. The earthquake itself was felt over a huge region but the tsunami that it generated was the principal cause of the estimated death toll of 245,000, spread over 11 countries around the Indian Ocean basin.

The impact of the 30 m high tsunami wave was indiscriminate, destroying both luxury tourist resorts and poor fishing settlements. The destruction was most severe in the Indonesian province of Aceh, the island of Phuket in Thailand, along the southern shores of Sri Lanka and the south Indian state of Tamil Nadu. In places the tsunami wave swept up to 3 km inland and it destroyed over 140,000 homes. Even 12 hours after the earthquake the tsunami still had the power to kill, when two people died in South Africa, 5000 km from the epicentre. A warning system has been established for Indian Ocean tsunamis to replicate the one in the Pacific Ocean.

Attempts to predict seismic events

Despite years of research, accurate prediction of earthquakes remains an elusive goal. Even our knowledge of where these phenomena happen is incomplete. In 1993, an earthquake of magnitude 6.4 struck Maharashtra in Western India, a region regarded as tectonically stable. No preparation existed, as it was believed that none was needed and 25,000 people perished as 50 villages and towns were destroyed. Most died as they slept, when the quake struck at 4 am. The region's poverty, especially in rural areas, meant that many injured were not adequately treated and disease broke out.

Even in the more advanced nations, surprises occur. The 1995 Northridge earthquake near Los Angeles, California, was on a previously unknown fault line running laterally to the San Andreas, arguably the world's most intensely studied fault.

While we can determine the regions in which the vast majority of earthquakes are likely to occur we cannot yet predict when they will happen or their magnitude. Some researchers argue that anything less than a fully accurate prediction in terms of location, time and scale would be a waste of time and effort and potentially dangerous, socially and economically.

The Japanese spend over £80 million each year on earthquake prediction studies, yet they have never successfully predicted a quake and currently say that they will have less that one minute to warn the population of Toyko-Yokahama of an imminent event. This minute is not really prediction time rather it is the maximum time lapse between an earthquake happening at sea, which they hope to detect, and the first seismic shaking arriving at the coast.

Precursors: The harbingers of doom

What would a class of A2 students think if their teacher went through the following steps at the beginning of their Geography class?

1. Directs them to leave their books at the front of the class.
2. Asks them to sit at separate desks.
3. Gives everyone a sheet of lined paper.
4. Guides them to write down their name and the numbers 1 to 10 down the left margin.
5. Instructs them that no communication, verbal or written will be allowed.

Most will be expecting a test or assessment of some sort to follow. Why? Because all these events point towards one course of action and perhaps they have experienced the same sequence before. This is an illustration of one of the main concepts behind earthquake prediction – the precursor: an event or action that signifies that another event, in this case an earthquake, will happen. Many suggestions have been made about things that may happen before an earthquake. Some, such as strange animal behaviour and 'earthquake weather', may be based on less than scientific observations; other signs are more measurable and therefore potentially reliable.

If we accept the idea that earthquakes are a sudden release of energy along a fault line, after stress has built up over time then all that is needed is to find and measure the characteristics that indicate growing levels of stress. These would be precursors. Potential characteristics include ground level uplift, subsidence or tilting. After several Japanese earthquakes, scientists studying records have shown that nearby surface changes have occurred. Sadly, after the event is too late.

An example of 'earthquake precursors' noticed after the event!

Well water at Kobe

An article in *New Scientist* in 1995 reported that a well 30 km from the epicentre of the Kobe earthquake had been studied for months before the earthquake. Researchers had continuously monitored the level of radon gas in the water of the well and on 7 January 1995 the level surged to very high levels and dropped to very low levels by 10 January. The earthquake struck one week later. Had the rapidly changing radon level been a precursor? Could a warning system be developed?

Dilation theory

The search for earthquake precursors is closely linked with dilation theory (dilatancy). This states that as the rocks along fault lines become stressed they expand (dilate) and numerous microscopic cracks open up. In turn, such micro cracks may change some characteristics of the rocks which, if measured, can warn of an impending quake. Dilating or expanding rocks are therefore linked to the suggested geophysical changes of rising, tilting or subsiding land. More subtle characteristics have been examined, such as the water levels in wells and the increasing release from the ground of radon gas which is a natural process. Laboratory experiments show that stressed rock samples will show small alterations in their ability to conduct electricity, a value known as electrical resistivity. Other measurable changes include the potential decrease in the speed of transfer of seismic waves along with temperature, local gravity or magnetic variation. Ground testing equipment and remote satellite based imagery have been employed to test these ideas but none have yet been successfully used to predict an event with any accuracy.

Figure A71: The seismic gap at Loma Prieta

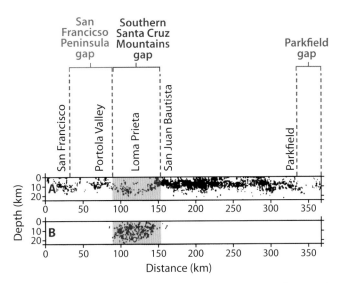

A – Earthquake foci between 1969–1989 along San Andreas Fault, San Francisco to Parkfield. Three gaps are identified.

B – The 1989 Loma Prieta earthquake and aftershocks 'fill in' the gap.

A second theory of earthquake prediction was based on work by American and Russian scientists and is known as the seismic gap theory. In brief, the concept suggests that in areas where earthquakes are known to happen regularly, but recent records show little activity, then stress must be building and seismic activity becomes more and more likely. One suggested example was that of the 1989 Loma Prieta earthquake along the San Andreas Fault (Figure A71). Before this earthquake, the seismic activity of the previous 20 years showed that three sections of the fault had shown little activity – one around San Francisco in the north, a second to the south near Parkfield and the third around the Santa Cruz Mountains south of San Francisco. The Loma Prieta earthquake and its aftershocks effectively filled in the Santa Cruz Gap, as Figure A71 shows. Ominously the San Francisco Gap remains.

Figure A72: The pattern of earthquake epicentres on the North Anatolian Fault, 1939–1999

Source: Data from U.S. Geological Survey

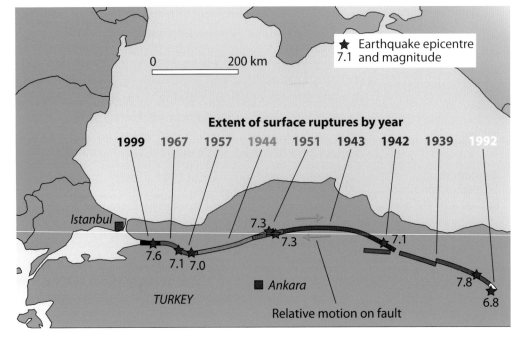

In another context, this seismic gap concept has been applied to a fault line, the North Anatolian Fault that runs along the northern coast of Turkey. Here a series of earthquakes has taken place over the last 80 years, each one with its epicentre a little further west along the fault. This has been likened to the closing of a zip. The idea is that the next earthquake epicentre will lie further west again. Unfortunately, this puts the city of Istanbul, with its population of over 14 million people directly in harm's way (Figure A72).

Figure A73: Video camera looking along the San Andreas fault at Parkfield

Source: J Adieman, U.S. Geological Survey

The Parkfield Experiment

After the 1989 Loma Prieta earthquake, researchers in California decided to catch a quake. Ironically the greatest difficulty of studying an earthquake to predict is to know when and where it will happen! What Californian scientists knew was that medium size earthquakes seemed to occur with regularity in and around Parkfield on the San Andreas Fault (Figure A73).

At Parkfield, medium sized earthquakes have been recorded at similar intervals – in 1857, 1881, 1901, 1922, 1934 and 1966. Based on this, Californian seismologists invested heavily in monitoring the San Andreas Fault in and around Parkfield. Laser ranging devices, tiltmeters and seismographs were deployed across the area. Ground deformation, electrical resistivity, magnetism, gravity and temperature were continuously monitored. The experts waited not for the expected 5 years but for 15. Then in 2004 the medium strength earthquake happened. Scientists spent the next year analysing all their collected data. The conclusion was long and technical in its language but essentially they failed to identify any pattern or precursors. One scientist said that in effect, "…it just happened, one moment nothing – the next an earthquake."

Some researchers suggested that the data needed to be gathered much nearer the focus and so a borehole has now been drilled several kilometres deep down to the San Andreas Fault and instruments are being installed, ready for the next event 20 or 30 years in the future.

Preparing for and responding to seismic activity

"Earthquakes do not kill people, falling structures do." This statement, while not entirely true, does stress that on many occasions it is the human built environment that contributes to the impact of these seismic events. The social and environmental impacts of earthquake activity are numerous:

Social impacts

- Death and injury.
- Human fear, anxiety and bereavement.
- Buildings collapse, wholly or in part, burying or trapping people.
- Other structures collapsing – bridges, flyovers or elevated route ways.
- Phone, road, rail and other communication links disrupted.
- Fracture of underground services – water, gas and sewage pipelines.
- Fires may be started or made worse by gas leaks.
- Homelessness, lack of adequate shelter, refugee camps and out-migration.
- The huge cost or debt in rebuilding infrastructure.
- Loss of jobs, closure of businesses and factories.

Environmental impacts

- Landslides moving or overwhelming buildings or whole settlements. Alternatively they may disrupt drainage causing flooding.
- Liquefaction and ground failure causing building foundations to sink or subside.
- Tsunamis have a devastating impact on coastlines and coastal settlement.

Any or all of these impacts may follow an earthquake but their intensity and severity may have less to do with the magnitude or nature of the earthquake than with the country or region involved. In general terms, nations that are more scientifically and economically advanced are better placed to prepare for and respond to an earthquake episode. Knowledge and perception are critical aspects concerning earthquake response. Knowledge relates to the scientific understanding of the nature and location of potential earthquake hazards, whereas perception is the broader awareness of these hazards and the degree to which awareness leads to action in preparation and planning.

Management of earthquake impact

The impact of an earthquake does not solely depend on its magnitude and duration but also on the degree to which the region is prepared for such a hazard. The management of earthquake activity starts before any event and can be summarised by the three Ps of: Prediction, Protection and Preparation.

Prediction

As discussed on pages 52–56, in the case of seismic activity, the many theories of prediction have not yet provided a working model. However, on the broader scale it is safe to suggest that significant earthquakes are certainly going to be experienced in some places given their tectonic setting: California, Alaska, Japan, New Zealand and Italy are an obvious few.

Protection

Protection is an area of earthquake management that has been rapidly developing, with the increasing use of information technology and computer modelling in engineering and building design. Hit and miss attempts to build earthquake resistant structures have been replaced by scientific design and testing. One example of this approach is Building Information Modelling (BIM). Each new seismic event for which data has been gathered adds to our understanding of their impact and threat. Designs can be tested 'to destruction' not just on physical shaking tables (Figure A74) but on screen by sophisticated simulation modelling. A number of the techniques employed to reduce the damaging impact to buildings in earthquake prone zones are illustrated by Figure A63.

One popular technique for engineers working in seismically active regions is base isolation. As the name suggests, this approach involves separating a building from its foundation. In one system a building sits on bearings made of rubber and lead. When an earthquake occurs the foundation can move without moving the structure above.

Japanese engineers have developed a new form of base isolation in which the system actually lifts buildings on a cushion of air. Ground sensors in the building automatically detect seismic activity and activate an air compressor system which forces air between the building and its foundation. In less than one second the cushion of air lifts the structure 3 cm above its foundations. After the event the compressor turns off, and the building settles back down to its foundation.

Figure A74: A four storey wooden frame building is tested using the world's largest outdoor shake table by researchers at the University of San Diego California on 17 August 2013

Source: REUTERS / Alamy Stock Photo

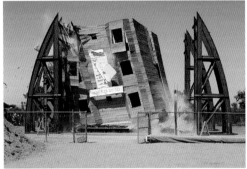

Protection is also about avoidance and reduction of risk. Land-use zoning may play an important role in reducing the impacts of seismic activity. Buildings should ideally avoid low-lying coastal plains where tsunamis are a threat and structures should not be placed on unconsolidated ground where liquefaction is likely to occur, amplifying the ground movement and increasing the threat of collapse.

Preparation – getting people ready

Preparation and perception go hand in hand. Regular emergency and evacuation drills can be used to educate the public, as well as the emergency services on how to be ready for a seismic event. Schools in earthquake prone countries have emergency procedures written into their teaching programs including the 'Duck and Cover' procedure used by Japanese and American children from an early age. California runs online simulation events and Japan now has both an earthquake practice event on September 1st and a similar national tsunamis event in November. In the more developed nations the emergency and military forces are required to draw up contingency plans in conjunction with other civil authorities to ensure that the co-ordination after the event is as efficient as possible.

Individual preparation by citizens includes taking steps to reduce the hazards posed by their own homes and having an emergency kit available that allows the family to be independent for up to 72 hours after an event.

Common safety advice tips issued to residents in earthquake prone regions

Have an earthquake response plan for your home and family:

- Take professional advice on how to make your home safer, such as bolting bookcases, fridges and water heaters securely to walls, and installing strong latches on cupboards.
- Identify a safe place in each room where nothing is likely to fall on you, where you can go to in an earthquake.
- Open a door as an emergency exit – doors may get wedged closed if the frame twists.

- Keep a supply of canned food, an up-to-date first aid kit, 12 litres of water per person, dust masks and goggles, a working battery-operated radio and flashlights, and a bottled gas stove.
- Know how to turn off your gas and water mains in case of leaks.

When the shaking begins:

- Drop down, take cover under a desk or table, protect your head and hold on.
- Stay indoors until the shaking stops and it is safe to exit.
- Stay away from windows. In a high-rise building, expect the fire alarms and sprinklers to go off during an earthquake.
- If you are in bed, stay there, protecting your head with a pillow.
- If you are outdoors, find a clear spot away from buildings, trees, and power lines. Drop to the ground.
- If you are in a car, slow down and drive to a clear place. Stay in the car until the shaking stops.
- Evacuate to a designated safety evacuation zone if a fire or other danger approaches.
- Tune in to local radio and do not act on any rumours that you hear.

CASE STUDY: Tohoku (2011), a small-scale study of preparing for and responding to seismic activity in Japan

In Japan, a wealthy, industrialised nation, earthquake preparation is one element of the national 'Disaster Management Plan'. The country also faces threats from volcanic activity, river floods, typhoons and storm surges. For much of the past 100 years Japan's awareness of the threat posed by seismic activity has been dominated by one event on 1 September 1923. That day the Great Kanto Earthquake struck the nation's capital, Tokyo, and Yokohama, leaving two devastated cities and over 140,000 people dead. The date is remembered annually when the whole nation practices an earthquake based evacuation and response drill. Japan's response was to study, map and understand the complex geology of its location on the boundary of three tectonic plates: the Pacific, Philippine and Eurasian Plates. The aim was to predict when and where the next major earthquake would strike. Despite decades of funding and research, the Japanese authorities have never managed to predict a single seismic event with enough accuracy to make it worthwhile.

Japan's long-term response to seismic activity

Japan's policy on disaster management in general is based on a report commissioned and published in 1963. This is reviewed, edited and re-published on an annual basis, taking into consideration new evidence from events and research. After each major earthquake event the report in subsequent years reflects on the lessons learned for both planning and response aspects of management in the short and long-term. The overall aim is to mitigate the impacts of disaster through DRR – Disaster Risk Reduction. The Japanese government takes the approach that the price of planning and implementing disaster countermeasures should be seen as an investment rather than a cost.

In the reconstruction phase after an earthquake, the aim is to apply the lessons that have been gained and in particular use the 'Build back better' principle. Japan has a

Figure A75: The Disaster Reduction and Human Renovation Institution (DRI) in Kobe, Japan

Source: 663highland

Figure A76: Published seismic hazard map of Japan based on NTE and TIE scenarios

well-deserved reputation for rapid recovery of its built-environment after an earthquake but the policy is for 'creative reconstruction' and not merely restoring what was there before. An earthquake that struck the city of Kobe in 1995 was an important test of the stricter building regulations introduced in 1981 and while some modern structures proved effective in resisting earthquake damage, others failed. As a result not only were homes and office blocks rebuilt but the new structures incorporated proven technology: deeper foundations in areas prone to liquefaction, shock absorbers in building foundations and the use of fire proof building materials. Extensive retrofitting was undertaken not only in the Kobe district but also across the country for both private and public buildings. After cases of falsified earthquake safety data involving new hotels and apartment blocks, additional regulations using independent double-checking of new buildings were introduced in 2007.

The Japanese government went further and developed the Disaster Reduction and Human Renovation Institution (DRI) (Figure A75). This led to the building of a research centre and a museum in central downtown Kobe, dedicated to earthquake research and the training of practitioners of Disaster Risk Reduction (DRR). The UN campaign 'Making Cities Resilient' in 2010, used Japan's DRI as its model of good practice.

Seismic planning in Japan is now based on two different scenarios: the Tokyo Inland Earthquake (TIE) and the Nankai Trough Earthquake (NTE). The TIE relates to potential events with a focus beneath the island and a land based epicentre, the NTE is the offshore event along the deep ocean trench that parallels the south eastern coast of Japan's main island (Figure A76).

Figure A77 is based on the plan for disaster mitigation for a TIE – Tokyo Inland Earthquake. Starting in 2014 the plan projects up to 2024 and includes the city's hosting of the 2020 summer Olympics and Paralympics.

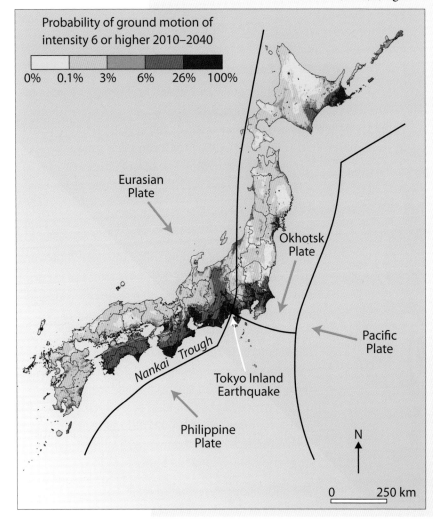

Probability of ground motion of intensity 6 or higher 2010–2040

0%   0.1%   3%   6%   26%   100%

Eurasian Plate

Okhotsk Plate

Pacific Plate

Nankai Trough

Tokyo Inland Earthquake

Philippine Plate

N

0   250 km

Figure A77: The development of the disaster mitigation plan for the Tokyo Inland Earthquake (TIE) emergency

Source: Information from 'White paper disaster management plan in Japan 2015, Summary', Cabinet Office, Japan

History of the measures for the Tokyo Inland Earthquake emergency	The disaster mitigation goals (next ten years)	Measures to achieve these goals
2005 Outline of the Tokyo Inland Earthquake measures. 2006 Risk reduction strategy for the Tokyo Inland Earthquake. 2011 **The Tohoku event in March**. 2013 The Special Measures Act for Tokyo Inland Earthquake passed. Report on damage estimates and countermeasures for Tokyo Inland Earthquake. 2014 Basic plan and Business Continuity Plan of Tokyo Inland Earthquake approved.	1. Reduce the potential fatalities by half from the estimate* of 23,000 people. 2. Reduce the number of potentially destroyed or burned buildings by half from the estimate* of 610,000 buildings. * The estimates are based on a projected large earthquake epicentre in the south of the Tokyo Metropolitan Region.	(i) Ensure function of central government: • Personnel (aiming for 100% by 2016). • Stockpile supplies (aiming for 100% by 2016). • Alternative buildings for all government departments and agencies (aiming for 100% by 2015). (ii) Response to the massive human casualties and property damage: • Reinforce housing (was 79% in 2008, aiming for 95% by 2020). • Expand Disaster Rapid Response units (form 12 units by 2018). • Disaster waste disposal (was 24% in 2014, aiming for 100% by 2024).

Japan 2011 – The Tohoku or Great Eastern Japan Earthquake

This earthquake registered 9 on the Richter scale and struck on Friday 11 March at 2.46 pm. Its epicentre was 72 km off the east coast of Honshu, Japan's main island, and its shallow focus lay 24 km below the ocean surface. The seismic shaking was unusually long at six minutes. In this region, the Pacific Ocean Plate subducts beneath the overriding Eurasian Plate. Centuries of stress built up between the two tectonic plates was released by the event.

Figure A78: Location of the Tohoku earthquake and tsunami, 2011

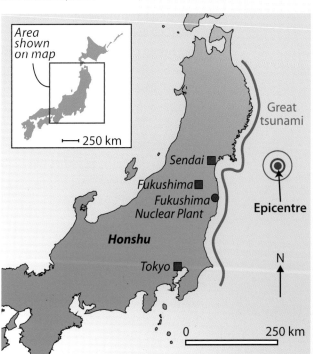

The impacts

The death toll was 16,000, (officially over 2000 were still recorded as missing five years after the event). Most were drowned by the 30 m tsunami waves which arrived at the coast within an hour of the earthquake. These waves swept over and destroyed the defensive tsunami seawalls. The presence of tsunami defences indicates that such a threat was recognised but most scientists had vastly underestimated the potential scale of an earthquake in this region. Over 47,000 buildings were destroyed with a further 144,000 damaged and the total cost was estimated at US$360 billion.

The authorities were able to issue a warning to the residents of Tokyo one minute before the strong shaking hit the city, thanks to Japan's earthquake early warning system. The country's stringent seismic building codes and early warning system prevented many deaths from the earthquake, by stopping high-speed trains and factory assembly lines. Some people in Japan also received texted alerts of the earthquake and tsunami warnings on their mobile phones.

However, the earthquake triggered a major secondary threat when the tsunami it generated caused a cooling system failure at the Fukushima Nuclear Power Plant, which resulted in a nuclear meltdown and the release of radioactive materials. Over 40% of the nation's nuclear power supply was shut down and environmentally the area adjacent to the plant may remain hazardous for up to 30 years. Due to the shutting down of the power plants damaged in the earthquake, sporadic nationwide power cuts were necessary and factories including Toyota and Sony halted production.

The response

Immediately, the Japanese Government declared an emergency in the affected area, mobilised the national defence forces of over 100,000 soldiers and initiated the national disaster plan. Central government declared that all the main highways in the region were for emergency response traffic only and the disaster response offices in each local prefecture (district) began operations. A tsunami warning was issued three minutes after the earthquake, giving coastal residents 20–40 minutes to evacuate. The government asked for international help with specialist search and rescue teams and 91 other nations offered aid. Modern social media sites, such as Twitter, brought people information updates more rapidly than the traditional media. Medical teams, therapists and social workers were dispatched to the area by the health ministry and treatment gradually shifted from dealing with physical injuries to psychotherapy needs. The scale of the tsunami had overwhelmed the coasts' purpose built defensive walls and while these would be rebuilt, it is unlikely that they will be any higher than before. The speed with which the Japanese authorities rebuilt some of the regional infrastructure was impressive. Within a week motorways were reopened and new accommodation for those made homeless was being constructed.

The Tohoku mega earthquake was recorded by more precise instruments than any previous event, generating the data for researchers to significantly improve earthquake models and forecasting, both in Japan and beyond.

In 2011 two warnings were needed, firstly for the earthquake itself and then for the subsequent tsunami. Japan's existing high-tech warning system to alert the public of an imminent earthquake was activated just eight seconds after the first wave of the earthquake was detected. The message was sent to 124 television stations and it automatically stopped bullet trains and lifts.

Secondly, tsunami warnings were broadcast through television, radio and officials on loudspeakers. Firemen drove around directing citizens to flee to high ground. However, one consequence of the earthquake was that power cuts had put some television and radio systems out of action so the tsunami warning did not reach many coastal residents. One official reported that, in relation to the tsunami, "Many people said they weren't able to hear any of the broadcasts, the waves were bigger than expected, and many went back after the first wave to check things out." As a consequence of these issues, warnings are now sent to every mobile phone in the area, along with email messages and broadcasts on local radio. To improve the speed of people's response, broadcasters are now directed to use urgency in their voices. Due to the death of 18 foreign nationals, one channel now broadcasts its warnings in English, Chinese and Korean to alert foreigners working or visiting Japan. Overall, a simpler evacuation message is now used just directing people to get away from the sea and on to higher ground. The exception is for ships in harbour that are directed to head out to sea and deeper water as quickly as possible.

The mega earthquake and tsunami in 2011 was located off the north eastern coast and was not fully anticipated by the seismologists, its scale shocked the Japanese authorities. As noted, Japan has a national earthquake drill on 1 September each year but as a result of the 2011 seismic event additional drills were developed. The Promotion of Tsunami Countermeasures Act was passed and this introduced 5th November as Tsunami Preparedness Day. Around this date local government departments, in conjunction with private companies, are required to run practice drills based primarily on the evacuation of people from tsunami risk districts. In 2014 there were eight earthquake or tsunamis drills across Japan involving private and public transport networks. Another outcome of the 2011 event was the clarification of two terms linked to evacuation: 'Evacuation sites' are designated places for immediate escape from tsunamis while 'Evacuation shelters', such as schools or community centres, are designed for longer term accommodation of people in the aftermath of a tsunami.

Figure A79: The devastated aftermath of the 2011 earthquake and tsunami

Source: U.S. Navy photo by Mass Communication Specialist 1st Class Matthew M. Bradley/ Released

Exam Questions

1. With reference to the nature of seismic events distinguish between P, S and L waves. [7]

2. Study Resource A which shows a model used in Japan to plan for a tsunami in a coastal town.

   Describe and explain how the different elements of the plan relate to the hazard posed by a tsunami. [9]

Resource A: Tsunami response plan

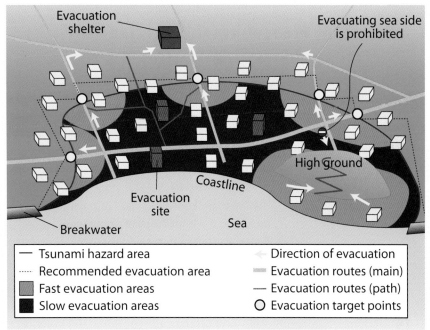

3. Explain how seismic gap theory and dilation have been used to attempt to predict seismic events. [8]

References

Geofile articles:
'Christchurch: back from the brink', *Geofile* 755, series 34, 2015–2016

Geo Factsheet:
'Haiti earthquake 2010', *Geo Factsheet* 285, Curriculum Press
'After the tsunami: learning the lessons', *Geo Factsheet* 341, Curriculum Press
'Lahars, landslides and tsunami – the devastating impacts of secondary hazards', *Geo Factsheet* 348, Curriculum Press

Disaster planning in Japan:
http://www.bousai.go.jp/kaigirep/hakusho/pdf/WPDM2015_Summary.pdf

Earthquake nature and hazards:
http://earthquake.usgs.gov/hazards/

Tropical Ecosystems – Nature and Sustainability

1. LOCATIONS AND CLIMATES OF MAJOR TROPICAL BIOMES

Case studies

Global distribution, location and nature of biomass

Students should be able to:

(i) demonstrate knowledge and understanding of the distribution, climatic and biomass (flora and fauna) characteristics of tropical forest, tropical grassland and desert ecosystems

(ii) demonstrate knowledge and understanding of the role of the Hadley Cell, including the Inter Tropical Convergence Zone (ITCZ), in the location and climate characteristics of tropical forest, tropical grassland and desert ecosystems

Living on the islands off the coast of continental Western Europe, it is difficult to imagine any connection to the climatic extremes of the tropics but in reality geologically, geographically and ecologically speaking, the links are strong. The history of the rocks of these islands reveals that slowly shifting continents have drawn them on a 100 million year journey through the low latitudes around the Equator (Figure A13). The jungle, grassland and desert climates of our past have left traces such as the desert sandstones beneath the summit of Scrabo, County Down, and seams of coal, the fossilised remains of a wet equatorial forest, that later fuelled our industrial revolution. Today the fear of global climate change firmly links our futures to the regions where the sun rises high throughout the year – the tropics.

The Tropics of Cancer and Capricorn are the lines of latitude that respectively circle the world at 23½° north and south of the Equator (0°). They mark the locations on the Earth's surface where the overhead sun reaches its most northerly and southerly position each year. The large section of the Earth's surface between these lines is known as the tropics and within these low latitudes lie a variety of environments with distinctive communities of flora (plant) and fauna (animal) life. These include the most biodiverse land and ocean based ecosystems on our planet.

These large-scale tropical ecosystems are examples of biomes and our aim is to examine their nature and the sustainability or otherwise of their management. Figure B1 shows the global extent of three tropical zones – the tropical forests, tropical grasslands and tropical deserts.

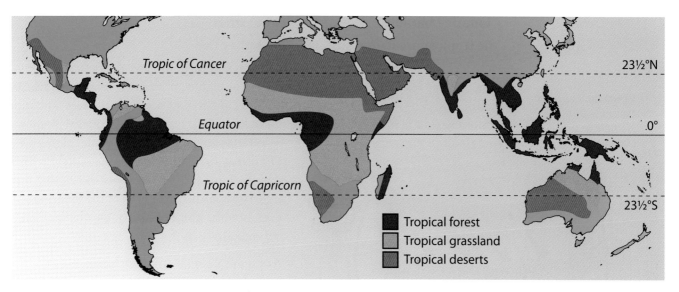

Tropic of Cancer   23½°N

Equator   .0°

Tropic of Capricorn   23½°S

Tropical forest
Tropical grassland
Tropical deserts

Figure B1: The global distribution of tropical biomes

Distribution of tropical biomes

1. Forest covers about one quarter of the tropics' land area, representing 5% of the Earth's surface area. Tropical forest coverage has been declining significantly in many regions. Most tropical forest lies between 10° latitude north and south of the Equator, with three concentrations:

   • Latin America, including the Amazon and Orinoco basins, 53% of the world total.

   • Equatorial Africa, including the Congo basin, and Madagascar, 26% of world total.

   • South East Asia, stretching from India to Northern Australia, 20% of world total area.

2. Tropical grassland or savanna covers a wide zone within the tropics. This biome incorporates a range of vegetation communities, from open woodland with grass, through pure grasslands to scrub. Most are located between 5° and 20° north and south of the Equator. Africa dominates the distribution, with a belt stretching across the continent from West to East Africa and as far as Zambia in the south. In South America it comprises the Llanos of Venezuela and the Campos of the Brazilian Plateau. Finally, in North Australia, Queensland and the Northern Territory have tropical grasslands.

3. Tropical desert is also found across a range of continents, most lying between 15° and 30° north and south of the Equator, and commonly in the centre or towards western coasts. In the northern hemisphere lie the Mohave and Sonora deserts of South West USA (North America) and the largest of all deserts, the Sahara across North Africa. Further east the desert biome runs across Saudi Arabia, through Iran, to the Thar Desert of Pakistan in Asia. Their counterparts in the southern hemisphere are the Atacama Desert of South America, the Namib or Kalahari Desert of southern Africa and the Great Australia Desert.

Within each tropical biome there may be great variation. In North Africa alone at least four types of tropical grassland are normally distinguished. For our purposes we will describe and study each of the three major tropical biomes by examining their common features.

Many physical factors influence the characteristics of ecosystems including geology, relief, time for development and most importantly of all climate.

Climatic characteristics of tropical biomes

The tropical circulation system – The Hadley Cell

In the tropics, or low latitudes, one circulation feature dominates the pattern of annual climate – the Hadley Cell. First described in the eighteenth century by the then British Astronomer Royal, George Hadley, this model of circulation of both surface and upper atmosphere air is fundamental to the climatic controls on our three tropical biomes. The Hadley Cell is one element in the tri-cellular global circulation model of the dominant airflows around planet Earth. Although modern research has shown that the mid-latitude and polar cells of the model are oversimplifications of reality, the Hadley Cell still remains a useful starting point.

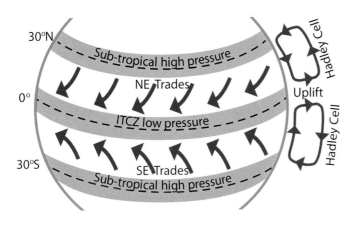

Figure B2: The Hadley Cell – the primary element in tropical circulation

As Figure B2 shows, in each hemisphere the surface element of its Hadley Cell is a pattern of persistent winds, blowing from about 30°N or S, towards the Equator. These are the north-east and south-east trade winds. These winds meet around the Equator at a zone dominated by surface low pressure and the related vertical uplift of air. This is the ITCZ (Inter Tropical Convergence Zone) and above this region convection currents of rising air commonly lead to the development of cloud filled skies and heavy convection rain, especially in the late afternoon. Higher up in the atmosphere, near the tropopause (16 km), the rising air moves laterally away to the north and south to eventually sink back towards the Earth's surface at around 30°. Here, this subsiding air creates the sub-tropical high pressure zones found on the surface at these latitudes. As the air descends towards the surface it is compressed and is warmed. This means any condensation of water vapour in the air is unlikely, so clouds and rain rarely develop. Consequently, under this subsiding air at the sub-tropical high pressure zones lie the tropical desert biomes (hot and dry).

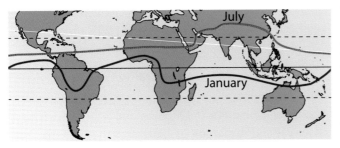

Figure B3: The annual migration of the Intertropical Convergence Zone

While the Hadley Cell dominates the circulation of air and energy in the tropics, it is not fixed in location. As Figure B3 illustrates, its position follows the annual migration of the overhead sun so that in the northern hemisphere summer (June–August) it moves north, shifting the winds, pressure belts and the region of equatorial rainfall. Surface weather conditions near 30°N and S remain hot and arid all year. At the Equator the climate remains hot and wet all year round, but between these regions lie the tropical semi-arid grassland regions where rain falls for only part of the year and temperatures are high.

Tropical climates

The climate characteristics of tropical forests

The climate statistics for Uaupes in the Amazon Basin (Figure B4) show this region typically has:

1. high temperatures, around 25°C throughout the year, with a low annual temperature range of only 1 or 2°C. This is due to days that are consistently around 12 hours long, giving large quantities of solar insolation along with a high overhead sun angle.

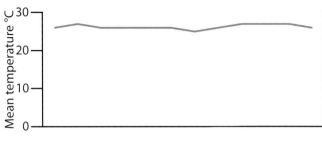

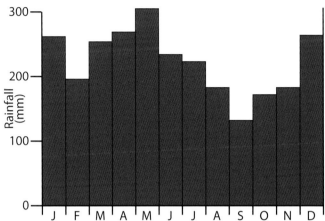

2. high annual rainfall, a total of at least 1800 mm a year but often up to 2800 mm. This rain falls in thunderous downpours on most days of the year. The total annual rainfall varies by 15–20% from the long-term average (similar to UK variation).

Explanation of the nature of the tropical forest climate

Despite its annual migration between the Tropic of Cancer (23½°N) and the Tropic of Capricorn (23½°S) (Figure B5) the sun always remains high in the sky in the vicinity of the Equator, where it shines for around 12 hours every day. This accounts for the consistent high monthly average temperatures in this region, which rarely vary by more than a few degrees. Rainfall is likewise persistent. The region is dominated by the meeting at the surface of the trade winds, the north-east trades from the northern hemisphere and the south-east trades from the south; the region known as the Inter Tropical Convergence Zone (ITCZ).

Uaupes, Amazon Basin, Brazil, latitude 0˚
Annual temperature range is 2˚C
Total rainfall = 2677 mm

Uaupes (0°)	J	F	M	A	M	J	J	A	S	O	N	D
Temp (°C)	26	27	26	26	26	26	25	26	27	27	27	26
Rain (mm)	262	196	254	269	305	234	223	183	132	172	183	264

Figure B4: Climate statistics for a tropical forest location

Despite this year round convergence of winds the surface air pressure remains low. The only possible explanation is that the air rises upwards into the atmosphere as a series of convection currents. Indeed this is the main mechanism at the ITCZ, where cells of rising air lift and expand up to the tropopause, on average some 16 km above the surface. As the warm, humid air rises it expands and cools reaching its dew point temperature. Condensation of water vapour commences and clouds form. The strong uplift continues, especially in the late afternoon when the ground is at its maximum heat, and towering vertical clouds develop. These are cumulonimbus clouds and are associated with thunderous bursts of intense rainfall. The equatorial forests have such late afternoon heavy rain for an hour or so most days of the year. In the city of Manaus (3°S) on the Amazon River in central Brazil, rain falls on average 265 days a year.

Figure B5: Annual migration of the overhead sun

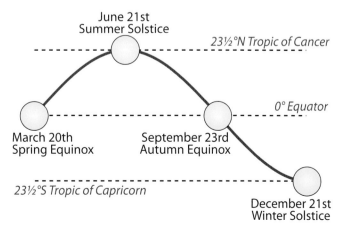

These conditions of abundant heat, light and water are an ideal growing environment, helping to explain the abundance, productivity and biodiversity of tropical rainforests. It is worth noting that with increasing distance from the Equator a marked seasonal variation in rainfall emerges, with a drier season during

Figure B6: Annual migration of the overhead sun

'winter' months. This seasonality does not restrict the growth of forest until 10–15 degrees away from the Equator (Figure B6).

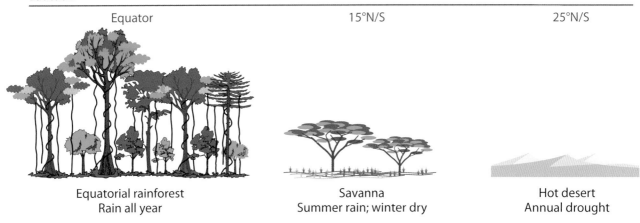

Equatorial rainforest
Rain all year

Savanna
Summer rain; winter dry

Hot desert
Annual drought

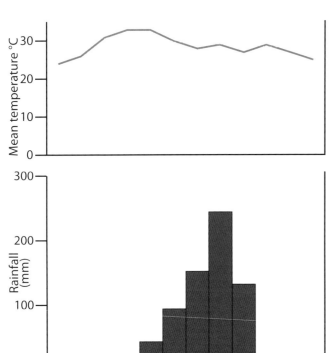

Sokoto, Nigeria, latitude 13°N
Annual temperature range is 9°C
Total rainfall = 691 mm

The climate characteristics of tropical grasslands

The climate statistics for Sokoto in Nigeria (Figure B7) show the seasonal contrasts of the tropical grassland region between a 'winter' drought and the 'summer' rain. The wet or rainy season lasts 5–9 months, with annual totals of 400–1500 mm. The annual rainfall total often varies unpredictably by 50–70% from the long-term average. Temperatures vary little, remaining hot, normally over 22°C during the year. The expected summer maximum is reduced by the cloud cover associated with the seasonal rains. Annual solar energy inputs are high and desiccating (drying) winds are common, especially in the winter drought season.

Figure B7: Climate statistics for a tropical grassland location

Sokoto (13°N)	J	F	M	A	M	J	J	A	S	O	N	D
Temp (°C)	24	26	31	33	33	30	28	29	27	29	27	25
Rain (mm)	0	0	3	10	43	94	152	244	132	13	0	0

Explanation of the nature of the wet and dry tropical grassland climate

The tropical wet and dry climate is one of the most significant in the world. Around one third of the world's 7.5 billion population lives under it. The most extreme version is the monsoon climate of South East Asia but it is common to all regions between the Equatorial hot, wet climate and the hot dry deserts. At its simplest, these areas are the transition zone between the wet tropical forest and the dry tropical desert.

The low pressure and rains of the ITCZ follow the overhead sun as it migrates during the year, so regions further from the equator receive a period of rain during their summer months. Six months later, as the overhead sun moves away, the high pressure dry conditions of the higher tropics move in to give a dry winter season. It should be noted that while the position of the overhead sun travels between the Tropics of Capricorn (23½°S) and Cancer (23½°N), a total 47 degrees of latitude, the pressure and wind belts do not normally shift so far. This is the only tropical biome that has a strong seasonal contrast during the year but, unlike our own in temperate Europe, this change is based on rainfall patterns and not temperature differences (Figure B8).

Figure B8: Map of low latitude surface winds and pressure belts

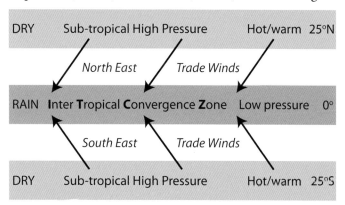

The climate characteristics of tropical (hot) deserts

Figure B9: Climate statistics for a tropical desert location

The graph and statistics for Ain Salah (Figure B9) illustrate the nature of the tropical desert climate.

1. Temperatures are high due to:
   - the clear skies that allow for high levels of daily and annual insolation.
   - the long days and high angle of the sun during the summer.

2. The seasonal difference in temperatures is between warm and very hot.

3. Rainfall totals are low; the technical desert limit is an annual total below 250 mm. Any rainfall is more likely in the summer months, and is often confined to a few scattered periods of rain or in some places mist or coastal fog.

Explanation of the nature of the hot tropical desert climate

The hot desert climate is primarily the product of the second limb of the Hadley Cell. Around 20–30° north and south, air descends from the tropopause towards the ground surface. This same air had risen above the equatorial region becoming dry as it lost its moisture as convectional cloud and rain. Having travelled away from the Equator in the upper troposphere, the air

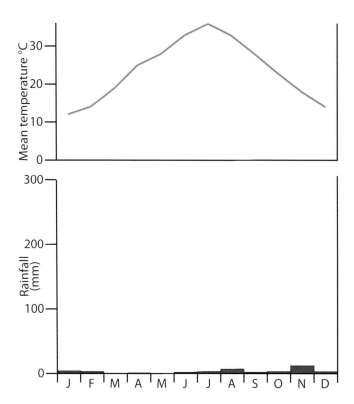

Ain Salah, Algeria – latitude 27°N
Annual temperature range is 24°C
Total rainfall = 40 mm

Ain Salah (27°N)	J	F	M	A	M	J	J	A	S	O	N	D
Temp (°C)	12	14	19	25	28	33	36	33	28	23	18	14
Rain (mm)	4	3	0	1	0	2	3	7	2	3	12	3

Figure B10: Detail of subsiding limb of the Hadley Cell

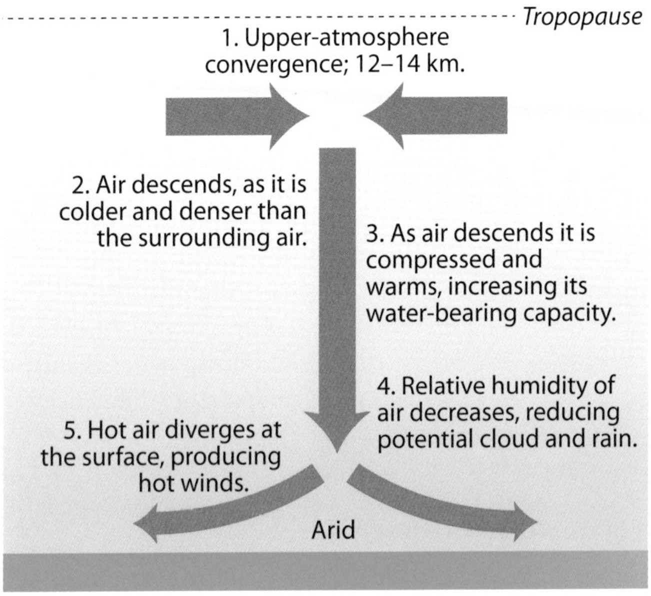

now sinks to form high pressure conditions on the surface. The tropical high pressure region is the source of the surface trade winds (Figure B2). As the air descends it becomes compressed and warms; this ensures that condensation of water vapour is unlikely and so cloud and rain rarely form over these regions (Figure B10).

- *Tropopause*

1. Upper-atmosphere convergence; 12–14 km.

2. Air descends, as it is colder and denser than the surrounding air.

3. As air descends it is compressed and warms, increasing its water-bearing capacity.

4. Relative humidity of air decreases, reducing potential cloud and rain.

5. Hot air diverges at the surface, producing hot winds.

Arid

As skies are clear in these latitudes then daytime temperatures are likely to become hot (up to 45°C), especially in the summer when the sun is at its highest and the days may be up to 14 hours long. A feature of the tropical deserts is that the daily or diurnal temperature range is often very high, even 30°C or more. Surfaces heat up rapidly during long cloudless days but under the same clear skies they cool rapidly at night.

Other than the Sahara and Arabian Deserts, most tropical deserts are focused on the western sides of continents. This is due to the occurrence of off-shore cold ocean currents that prevent moist air being carried onto the land bringing rain to these regions. The Atacama Desert of Peru is the world's driest, with some places having no recorded rainfall for centuries.

Biomass (flora and fauna) characteristics of tropical biomes

The term biomass is used to describe the total amount of living organic matter in an area or biome. It comprises both plant and animal material and is usually measured by weight either as a total or an average per unit of area. In a particular woodland area the biomass could be stated as the total weight of all the trees, all other plants and animals living in or on the trees and in the soil. The table in Figure B11 contains biomass figures, both total and average, for the three major tropical biomes.

Figure B11: Biomass and productivity figures for three tropical biomes

Biome	Total biomass (billon tonnes)	Average biomass (kg/m²)
Tropical grassland (savanna)	60	4.0
Tropical rainforest	765	45
Tropical desert	13	0.7

Tropical forest

Tropical rainforests cover 5% of the Earth's land surface. The forest varies in nature from swamp or wetland forest, mountain forests in highland regions, to the classic closed canopy forest of lowland equatorial regions known as selvas. Plant and animal species are numerous and the number of known species increases almost daily as remote forests in places such as the Congo Basin, Peruvian highlands and Borneo are subject to scientific exploration.

Statistically the tropical forest's enormous biomass and its incredible rates of productivity make it the world's leading land-based ecosystem. A typical biomass figure for the tropical forest is 45 kg/m² compared to 26 kg/m² in the temperate deciduous forests of Europe. The ideal climatic growing conditions have ensured that a vast range of species thrive in these regions. There are over 40,000 recorded plant species in the

Figure B12: Tropical forest structure and plant adaptation

Amazon forests, including some prized for hardwood timber (mahogany, ebony, rosewood and greenheart), food (Brazil nuts from the castanheiro tree, cocoa and sweet potato) and industrial raw materials (the rubber tree, Hevea brasiliensis).

Structure	Micro-habitat	Organisms
Emergent layer	Exposure to winds and full sunlight. Large daily temperature variation.	The tallest trees with broad crowns, slender trunks (boles) with few branches. Lianas and epiphytic flowers.
Canopy layer	Absorbs 70–80% of solar insolation.	Continuous layer of crowns of smaller or younger trees. Lianas and creepers. Main habitat for forest animals, including climbing mammals.
Shrub layer	Dark, drier with less temperature variation.	Young trees, often species that bear flowers and fruit on trunks and branches. Animals often move between trees and ground.
Ground layer	Sheltered, little daily temperature change. Little wind and slow growth due to heavy shading.	Tall ferns but little else, buttress roots of trees and some seedlings especially below any gaps in canopy. Termites, ants, bacteria and fungi are common.

The flora of tropical forests forms a strongly layered structure as plants compete for the available sunlight. Figure B12 shows a cross-section view of the four strata in the forest biome, with the key habitat and plant features identified. Trees are very tall, with the highest emergent species reaching 50 m, the height of an 18 storey building. The trees have long, smooth, relatively narrow trunks, with few branches until the large crown near the top. This height, trunk form and heavy crown, combined with shallow roots makes for an unstable tree but many have buttress or plank roots (Figure B13). These extend above ground, reaching three or four metres above the soil surface to support these giant plants. The tree root networks are shallow as only the surface organic layer of these deep soils stores any useful nutrients. Beneath the taller emergent trees is a continuous canopy of green, like a vast sea when viewed from above. In the gloom beneath this is an understorey or shrub layer of young tree saplings, the immature future canopy, along with smaller tree species.

In the closed forest the canopy created by tree crowns blocks out almost all light, 90% in places, severely limiting any ground plant growth. Unable to survive beneath the canopy, numerous smaller plants actually live on the trees. These are epiphytes – ferns and flowers including orchids, which commonly seed themselves where a branch meets the main trunk. The Amazon Basin alone supports over 500 species of orchid. Woody lianas hang down from the tree branches and take root in the ground. Other parasitic plant species, such as the strangler fig, grow up other trees using their support to reach for the sunlight and may eventually kill their hosts.

The fauna of the forest also has a layered element, often termed stratum specificity. Apes, monkey and bird species are found high in tree canopies, with frogs, lizards and deer species on the ground, while insect species by the thousand inhabit every possible habitat. Some 600 bird species (20% of the Earth's total) are found in the Amazon Basin. However, such abundance does not mean that the biome is a stable and resilient system. Despite the biodiversity of these forests, the number of any one species may be small as they inhabit highly specific niches in the habitat. This in turn means that plants and animal species are vulnerable and that any interference, even over a small area, may cause extinction. The interrelationships within the ecosystem are incredibly complex and research has only begun to comprehend their nature.

The vast productivity of the tropical forests reflects two key factors: climate and time.

1. Climate is fundamental to the richness of the forest's luxuriant flora and fauna. As far as vegetation is concerned, the bright, hot and humid climate of this region represents the perfect environment for growth:

    • Long hours of uninterrupted photosynthesis throughout 12 months of the year.

    • No temperature limitation – frost is unknown.

    • A continuous and abundant water supply from rainfall.

2. Tropical forests are ancient. While successive glaciations have repeatedly rewritten the landscapes and climate of the higher latitudes, including the hot deserts, many equatorial regions have remained stable. This fact alone may explain the biodiversity, as evolutionary processes have developed numerous responses to the various ecological niches available.

Figure B13: Rainforest producers and consumers

Forest cross-section a river bank, Madre de Dios, Peru

Epiphytic mosses and orchids on canopy tree species

Buttressed root base of an emergent giant, Tambopata Nature Reserve, Peru

A well camouflaged, four metre long, bushmaster snake awaits prey by a forest path

A curl-crested aracari toucan perched high in forest canopy

A cayman basks in stealth mode on a river bank

Tropical grasslands

The tropical grassland or savanna is, in effect, a transitional biome between the forest and the desert. While the dominant species, as the biome's name suggests, are grasses, specialist trees are also found in the areas closer to the equator where the dry season of 'winter' is short. Uniquely, of the three tropical biomes the grasslands are seasonal and the visual contrast between the abundant biomass of tall grasses of the wet season and the parched scrubland of the dry months is strong (Figure B14). Local conditions, including geology, relief and the length of the dry season will determine the exact amount of vegetation ground cover. Figures for biomass in tropical grasslands are averaged over the year at 4 kg/m², less than 10% of the tropical forest. Three metre high grasses can flourish in summer providing rich grazing for herbivores. The dry season lasts between two and nine months, increasing roughly with latitude from the forest regions. In this annual drought the grasses die back leaving only tussocks (clumps) of dried blades of grass, with seeds or rhizome roots beneath the surface. The tussocks of grass help protect the plants by conserving moisture. The grass leaves or blades are waxy to reduce respiration losses and silver in colour to reflect away light. Scattered amidst the grasses are highly adapted tree species: acacias, thorn trees and the distinct baobab or bottle tree. These are more common along water courses or in low-lying hollows where water may be found in the dry winter season. Baobab trees (Figure B15) use thick bark, stubby branches and small leaves to reduce their loss of moisture, and have a wide net of shallow roots to find water. Acacias also reduce water loss by replacing leaves with thorns and have tap roots that penetrate deep into the soil to source moisture that the roots of grasses and other trees cannot reach. The savanna grasslands of Africa are not only the largest extent of this tropical biome, they also provide the best examples of both plant and animal species that are closely adapted to this one ecosystem.

Figure B14: Tropical grassland flora change between the wet (top) and dry (bottom) seasons

Source: Rod Waddington (top) and © Nevit Dilmen (bottom)

The East African Rift Valley is home to the world's greatest concentration of grassland grazers, along with their iconic predators and (probably) wildlife documentary film makers. Across wide stretches of savanna herds of hooved mammals migrate, following the arrival of the summer rains that produce their vegetation food supply. Elephants, zebras, wildebeest, giraffes, impalas, gazelles and antelopes graze on the grasses and browse trees in huge numbers (Figure B15). In turn, this mobile 'larder' is the prey for lions and leopards, along with the scavenging hyenas and vultures. In Australia, the equivalent primary and secondary consumers are the kangaroo and wallaby, and the dingo and fox.

Figure B15: Tropical grassland fauna

Source: Michael Taylor (top two) and Ferdinand Reus (bottom)

Giraffes browse in woodland savanna

Savanna grazers

A baobab tree and an elephant, Tanzania

Tropical deserts

The plants and animals of the tropical deserts are highly specialised, having adapted their features and their behaviour to this very challenging environment. Food chains in the desert biome tend to be short but food webs can be complex, as many species of animals are omnivorous, eating any available food source in the limited biomass of the desert.

Most of the flora has evolved to deal with long periods of drought and high temperatures; unlike animals they cannot relocate to avoid the harsh conditions. Desert biomes have a small biomass, averaging less than 1 kg in each square metre, or 2% of the tropical forest average biomass. Plants are often slow growing and

Figure B16: Tropical desert flora

Oasis town and sparse vegetation on the edge of Sahara Desert, Morocco

South American cacti species, Yves St Laurent garden, Marrakesh

Prickly pear cactus in North Africa, native of the Americas

Figure B17: The desert fox is physically and behaviourally adapted to the rigours of the desert

Source: Kkonstan

long-lived and the bio-diversity is restricted. Plants deal with the limited availability of water using a range of mechanisms:

- Succulents store water and have thick skins that reduce water loss. Cacti originated in Central and South America but have now been spread across most tropical arid and semi-arid regions. The prickly pear uses its fleshy stem and waxy skin to conserve moisture.

- Phreatophytes are plants with long tap roots that penetrate deep into the ground to access groundwater; the tamarisk bush native to North Africa is an example.

- Halophytes are plants adapted to cope with the salty conditions created by high rates of evaporation in deserts.

- Some species have seeds that can remain dormant in the ground for years until rare rainfall triggers their growth. Such plants may germinate, flower, develop new seeds and die back, all in a few short days. The saltbush, native to the Australian desert, is one such plant. In South America the Atacama Desert has been described as a 'sea of flowers' after rainfall, only to appear a barren landscape again within days.

- Many desert plants, including cacti, have thorns to replace leaves. These allow photosynthesis to take place within a minimum loss of water and also protect plants from grazing animal species in search of the moisture they store.

Desert fauna is equally specialised but may also have the advantage of moving underground to escape heat, or migrate seasonally to both cooler and moister environments. Examples of morphological (shape) adaptation in animals include:

- the large bat-like ears of the jack rabbit (Americas) and the desert fox or fennec (North Africa).

- longer legged species to raise bodies off the hot ground – the stilt walking lizard.

- humps to store fat used as fuel when the food supply is limited – the camel.

- light coloured skins that reflect away light and broad flat feet – the addax antelope (Sahara).

Behavioural adaptations include:

- drinking water from fog that condenses on skin – the sidewinder adder of the Namib Desert.

- using only nocturnal hunting activity – the golden mole again from the Namib.

- hibernating during the hot season – the desert tortoise in North America.

- migrating away in the hottest season – mainly by desert birds.

- the red kangaroo (Australia) seeking shade and spreading saliva on its skin for evaporative cooling.
- entering long dormant phases – some grasshoppers can shut down active life for months and even years.

Exam Questions

1. Describe and explain the climatic and biomass (flora and fauna) characteristics of the tropical grassland ecosystem. [10]

2. Study the map of West Africa in Resource A:

   (i) Identify the tropical biome likely to be found at:
   - Tombouctou
   - Ouagadougou
   - Ibadan [3]

   (ii) Explain the variation in the seasonal pattern and total annual rainfall across West Africa. [6]

Resource A: Variation in annual rainfall in West Africa

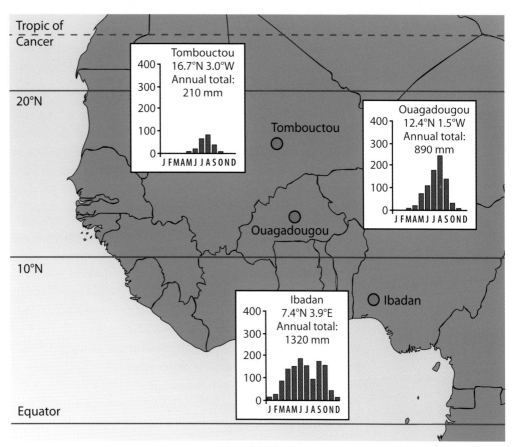

References

Geofile articles:
'The Savanna Biome', *Geofile 667, series 31, 2011–12*

Geo Factsheets:
'Energy flows and nutrient cycling in Tropical Rainforests', *Geo Factsheet 25, Curriculum Press*
'Grassland Biomes', *Geo Factsheet 125, Curriculum Press*

Rainforests and deserts:
http://www.geographypods.com/24-rainforests--deserts.html

2. MANAGEMENT AND SUSTAINABILITY IN ARID/SEMI-ARID TROPICAL ECOSYSTEMS

Case studies

Regional case study of irrigation in an arid/semi-arid tropical environment: Pakistan

Students should be able to:

(i) demonstrate knowledge and understanding of the use of irrigation in arid/semi-arid tropical environments

(ii) demonstrate knowledge and understanding of the environmental and socio-economic benefits and problems associated with the use of irrigation

(iii) demonstrate knowledge and understanding of possible solutions to the problems of using irrigation in arid/semi-arid tropical environments

It is probable that the origin of our own species, Homo sapiens, was in the tropics and in the wooded grassland savanna of East Africa. The tropics certainly helped stimulate the rise of human culture and some of the world's earliest civilisations. In the dry and seasonally dry tropics the need to maintain an adequate food supply encouraged the growth of effective agricultural systems along rivers that flooded annually. Based on this, water management developed through the deliberate addition of water to land – irrigation.

In the equatorial forests small groups of people have supplemented a hunting and gathering economy with small-scale agriculture for thousands of years. In most places, trial and error led to systems that were in balance with their environment and therefore sustainable. In the last 200 years, the tropics have seen an unprecedented change, with world population growth and mass migration putting pressure on many of these tropical environments and threatening their destruction.

The rapid clearance of rainforests and the desertification of marginal lands on desert fringes in the 1970s revealed the global environmental threat of poor land management. In response, the concept of sustainable development was born. Satellite images showed the Amazon Basin forests disappearing as roads opened the interior to thousands of migrants. Environmentalists quoted rates of expediential destruction that would leave the world without tropical forests within a lifetime. By the 1980s, tropical environments were constantly in the news with headlines of drought, desertification and famine in the semi-arid regions and wanton clearance for short-term gain in the forests. The outcry reached a peak at the Earth Summit at Rio de Janeiro in 1992. This UN conference produced three documents fundamental to a new approach to development:

1. The Climate Change Convention, an international response to the threat of global warming.

2. The Biodiversity Convention, concerning the protection of plant and animal species.

3. Agenda 21, a document proposing the adoption of policies to conserve and protect resources and the environment, ie Sustainable Development.

All three have important implications for the development of tropical environments.

Sustainable development

Entire texts have been written attempting to define this term, but in essence it can be described as economic growth and social progress that does not damage the prospects of future generations. One approach to the issue is to identify distinct aspects of sustainability that need to be addressed in any integrated management scheme. In the context of a region where a subsistence primary economy exists then three forms of sustainability might be identified:

1. Environmental sustainability – Can a management system be devised so that both local and global natural systems (ecosystem, soil, water and climate) remain undamaged?

2. Agricultural sustainability – Can the region produce a profitable output that can be maintained over the long-term?

3. Social sustainability – Can the system maintain the existing social structure and avoid exploitation, overpopulation or serious cultural change? Will all the local social groups benefit from the system?

Management and sustainability in arid and semi-arid tropical environments

Water management in all its forms has many implications for arid and semi-arid environments. These implications may be positive or negative, in economic, social and environmental terms. Semi-arid environments are inherently fragile and reliance on their productivity is hazardous. Repeatedly the evidence indicates that people, both within and outside the region, must take a large proportion of the responsibility for the problems that have been created. Irrigation has a long tradition in semi-arid tropical regions, including river floodplains such as the Nile in Egypt, the Indus in Pakistan and the Colorado in the USA.

Figure B18: Irrigation and irrigated land in Egypt and India

Irrigation is necessary if the limited and/or unreliable nature of rainfall in these regions is to be overcome. In arid or semi-arid tropical regions the length of the growing season is only limited by water supply: the bright, warm tropical conditions means crops can be grown throughout the year if water is made available. Indeed, two or even three annual harvests may be possible. In places irrigation has been in regular use for thousands of years, creating an effective and sustainable system. However, in others irrigation schemes have created serious environmental and socio-economic problems.

Irrigation is the artificial addition of water to the land. Some irrigation schemes entail simple redirecting of water; others are more radical, both in their scale and the transfer of water. Surface irrigation is the most common form found globally, using gravity to move water onto the land in a variety of ways. The alternative is where energy is needed to transfer water, such as the use of diesel, electrical or solar-powered pumps.

The water used for irrigation in the arid or semi-arid tropics comes from one of two sources:

1. Groundwater stores
2. Surface water stores either
    - permanent rivers that originate in wetter regions; or
    - reservoirs in which rainwater is collected during wet seasons.

Traditional schemes include flood or basin irrigation. In this water, usually diverted from a river in purpose-built channels, inundates the flat fields of the floodplain and soaks downwards. Alternatively, water may be raised from rivers or wells and transferred by gravity flow along small channels or furrows onto the land. In either case, water may be raised using a variety of traditional, human or animal powered devices. More modern systems can simply replace the lifting mechanisms with diesel-powered pumps or use more sophisticated and more water efficient distribution systems, such as trickle/drip and overhead sprinkler irrigation. There are numerous large and small-scale irrigation schemes operating in the tropical dry lands of Australia, Africa, North America and the Indian sub-continent. Their aims are often similar and they also share common problems.

Figure B19: Methods of irrigation

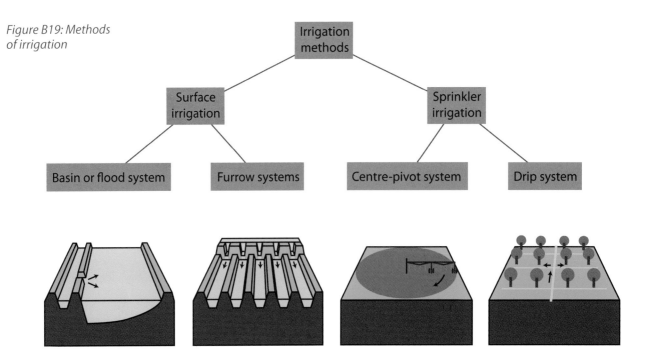

The benefits of irrigation

Environmental

Irrigation schemes are employed to improve the growing environment for crops in one of three ways:

1. To extend the length of the growing season beyond the natural wet summer period, even allowing multiple cropping.
2. To overcome the problem of the unreliability of seasonal rain, which varies widely year to year in semi-arid tropical regions.
3. To increase yield by maintaining soil moisture levels as crops mature and ripen.

Water in soil not only allows crops to maintain their moisture content but it is also essential in the transfer of soluble nutrients to the growing plants. Maintaining optimum water levels in soil by irrigation can improve food quality, for example increasing the sugar content of fruit and berry crops. In arid regions, soil surfaces are dried rapidly by desiccating winds and irrigation water helps bind particles to prevent erosion of the precious top soil. Evaporation levels are high in the arid and semi-arid tropics, which leads to salt deposits near the surface. Irrigation water can flush these potentially toxic salts back down into and, with adequate drainage, out of the soil.

Socio-economic

The world's population is projected to exceed 9 billion people by 2050. This, and its growing affluence and diet diversification, means twice as much food will need to be produced globally. Around 70% of this increase will have to come from irrigated land. Irrigation has been used for 8000 years and its use is only going to grow. Currently, it is estimated that over 40% of the food crops grown across the world requires some degree of irrigation. Not all of this is in the tropics but the majority of people in the world live in regions where irrigation is fundamental to maintaining crop production. As only 16% of the world's farmland is irrigated, yet this produces 40% of the world's food output, irrigated land is 2½ times more productive than land that is not irrigated. Irrigation is not only in use for subsistence food crops but also for cash crops of both food and industrial goods such as cotton that can earn producers an income. Today, some nations have an economy that depends on the output of their irrigated land, including Egypt and Pakistan. A recent United Nations report on the role of irrigation noted that, "Irrigation makes a significant contribution to poverty reduction, better food security and improving the quality of life for rural populations".

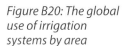

Figure B20: The global use of irrigation systems by area

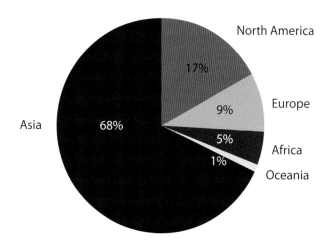

The problems of irrigation

Environmental

Irrigation schemes, in particular those that are poorly planned or managed, can create a range of significant environmental issues. These include:

- soil salinisation
- waterlogging
- ecological damage, including reduced river flows

Salinisation

Salinisation is a natural process. It is associated with environments in which evaporation rates are high and the water table is also high – close to the soil surface. Salinisation is a problem for, and often created by, irrigation schemes. The mechanisms that cause salinisation are illustrated in Figure B21.

Figure B21: The salinisation process

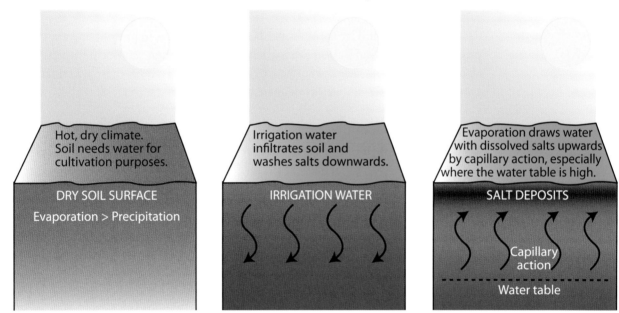

High temperatures rapidly dry out the top soil and a process of capillary action then draws moisture in the soil upwards towards the surface. Soil moisture contains soluble salts which, when the water evaporates into the air, are left at or near the soil surface. The most common deposited salts are various compounds of sodium, calcium, magnesium and potassium. At between 0.5 and 1% concentration, salt will inhibit healthy plant development by preventing the uptake of water and essential nutrients. Consequently crop yields fall, reducing the economic viability of schemes. In extreme cases, a salt crust forms on the soil surface and the land is abandoned entirely. The key factor in the salinisation issue is excess water at or near the surface. If the supply of irrigation water matches the plant's water use, or if an effective drainage system exists, then salinisation is less likely to develop.

Several factors increase the risk of salinisation as the result of irrigation in tropical regions:

- Saline water sources due to high evaporation rates associated with these climates. Even irrigation water of good quality, with a salt content of only 100 parts per million (ppm), may deposit 314 kg of salt on each hectare of irrigated land per year. If poor quality water is used, with a dissolved salt content of say 500 ppm, then evaporation could leave 5000 kg per hectare per year on or in the soil.

- Semi-arid tropical areas have high rates of evaporation as a consequence of their hot and dry climate.
- The zonal soils of arid regions are aridisols and their lack of organic matter and chemical weathering gives them an open texture encouraging capillary action to occur.

Globally, the Food and Agriculture Organisation (FAO) has calculated that for every new hectare of irrigated land, another hectare is being abandoned somewhere as a result of salinisation.

Waterlogging

While the aim of irrigation is to add water to the soil to aid plant growth, excessive irrigation can raise water table levels to within two or three metres of the surface. Ironically, this may then waterlog the sub-soil and the plant root zone. The soil's pore spaces are filled with water and this will hinder healthy plant growth as roots suffocate due to a lack of oxygen. A waterlogged soil also encourages capillary action, evaporation and salt deposition. In low-lying areas of land that have poor natural drainage, unused irrigation water can gather at the soil surface leading to evaporation and the risk of increasing salt concentrations in the upper soil. Studies of irrigation schemes across the world, both traditional and modern, have concluded that between 40 and 60% of water added for irrigation is not used by plants. Instead it percolates into the groundwater storage, raising the underground water table and increasing the risk of damage. In both India and Pakistan, over two million hectares of irrigated land is described as suffering from waterlogging. Meanwhile, in Egypt, artificial drainage is being added beneath millions of hectares of irrigated land at considerable expense. Worldwide, it is estimated that 10% of all irrigated land suffers from waterlogging related issues.

Ecological damage

If poor management of irrigation leaves ponds of stagnant water on the soil surface, then these can become breeding grounds for some of the tropics' most dangerous vectors of disease including mosquitoes carrying malaria and dengue fever. Also, as much irrigation water is extracted from rivers, the result can be a reduction in both the quantity and quality of water downstream. River valley and delta habitats at the large and micro-scale can be severely impacted. The deltaic areas of both the Nile, in the Mediterranean, and the Colorado, in the Gulf of California, have been very negatively impacted. Areas have subsided into the sea, salt water has seeped into groundwater stores and plant and animal species have lost their natural habitats.

Socio-economic

Closely linked to the environmental issues of waterlogging, salinisation and ecological damage, socio-economic problems vary in scale from local to national levels. In the 1980s loss of agricultural land in Pakistan due to waterlogging and salinisation threatened the nation's whole economy and remains a significant issue today. Elsewhere, the downstream loss of water quality has undermined livelihoods in fish farming. Modern irrigation has increased the rate at which groundwater stores can be used. Diesel and electric pumps can now extract water from aquifers faster than these are recharged by rainfall and percolation. This is a threat in China, the dry lands of the USA and the Punjab region on the India/Pakistan border. The loss of aquifer capacity, reduction in water quality and possible ground subsidence all threaten the wider community, much of which derives no benefit from irrigation. Rivers or aquifers that cross international boundaries are of particular concern, as the nation controlling the headwaters of rivers that are used for irrigation downstream may extract water for their own development. This factor has led to bitter disputes between neighbours, such as Mexico and the USA, Israel and Syria, India and Pakistan. The shift to using irrigation, especially if due to government policy, may also lead to a switch from food production to cash cropping. While this can help individual and national development, it may produce food shortages or an economy that is overly dependent on foreign market prices.

The risk to human health is another significant problem; as noted, stagnant water is a breeding ground for many deadly or debilitating tropical diseases including malaria, cholera and bilharzia. One of the most successful past civilisations based on irrigation was found in Sri Lanka. Here, 2500 years ago, the world's first artificial reservoirs were created and for centuries a well-managed water system formed the basis to a highly advanced city-based culture. Only when canal and water management fell into disrepair, allowing malarial marshes to develop, did the civilisation finally abandon the area. In the 1990s, this region was finally cleared of the malaria threat and people returned to live and work there.

Solutions to the problems of irrigation

Most of the issues that result from irrigation – environmental, social or economic – can be addressed by more effective and appropriate management of water resources. For irrigation to be successful the supply of water must be enough to promote healthy plant growth, while at the same time there must be efficient drainage of any surplus water. There are various options and much will depend on the nature and scale of the problems. In many cases, switching to new irrigation systems such as drip/trickle or overhead sprinkler schemes may be the answer. The first involves underground or surface piping of water directly to plant roots and so virtually all water is used by the plants and returned by transpiration to the atmosphere without any infiltration or percolation to soil stores (Figure B22). The second entails a long boom-arm sprinkler that rotates slowly, spraying water onto the soil surface, forming a large circular field (Figure B23). Both use much less water than traditional systems, so reducing the risk of salinisation or waterlogging, and they can also be used to introduce soluble fertilisers, herbicides and pesticides to the plants being irrigated. However, in both cases significant high capital investment costs are involved, making this unrealistic in developing economies. With respect to salinisation and waterlogging, an alternative is to improve the sub-surface drainage network for surplus water but this too is an expensive option when the irrigation scheme is of any significant scale. In places,

Figure B22: Drip or trickle irrigation system
Source: U.S. Department of Agriculture / NRCS Agricultural Water Enhancement Program (AWEP)

Figure B23: Boom-arm sprinkler system in use, Nevada, USA
Source: U.S. Geological Survey/photo by Michael T. Moreo

desalinisation plants can be used to reduce the salt content of water from irrigated areas, but even the USA has found this to be too costly to be a realistic solution.

Numerous other approaches have attempted to address some or all of the issues that arise from irrigation, including:

- switching to crops that have a higher tolerance for salinity (halophytes) and/or high moisture levels in soils.

- growing crops that extract water and salt from soils acting as 'biological pumps'.

- using genetic modification and conventional plant breeding to develop strains of wheat, rice and other staple crops that have increased salt tolerance.

Research into maximising the potential of land damaged by salinisation is known as saline agriculture.

CASE STUDY: Pakistan, a regional study in an arid/semi-arid tropical environment

The nature and development of irrigation

Pakistan, a developing nation, struggles to meet the basic needs of its large and rapidly expanding population; currently 200 million and increasing by almost four million people each year. The region's ancient civilisation was based on the waters of the River Indus flowing through the Thar Desert. At their height, the cities of Harappa and Mohenjo-daro rivalled any contemporary culture in Egypt or Mesopotamia. The climate of Southern Pakistan is that of a true hot desert, with less than 250 mm of annual rainfall, most of which falls during the brief summer wet monsoon in July and August. The high summer temperatures, averaging 38°C, ensure a high rate of evaporation, leaving little effective rainfall for plant growth. The north of the country has more rain, as the foothills of the Himalayas create orographic or relief rainfall. These rains and melting glaciers feed the River Indus headwaters; the water source vital for the rest of the nation. Today, most of Pakistan's farmland (80%) is based on irrigation systems from the Indus River network. The modern irrigation era dates back to the mid-nineteenth century when the region was under British colonial control (the Raj). The gently sloping canal systems, totalling 650,000 km today, carried water to the farmlands. An older traditional system, the karez, was developed to raise ground water using long, sloping tunnels and the land's natural gradient (Figure B24).

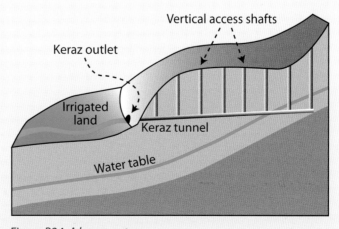

Figure B24: A karez system

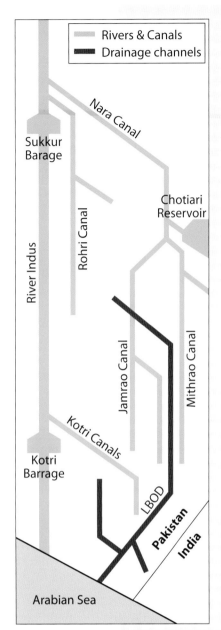

Figure B25: Schematic view of irrigation canals and drainage systems in Sindh province, Pakistan

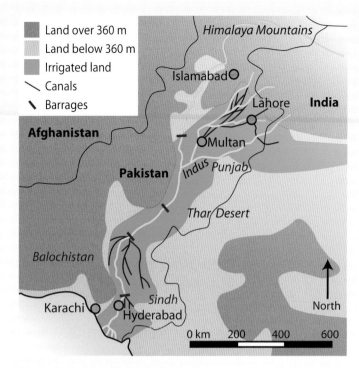

Figure B26: Map of irrigated area, barrages and main canals in Pakistan

Pakistan's modern irrigation system is dominated by the series of barrages and canals that comprise the Indus Basin Irrigation System (IBIS). During the 150 year long Raj period, when the entire Indian sub-continent was administered by the British, an irrigation water distribution system was developed. Water from the Indus and its tributaries would be partially blocked behind barrage dams, flooding the low-lying valleys. From these water stores, canals were created to carry and spread the irrigation water across the flat and fertile soils of the floodplain (Figures B25 and B26).

From large canals, water travelled in smaller and smaller channels branching out to supply farmers with the vital water. For decades this system successfully helped the region's people maintain agriculture production. The system requires careful control of water flow, including regular clearance of vegetation from the canals. The IBIS now has 3 large dams, 85 small dams, 19 barrages, 12 canals linking rivers and a total canal network over 650,000 km long. This huge infrastructure represents an investment of around £250 billion.

In recent decades, in common with most semi-arid regions, tube wells have been introduced in large numbers. Over one million tube wells have been drilled and the majority of these (87%) are diesel powered.

In Balochistan, a large arid province covering 44% of Pakistan's territory, irrigation relies on tube wells and 15 renewed traditional karez systems. Balochistan's relatively small population of nine million people have received World Bank funding to improve their irrigated agriculture. The cultivated land has increased by 50% and for the first time the region grows enough wheat to supply its own needs.

Crops grown	Area (hectares)	World rank in production
Wheat	7 m	8th
Rice	2.5 m	7th
Maize	0.9 m	–
Cotton	3.1 m	4th
Sugarcane	1.2 m	5th
Fodder	2.5 m	5th
Other	4.5 m	
TOTAL	21.5 m	

Figure B27: Irrigated crop production in Pakistan, 2015

The benefits of irrigation in Pakistan

Environmental

The purpose of using irrigation water is to improve the soil and micro-climatic environment to promote healthy plant growth. In Pakistan, the brief summer rainfall is inadequate and too unreliable for agriculture in much of the country. Irrigation extends both the growing season (by making water available in the dry period of the year) and the land area available (by transporting river water or raising groundwater through wells). Crops yields are two to three times higher as a result of the improved environmental conditions promoted by irrigation. In Pakistan, irrigation gives greater control over field systems, making crop output more reliable, avoiding the risk of crop failure and increasing the diversity of food and cash crops produced. While the potential environmental damage caused by irrigation is often discussed, it should be noted that providing the same food without irrigation would most likely have even greater environmental implications.

Socio-economic

The vital importance of irrigation for Pakistan is reflected by the fact that irrigated land supplies 90% of the nation's agricultural output, accounts for 26% of the annual GDP and employs over 44% of its labour force. Today the complex system is responsible for most of the country's food crops (wheat, rice and maize) and industrial crops (cotton, sugar cane, tobacco and oil seed). These supply the domestic needs and through exports bring vital foreign revenue to the nation, currently over 12% of income. Without the use of irrigation, Pakistan could not provide the food and fibre needs of its large and rapidly growing population.

The causes of irrigation problems in Pakistan

Physical factors

In some respects, nature has been unkind to Pakistan because several natural physical factors serve to make waterlogging and salinisation real risks:

1. In the distant geological past, the region was a shallow tropical seabed. This has resulted in a large store of chemical salts in the rocks underlying the country. In Western Pakistan are the Salt Mountains, their name reflecting the saline nature of the local geology.

2. The extreme aridity and heat of the region's climate produces high rates of evaporation.

3. The fact that the relief of the Indus basin is low-lying, with gentle slopes that do not drain easily, means that waterlogging is a constant threat. The average slope in the Indus River basin is only 20 cm for each kilometre.

4. In parts of Pakistan the groundwater available is of poor quality, with a high salt concentration.

The scene is set for problems once attempts were made to manage and redirect water for irrigation.

Human factors (management)

From the outset, the IBIS had built-in weaknesses that promoted waterlogging and salinity. Firstly, the lack of lining in the canal systems meant that water infiltrated into the land below, reducing the water flow and raising the water table. Secondly, there was very limited development of drainage for surplus water, unused by plants, allowing it to evaporate or percolate into ground water stores, thereby encouraging salinisation and waterlogging.

In 1947, independence from Britain involved the division of the Indus basin between a Hindu India and a Muslim Pakistan (West). Conflict between the states was an on-going problem and it often involved water supply issues. To some extent the management of the irrigation system was neglected and in places it fell into a state of disrepair. The largely unlined canal network allowed water to seep away into the soil and groundwater. In places this raised the underlying water table from 25 m deep to only a few metres from the soil surface. Soils are described as waterlogged if the water table reaches the plant root zone that is within 2–3 metres of the soil surface. At this level, salty water can be drawn up into the plant roots by capillary action, initiating the process of salinisation. Annually some 120 million tonnes of salt are added to Pakistan's soils but only 20% of this is removed and carried to the sea by surplus water drainage systems.

By 1995 the IBIS, begun one hundred years earlier, was largely completed, becoming the world's largest single irrigation system. Not only was the country one of the world's top five in total irrigated land area but at 52% it had the highest proportion of its cultivated land irrigated. By 2015, the total area of irrigated land in Pakistan was 21.5 million hectares (Figure B27).

Figure B28: The top 10 countries in terms of area of irrigated land (2012)

NATION	Irrigated land (million hectares)	% of cultivated land that is irrigated	Estimated % of irrigated land area damaged by salinisation or waterlogging
CHINA	69.0	11	15
INDIA	66.7	35	13
USA	26.4	6	25
PAKISTAN	20.2	52	30
INDONESIA	6.7	15	10
MEXICO	6.5	23	6
THAILAND	6.4	30	7
TURKEY	5.2	14	10
IRAN	4.5	17	33–60
RUSSIA	4.3	2	18
WORLD	300	11	10

Between 1964 and 1993 the Pakistan government and private landowners sank tube wells to access groundwater supplies. In this period the number of such wells across Pakistan increased from 25,000 to 360,000. These wells were designed to help lower the water table and therefore reduce the problems of salinisation and waterlogging. Ironically, tube wells encouraged the use of poorer quality saline water (over 500 ppm) for irrigation purposes potentially increasing surface salt.

The problems of irrigation in Pakistan

Environmental

By 1970, salinisation levels across Pakistan had become a very real problem for the country and the first scientific investigations into the scale and cause of this were launched. Aerial photographs and field surveys showed that five million hectares were highly saline and a similar sized area suffered local salt problems. Several irrigation related issues impacted the country; in the western province of Balochistan, over-pumping from tube wells had reduced the water table to a level below the karez shafts and in the dry season many wells ran dry. In the Sindh (south-east) and Punjab (north) the issues were waterlogging and salinisation associated with a rising water table. By 1992, 98% of Sindh irrigation land was saline to some degree, with 50% heavily affected, and with the Punjab having equivalent figures of 25% and 6%.

In the sub-soil the range of chemical salts has increased, reducing crop yields, especially of vital wheat production. Current estimates suggest that between 30% and 60% of Pakistan's irrigated farmland is affected, and in places a salt crust has formed on soil surfaces and cultivation is abandoned. Despite attempts to address the issue, around 40,000 hectares of saline land is taken out of production annually in Pakistan. Testing by the International Water Management Institute showed that even after 40 years of intervention, the problems still persist in irrigated regions of Balochistan and the Punjab, where waterlogging still impacts between 75 and 80% of irrigated land.

One key failure in the management of the Indus irrigation system is its high cropping intensity. It was designed to operate at 65% cropping intensity. This suggests that land that is irrigated should be left fallow, or unused, for a third of the time. However, the growing population demands have resulted in a current intensity of cultivation of 111%. Values over 100% are due to land being used for more than one crop each year.

Socio-economic

Losing irrigated land for cultivation in Pakistan is deeply troubling, as the population and therefore demand is growing. The falling yields from remaining areas, with salty soil and the need to switch to less productive or valuable crops in some regions, undermines Pakistan's economy. Food may need to be imported and there is a decline in export wealth from selling cash crops, such as cotton. The country's balance of trade is affected and capital investment in development projects of both an economic and a social nature falls. By 2005, the various attempts to control salinisation had cost the Pakistan government over £1.5 billion and at one stage the remedial work used up 43% of all its annual spending on the nation's water supply system.

Solutions, possible solutions and sustainability in Pakistan

The response to these irrigation problems has included both individual and government action. Recently there has been a move towards small-scale schemes with more individual farmer responsibility for water management. This is seen as a key strategy in the long-term control of these issues in Pakistan.

Engineering solutions

Sinking wells

In 1986, the Pakistan government initiated SCARP (the Salinity Control and Agricultural Reclamation Programme) and with the help of the World Bank sank over 13,000 tube wells. These were designed to provide non-saline water for irrigated farmland and to lower the water table to end waterlogging and the risk of salinisation. The scheme was also designed to introduce improved drainage for the canal system but this was not developed. The government abandoned the scheme when private landowners took control and today there are over one million irrigation tube wells across Pakistan. Eventually, in the lower Indus region, groundwater levels were lowered by seven metres and 45% of the area with saline soil was reclaimed for sustainable food production.

Drainage engineering

Commonly proposed engineering solutions include building surplus water drainage systems and lining the canals to prevent water leakage to the groundwater store. In a National Drainage Programme the Pakistan government has initiated the development of both an RBOD and LBOD – Right and Left Bank Outfall Drainage schemes. These sub-surface drainage networks are designed to remove surplus groundwater to prevent excessive evaporation of surplus irrigation water and waterlogging in the lower Indus (Figure B25). In the last 20 years, a number of studies and proposals have been made for the concrete lining of key irrigation canals in both the Punjab and Sindh provinces. Some schemes have been completed and water losses have dropped from 30% to only 5%. However, in many cases progress is slow due to the high capital costs involved and the need to maintain flows for use with seasonal crops throughout the year. While the positive environmental outcomes represent good sustainability, the high economic cost of canal lining does not.

Using modern irrigation systems

Several modern irrigation systems have been developed that could improve the situation. These include the use of:

- drip irrigation systems, where valves in plastic hoses release water to the base of individual plants (Figure B22).
- boom-arm sprinkler systems, as seen in the mid-west of America (Figure B23).

Both of these systems have the advantages of using less water and requiring limited drainage. Additionally, fertiliser, pesticides and/or herbicides can easily be added to crops in the irrigation water. In Pakistan, the capital expenditure required by such schemes means that external help may be needed. One example is the Punjab Irrigated Agriculture Productivity Improvement Project (PIPIP), launched by the provincial government and supported by the World Bank. Set up in 2012, and initially to run until 2018, it aims to help the Punjab improve its productivity, increasing crop yields significantly while reducing water demand by 40%. This scheme provides Punjabi farmers with modern drip and sprinkler irrigation systems, working at a community level using improved agricultural technology, such as laser land-levelling.

One farmer reported, "The new and modern irrigation methods introduced by the project have done wonders. The productivity of my land has increased many fold. Now with drip irrigation, I can harvest multiple crops at the same time. It not only helps with the efficient use of water, it also reduces the labour and the number of man-hours."

The views of local landowners suggest this is a sustainable approach to the problems both socially and with respect to its environmental impact. Concern remains about the economic viability of rolling out such a hi-tech scheme across the millions of farms that currently use surface water, gravity-fed forms of irrigation.

Figure B29: Research on saline agriculture in Pakistan

Source: Adapted from information from the Nuclear Institute of Agriculture and Biology, www.niab.org.pk/

After more than two decades of research and experimentation, Pakistan is now learning to live with salinity. Almost 11 million hectares of land in Pakistan has salt deposits, making the land unsuitable for normal agriculture. Scientists estimate that finding a way to cultivate on this land could contribute up to £2 billion to the economy annually. Several salt-tolerant grain, fruit and fodder species have been identified for practicing saline agriculture. This approach, if carefully adapted, can help to reduce the need to import agricultural goods.

Crops suitable for moderately saline soil

i)   **cereals:** paddy rice, sugar cane, oat, sorghum
ii) **oilseed:** rape, canola, mustard
iii) **vegetables:** spinach, sugar beet, red beet, tomato
iv) **fodder and forage:** guar, lucerne
v)   **fibre:** cotton, sunhemp, kenaf
vi) **fruits:** fig, grape, pomegranate

Crops suitable for highly saline soil

i)   **fruits:** date palm, wild date palm and coconut
ii) **grass:** kallar grass, orchard grass, bermuda grass, para grass, sudan grass
iii) **woody species:** jojoba, guava, jujube, mesquite, mangroves, acacias, mustard tree
iv) **miscellaneous:** aloe, reed plant, bottle palm, cactus, drumstick tree, wild banana, senna

Changing agricultural practice

Saline agriculture

As a response to deteriorating soil conditions farmers have adjusted the crops they grow, for example, some have shifted from wheat to rice cultivation as rice can tolerate both more saline and waterlogged conditions. In the Sindh and Punjab provinces, kallar grass, a salt tolerant species, has been grown on badly damaged soils as a fodder crop for livestock. In places, salt tolerant plants (halophytes) have been used to extract soil salts and to help restore soils to commercial productivity. In Pakistan today, farmers periodically leave their farmland fallow for a time to allow the rains

Figure B30: Switching to rice cultivation in salinised and waterlogged soil

to wash salts out of the surface soil. Biological cross-breeding and even genetic modification of plants has been used to develop strains of food and cash crops that can thrive in the soils damaged by poor irrigation management. Environmentally, salinisation is a very difficult problem to reverse and it may be that preventing soils from further deterioration is a more realistic goal.

Exam Questions

1. With reference to a regional case study, discuss the environmental and socio-economic problems associated with the use of irrigation. [18]

2. Study the extract in Resource A which describes attempts to solve salinisation issues in the Mekong Delta.

   Use the resource to help you explain the possible solutions to problems associated with the use of irrigation. [9]

   Question from CCEA A2 2 Physical Geography and Decision Making, May 2015, © CCEA 2017

   Resource A: Breeding a solution for salinisation
   Source: adapted from 'The Science Behind Rice Hybrids', DuPont Pioneer

   Vietnam is the second largest rice exporter in the world, with the Mekong Delta at the heart of the country's rice-producing region. In an effort to feed themselves year-round and maximise opportunities, farmers in the Mekong Delta flood rice fields with saline water in the dry season to farm shrimp. In the wet season, they use rain and fresh river water to attempt to flush the salt out of the soil in preparation for rice planting. This practice poses severe challenges as rice crops do not adapt well to the high salinity so rice yields are adversely affected.

   Thanks to a new hybrid variety of rice, named PHB71, farming communities can now hope for a more secure income. This new rice seed prospers in salty soils, producing predictably higher yields in the short four to five-month summer planting season. Over a period of several years, the DuPont Pioneer Company has worked with research institutes and local partners throughout Asia testing PHB71.

   Adaptable to different environments, PHB71 has proven to be a top-performing hybrid across the board, standing up in rigorous tests in Vietnam, India, the Philippines, Indonesia and Cambodia. It demonstrated a strong tolerance for the high salinity of the Mekong Delta soil, producing a 30–40% higher yield than traditional varieties of rice.

3. Describe the methods and explain the reasons for the use of irrigation in your regional case study. [9]

References

Irrigation in Pakistan:
'Small scale irrigation: Large scale benefits for Balochistan' – *http://www.worldbank.org/en/news/feature/2014/06/16/pakistan-small-scale-irrigation-large-scale-benefits-for-balochistan*

Qureshi and Barrett-Lennard, 'Saline Agriculture for Irrigated land in Pakistan: A handbook' – *http://aciar.gov.au/files/node/2275/mn050_part_1_pdf_73685.pdf*

Videos:
Indus Basin engineering system – *https://www.youtube.com/watch?v=U68EOsnEN84*

3. MANAGEMENT AND SUSTAINABILITY IN THE TROPICAL FOREST ENVIRONMENT

Case studies

Regional scale case study of a tropical forest ecosystem: the Amazon Basin

Small-scale case study of attempts to achieve sustainable development: **either** agroforestry in Tomé-Açu, Brazil **or** ecotoursim in Tambopata National Reserve, Peru

Students should be able to:

(i) demonstrate knowledge, understanding and evaluation of the threat of large-scale development to the trophic structure, nutrient cycle and zonal soil of the tropical forest ecosystem

(ii) demonstrate knowledge, understanding and evaluation of attempts to achieve sustainable development (environmental and socio-economic) in the tropical forest ecosystem

The threat of large-scale development in the tropical forest

Today an increasing proportion of humanity lives within the tropics: 40% or three billion people in 2015 rising to 55% or 5 billion people by 2050. Those that live outside the tropics are largely dependent on tropical ecosystems for their food supplies, industrial resources, medical needs and even the air they breathe. It is true that European colonisation of tropical nations has impacted the world's tropical forests but in the last 50 years the rate and scale of that impact has increased enormously.

In the past, tropical rainforests were largely ignored by outsiders, protected by their remoteness and difficult climate. The indigenous people of the forests were studied by anthropologists, fascinated by their lifestyles and economies. The worldwide population explosion from 1950 forced the governments of many LEDCs to re-examine their available natural resources in order to address the potential threat of overpopulation and to improve their economies. Many tropical nations permitted or encouraged the opening up of their forests for development by their own people or by foreign companies. The most common reasons for such large-scale development of tropical forest resources are illustrated by Figure B31.

Figure B31: The reasons for large-scale deforestation of tropical forests

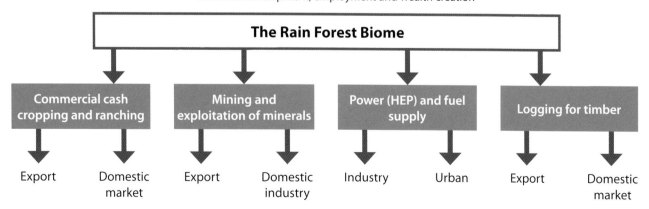

Population increase and the need for economic growth
Resource development, employment and wealth creation

In certain regions, some of the economic activities shown in Figure B31 have been practiced for centuries. African forests were first commercially exploited by Europeans in the seventeenth century and plantation farming in South East Asia goes back over 200 years.

Figure B32: The negative impacts of large-scale deforestation

Some regions are closely associated with one economic activity, for example in Sarawak, Malaysia, on the north coast of Borneo, commercial logging dominates forest development.

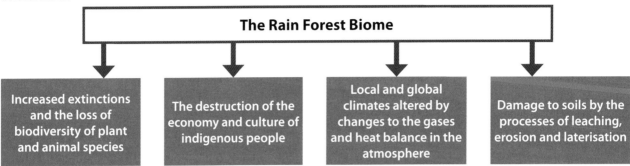

The Rain Forest Biome

| Increased extinctions and the loss of biodiversity of plant and animal species | The destruction of the economy and culture of indigenous people | Local and global climates altered by changes to the gases and heat balance in the atmosphere | Damage to soils by the processes of leaching, erosion and laterisation |

Today, the drive is to find ways to conserve the tropical forest sustainably: creating approaches that develop the resource for the benefit of tropical nations without damaging these special biomes. There can be no return to the traditional lifestyle of the hunter-gatherers or the shifting system of cultivation developed across these forests by the indigenous peoples: while their systems were models of sustainability (Figure B33), they support only low population densities and often at a standard of living unacceptable to most people today.

Figure B33: Shifting cultivation – the traditional sustainable economy of tropical forests

Until recent years, across the world the use of tropical forests has had a common theme – shifting cultivation or slash and burn agriculture. From Papua New Guinea in South East Asia, to Ghana in West Africa and the Amazon Basin of South America, tribes and indigenous groups have independently developed farming systems that are both effective and have a minimal long-term impact on the ecosystem. The clearance of small patches of forest, followed by a few years of suitable cultivation and a long period of abandonment is an attempt to maintain the cycling of nutrients within the local ecosystem. For many centuries, versions of this economic pattern have successfully allowed millions of indigenous natives to live in harmony with their forest home. Shifting cultivation only becomes an unsustainable economy when either the local population density rises above the capacity of the land or the amount of forested land available is reduced, often as a result of competing land use from outsiders.

CASE STUDY: The Amazon Basin, a regional study of a tropical forest ecosystem

Location and environment

Despite 50 years of large-scale clearance and development, the tropical rainforest of the Amazon Basin in South America remains the largest single extent of this biome on Earth. The Amazon, now officially the world's longest river, has a total of 80,000 km of channel and drains 40% of South America (6.4 million km²). While most of the basin consists of flat lowland below 200 m, in the west it rises on the high slopes of the Andes Mountains. The Amazon Basin extends beyond Brazil's borders into Ecuador, Bolivia, Colombia and Peru, but within Brazil itself covers 5 million km². This river carries to the sea each day a discharge equal to the total annual flow of the River Thames. The Amazon Basin includes land adjacent to its river channels, which is flooded annually. The river level at the city of Manaus, 1600 km from the mouth, varies annually by 12 m, with the result that places up to 50 km from the river itself are flooded. These floodplains, called varzeas, cover about 2% of the basin, have more fertile soils, and a distinct and abundant ecosystem. The higher drier forests are referred to as terra firme. Here, despite infertile soils, the diversity of plant and animal life is astounding, for example, one fifth of the entire planet's bird species live there.

Figure B34: The Amazon Basin

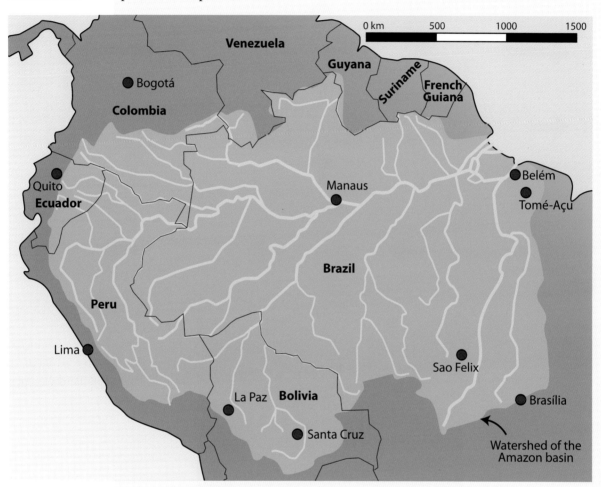

Trophic structure

All ecosystems are based on the 'capture' of solar energy (insolation) by the process of photosynthesis. This chemical energy (food) is then used, transferred or lost through a series of feeding steps or trophic levels. Figure B35 shows an outline trophic structure which may be applied to both large and small-scale ecosystems, terrestrial (land-based) and aquatic or marine (water-based). The diagram is commonly known as a trophic pyramid, as the energy and amount of living matter (biomass) declines from the base upwards.

Figure B35: Trophic Structure with examples of species from the Amazon Basin

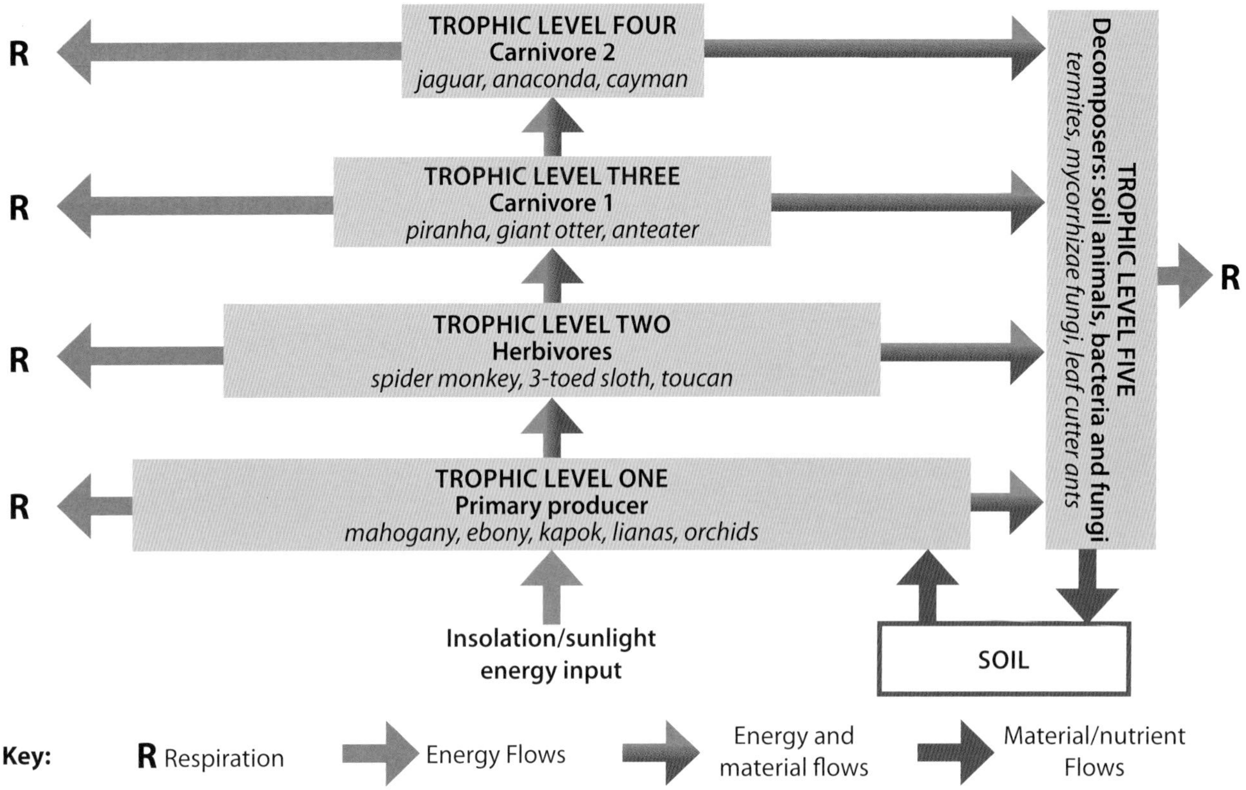

R ←

TROPHIC LEVEL FOUR
Carnivore 2
jaguar, anaconda, cayman

→ **R**

R ←

TROPHIC LEVEL THREE
Carnivore 1
piranha, giant otter, anteater

→

R ←

TROPHIC LEVEL TWO
Herbivores
spider monkey, 3-toed sloth, toucan

→

R ←

TROPHIC LEVEL ONE
Primary producer
mahogany, ebony, kapok, lianas, orchids

→

TROPHIC LEVEL FIVE
Decomposers: soil animals, bacteria and fungi
termites, mycorrhizae fungi, leaf cutter ants

→ **R**

Insolation/sunlight
energy input

SOIL

Key: **R** Respiration → Energy Flows → Energy and material flows → Material/nutrient Flows

---

Figure B36: The forest canopy from above

The trophic pyramid is a representation of the exchange of energy through an ecosystem. At every trophic level organisms use energy in their life processes (termed respiration) and this energy is lost from the ecosystem into the environment, usually as heat. Also, at each transfer of energy some is lost from the system. Figure B12 shows a cross-section view of the forest ecosystem with the key plant features identified.

Trophic structure in the Amazon

One common misconception of the Amazonian forests is that they are impenetrable at ground level. In reality it is only along river banks and in clearings that any ground flora is able to flourish. Elsewhere penetration of sunlight is prevented by the closed tree canopy (Figure B36). See pages 70–73 for examples of Amazon plant and animal species.

Figure B37: Amazonian consumers – bats, giant otters and spider monkeys
Source: (giant otter) © Raul Achahuanco / Explorer's Inn

Nutrient cycling

Energy is transferred through ecosystems but not recycled, as it is lost through the life and transfer processes into the environment (Figure B35). However, material, including essential plant nutrients, is recycled by decomposition and taken into the soil. This is nutrient cycling and it is vital in the efficient and long-term maintenance of any ecosystem. Plant foods or nutrients include a range of materials such as nitrogen, potassium, oxygen, sodium, calcium and phosphate. The key players in this recycling process are the decomposers (the fifth trophic level). These include bacteria and larger organisms, such as fungi, that break down the dead organic material (DOM) that falls to the ground as litter. Decomposers cause this material to decompose and to become incorporated back into the underlying soil. From here the nutrients are then available to be taken up in soil water by plant roots and re-enter the living part of the ecosystem. All these elements and processes are combined and illustrated in Figure B38.

The nutrient cycle model shows that any ecosystem, from a simple freshwater pond to the most complex global scale biome, has three stores of nutrient material:

1. Soil – The physical medium in which plants grow.
2. Biomass – The living material itself, plants and animals.
3. Litter – Dead organic material often on the soil surface.

Nutrients move between these three stores in a unidirectional way: from soil to the biomass, then to litter, before returning to soil. There are also two inputs and two outputs of nutrients in an ecosystem: rainfall and the parent rock are sources of nutrient material, while water in the form of surface run off and leaching through soils cause nutrient loss. The most useful feature of the nutrient model is that when it is applied to a particular ecosystem, the width of the arrows and the size of the circles may be used to indicate the relative importance of the flows or stores in the ecosystem.

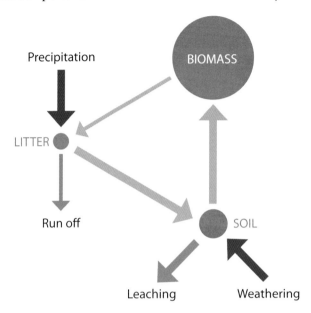

Figure B38: Nutrient cycling in the tropical forest

Key:

Stores:

Circle size represents the proportion of ecosystem nutrients found at any given time in that store.

Nutrient flows:

INPUT   EXCHANGE   LOSS

Arrow width shows nutrient flow as a proportion of the nutrients stored in the source compartment.

Nutrient cycling in the Amazon

The nutrient cycle model for tropical forests such as the Amazon Basin (Figure B38) indicates that most nutrients, up to 90%, are locked into the living elements of the ecosystem (the biomass store). Litter is continuously falling to the ground where it rapidly decomposes in the presence of hot, wet conditions and abundant active decomposers – bacteria, fungi and insects. Experiments have shown that leaves can be broken down and recycled ten times faster under tropical forest than in European forests. The soils contain minimal quantities of nutrients as these are rapidly taken up by plant roots or risk being leached downwards beyond their reach. In tropical forests the soil is less a store, as it is in most other ecosystems, and more a routeway for nutrients. In the Amazon Basin, organisms including termites, leaf cutter ants, moulds and parasites ensure that all litter decomposes rapidly under the forest cover. In this highly developed ecosystem some nutrient transfer processes actually by-pass the soil altogether. Litter may fall onto plant roots above the ground and these are commonly covered by specialist fungi termed mycorrhizae. These break down the litter and can directly transfer the nutrients to plants through the finer roots themselves. Experimental work in the Amazon showed that recycling was highly efficient, with up to 99% of nutrients such as calcium and phosphorus being taken up by vegetation, leaving only 1% in the soil water.

Despite the luxuriant vegetation and diverse animal life, the underlying soils, known as Terra Rosa in the Amazon, are often nutrient poor. The abundance of these tropical forests does not depend on good soil nutrition but rather on the ability of these ecosystems to recycle dead organic material extremely rapidly.

Figure B39: Decomposing fungi at work on the forest floor

Zonal soil of the tropical forest – the oxisol

Soils

Soils are defined as zonal when their nature is determined by and reflects the climatic nature of a world region. In reality soils vary over short distances, for example, at different points on a hillside or where the underlying rock type changes, but zonal soils illustrate the dominant control of a region's climate. Soils are commonly represented by drawing a cross-section showing their nature from the surface down to the underlying rock or parent material. Such a diagram, with layers or horizons identified along with other characteristics, is called a soil profile (Figure B40). All soils are said to have three horizons, each of which may be sub-divided to show distinctive characteristics. The layer or horizon near the surface is the top soil, organic or A horizon and often contains decomposing organic material from dead plants and animals. Beneath this is the sub-soil or B horizon, which rests on the underlying geological rock which may be hard rock or soft deposited material such as sand or clay – the C horizon.

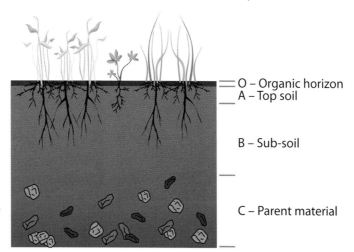

Figure B40: Outline soil profile model

O – Organic horizon
A – Top soil

B – Sub-soil

C – Parent material

The oxisol in the Amazon

Soils beneath most tropical forests have severe limitations due to acidity, low nutrient status or poor drainage. The terms oxisol, latosol or ferralitic soil are all used to describe the zonal profile. In the Amazon Basin forest, despite its luxuriant vegetation and diverse animal life, the underlying soils are often nutrient poor. The abundance of these tropical forests does not depend on good soil nutrition but rather on the ability of these ecosystems to recycle dead organic material extremely rapidly. The soil profile diagram (Figure B41) shows the most common features of these soils and the processes involved in their development.

Key soil characteristics

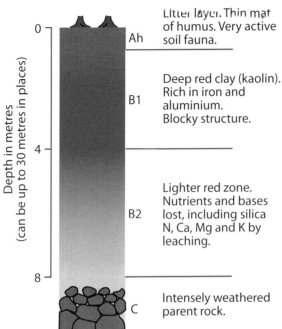

Figure B41: The oxisol profile, zonal soil of the tropical forest, such as the Terra Rosa soils of the Amazon Basin

- Deep profiles due to long-term and intense chemical weathering of the parent material. Terra Rossa soils are commonly 10–20 m deep, resting on even more weathered rock or regolith beneath.

- The high iron content of the heavily weathered and leached soils of the Amazon rainforest earned them the name Terra Rossa or red earths, though yellow-red soils are also common.

- In terms of fertility, studies show that 90% of Amazonian soils lack the essential nutrients nitrogen and phosphorus, while 80% are short of aluminium and potassium. Only on the varzea floodplains are fertile soils found: here the regular inundation of the land provides new nutrients to replace those so efficiently leached beyond plant roots by the intense rainfall (Figure B42).

Intense leaching and rapid organic decay creates acid soils with low pH values. Water passing through the soil increases its acidity from the organic acids released by decomposition. Hydrogen cations in the water replace soil nutrients carrying them down and out of the soil. Even the normally stable silica is leached and a concentration of iron and aluminium oxides (sesquioxides) is left in the soil. Stability is a critical element in the development of the complex interrelationships within an ecosystem.

Figure B42: Varzeas – the flooded forest of the Amazon

Source: H Adams and M Stanley

The cause and threat of large-scale development on the forest of the Amazon Basin

The root cause of such tropical forest clearance in the Amazon Basin has been rapid population growth and the need of the South American nations to use these resources for economic gain and social development. Foreign demand for goods from the tropical forests is an important factor but as the population and wealth of tropical nations themselves grow, the domestic market becomes a key factor on the pressure to use forest resources. In the Amazon Basin, the Brazilian government's drive to develop the region using tax

and loan incentives has led to the large-scale clearance of forests for a number of reasons (Figure B31 and B44).

Transport

Figure B43: The Madre de Dios River bridge, Peru that completed the Trans-Amazonia Highway in 2012

In the Amazon, the decision taken in the 1970s to drive a road network from Brazil's Atlantic coast across the basin to the Pacific was fundamental to all the development that followed. The Trans-Amazonian Highway opened up the forest to individuals and companies, local and foreign, for exploitation and development (Figure B43).

Agricultural expansion for subsistence cultivation (small-scale)

Encouraged by the Brazilian government and the improved access provided by the new roads into the heart of the Amazon Basin, thousands of poor, landless Brazilian families migrated from the overcrowded cities and the drought prone North-East territories. The promise of free land and a government built home enticed them to come and clear the forest back from the new roadways to farm the land (Figure B44).

Commercial agriculture

In the Amazon, governments have encouraged the development of land by offering tax incentives to national and foreign-based businesses. Territory in sparsely populated areas was opened up for cash grazing from cattle ranching or cash cropping (rubber, soya and oil-palm). It is estimated that 70% of deforestation in the Amazon Basin in the last 40 years is linked to the production of cheap beef from cattle ranching. In 2009, following reports from Greenpeace and Friends of the Earth, the Brazilian government persuaded the major cattle buyers to agree to ban the purchase of beef from deforested land. This has helped Brazil reduce the rate of deforestation as illustrated by Figure B45. Compared to the experience of other tropical forest regions in Southern Asia, plantation style farming has played a minor role in deforestation of the Amazon but until a suspension was agreed in 2006, the extension of soybean farming was causing widespread loss of pristine forest in the states of Pará and Mato Grosso. Following a Greenpeace report, 'Eating up the Amazon', companies, including McDonald's, agreed to stop buying soya produced from land cleared after June 2006. Actual soybean production has increased but this comes from multiple cropping on existing land. Soy or soya is a rich source of protein and while most is used as animal fodder it is also processed as soy sauce, tofu and as a meat substitute. Brazil produces 31% of the global output.

Figure B44: The reasons behind the deforestation in the Brazilian Amazon at its highest rate – 2000–2005

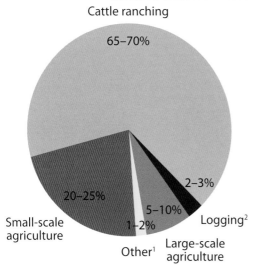

Cattle ranching
65–70%

20–25%

2–3%

5–10%

1–2%

Logging[2]

Small-scale agriculture

Other[1]

Large-scale agriculture

1. Including fires, mining, urbanisation, roads, dams.
2. Logging generally results in degradation rather than deforestation, but is often followed by clearing for agriculture.

Commercial logging (timber production)

Many tropical hardwood tree species are prized for their high quality timber (mahogany, kapok and rosewood). Unfortunately with clear felling methods, to access and remove the few desired trees many other species were wastefully cut down. In the Amazon, cattle ranchers work closely with loggers who clear the prize tree species from land being cleared for cattle grazing. Much of this logging is illegal and it is only through the use of satellite imaging that the true scale of forest clearance can be monitored.

Mining and quarrying

New techniques of exploration have revealed the vast wealth contained in the rocks beneath these forests, including mineral deposits, fossil fuels and metal ores. The world's largest iron ore mine has been developed as the Grande Carajas Project in the heart of Pará state. Designed to be as ecologically safe as possible, it is large in scale and with an estimated iron ore reserve for 400 years, it will continue having an impact into the future. The open cast mining system in use removes the whole ecosystem locally from the soil up. The use of toxic chemicals can pollute rivers and enter the food chain (trophic structure). In the Peruvian Amazon, oil companies have been operating for over 40 years and after 2008 more land was released by the government for potential exploration. In 2014, oil spills from pipelines impacted the forest ecosystem and the health of indigenous people along four headwater tributaries of the Amazon.

Hydro Electric Power (HEP) schemes – energy production

Population growth, industrial development and increased prosperity all increase the demand for energy supplies in tropical regions. On tropical forest rivers, HEP proves a ready energy source which, while non-polluting and renewable, creates large reservoirs that flood forest regions with the widespread loss of habitat and life. The Tucurui Dam on the Rio Tocantins, again in Pará state, first became operational in 1984 and a second phase was completed in 2012. The land behind the dam had

Figure B45: Deforestation rates in the Amazon Basin 2001–2013

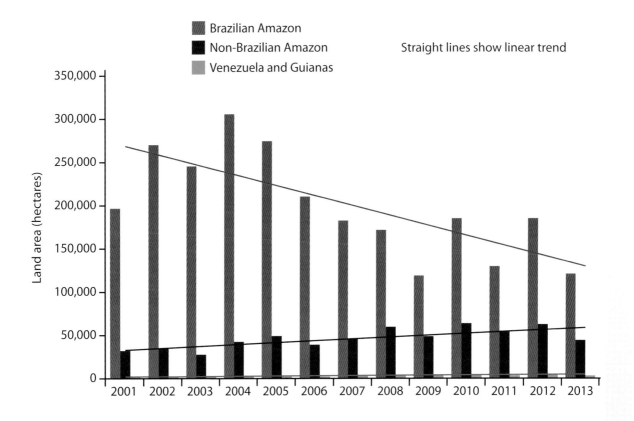

been cleared of its tribal population but little was done to help the numerous plants and animals that disappeared beneath its 2875 km² reservoir. The Belo Monte Dam on the Xingu River has been in planning since 1975. Despite environmental objections the first turbines are now operating and the huge project, in which a further 400 km² of forest will be flooded, is due for completion in 2019.

The best current estimate is that around 17% of the Amazon Basin forest has been lost to deforestation in the last 50 years. While some figures show that the clearance rates are now the lowest for a generation in the Brazilian Amazon (Figure B45) it is also true that other Amazon nations have seen an increase in forest clearance. The reality is that large-scale ecosystem clearance is on-going in the Amazon Basin, with all the potentially negative consequences that holds for its future.

Evaluating the damage done

This threat to the forest's trophic structure is obvious: any interference with forest plants disturbs the complex feeding structure on which the numerous animal species depend. Clearance of the flora not only disrupts the essential food supply but also removes the physical habitats occupied by the mammals, amphibians, lizards, birds and insects. Such development poses significant threat to the nutrient cycle, as it undermines the balance behind the nutrient stores and flows:

- Biomass stores are removed.
- The soil surface is left unprotected.
- There is increased run off of nutrients from surface litter stores.
- Leaching through the soil increases.

The sheer biodiversity of life in the forest hides its vulnerability. Individual species often depend directly on each other. Brazil nuts are a relatively expensive item; most are produced in the Bolivian Amazon forest rather than in Brazil itself. Attempts to develop the Brazil nut tree in a plantation normally fail. The main reason is that only one species of fat-bodied bee can pollinate the plant and it only survives in pristine forest environments. Also in nature the tree relies on the agouti, the only native animal that can gnaw into the nut and that buries them for storage, some of which then germinate and grow. Thus any development that removes the trees, the bees or the agouti will break the chain and the survival of the species, at least locally (Figure B46).

In the forest there are other animals that, like the agouti, act as keystone species. These are important in the widespread dispersal of plant seeds. The chance of survival of many plants relies on them being widespread and not clustered. While some plants produce seeds that can be blown or float over these distances, others rely on animals to carry them. Spider and howler monkey troops move through the canopy layer, eating fruit containing seeds. These seeds then pass through the animals and are deposited elsewhere, complete with 'built-in' fertiliser. Consequently some conservationists suggest that their effort should be focused on the survival of keystone species in an ecosystem to ensure its health and survival.

Another issue with deforestation is that many species need access to large unbroken areas of forest but as forests are cleared only smaller patches are left untouched across the landscape. Fragmentation of areas has direct and indirect impacts on the habitats available. Predators in particular need large areas of ecosystems and they may not be able to move across non-forested landscapes between forest areas. Light loving plant species, including lianas, do well with fragmentation as it creates more edges, with light stretching to the forest floor. On the other hand larger animal numbers often decline or disappear in small stands of tree.

Figure B46: The survival of agouti and Brazil nut trees are closely linked

As described earlier, the soils of the Amazon Basin are notably poor in nutrients. When they are exposed to the tropical sun and rain by the removal of the biomass they are prone to rapid surface erosion and increased chemical leaching. In the worse cases, the erosion can expose a stone-like deep redeposited layer in the soil, known as a laterite. This layer inhibits water movement and prevents plant root growth. In the severely damaged forests of West Africa, such laterite soils have created a barren landscape of little if any use.

Figure B47: Current estimates of tropical forest loss (hectares)

Country	Rank	Forest Loss 2014	Trend
Brazil	1	2,262,241	down
Indonesia	2	1,490,457	up
DR Congo	3	1,100,880	up
Malaysia	4	493,385	up
Paraguay	5	305,650	up
Bolivia	6	220,470	down
Myanmar	7	259,443	up
Madagascar	8	318,465	up
Cambodia	9	123,779	up
Peru	10	183,544	up
Colombia	11	165,507	down
Mexico	12	130,717	down
Laos	13	191,032	up
Mozambique	14	163,345	down
Tanzania	15	161,899	up
Total average for the top 15 countries is over 8,000,000 hectares a year			

Management for sustainability

Tropical forests are diverse and fragile environments. In recent decades their development has accelerated at a phenomenal rate and today pressure groups, both local and international, are seeking to slow down and even halt the process. Economic and environmental values have clashed and at times resulted in sporadic and sustained violence. In December 1988, the murder of Chico Mendes, a Brazilian leader of rubber tappers, by rival cattle ranchers was a pivotal moment in the global awareness of the conflict between sustainable and unsustainable exploitation of the forest. Since that event and the Earth Summit of Rio in 1992, the world's media has highlighted the issue, if not consistently, at least more frequently.

Today, it is recognised that somewhere between the reckless destruction of tropical forests for short-term economic gain and its traditional but limited use for subsistence agriculture lies a compromise – a newly evolving attitude of responsible and sustainable management.

Figure B48: Examples of sustainable development projects in tropical forests

Sustainable development, as noted earlier, involves the social and economic well-being of the local community, and environmental protection at both local and global scales. One lesson from the search for sustainable management systems is that no single approach will be applicable to all forest areas and that consequently a variety of solutions will be needed. While good examples of sustainable development are not abundant, their number and their impact are growing. Figure B48 contains some of the common approaches to the sustainable use of tropical forest resources.

System	Elaboration	Example
Agroforestry	An agricultural system that mimics the forest by having a canopy of productive trees with annual crops grown below.	The coconut farms on the islands of southern Thailand. The Tomé-Açu cooperative farms near Belém, Brazil (pages 107–110).
Forest product resources	Extracting resources from standing forest, such as rubber tapping or Brazil nut gathering.	The state of Acre in the Amazon Basin.
Ecotourism	Bringing in tourists to see and learn about the forest biome and its native people with minimal impact on the local environment.	The Explorer's Inn, Peruvian Safaris in the Amazon Basin, Peru (pages 111–114).
Mining	Controlled exploitation of mineral reserves beneath the forest	The Grande Carajas project in Pará state, Brazil.
Selective logging	Small-scale managed logging, including strip logging or 'highgrading' (the removal of only the most valuable trees).	The Amuesha Indians in the Yanesha Forestry Cooperative, Peru.
Nature reserves	Ranging from zero use, to areas for scientific research, including medical gene pools and tourism.	The Korup Nature conservation reserve, in South-West Cameroon.

The success of these and other schemes in tropical forests depends on many factors. The local people and their governments along with NGOs (Non-Government Organisations) play important roles in this process but market forces are critical. It is western economies that control market demand and if their suppliers adopt a policy to only handle goods from forests managed sustainably, they may hold the key to success.

Note:

The specification requires the study of only **one** sustainable development case study.

Two sample case studies of attempts to achieve sustainable development on a small-scale

1. Agroforestry system

Agroforestry combines agricultural and forestry techniques to establish an integrated, diverse, productive and sustainable land use system. The concept is that by mixing tree crops and short-term or annual crops, the land can provide an income without having to expose the delicate soil to the heat of the sun or the torrential rainfall of convectional storms. The trees provide both a canopy layer that intercepts rain and a root network that binds the soil. As most farmers cannot wait the ten or more years for trees to reach productivity, the interplanting of bush or ground crops produces a potential food or cash crop supply in the short-term.

Researchers into agroforestry schemes around the world have identified several necessary requirements to make these successful as sustainable enterprises:

- The locals or colonists must be aware of the limitations and problems of rainforest environments, including the nature of the soil and be held responsible for any environmental consequences.

- Schemes need to be well resourced and maintained so that any environmental issues can be addressed as soon as they appear – this requires appropriate technology and specialist labour.

- Both the profits made and any external subsidies must be controlled to prevent damaging, short-term strategies, where land is abandoned and new areas of forest cleared.

Agroforestry has the potential to produce a variety of food and industrial crops as illustrated in Figure B49.

Figure B49: Potential commercial agroforestry products

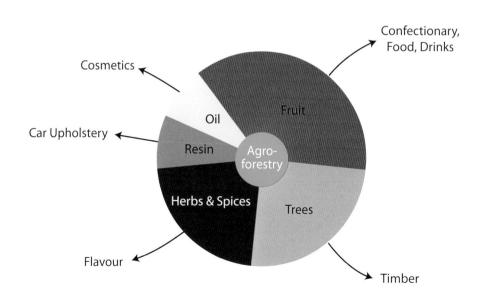

CASE STUDY: CAMTA Cooperative, Tomé-Açu, Pará, Brazil (Japanese community), a small-scale study of sustainable development

Figure B50: A location map of the Tomé-Açu region

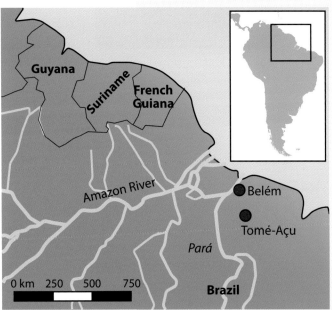

One of the few well documented and generally successful agroforestry schemes involves a small community of farmers in the Brazilian state of Pará. Over the last 60 years they have developed farming from a very poor subsistence economy to a cooperative-based commercial enterprise based on local plant species. The history of the community is an unusual one but the lesson of their past is that with care and attention it is possible to develop an economy that is sustainable in social, environmental and economic terms.

A brief history

During the 1920s and 30s the government of Japan, fearing overpopulation, encouraged many of its citizens to emigrate to find new lives elsewhere. One group of around 40 families arrived in Brazil and settled at Tomé-Açu, around 200 km south of the Amazon port of Belém (Figure B50). Over the next 20 years the immigrants cleared areas of secondary forest and subsisted on rice and vegetables, including varieties they had brought from Asia. After World War II the small community seized on a unique opportunity – the conflict had destroyed the black pepper plantations of South East Asia and consequently its market price soared. From a few seedlings that had been brought over in 1933, the Japanese farmers developed a highly profitable export economy based on a monoculture of black pepper. From 1947 until the mid-1980s production expanded and at one point the Tomé-Açu region supplied most of the world's black pepper. By 1985, the combination of a fungal disease, Fusarium, and foreign competition from renewed Asian producers undermined this success. Faced again with potential disaster, the community responded by developing a more diverse agricultural system based on small family farms. The community had learned the perils of over dependence on a single crop and unpredictable world markets. They also learned from the indigenous farmers, their neighbours, that a system based on tree crops could replicate the forest's natural pattern of nutrient storage. This means most nutrients are stored in the biomass itself, thus protecting the fragile soil below from erosion and potentially providing a constant supply of agricultural produce.

One advantage the community had was the farmer's cooperative, CAMTA (Cooperative Agricola Mista de Tomé-Açu), which they had established (Figure B51). From 1931 it had supplied seed, fertiliser and advice; while also helping the community socially by funding a hospital, schools and a supermarket. The cooperative promoted the new more sustainable form of agroforestry, when in 1987, it built a frozen fruit pulp processing plant, as local farmers began to experiment with local fruit crops for the growing drinks market. The processing plant separates the pulp using both hand labour and machinery; it then freezes the pulp in plastic bags. CAMTA sends the fruit pulp to major urban markets, including Sao Paulo through the port at Belém, and abroad to Japan under the company name Fruta fruta.

Figure B51: CAMTA's operations at Tomé-Açu

Source: Images from Camta, http://www.camta.com.br

The range of fruits that are supplied as pulp from the CAMTA processing plant.

Logo of CAMTA the cooperative organisation in Tomé-Açu.

pineapple
açaí
acerola
cashew
star fruit
cupuaçu
guava
graviola
passion fruit
murici
taperebá

The nature of the Tomé-Açu farms

Individual family farms are between 100 and 150 hectares in size; however, less than half of this may be in production at any one time. The cultivated plots are one to four hectares in size and normally have two, three or even four crops mixed and interplanted. For example, in one plot, under tapereba trees, bananas may be grown, while on an adjacent plot, cupuaçu and acai fruits may be found, beneath a canopy of coconut palm and citrus trees (Figure B52). Today, mostly native species are used, such as the shade tolerant cupuaçu and cacao. As many as 25 different species may be grown on one farm and a complex and sophisticated pattern of production emerges. This is a risk avoidance strategy, allowing flexibility if market conditions alter. In cultivated and regenerating areas, many farmers have planted valuable hardwood timber tree species, including mahogany, rosewood and jacaranda, as a future income for their children and future generations. Currently, less than one in five farmers grows staple food crops, such as rice, beans or corn, due to the confidence in the long-term commercial success of this enterprise.

Figure B52: A typical farm pattern in Tomé-Açu

Scale: ☐ = 1 hectare (100 m × 100m)

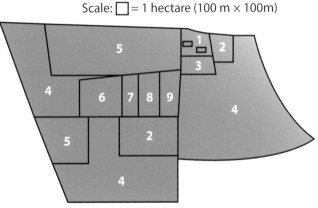

Land use:
1 Home and farm buildings
2 Brazil nut, cacao, pineapple
3 Mahogany, papaya, vanilla
4 Secondary forest regeneration
5 Coconut, citrus, cupuaçu
6 Rubber tree, passion fruit
7 Cacao, mangosteen, banana
8 Rubber tree, black pepper
9 Andiroba, cupuaçu

Economic sustainability

CAMTA annually trades over £10 million worth of fruit pulp exclusively through Fruta Fruta to Brazil, Japan and the USA, making it one of Brazil's most successful cooperatives. It has over 200 member farms, two thirds of which are owned by the Japanese community. The fruit pulp comes from 13 different species and cacao and black pepper are also traded, though mainly for the domestic Brazil market. This broad based and growing market has helped to avoid the dependency of the past and the risk of a collapse due to world market prices or the blight of plant disease. One concern is that setting up new farms of this type is capital intensive. Income is low in the early years and costs are high. The cooperative, however, can provide access to credit and reduce costs by its bulk purchase of seeds, fertiliser and other inputs.

The company Fruta Fruta Incorporated was floated on the Tokyo stock exchange in 2014 and had a revenue of 1.4bn yen (£9.4m) in 2017. However, it should be noted that the value of shares in the company has fallen by 50% at times during its first few years of trading – an indication of the volatility of world trade and commodity prices.

Social sustainability

At one time, concern was voiced that the complexity of these systems meant that only the specialist farmers from Japanese families could maintain these farms. Today, nearly a third of CAMTA members are Brazilian in origin and many are migrants from outside the Amazon region. The farms themselves are labour intensive, with each small farm needing a skilled workforce of seven or eight people. This is an advantage in a region with high population growth and in-migration. One issue is that in recent years members of the younger generation, including the Japanese community, are leaving for the bright lights and opportunities in the cities of Brazil or beyond.

While it is true that the Tomé-Açu farms have not received help from outside foundations or NGOs (Non-Government Organisations – charities), it is not strictly true to say they are fully independent. Many families gain income from members working outside the area, including in Japan, for periods of time.

Environmental sustainability

The model mimicking the natural structure of a tropical forest for cultivation seems to work. Testing at Tomé-Açu shows that the creation of a tree canopy, with a second under-storey layer, is both productive and has maintained soil quality even after 20 years. This is superior to the two to three year output under traditional shifting cultivation systems or the eight to ten year use under cattle ranching. Some simpler agroforestry systems have been shown to be capable of maintaining a significant range of bird, small mammal, reptile and insect species. While more research needs to be completed on the impact of the Tomé-Açu system on natural biodiversity, it is worth noting that most of the farms were established in areas of damaged forest, including the pepper plantations and land previously clear-felled by logging companies. Little virgin forest is now cleared and it is claimed that, even to the trained eye, a typical farm in normal production appears similar to the natural forest. To maintain soil fertility the black pepper plantations had relied on large inputs of inorganic chemical fertiliser brought into the area, but the new system focuses on the recycling of organic material. Cacao produces beans for chocolate but their hulls can be recycled, returning nutrients such as potassium to the soil. Weeds are routinely cut but left to decay and decompose as mulch for the soil. The Fruta Fruta Inc website (www.frutafruta.com/global/) addresses the importance of sustainability in its business stating that:

"Today, Agroforestry in Tomé-Açu … covers as much as 7000 ha, and it has been calculated that the greenhouse gases (CO_2) locked up by the taller tree species are as much as 53,185 tons annually."

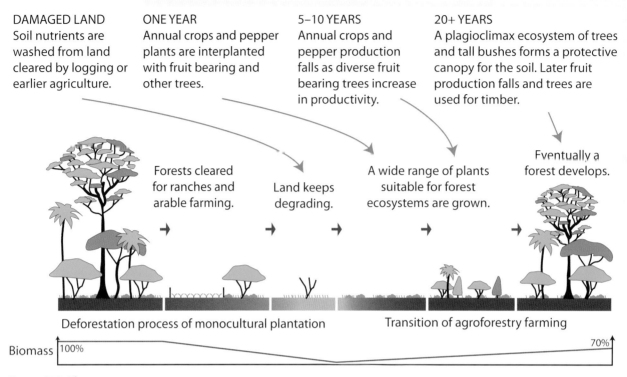

DAMAGED LAND
Soil nutrients are washed from land cleared by logging or earlier agriculture.

ONE YEAR
Annual crops and pepper plants are interplanted with fruit bearing and other trees.

5–10 YEARS
Annual crops and pepper production falls as diverse fruit bearing trees increase in productivity.

20+ YEARS
A plagioclimax ecosystem of trees and tall bushes forms a protective canopy for the soil. Later fruit production falls and trees are used for timber.

Forests cleared for ranches and arable farming.

Land keeps degrading.

A wide range of plants suitable for forest ecosystems are grown.

Eventually a forest develops.

Deforestation process of monocultural plantation

Transition of agroforestry farming

Biomass 100%   70%

Figure B53: The environmental benefit of using sustainable agroforestry on deforested land

Source: Information from www.frutafruta.com

2. Ecotourism

Tourism in tropical biomes has long been associated with the grassland biomes, where herds of migrating herbivores and the carnivores that prey on them are more readily seen than in forested regions. Safaris, initially as hunting expeditions, have been popular, albeit with wealthier westerners, for a hundred years or more. Until the last few decades, tropical forests have been regarded as the preserve of the adventurer. Mass tourism and improved access have allowed for the development of tourism and its supposedly sustainable cousin, ecotourism, bringing visitors and their valuable foreign currency into many LEDC nations.

Figure B54: Images of tropical forest tourism. Do they represent sustainable ecotourism?

Elephant trekking in Thailand

Mounted Red-bellied Piranha from Manaus, Brazil

Orangutan feeding in Sarawak, Borneo

CASE STUDY: Tambopata National Reserve, Peru, The Explorer's Inn (Peruvian Safaris), a small-scale study of sustainable development

Tambopata is a nature reserve on the Peru-Bolivian border within the Amazon Basin. Its establishment in 1990 is in part the result of a successful research centre opened in 1975/76, called Explorer's Inn and run by the Peruvian Safaris company in cooperation with the Peruvian government. By 2000, the Tambopata National Reserve (TNR), with 275,000 hectares, was linked to the newly designated 1.1 million hectare, Bahuaja-Sonene National Park. Across these protected regions it is estimated that 20,000 tourists visit each year. Most stay at 13 purpose built lodges, generally outside the protected zone. Explorer's Inn and the nearby Posada Amazonas Lodge, run by an indigenous community, lie within the TNR. The lodges vary in nature from basic to luxury, with most focusing on direct observation of wildlife. One claim for the area is that it has the world's highest species count for birds and butterflies at nearly 600 and 1200 respectively.

Figure B55: Map of the Tambopata National Reserve and location of Explorer's Inn

The Explorer's Inn

Situated within the TNR, the lodge is located near the confluence of the Tambopata and La Torre rivers. Designed as a base for scientific research, it has combined this role with educational ecotourism. Visitors stay at the complex in a small clearing a few hundred metres from the river bank (see Exercise on page 112). The Inn consists of seven separate bungalows with palm-thatched roofs, and a central hexagonal building that houses the dining area, lounge, research area, bar and a small library and museum (Figure B56). Local materials were used in the original construction of the Inn and today materials are supplied by local people from sustainable sources. The bedrooms are lit by candlelight, with electricity only available in the public areas. The electricity is supplied by solar cells, which also power the radio link to headquarters in Puerto Maldonado. In the surrounding forest over 37 km of walking trails are regularly maintained. These lead to a variety of environments including the rivers, ox-bow lakes and pristine forest. Additional facilities include 11 viewing platforms, high in or above the canopy, from which wildlife can be observed by day and night. All visitors come in from Puerto Maldonado, some 60 km downstream, by motorised long boat. On-route they have to check into the biological reserve at a nearby riverbank control post, one of five in the reserve. Tourist stays vary from two to five nights, during which guided walks and open canoe trips are undertaken. Highlights of the 'Jungle Expedition' package include:

- the giant otters at Cococcha, a large ox-bow lake about four kilometres north east of the Inn.
- the macaw claylick, Colpa de Guacamayos (Figure B56), where hundreds of these exotic birds feed on a clay river bank.
- night boat trips to spot cayman and turtles on the riverbanks.

The Library

The macaw claylick

Accomodation

*Figure B56:
Photographs of
the Explorer's Inn*

Source: Owen Glenn

Exercise

1. Enter (or download) Google Earth.

   Type in these latitude and longitude coordinates: 12 50' 12"S   69 17' 37"W

   This location will take you to the clearing containing the Explorer's Inn, near the confluence of the Tambopata and La Torre rivers. Zoom in to study the buildings on the site itself. You can use the scale icon to measure the size of the clearing.

   - Scroll 4 km to the north-east to the Cocococha ox bow lake where the hide for giant otters is found. Click on the blue squares that are normally photographs, showing the buildings, river or wildlife in the region.

   - Scroll the map downstream (north and north-east) towards Puerto Maldonado. Notice how agricultural clearings, including cattle pastures, appear along the river and widen to dominate the area around the town. Note also the largely pristine forest of the TNR itself, especially away from the rivers.

   - Other tourist lodges in the region can be seen, invariably near the river. These include Posado Amazonas, a native run lodge downstream and Libertador Tambopata, upstream of the Explorer's Inn.

Sustainability at the Explorer's Inn

The express purpose of the Explorer's Inn is part of "a unique experiment in cooperation where research, tourism and rainforest conservation are being combined to the mutual benefit of all involved and for tomorrow's generations". To this end, the Inn under its 'Resident Naturalist' programme offers free accommodation and food for researchers in return for their acting as guides to visitors. Numerous theses, published and unpublished, along with many well informed tourists have resulted from this creative, symbiotic relationship. One study identified the risk of soil compaction along the walking trails. Consequently the centre built a raised walkway over paths in the lodge clearance and each year some

Figure B57: Local food production (cacao plants and plantain bananas) near the Explorer's Inn

trail routes are left unused to allow restoration. The same research suggested that trail clearance may allow more light to reach ground plants, positively promoting greater species diversity and helping insect life on the forest floor. The first clue to the number of species contained by rainforest canopies was from experiments carried out at Tambopata by Terry Erwin of the Smithsonian Institution. Biodegradable insecticides released into the canopy brought down a rain of thousands of unknown insect species. EO Wilson, who helped introduce the term 'biodiversity', found more species of ant in just one Explorer's Inn tree than in the entire British Isles.

Visitors enjoy three meals a day, including traditional dishes made using locally sourced food. The reserve runs agroforestry farms that not only supply the lodges but also share sustainable farming practice with local farming communities. Waste disposal is an important issue in these vulnerable environments. At the Explorer's Inn any biodegradable waste is buried where it can decay safely and not attract unwanted visitors. Non-biodegradable waste is routinely removed downstream to the town of Puerto Maldonado, outside the TNR, to be added to its urban waste system. Current threats to the environment include gold mining, illegal logging, hunting and expansion of farming along the rivers (Figure B58).

Figure B58: Pollution threat from the panning for gold on Tambopata River

Figure B59: Extract from the Explorer's Inn website regarding social sustainability

Source: Explorer's Inn, www.explorersinn.com

Communities

From its inception, Explorer's Inn in Tambopata Reserve has been deeply committed to supporting local communities and ensuring that the benefits of both our business and our conservation work are shared with them as much as possible. In addition to employing local people and sourcing most of our supplies from nearby family producers, we also support local communities in their efforts to achieve community-based sustainable development.

More than 90% of Explorer's Inn in Tambopata Reserve rainforest staff come either from communities along the Tambopata River or from Puerto Maldonado. Most of the perishable food items, in particular fruit, vegetables, grains and tubers such as potatoes and cassava, are sourced locally. Even our boats are still made the traditional way, from a hollowed-out tree trunk, by local boat-wrights in Puerto Maldonado, although comfortable seats have now been added to these dugout canoes!

We also go out of our way to help create sustainable economic opportunities for local communities. Whilst staying at the Inn, guests can visit and interact with local families who benefit from cash payments per visitor as well as from the sale of handicrafts to guests. All craftwork sold in the Inn's shop is sourced locally in the Tambopata area, with many of the items made by native indigenous artisans — often women — including necklaces, earrings, basketry, bows and arrows, and many other items painstakingly made from sustainably-harvested forest products collected from the local area.

Explorer's Inn Tambopata Eco lodge is also well known locally for taking on recently qualified local guides from the ecotourism guiding schools in Puerto Maldonado, and providing them with training in languages, natural history and ecology, with the help of our experienced guiding team, Resident Naturalists and other visiting research scientists. Indeed, most rainforest guides in Tambopata have passed through Explorer's Inn Tambopata Eco lodge at one stage or another during their career.

Through strategic alliances with nonprofit organisations, such as Fauna Forever and Trees-Peru, the Inn also supports a range of community and family based projects …. the development of rural guest houses or home-stays in communities, with the lodge providing logistical support, tourism know-how, contacts and marketing channels … the establishment and maintenance of conservation corridors on family-owned lands in exchange for monetary, educational and health benefits (also funded by donations from guests). These corridors serve to bridge the deforested gaps between the Tambopata National Reserve and the intact forests of protected areas and Brazil nut concessions to the north and west of the lodge.

Exam Questions

1. "Long-term socio-economic and environmental sustainability is the ultimate goal of the management of tropical forests."

   With reference to a small-scale case study in the tropical forest ecosystem, describe and evaluate the attempts to achieve this goal. [18]

   Question from CCEA A2 2 Physical Geography and Decision Making, May 2013, © CCEA 2017

2. Study Resource A which describes one attempt to maintain sustainable development in the tropical forest ecosystem. Discuss how the management approach aims to achieve socio-economic and environmental sustainability. [9]

   Question from CCEA A2 2 Physical Geography and Decision Making, May 2014, © CCEA 2017

Resource A: Inkaterra, Peru's pioneer of responsible tourism in the rainforest

In 1975, before the term 'ecotourism' was in use, a group of rainforest enthusiasts developed an idea to bring small groups of tourists and scientists into the remote virgin forests of Madre dc Dios, a slate of Peru. The state with an area 84000 km², similar in size to Ireland, has a population of only 90,000 people. Over the next 30 years the Inkaterra Reserva Amazonica became a leading example of sustainable activity in the delicate forest ecosystem. The site itself has a central two storey lodge and 35 simple palm roofed cabanas (cabins) modelled on the huts of the local Ese-Eja people. The buildings are made using local material and techniques. Everything is bare wood including the sinks carved from rock-hard quinilla timber. Alongside the tourist expeditions, on foot and river to the nearby nature reserves, groups of scientists record the health of the environment and uncover the complex interactions of native plants and animals with their natural abiotic environment.

Cabanas and raised timber pathways at the Reserva Amazonica lodge

Local subsistence farmers are employed as guides for these scientific expeditions. Money from this tourist development funds the scientific work through the Inka Terra Association (ITA). A short distance from the lodge is Gamitana Farm where much of the food for guests is produced and a programme for training farmers in sustainable agroforestry techniques is provided.

Drying plantain bananas at the Gamitana Farm on the banks of the Madre de Dios river

The company now also runs two forest centres, one close to the largest local town Puerto Maldonado, for environmental education and an interpretation centre for young children. Most of the staff at the lodge are local and, while many have little formal education, the company aims to develop their skills by providing training in environment awareness, catering and hospitality. Meanwhile the native wildlife are never far away: agoutis (giant guinea pigs) roam freely, macaws and parrots sing for hours at dawn, and hummingbirds throng to visit the flowers that surround each cabana. The reception area doubles as a butterfly farm but less welcome are the venomous bushmaster snakes that can still be seen at times slithering their way through the vegetation.

3. With reference to a regional case study of a tropical forest ecosystem, describe and explain the threat that large-scale development poses to **any two** of the following elements of the ecosystem:

   - The trophic structure
   - The nutrient cycle
   - The zonal soil [18]

References

Geofile articles:
'Deforestation success stories (Amazon)', *Geofile* 742, series 34, 2015–2016
'Rainforest Biodiversity – management: Case study Tambopata…', *Geofile* 653, series 30, 2011–2012
'Case study of a Rainforest zone: Amazonia', *Geofile* 640, series 29, 2010–2011
'An Eco-tourism Case Study: Ecuador', *Geofile* 618, series 28, 2009–2010
'Eco-tourism Case Study: Costa Rica', *Geofile* 598, series 28, 2009–2010

Geo Factsheet:
'Biofuels versus Biodiversity – A resource debate', *Geo Factsheet* 263, Curriculum Press
'Managing Tropical Rainforest- Ecosystem approach', *Geo Factsheet* 02, Curriculum Press

Open University articles on the Amazon:
http://www.open.edu/openlearn/nature-environment/expert-insight-amazonian-challenges-and-policy-responses

'Global Ideas: Forests: Case Studies', Classroom Video Limited

Explorer's Inn, Tambopata Reserve:
www.explorersinn.com/en/tambopata

Fruta Fruta Inc:
www.frutafruta.com/global/agroforestry/index.html

1. COASTAL PROCESSES AND FEATURES

Case studies

General reference to places for illustration purposes

Students should be able to:

(i) demonstrate knowledge and understanding of coastal processes – wave action, refraction, erosion, transport, swash and drift-aligned coasts

(ii) demonstrate knowledge and understanding of the formation of landforms at:
  – high-energy coasts: headlands, cliffs, arches, stacks and stumps
  – low-energy coasts: beaches and dunes, spits, tombolos and bars

Coasts are dynamic, complex and ever changing environments; a battlefield where the physicality of the land meets the vibrant fluid dynamics of the sea. If the land provides the material for coastlines – rock and sediment – then the sea provides the energy that forms and shapes these materials. Add to this conflict zone the fact that coasts are attractive environments for development and therefore subject to increasing human demands and pressure. At any point in time the landforms created along this distinctive boundary represent a dynamic equilibrium between the nature of the land, the forces of the sea and human activity.

Figure C1: Factors acting on coastal landforms

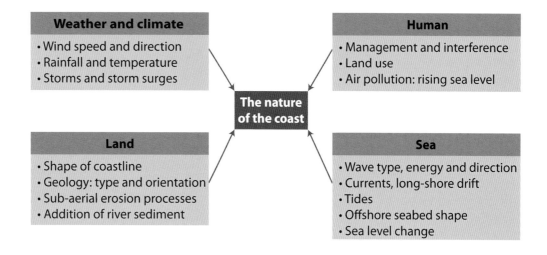

Weather and climate
- Wind speed and direction
- Rainfall and temperature
- Storms and storm surges

Human
- Management and interference
- Land use
- Air pollution: rising sea level

The nature of the coast

Land
- Shape of coastline
- Geology: type and orientation
- Sub-aerial erosion processes
- Addition of river sediment

Sea
- Wave type, energy and direction
- Currents, long-shore drift
- Tides
- Offshore seabed shape
- Sea level change

Coastlines can be described as consisting of three zones: the backshore or upper beach (backed by cliffs or sand dunes), the foreshore (uncovered at low tide) and the offshore (covered by water).

Coastal processes – the energy from the sea

Waves, tides, currents and changing sea level provide the flows and forces to modify and alter the shore. Coastal environments vary greatly over time and space. Twice daily tides, generated by the gravitational pull of the moon and sun, sweep across the coastal zone, constantly altering the point at which waves arrive. The coast of Western Europe has some of the highest tidal ranges in the world, meaning that, at low tide, huge stretches of land may be exposed, only to be covered again in a few hours.

Waves are created by the wind that blows over the water surface and the waves then transfer the energy across the oceans until they reach land. Waves vary in their nature and impact. Steep, plunging waves may cause severe erosion of the coastline, while shallower but powerful surging waves may carry sediment towards the shore.

The nature of waves

Sea waves are generated by the friction of winds blowing over the open sea. The power of a wave reflects the speed of the wind and the time and distance (fetch) over which it blows. This is why waves on the west coast of Ireland tend to be powerful, as they can be generated across the width of the Atlantic Ocean, while east coast waves are restricted by the shorter potential fetch of the Irish Sea. Waves in the open sea merely transfer energy as waves of transfer; water particles move in a circular motion as waves pass through. Figure C2 illustrates the terms used to describe a wave; the wavelength is the distance between wave crests and the wave height the vertical difference between the trough and crest.

Figure C2: Wave form and terminology

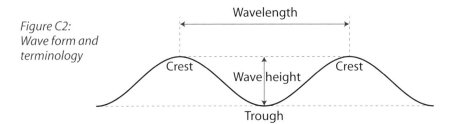

Wave steepness = wave height : wavelength
Wave period = average time between successive crests

Eventually, when waves enter shallower water near the coast, an important change takes place. At this point friction with the seabed slows the base of the wave, the circular water movement becomes increasingly elliptical and eventually breaks down forming waves of translation, throwing water forward onto the shore – the swash. The same water then runs back down the shore pulled by gravity – the backwash.

The relative power of the swash and backwash will determine if each wave deposits or erodes material from the shore. The precise nature of a wave or wave train (as a group is called) varies according to variables of the wind and the shape of the shoreline. Winter storms often form high energy plunging waves, termed destructive waves, which commonly remove material from the foreshore, making beaches steeper and forming a ridge where the wave breaks. Gentler summer winds over the open ocean create lower energy swell waves that, when they break, push material onto the shore, adding to beaches. These are termed constructive waves.

Figure C3: Constructive and destructive waves

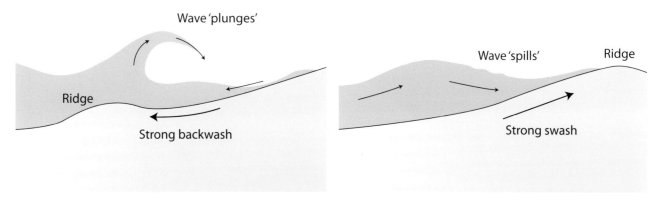

Destructive wave	Constructive wave
Short wavelength	Long wavelength
High wave height	Low wave height
Short period – high frequency (12–14 per minute)	Long period – low frequency (6–8 per minute)
Dominant strong backwash	Dominant strong swash
Material 'combed' from beach and moved offshore	Material moved onshore – building the beach
Waves often formed by local storm winds	Waves often formed far offshore

Wave refraction

An important relationship with coastlines is the direction from which waves approach. At first it would appear that this would be determined by wind direction. For example, to the west of Ireland the most persistent winds are from the south west so waves will commonly come from this direction. However, as waves approach the land and shallower water, the shape of the seabed will alter their form and, as they slow down, they often become increasingly parallel to the shape of the coastline. This important process is known as wave refraction (Figure C4).

Most often waves will approach the shoreline at an oblique angle: at one end of the wave front friction between the wave base in shallow water slows the wave and then the wave front appears to turn towards the shore. If refraction is complete, each wave front will break directly onto the shore and the swash and backwash will run up and down the beach.

Figure C4: Wave fronts turning parallel to shore by wave refraction

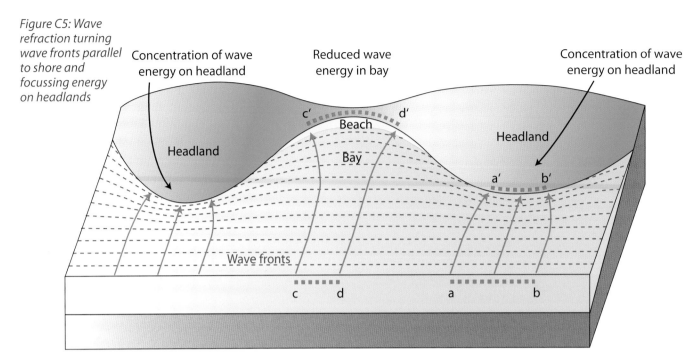

Figure C5: Wave refraction turning wave fronts parallel to shore and focussing energy on headlands

In Figure C5, waves are approaching a complex coastline with headlands and bays. As waves approach the headlands they feel the shallower shore and friction slows them down. Further along, the same wave in the bay continues to move onshore, only slowing later. The diagram illustrates how each wave can change shape to parallel the coastline and break directly onto the shore. At the same time it shows how wave energy will be concentrated onto the headlands, causing erosion. The wave energy represented by the line a-b becomes focussed on the smaller area a'-b' Meanwhile, in waves approaching the bay, their energy, represented by the line c-d will be spread across a wider area on the shore, c'-d', reducing erosion and allowing the deposition of material.

Despite the process of refraction, waves often reach the coast at an angle to the shore. In this case the swash of each wave will break at an angle onto the shore and carry water and sediment up the beach at the same angle. The subsequent backwash of each wave will run directly back down the beach, under gravity to the sea. This initiates a process known as longshore drift (LSD), by which material, such as sand and shingle, is moved along the coastline in a zigzag or saw tooth manner (Figure C6).

Figure C6: The process of longshore drift

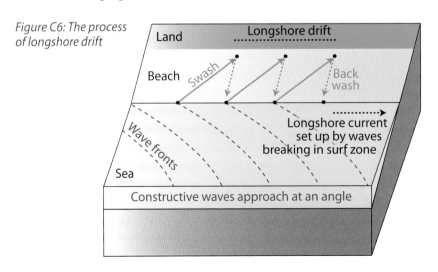

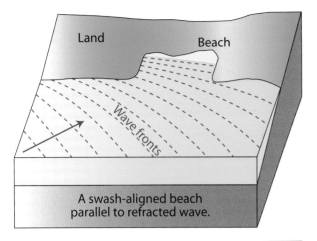

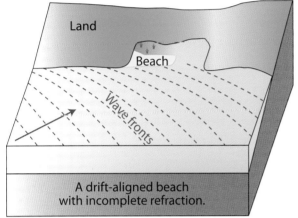

Figure C7: Swash and drift-aligned aligned beaches

Swash and drift-aligned coasts

Shorelines that are dominated by the continuous movement of sediment along the coast, due to the local prevailing winds driving waves at an angle to the shore, are known as drift-aligned coasts. These are associated with distinctive deposition features including spits, bay bars, tombolos and cuspate forelands. The alternative is swash-aligned coasts which, as closed sediment-cell systems, involve limited movement of materials along the coastline. Features of swash-aligned coasts include bay head and barrier beaches (offshore bars). On swash-aligned beaches the swash and backwash of waves move material up and down the beach, sorting it into different sizes of materials and forming long ridges or berms across the beach. In some cases, ridges of pebbles are deposited near the high tide mark, often with a cusp or saw tooth shape along their edge. At low tide, ripple marks stretch across the sandy beach and shallow ponds or runnels lie parallel to the coast. Wide beaches may form the source area for wind-blown sand to form sand dunes above the high tide mark of the beach (Figure C7).

Coastal erosion

Both the sea and the atmosphere are at work on the coast to break down the rocks that form the shore. The common sub-aerial processes of weathering – mechanical, biological and chemical – will all operate here. On rock faces, freeze thaw weathering will cause rocks to fall to the foot of cliffs; plant roots and wildlife can widen cracks and weaknesses in rocks; and the dissolving of calcium carbonate by rainfall will continue in limestone deposits. The coast has some special forms of mechanical and biological weathering processes. The abundance of sodium and magnesium compounds at the coasts produces salt weathering. As these compounds crystallise, they expand within the cracks and joints of the rocks, widening these lines of weakness. Additionally marine organisms such as molluscs, sea urchins, sponges and boring worms biologically attack rock surfaces along the shore.

Marine erosion

Waves use their energy and chemistry to erode coastlines in four complex and interacting processes: hydraulic action, abrasion, solution and attrition.

- **Hydraulic action** occurs when the air in cracks in the rocks is compressed by the force of breaking waves. As the wave subsides, this air expands again and these pressure changes can open the joints and weaken the rock. The sheer weight of waves hitting rocks can exert pressures over 10 tonnes per m² on cliffs. This process is also known as wave pounding.

- **Abrasion (corrasion)** is a highly effective form of erosion along exposed coastlines. Waves throw sediment, including sand, pebbles and shingle, against the base of cliffs, wearing them back. Abrasion and hydraulic action are both concentrated between the high and low tide marks.

- **Solution** results from salts and organic acids in the seawater attacking the chemistry of rocks. It is particularly effective on lime-rich strata and is often evident in rock pools on rocky shorelines.
- **Attrition** involves the wearing down of the material eroded from the cliffs. It provides the tools used in abrasion, as well as the wide variety of sediment that forms beaches and other depositional features. The rapid rounding and polishing of beach materials, including broken glass, is evidence of the effectiveness of this process.

Coastal transport and deposition

Sediment on coasts has many sources including eroded cliff material, river sediment, glacial deposits and offshore marine material. The sea moves this material as bedload by traction and saltation (rolling, dragging and bouncing sediment along), or as suspended load (with silt or sand held up by turbulent flow). On the shore, transport is associated with the swash and backwash of waves and the longshore drift process noted earlier.

Sediment cells

The coastal sediment system (littoral cell system) is a model for the study of processes and patterns on a section of coast. Each cell is treated as a self-contained unit in which inputs and outputs are balanced and sediment is transferred within the cell (Figure C8).

Figure C8: A sediment or littoral cell

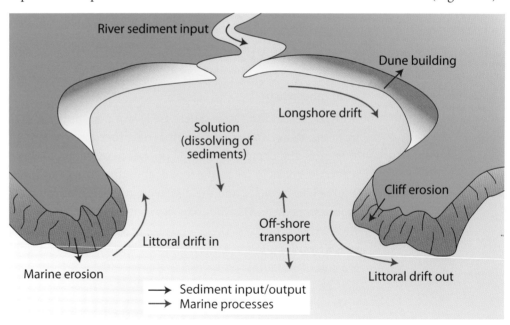

Formation of coastal landforms

The geology of the coastline is a key factor in determining the outcome of the interaction between land and sea. At its simplest, rocks may be classified as those that are easily eroded and those that resist erosion. Often it is the arrangement of the rocks that guides the coastline that is formed. Alternating bands of hard and softer rock, running at right angles to the shore can form a headland and bay topography (Figure C9). Differential erosion rates will also be associated with existing weaknesses in geology, such as fault lines or the existence of river or glacier valleys. The distinctive indented coastline of South West Ireland, Western Scotland and Western Norway are all the consequence of the sea invading and eroding valleys that were created by glaciers (Figure C10).

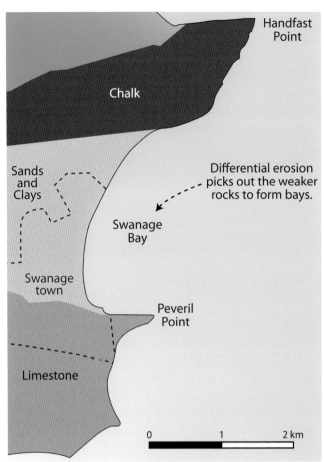

Figure C9: Headlands and bays near Swanage, South East Dorset

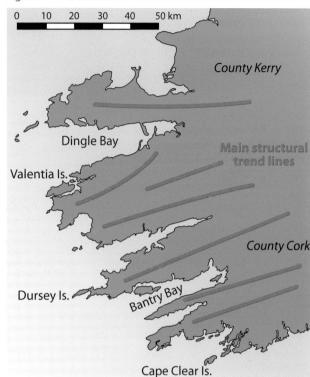

Figure C10: The indented coastline of South West Ireland

High-energy coasts

Figure C11: Praia da Marinha, Algarve, Portugal, a high-energy coast

These are coasts that are subject to regular strong wave impact for much of the year. They often face the open sea, where the prevailing wind has a long fetch over which powerful waves can form. The west coasts of Scotland and Ireland are good examples. High-energy coasts are associated with erosional landforms including cliffs, headland features and coarse sand and shingle beaches in the bay environments.

The primary coastal landform associated with erosion is the cliff or cliff line. This is a break in slope between the land and sea that may be low and gentle, or high and steep. Cliffs are the outcome of sustained erosion along the shore and active cliffs are associated with retreating coasts. Figure C12 illustrates how cliffs are formed and how they can grow in size as the coastline retreats, creating the related feature of the wave-cut platform. Initially, erosion is focused in the relatively narrow zone between high and low tide. At this point, a small notch will form as material is weakened and removed. Over time this wave-cut notch will undermine the rock above and collapse will occur. The fallen material can prevent further erosion for a time along the cliff base but eventually attrition and other marine erosion processes will remove this material and erosion of the cliff base will be renewed. Gradually, the cliff face retreats and the residual wave-cut platform, often covered by sediment, is widened. The rate of cliff retreat, assuming the wave energy conditions are unchanged, will slow over time as waves will have further to travel across the wave-cut platform before reaching the cliff base. Finally, sea erosion of the cliff base may virtually cease and cliffs become degraded by sub-aerial processes. In the UK, cliff retreat rates of 50 cm per year are not uncommon, while the government regards rates of 100 cm or more per year as a cause for concern.

Figure C12: The formation of cliffs, cliff retreat and wave-cut platforms

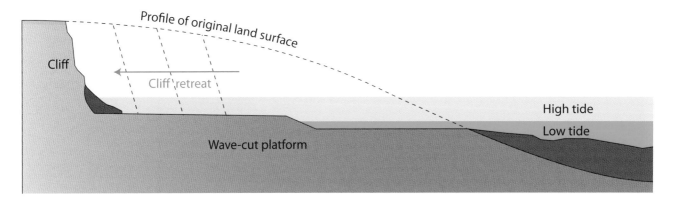

The precise cross-section shape and plan form of a cliff depends on wave energy and the nature and structure of its geology. Hard rocks that are horizontally bedded can form vertical cliffs, such as the 210 m high shale and sandstone Cliffs of Moher in western Co Clare. Softer geology or rocks that dip towards the sea create more gentle profiles. The cliffs along the coast of Holderness in Eastern England are formed in unconsolidated (loose) glacial mud and are among the most rapidly retreating in the world.

Figure C13: Mud flow on clay cliff line, Dorset

Figure C14: Vertical cliffs, Co Antrim

Figure C15: Cliff and wave cut platform, Fife Scotland

Headlands, arches and stacks

Figure C16: The erosion landforms associated with headlands

Earlier in the discussion of wave refraction (Figure C4) it was demonstrated that wave energy can become focused onto headlands and in such settings a series of distinctive erosion landforms is often found.

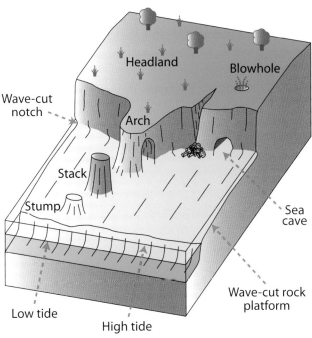

The north coast of Ireland has many dramatic erosion landscapes. At Fair Head (Benmore), Co Antrim, a band of hard volcanic rock known as a sill juts dramatically out into the North Channel. To the south, along the Co Antrim coast, each of its famous Glens is separated by headlands and promontories, between which lie long curving bays and beaches. Many headlands show the impact of concentrated wave erosion at their base, where a wave-cut notch is evident, especially at low tide. Where there are weaknesses in the geology, faults, jointing or weaker strata, the sea will widen and open caves. Caves in a headland can be worn backwards, perhaps to meet a similar feature developed along the same line of weakness from the opposite side of the headland. Where this happens, a hole through the headland leaves the upper rock spanning an arch.

Figure C17: Coastal erosion features at White Rocks and Magheracross, North Antrim

Note that due to isostatic uplift in this region, some stacks, arches and stumps are raised out of the sea except at high tide.

Figure C18: Double Arch on headland, Portugal

Ongoing erosion, both by waves and sub-aerial processes, will widen the arch, undermining the spanning rock until it collapses to the sea below. The remaining part of the headland is now separate from the land and often surrounded by the sea as a stack. Even stacks in their turn will be eroded and reduced to stumps of rock that only appear at low tide. Figures C16, C17 and C18 describe and illustrate examples of these features of coastal erosion.

At White Rocks in Co Antrim there are a number of caves, arches and stumps, including the Wishing Arch (Figure C17). The collapse of an arch is a dramatic event and several have happened in recent decades, including the collapse of one of a double arch known as the London Bridge, in a headland in South East Australia. Well known stacks include Dún Briste (The Broken Fort), Co Mayo and the Old Man of Hoy, in the Orkneys (Figures C19 and C20). Historic paintings reveal that 200 years ago the Old Man of Hoy was an arch, the two legs giving its name. Later its collapse left the 137 m high stack detached from the cliff and the ground between covered by rubble from the arch.

Figure C19: Dún Briste Stack, Co Mayo, Ireland

Other landforms of erosion that can be seen at coastlines include blowholes and geos. These may form in headlands or along cliffs. A blowhole, as the name might suggest, involves the blowing out of water at the top of a cliff. This is the result of the sea eroding a hole in the roof of a cave. At high tide waves sweep into the cave and force air and water out through this hole. These dramatic features can be short lived as erosion continues. A geo is a narrow, steep sided inlet that may have been a constricted cave in which the roof has collapsed (Figure C21).

Figure C20: The Old Man of Hoy, Orkney, Scotland

The sediment created by erosion of the coast must be transported and deposited somewhere. While some of it is carried offshore into deeper water, much is moved along the shoreline to lower energy environments, where it is deposited forming other distinctive coastal landforms.

Figure C21: Fault aligned geo, Orkney   *Figure C22: Fingal's Cave, Isle of Staffa, Scotland*

Low-energy coasts

Figure C23: Marble Hill Beach, Donegal, a low-energy coast

Just as the features of coastal erosion are associated with areas of high-energy, including wide tidal variation and powerful storm waves, so the landforms of deposition are closely associated with low-energy coastal zones. Low and high-energy zones are frequently close together. An offshore island can shelter a section of otherwise storm torn coast or the change in orientation along a shore, from say north to north-west, may expose the coast to the full force of an ocean wide fetch, creating surfing breakers. The earthquake induced tsunami wave of Boxing Day 2004 devastated many coastlines. However, in places shores only a few metres from destruction were virtually untouched, as the shape of the land and seabed sheltered them from the enormous waves. In short, it is possible to find erosion and deposition landforms adjacent to each other. Between most headlands bays are found, which are dominated by the most common of all deposited landforms – the bay-head beach. Clay and silt sized particles are often too light to remain on beaches, so the coarser sand particles are left. Beaches can be made of a wide variety of materials, including sand, pebbles and cobbles. These particles in turn are often sorted into size either up and down the beach or along the shore

As noted earlier, two forms of beach/deposition coastlines can be distinguished: the swash-aligned and the drift-aligned shore. In swash-aligned environments the prevailing wind, and thus wave direction, acts at right angles to the shore, whereas in drift-angled environments the wind and wave fronts arrive at an angle to the shore, driving water and sediment along the beach (Figure C7).

Figure C24: The variation of beach materials on the shore of Dundrum Bay near Newcastle

Beaches

The shape and form of beaches are influenced by many factors and they often change seasonally. Destructive storm waves are more common in winter, with constructive swell waves dominant during summer months thus beaches may become wider and steeper in summer as material is added.

Beaches consist of sediment material that lies between the low and high water, marked with the upper beach created by sediment thrown up by storm waves. Successive ridges created by high tide lines are known as berms and further down the beach long transverse ridges separate parallel hollows called runnels where water lies at low tide (Figure C25).

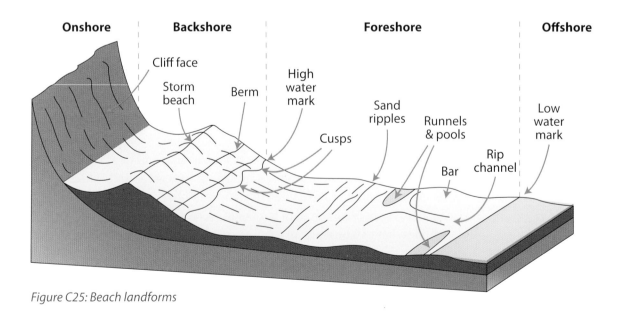

Figure C25: Beach landforms

Dunes

Strong onshore winds blowing across a wide stretch of beach can lift and transport fine sands onshore in a bouncing motion termed 'saltation'.

Figure C26: Wind-blown sand moves by saltation along Magilligan Beach, Co Londonderry

Above the strand line high water mark, organic material and/or litter obstacles can trap this sand, forming small embryo dunes. Specialist plants that are adapted to this salty, windy and arid environment thrive in this shifting sand, including sand couch and marram grasses. The complex root network of the vegetation binds these embryo dunes, allowing them to grow in height and breadth. A cover of marram creates a 'dead-zone', some 10 cm above the dune surface, where wind falls to almost nothing and windborne sand is trapped. Over time, assuming a continuous supply of fresh sand, a successive line of dunes can develop with linear low-lying dune slacks running between them. Near the beach, dunes are almost pure sand and are described as mobile yellow dunes. Inland, older fixed dunes have a wider range of vegetation and plant species, and the soil is less alkaline and arid. These are termed the grey dunes. Dunes may be 15 or even 20 m high but are very fragile features. Damage to the vegetation cover or storm waves at high tides can cause them to erode rapidly. Blow-outs are large hollows where exposed loose sand has been swept away by storm winds.

Figure C27: Dune formation and structure at Murlough National Trust Reserve, Newcastle, Co Down

Figure C28: Landforms of coastal deposition on low-energy coasts

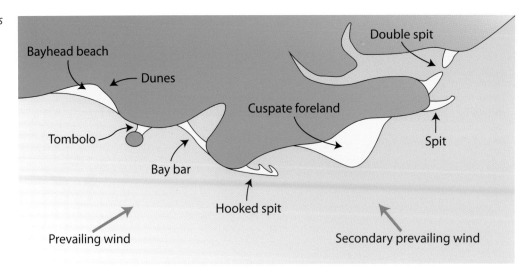

Drift-aligned environments

As noted previously, drift-aligned beaches form where the prevailing onshore wind generates waves that arrive at an angle oblique to the trend of the coast. These carry sediment along the shore in the zigzag process – longshore drift (Figure C6). The beach will be maintained as long as there is a continuous supply of sand available, for example from an eroding cliff line or from sediment brought down to the coast by rivers. If no such supply exists, the beach will gradually be depleted of sand at one end, possibly leaving only coarser pebbles or cobbles which the waves cannot easily remove. In this case, people have often attempted to keep the sand beach in place or increase its depth and width by building barriers across the beach to trap the drifting sediment. These are called groynes. Normally made of wood, concrete or simple boulders these run across beaches at right angles to the shore in groups known as groyne fields (Figure C29).

Figure C29: Groyne management

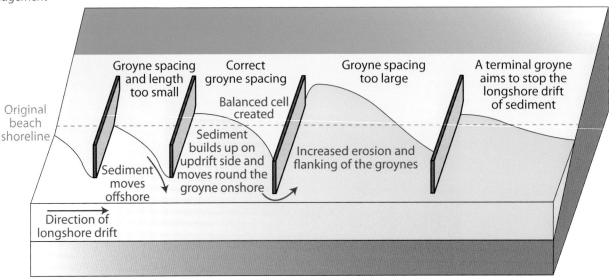

In either case, the longshore drift of sand down the coast will continue only until the shape of the coast changes. If the coastline turns away from the direction of drift by 30°or more, such as at an estuary or river mouth, then one of the coast's most distinctive landforms may develop – a spit. Essentially, a spit is simply a beach that continues to extend out into the sea (Figure C30).

Figure C30: Longshore drift and the formation of a spit

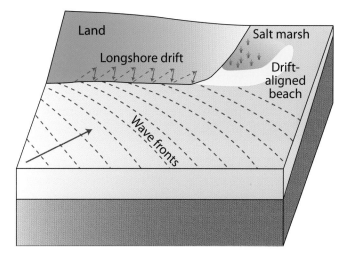

(a) Longshore drift and the initiation of a spit

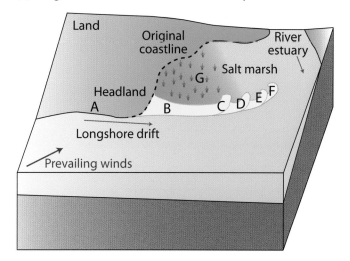

(b) The development of a spit

Figure C31: Map of Holderness coast and Spurn Head spit

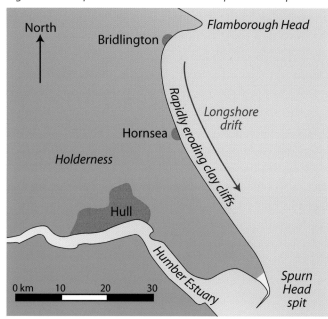

Spits

These are stores of sediment that form as drift processes continue at the change of trend of the shoreline and where the tidal range is not too extreme. Figure C30 (b) shows the formation sequence of a spit:

- The dashed line shows the position of the original coastline. In this region the prevailing winds and the direction of maximum fetch are from the south west. As a result, the strongest and most common waves come from this direction, transporting material eastwards by longshore drift along the beach at A.

- Where the trend of the coastline changed direction dramatically, at the headland, the drift of material continued out into the river estuary, and pebbles and cobbles were deposited on the bed at B.

- This material builds up over time to reach the sea surface, initiating the extension of the beach as a spit.

- Deposited materials continue to extend the beach to C. Storm waves and winds add sand to the upper beach.

- The beach continues to grow across the estuary to points D and E. At this end of the spit, the distal end, occasional storm winds or a second common wind/ wave direction can curve the end into a distinctive hook.

- Onshore winds carry sand landward, forming sand dunes above the high tide mark. Behind the spit, the sheltered area of the estuary allows fine silts and mud to settle to form a flat, wet saltmarsh at G.

- The spit reaches point F but deeper water and the scouring effect of the river flowing into the sea prevents further growth and expansion.

- Spits may be breached by winter storms and their position and size can be altered, slowly or dramatically.

Spits are fed by active erosion further back, 'upstream', along the coast. A classic example of such a situation is the Spurn Head Spit, Yorkshire, where erosion from the cliffs along Holderness feeds its growth (Figure C31).

Figure C32: Map of Murlough Nature Reserve, Dundrum Bay

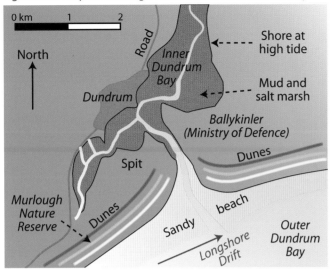

Another example is the spit that is home to Murlough Nature Reserve, Co Down and helps form Inner Dundrum Bay (Figure C32). The source of this sediment lies offshore and was deposited during the last Ice Age.

It appears that, in recent decades, this source is declining as the beach is reducing in width and scale, providing less natural protection from storm winds. Remedial action has been taken to protect the foredunes from erosion by waves, especially where Royal Co Down Golf Links is threatened (Figure C33).

Spits come in many forms, such as double spits where two extend across from both sides of a bay or estuary.

Figure C33: Groynes and other coastal defences near Newcastle

A) Degraded groyne field with boulder rip-rap at foot of dunes

B) Simple railway sleeper revetment in front of boulder rip-rap

Tombolo

Where a spit extends from the mainland and links a former island to the shore it is referred to as a 'tombolo'. The most famous UK example is at Chesil Beach (Figures C34 and C35), where a shingle spit, 25 km long, connects Dorset to the Isle of Portland. It varies in height from 5–15 m and in width from 50–200 m. The sediment along the beach is graded in size from pea-sized gravel in the north to potato-sized in the south. There are many theories about its origin and the movement of sediment along the beach. It is widely agreed that Chesil is a relict landform feature, an offshore bar formed after the last Ice Age ended from material deposited on the seabed. As the ice melted, raising world sea levels, this bar was driven onshore to form the tombolo we see today. Chesil Beach protects a 13 km long tidal lagoon called the Fleet, a rare feature on Europe's coast and the largest in England. The Fleet has a national conservation designation as a Site of Special Scientific Interest (SSSI), European status as a Special Protection Area (SPA) and internationally it is recognised as a Ramsar site for its wetland bird habitat.

Figure C34: Map of Chesil Beach tombolo, South Dorset

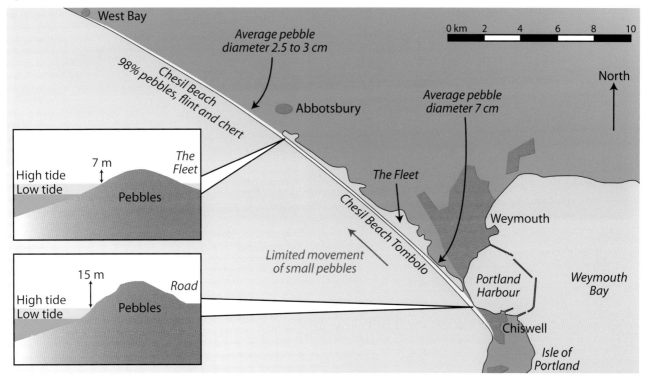

Figure C35: Graded sediment along Chesil Beach tombolo, South Dorset

However, tombolos are often much smaller features, for example where an island causes wave refraction to build a spit (causeway) from the land to the island itself. Some tombolos are only evident at low tide when they form a natural causeway giving access to the connected island. (Figure C36).

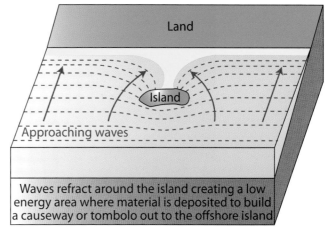

Figure C36: Refraction by island creating a tombolo

Figure C37: Embryonic tombolo, Dorset

Figure C38: Tombolos connecting islands near Koh Tao, Gulf of Thailand

Bars

Ridges of sediment lying offshore but parallel to the coastline are known as bars and form in very distinctive environments. These are a common feature along the eastern seaboard of the USA, where they form almost 300 separate long islands stretching from Florida in the south to New York State in the north (Figure C39). There are several theories about the formation process of these so-called 'barrier beaches' and it is probable that more than one theory may be correct. Changing sea levels in the post-glacial period and the partial drowning of existing sand dunes or beach berm ridges seem to be relevant in some cases. Bars can be formed 20 km offshore from low-lying shallow coasts or be driven onshore to lie within metres of the beaches themselves.

The term bay bar is used to describe the situation where a bar extends across an inlet or bay, cutting off an area of open water from the sea – a lagoon. These may be formed when an offshore bay is driven onto the shore in a swash-aligned coast or alternatively where a spit grows right across a bay or inlet in a drift-aligned coast. One example is found at Slapton Ley in Devon (Figure C40).

Figure C39: Map of the Virginia Eastern Shore USA showing the line of barrier beaches

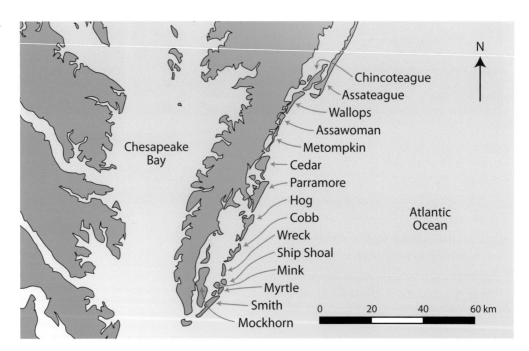

Figure C40: Bay bar at Slapton Ley, Devon

Source: Jim Linwood

Exam Questions

1. Explain, with examples, the difference between swash and drift-aligned coasts. [8]

2. With the aid of a diagram(s), explain wave refraction in coastal environments. [8]

3. With reference to places for illustration purposes, describe and explain the processes and landforms associated with high-energy coasts. [18]

References

Geofile:
'Coastal systems: waves, tides, sediments and sediment cells', *Geofile* 575, series 27, 2008–2009

Geo Factsheets:
'Coastal erosion landforms on the Gower Peninsula', *Geo Factsheet* 356, Curriculum Press
'Coastal deposition', *Geo Factsheet* 145, Curriculum Press

2. REGIONAL COASTLINES

Case studies

National scale study of a coastline under threat from sea level rise in an LEDC: The Maldives

Students should be able to:

(i) demonstrate knowledge and understanding of the processes (eustatic and isostatic) and features (fjords, rias, raised beaches and relict landforms) associated with coastlines of submergence and emergence

(ii) demonstrate knowledge and understanding of the threat of rising sea levels due to climate change on the human and physical environment

Eustatic and isostatic change

Added to the already complex relationship between the land and the sea is the fact that sea level is constantly changing. It not only changes daily with tides and seasonally with winter storms but over the long-term due to the forces of plate tectonics and in particular climate change. Today world sea level is rising globally, as a consequence of a warming climate, but in the past two million years a series of ice ages has caused repeated changes to ocean levels. Such worldwide sea level adjustments are termed eustatic change. Eustatic change is global and is due to variation in the volume of water in the world's oceans. This is the result of climate change. Natural climate change is due to several cycles including:

- variation in the Earth's orbit, a 400,000 year cycle.
- variation in solar energy output (sun spots), an 11 year cycle.
- variation in the tilt of the Earth's axis, a 41,000 year cycle. (See page 169.)

In addition, periodic major volcanic eruptions can cool the Earth as debris in the upper atmosphere blocks out insolation. Falling world temperatures means more precipitation will fall as snow, which will turn to ice storing water on the land. As a result world sea level will fall. When global temperatures rise again, the water stored as ice on the land, as glaciers and ice sheets, will thaw and return to the ocean raising the sea level. Today, the human induced warming of the world's climate has caused a 22 cm rise in global seas level since 1880 and projections suggest a further rise of between 30 and 120 cm before the year 2100.

However, not all relative sea level change is worldwide. Locally, vertical changes in land height occur. Isostatic change is the local rise or fall in land level relative to the sea. This is caused by physical processes of plate collision or the addition or removal of the weight of ice during a glacial period. Land buried under deep ice, such as Greenland, is depressed down under the sheer weight of the ice sheet. If and when the ice melts, the burden will be removed and the land will slowly rise upwards. The last glacial era, which covered most of Northern Europe in deep ice, ended around 10,000 years ago. Today, Scotland and the northern coast of Ireland are still slowly recovering, with the land rising upwards through isostatic change by as much as 7 mm a year. As a result of this process, around the present day coast former beaches, cliff lines, caves and other coastal features can now be seen high and dry above our current sea levels (Figure C41).

Figure C41: Former cliffs, beaches, arches and stacks on the emergent coast of Co Antrim

Red Arch, a natural raised sea arch, Red Bay, Co Antrim

Raised beach, fossil cliff and caves, Ballintoy Harbour, Co Antrim

Raised beach and cliff line between White Park Bay and Ballintoy Harbour, Co Antrim

Fossil stack near Ballintoy, Co Antrim

Figure C42: Islands and pladdies (drowned drumlins) caused by the submergence of Strangford Lough

Elsewhere the consequence of rising sea levels in the past can still be observed. In the shallow sea inlet of Strangford Lough the numerous islands and pladdies (drowned drumlins exposed at low tide) are the result of the sea drowning the rolling drumlin hills of that part of Co Down (Figure C42).

During the geological era known as the Quaternary, the dominant pattern has been a series of climate changes producing about 20 separate periods of glaciation. During each of these, world sea level has fallen as water becomes stored as ice on land only to rise again between glaciations during warmer eras known as interglacial periods. During the last glaciation, world sea levels were 100–120 m lower than today so large areas of the continental shelf around Ireland and Great Britain were dry land. During the current interglacial period, the Holocene, which started about 10,000 years ago, the sea level has risen to its present level, flooding much of this land and transforming Western Europe from a large peninsular area of the Atlantic into the numerous islands we see today.

Figure C43: The north west coast of Europe near the end of the last Ice Age

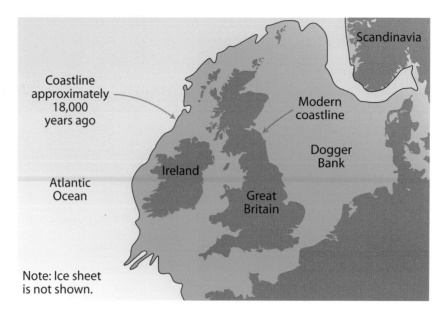

Regional coastlines of submergence and emergence

At a regional scale, such changes in the relative height of sea level can create two distinctive coastlines:

1. Coasts where the land is falling relative to the sea, due to rising sea level or falling land, or both causing submergence of the shore.

2. Coasts where the land is rising relative to the sea, due to falling sea levels or rising land, or both causing emergence of the shore.

Figure C44: The variation in current, post-glacial, relative land level change in the UK and Ireland

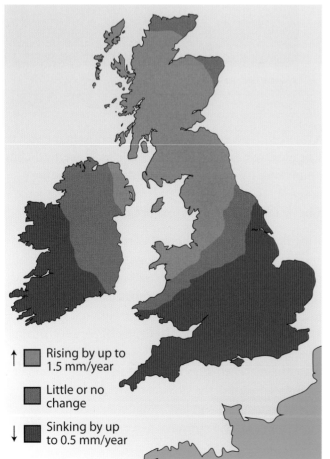

While eustatic change in sea level is global, its impact on coasts will be adjusted by any local scale isostatic changes that occur. This helps to explain why parts of the UK and Ireland, the south east coasts in particular, currently display evidence of submergence while western Scotland and the north of Ireland show the features of an emergent coast.

Submergent coastlines

Submergent or drowned coastlines are marked by marine transgression: the sea spreads over the land and the coastline retreats. The landforms created will vary on whether the coast was a lowland or upland area and on the trend of the local geology. In Northern Europe, including the west coasts of Norway and Scotland, during the last Ice Age, glaciers created broad and steep sided valleys. Post-glaciation these have been drowned by the sea forming dramatic deep fjords running at right angles or discordant to the coast. These have steep sides often with waterfalls plunging from hanging valleys down the sides of their distinctive U-shaped cross-section. The mouth of a fjord is often shallower, possibly due to the dumping of material by ice as a moraine or because at that point the sea had caused the valley glacier to float, lifting it from the bed of the valley. Fjords coasts are also seen in the former glaciated regions of West Canada and in Chile and New Zealand in the southern hemisphere.

Figure C45: Plan, cross-section and long profile section of a fjord

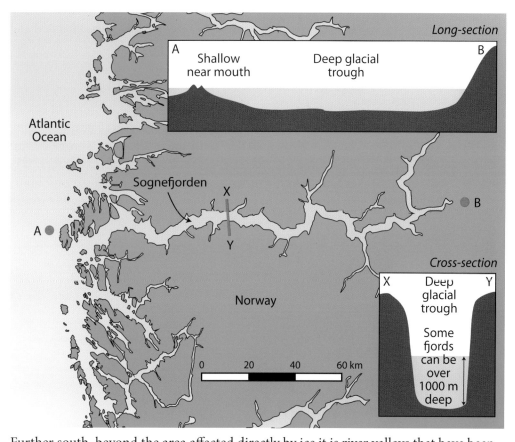

Further south, beyond the area affected directly by ice it is river valleys that have been flooded by the rising sea. These are termed rias, and typically show the winding tree-like (dendritic) pattern associated with a river and its network of tributaries. Rivers such as the Exe and Teign on the south coast of Devon and Cornwall are good examples of such rias. If the trend of the pre-submerged coast was of ridges and valleys running parallel to the shore then the flooding sea forms long narrow inlets as 'sounds' and leaves long islands that lie parallel or concordant to the coast. Named after the coast that forms the eastern shore of the Adriatic Sea, these are known as Dalmatian coastlines.

Figure C46: Plan, cross-section and long profile section of a ria

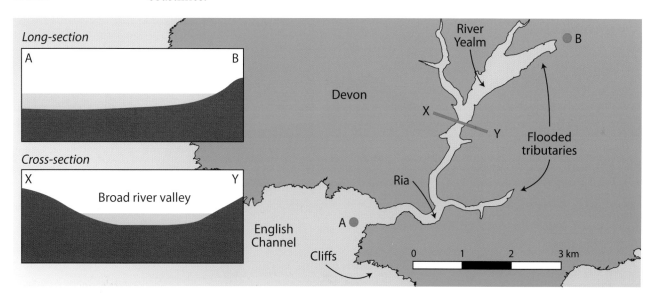

Along low-lying coasts the 'invading' sea creates flooded valleys, wide sandy beaches and large salt marshes. The East Anglian coast including the counties of Norfolk, Suffolk and Essex show these features well and land is continuing to be lost here to the rising sea. Across the North Sea the very flat coastal lands or polders of the Netherlands are in fact below sea level and only inhabited and farmed as they are protected by an extensive and expensive series of dams, dykes and barrages.

Emergent coastlines

Emergent coastlines are distinctive in that landforms of coastal erosion and deposition will be found above the present day sea level (Figures C41 and C48). These are a common element in the landscape of Northern Europe and in particular the presence of former beaches and wave-cut platforms as raised beaches. While world sea levels rose by up to 120 m after the end of the last ice age later isostatic uplift raised newly formed

Figure C47: Relict landforms on the emergent coast of Co Down

beaches up out of the sea to where they now stand several metres or tens of metres above the sea. At least one such raised beachline can be traced around most of the coastline of Northern Ireland. Parts of the coastal road network of Antrim and Down are built onto the conveniently flat raised beachline. Not only do the relict landforms provide evidence for previously higher sea levels, but the raised beaches themselves are often still covered by marine sands and shell fragments. Figure C41 illustrates examples of many of the raised or relict coastal landforms in Co Antrim while Figure C47 shows a small bay with a former cliff line, beach and wave-cut platform near Ballyhoran in Co Down.

Figure C48: Relict landforms on an emergent coast

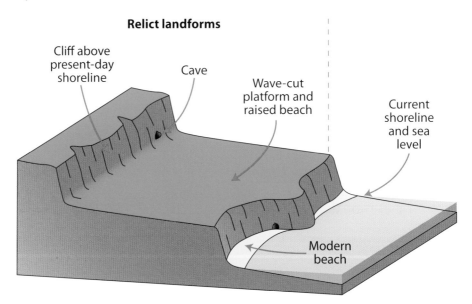

Gradual emergence of land allows the formation and extension of depositional features such as salt marshes and mangrove swamp ecosystems. In sheltered bays around Ireland the growth of wide sand beaches has, in turn, encouraged the formation of extensive sand dunes systems above the high tide mark. Many of these have been growing seaward for 5000 years or more and some are backed by the original cliffs of the coast such as the dune system at White Park Bay in Co Antrim. Ireland's largest deposition landform is the striking cuspate foreland at Magilligan, Co Londonderry. This low-lying triangular landform feature is backed by the steep cliffs of Benevenagh and extends several kilometres north to Benone beach and the Umbra sand dunes. Cuspate (tooth-shaped) forelands are complex deposition landforms involving the working of river, beach and wind-blown sediment in a sheltered environment in which both swash and drift alignment processes are incorporated. At Magilligan, the gradual emergence of the seabed due to isostatic rebound after glaciation has facilitated these deposition processes in the creation of over 32 km² of land, much of which, as shown in Figure C49, is in use for agriculture or tourist purposes.

Figure C49: Cuspate foreland and Benevenagh cliffs, Magilligan, Co Londonderry

Rising sea levels due to climate change

Research suggests that global sea levels have been stable for the last 2000–3000 years, although isostatic changes mean that local or regional change in relative sea level has taken place. However, in the last 200 years a different pattern has emerged with a significant eustatic rise in sea level approaching 30 cm recorded across the planet. Linked to global warming this increase is expected to continue in future. In fact scientists suggest that even if global warming was stopped the worldwide sea level will continue to rise for many years to come. As stated by the 5th report of the Intergovernmental Panel on Climate Change (IPCC):

> "It is virtually certain that global mean sea level rise will continue for many centuries beyond 2100, with the amount of rise dependent on future emissions."

Figure C50: Projected rise in global sea level by 2100

IPCC Report	Estimated increase in sea level by 2100
4th 2007	Between 20 and 50 cm
5th 2013	Between 28 and 98 cm

Many scientists have suggested that the 2013 5th IPCC Report figures (Figure C50) represent the lower estimated range of sea level change for the twenty-first century. The recent rate of sea level rise has increased from the 1900–1970 period through a more rapid annual change between 1970 and 2010 with a further rate increase predicted for the present period. At first the rising global sea level was simply due to thermal expansion – as ocean water warms it expands upwards, its only option. Later some of the sea level rise was due to the melting of mountain glaciers reported from all continents and mountain ranges. Added to this is the melting of major ice sheets in Greenland and Antarctica, currently the least predictable in terms of scale and timing. In regions where local isostatic change is causing land to sink, the impact of rising eustatic sea levels will be greater. For example, on the Gulf of Mexico and North Atlantic coasts of the USA a further 30 cm rise in relative sea level is predicted by 2050. Other global warming related changes include the increased violence of storms. In North Carolina, USA, recent studies show that extreme coastal storms that were formerly regarded as one in 100 year events are now expected once in 30 years.

The threat of rising sea levels on the human and physical environment

The degree and the form of the threat posed by rising sea levels will depend on the nature of the coastline in both physical and human terms. Coasts dominated by steep plunging cliff lines are unlikely to change dramatically whereas beaches and low-lying coastlines may be rapidly altered by erosion. Similarly, for the developed nations of Europe the threat may entail cost and inconvenience but some LEDCs may be facing the demise of their nation. It is estimated that globally, one billion people face increased physical hazards from coastal flooding, storm surges and violent storms. Inevitably land will be lost to the sea impacting on agriculture, fishing, aquaculture, tourism and coastal residential settlements. Higher sea levels will cause the destructive erosion of beaches and cliffs producing more sediment, which in turn must be deposited elsewhere: in short the coastal sediment budget becomes highly disrupted. Coastal wetlands will be inundated changing the abiotic conditions for these ecosystems including raised salinity levels in rivers, bays and groundwater. Saltwater penetration of terrestrial groundwater sources impacts on the local supply of fresh water for domestic, industrial and irrigation uses.

Environmental threats include the potential loss of the distinctive and globally important coastal coral and mangrove ecosystems. In the tropics, around 75% of all coastlines are home to tidal forests known as mangroves. Lying between the land and sea these specialist ecosystems formed by salt-tolerant trees provide a vital habitat for many fish, insect, bird and mammal species. Mangroves are recognised as a natural defence from the sea and their loss by human activity in the past has led to increased rates of coastal erosion. Bangladesh is one of the world's lowest lying nations and also one of the most densely populated. Around 25 million Bangladeshis live on coastal delta land less than 1 m above sea level. Of the nation's 735 km coastline, 20% is lined and protected by natural mangrove forest, known locally as the Sunderbans. Rising sea levels threaten the loss of these forests along with the numerous species that depend on them. This in turn will increase the rate of coastal erosion and the loss of rich agricultural land. The government of Bangladesh has invested huge sums of money to reinforce their coastal defences but many argue that this is a hopeless task in the face of global sea level rise. Human activity including shrimp and rice farming has already caused the loss of most of the mangrove forests of the Caribbean and Pacific. Global warming and rising sea levels now threatens those that remain.

Linked to mangroves is an equally important and threatened ecosystem – coral reefs. Coral reefs are created by a group of species of soft bodied polyps, known as reef building stony corals that excrete calcium carbonate to build an external skeleton. The polyps survive in a symbiotic (mutually beneficial) relationship with algae – a plant that provides

oxygen and food. In tropical waters corals grow by 2–60 cm each year and th[...]
have created some of the largest organic structures on Earth. The 2600 km lo[...]
Barrier Reef, off Australia's north east coast, took five million years to form. [...]
only occupy 0.25% of the oceans but they are home to around 25% of all the [...]
marine species – polyps, fish, mammals, turtles, molluscs and crustaceans. Reef building
corals thrive in a very specific range of conditions, as noted in Figure C51.

Figure C51: The conditions for coral growth

Factor	Conditions
1. Temperature	Mean annual temperature above 20°C but below 29°C. Best between 23–25°C.
2. Water depth	Most form in water less than 25m deep – shallow coastal locations.
3. Light	Light is vital for the photosynthesis of the algae that the coral polyps feed on.
4. Salinity	Coral polyps require salt-water and can tolerant relatively high levels of salinity.
5. Sediment	Corals thrive in clear water as sediment blocks light and clogs feeding systems.
6. Wave action	Wave action keeps the water oxygenated and supplies micro plankton.
7. Air exposure	Corals can survive exposure to air only for a short time.
8. Acidity	Sea water pH is 8–8.3. In more acidic conditions corals cannot grow as effectively.

Global warming is causing the oceans to absorb more carbon dioxide increasing its
acidity. Higher acidity can chemically dissolve existing coral and reduces the rate at
which corals can grow. This combined with sea level rise is threatening many of the
factors needed for the healthy development of coral reefs noted in Figure C51. One major
impact on coral reefs is described as coral bleaching: under environmental stress the
algae on which polyps depend can abandon the coral leaving it to die. A 2010 report by
the Global Coral Reef Monitoring Network suggested that coral reefs were the first
ecosystem to show major damage as a consequence of climate change. A combination of
rising sea levels, increased storm strength, higher sea temperatures and acidification has
led to the loss of 20% of the planet's coral reefs, with another 35% under serious threat of
destruction. It is estimated that by 2050, 90% of coral reefs will be negatively impacted by
local and global threats. The United Nations states 500 million people depend on coral
reefs for food, protection, building materials or for income from the tourist industry. It
estimates the net economic worth of coral based goods and services at $100 billion a year.

The threat of global sea level rise to MEDCs includes a threat to many of their large cities. London, Rotterdam and Venice (Figure C52) have all built barrage systems to protect the threat coming from the sea. The large, complex and expensive engineering schemes may only be realistic and practical for such special cases. Elsewhere, even MEDCs will need to accept the real loss of land along

Figure C52: Construction of barrage scheme across the Venetian Lagoon, Italy

with infrastructure and resources. While LEDCs have relatively fewer resources with which to address the rising global sea level issue, many are vulnerable both in their location, coastal and low-lying, and in their economic structure, subsistent often farming and fishing base.

CASE STUDY: The Maldives (Republic of Maldives), a national study of a LEDC coastline under threat from sea level rise

Figure C53: Map and location of the Republic of Maldives, Indian Ocean

Over 30 years ago an extreme weather event flooded Malé (prounced *Ma-lé*), the capital city of the Maldive Islands. In the aftermath the nation's president commissioned a report on the likely impact of climate change on the country's future. The report when published propelled the Maldives to the front page of newspapers around the world; as it declared it would be "….the first nation wiped out by climate change", becoming uninhabitable before 2100.

The Maldives is a 1000 km long string of tiny coral islands in the Indian Ocean. The nation consists of 1200 separate patches of land grouped into 26 atolls (ring-like groups of coral). Fewer than 200 of the islands are inhabited and the total land area is only 298 km², meaning they would all easily fit into the surface area of Lough Neagh (390 km²) (Figure C53).

Much of the land is less than 1 m above sea level with a mean height of only 1.5 m, less than the average height of an adult. The highest point is said to be an artificial hill on a golf course at nearly 5 m. The Maldives is officially the world's lowest nation; this is because the islands are built entirely of coral growing on top of a submarine volcanic ridge and coral sand, eroded and deposited by wave action. Figure C54 shows a typical island, in this case where a luxury tourist development has taken place. Notice the tiny low-lying islands in the background, which are part of the same atoll group.

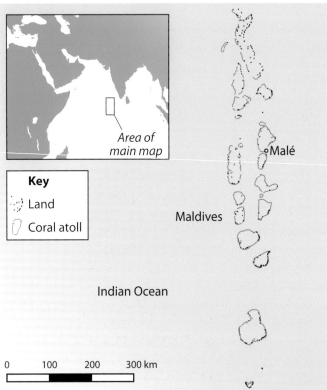

Figure C54: Aerial view of a tourist resort development Baros Island, Kaafu Atoll, Maldives

Source: © Baros

Figure C55: Diving on the pristine coral reefs of the Maldives

Source: © Baros

The total population of the Maldives is 375,000 (2017). This number has doubled in the last 30 years. Thirty percent of Maldivians live in the capital city Malé, which covers only 2 km² making it the world's most densely populated city.

The economy of the Maldives is based on fishing and tourism, which together employ 88% of the country's workforce and generate 95% of the government's income. The Maldives has virtually no agricultural land and the nation can supply only 10% of its food needs. Fishing, despite using the most sustainable method of pole and line, faces the issue of overfishing of the large reef-dwelling species. Consequently, fishing has reduced its economic significance to about 15% of foreign earnings. International tourism has increasingly dominated the economy after the airport near Malé was upgraded to International standard in 1981, now named Velana airport. Marketed as a tropical ocean paradise many of the nation's uninhabited islands have become luxury tourist destinations (Figure C54). Such developments are usually separate from the inhabited islands, partly to avoid cultural conflict with the nation's mainly Islamic population over issues such as alcohol consumption, dress for sunbathing and dietary choices including eating pork. The economy's dependency on tourism makes it vulnerable to natural, economic and political events; the 2004 Indian Ocean tsunami, the global economy crash of 2008 and local political tensions in 2012 all lead to a 5% fall in the industry in the following years. Nevertheless, the number of tourists has grown, exceeding 1.2 million in 2017 and there are plans for dozens of new resorts, including some on yet undeveloped islands. The Maldives' economy is in debt largely due to the need to import food and fuel from elsewhere. Unemployment rates are high at 20% of the workforce and most of the people have little or no contact with the international visitors who often remain entirely at the purpose built resorts. Part of the attraction to the Maldives is the amazingly diverse and colourful marine life based on the tropical corals that flourish in the Indian Ocean waters (Figure C55).

The predicted global rise in sea level was the threat that initiated concern for the Maldives but in reality the threats are more diverse and complex. Firstly, higher sea levels are not necessarily a risk for coral reefs, if their growth can keep pace with the rate of increase. However, add to this the other climate change impacts of stormier weather and the acidification of water, then increased physical erosion damage and slower growth of coral may well combine to threaten the coral reefs and atoll islands. There are signs of these negative impacts across the islands:

- The incidence and degree of coral bleaching has increased both weakening coral reefs as a defence and reducing their tourist appeal as species diversity declines.

- Extreme and coral damaging storm events are twice as common as ten years ago.
- Growing population and tourist numbers increases pressure on freshwater supplies.
- Natural freshwater stores are becoming more saline as waves sweep over the islands more often.
- Higher rainfall in the wet season and higher temperatures have increased the incidence of dengue fever – a mosquito borne illness.
- A 40% reduction of tuna catch in a recent five year period is thought to be due to fish migrating to find cooler waters.

The response to the threat

In the Maldives the strategies dealing with the economic and environmental threat of climate change have been strongly influenced by the country's political situation, which has changed several times. Responses can be studied under two headings: Mitigation (prevention) and Adaptation (preparation).

Mitigation (prevention)

The Maldives' call for international recognition of its plight was one of the first steps towards a worldwide response to global warming. As an LEDC, the Maldives believed that it was MEDCs that were to blame for current climate change and they were therefore responsible for finding a solution. For the last 30 years its various leaders are said to have had a 'loud voice' but 'little power' in the global warming debate. The Maldivian president between 2008 and 2012, Mohamed Naseed, took on the role of spokesman for AOSIS (the Alliance of Small Island Nations) to promote the cause of 'at risk' low-lying nations. His approach included an eye catching publicity stunt when, in 2009, he held an underwater cabinet meeting. The various government ministers of the Maldives met around a submerged table wearing wetsuits and scuba gear to draw global attention to the sea level issue. Recently, the Maldives have pledged to a carbon-neutral future themselves by switching from their use of imported diesel and other fuels to renewable solar and wind energy sources. In truth, even if they succeed, such a change will have a minimal effect on the global situation. Consequently, more time and effort has been made on the second strategy approach: adaptation to the seemingly inevitable rise of sea level.

Adaptation (preparation)

One of the extreme storms of the 1987 El Niño event caused widespread flooding in Malé. The government of the Maldives set about constructing a 3 m high sea wall around the island capital. Lacking the money to complete the task the Japanese government agreed to fund 99% of its cost. The wall cost $63 million and took 14 years to complete. A second approach was to create more land and in particular an artificial island near Malé to relieve its congestion and allow for future population growth. Named Hulhumale (or 'new Malé') it was planned to be 2 km² in area, surrounded by a sea wall and raised 2–3 m above sea level. Reclamation started in 1997 and by 2015 it had become home to 30,000 people, mostly living in high rise blocks. The plan is that by the year 2020 it will accommodate 120,000 Maldivians. The same land reclamation approach has been used to extend a number of existing islands, building 2 m high sea dykes and infilling with sediment from a harbour dredging scheme and the seabed to reclaim the land. Up to 40 hectares of land has been added to some small islands and the higher land level protects them from future flooding. These engineering approaches are seen as the one way that the Maldivians can remain on their islands. However, this approach is expensive and potentially damaging to the environment, both visually and with respect to habitats. It is therefore not a solution for many of the nation's 1200 islands.

Government permission for the development of new tourist resorts has increasingly stricter requirements. Tourist resort islands have to provide some sea wall protection (Figure C54) without undermining the attractive coral-based habitats. Also, many now promote low or carbon neutral systems in their power generation and use desalinisation systems. Another approach developed by the Maldives' government was the proposal that when their islands eventually become uninhabitable they would become environmental refugees and move en masse to land purchased by the government in a neighbouring country – suggestions have included India, Sri Lanka and even Australia. In 2008, to pay for this strategy, President Naseed proposed the setting up of a sovereign wealth fund to divert a proportion of the tourist income directly to a government held fund. Such a fund has not yet been established.

Exam Questions

1. What is meant by eustatic and isostatic sea level change and explain the causes behind the two processes. [8]

Resource A: Coastal landforms near Birsay, Orkney Islands

Steep rock face

Sloping rock platform

2. Study Resource A which shows a coastline at Birsay on the Orkney Islands, Scotland. With the aid of a diagram explain the formation of the steep rock face and the gently sloping platform, and why they are no longer impacted directly by the sea. [8]

3. With reference to a regional or national LEDC case study, explain the threat posed by rising sea levels on the human and physical environment. [18]

References

Geofile:
'Emergent and submergent coastlines: case studies', *Geofile* 756, series 34, 2015–2016
'Sea level change: causes and coastal landforms', *Geofile* 600, series 28, 2009–2010
'Post-glacial sea-level changes and resulting coastal landscapes', *Geofile* 449, series 21, 2002–2003

Geo Factsheet:
'Coastal landforms of sea level change', *Geo Factsheet*, Curriculum Press, 324
'The Maldives: on the frontline of climate change', *Geo Factsheet*, Curriculum Press, 296

GeoActive:
'Sea level change: impacts and strategies (case study – the Maldives)', *GeoActive* 526, series 26, 2014–2015

Sea level change:
https://www.bgs.ac.uk/discoveringGeology/climateChange/general/coastal.html?src=topNav
http://thebritishgeographer.weebly.com/sea-level-change.html

3. COASTAL MANAGEMENT AND SUSTAINABILITY

Case studies

Regional scale study of coastal management: South Devon and Dorset

Students should be able to:

(i) demonstrate knowledge and understanding of the role of Environmental Impact Assessment (EIA), Cost-Benefit Analysis (CBA), Sediment Cells and Shoreline Management Plans (SMP) in coastal management

(ii) evaluate the impact and sustainability of hard engineering (sea walls, revetments, rip-rap, gabions and groynes) and soft engineering (beach nourishment, dune regeneration and managed retreat) strategies on the human and physical environment

Demands on the coast

In the UK and Ireland one in three people live within the coastal zone. Around the coast dramatic erosion events, such as railway lines collapsing onto beaches and lighthouses having to be jacked-up and moved inland, suggest coastal processes cannot be ignored. Figure C56 illustrates the range of demands applied to coastlines and the potential outcomes. It is this increasing pressure that has led governments to seek to develop management strategies that are both effective and sustainable.

Figure C56: The demands and potential outcomes on the coast

Activity	Development consequence	Potential outcomes
Urbanisation and transport infrastructure	Land-use change – housing, ports and airports. Harbour and seabed dredging. Sewage and waste disposal.	Habitat loss and reduced species biodiversity. Increased surface run off. Visual and water pollution. Changes to coastal sediment flows.
Agriculture	Reclaimed land – drainage of salt marshes. Water abstraction. Increased use of chemical fertiliser and pesticides.	Reduced species diversity and habitat loss. Water pollution including eutrophication.
Fishing and Aquaculture	Port, offshore fish farm and onshore fish processing facility construction.	Water and beach pollution. Impacts on marine habitat and species.
Industry and energy generation	Construction of plants and power stations – tidal barrages. Resource extraction sites.	Habitat loss. Air, water and visual pollution. Changes in sediment movement and increased coastal erosion.
Tourism and recreation	Land-use changes – golf links, marinas and water parks.	Loss of species and habitats. Water and land pollution.

By the end of the twentieth century it was recognised that the management of coasts in the UK and Ireland was frequently chaotic, with dozens of different government departments and non-government interest groups making decisions and taking action without any meaningful coordination. The threat of rapid sea level rise, as a consequence of global warming, helped to focus attention on the need for a sustainable and integrated approach.

The physical division of coasts into littoral or sediment cells was a key starting point for recent management plans. In nature, sediment is transported within sediment cells

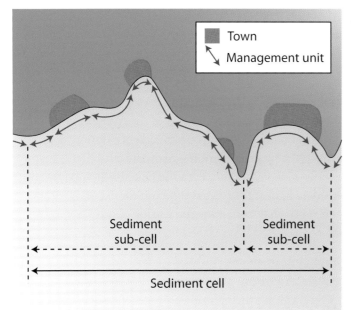

Figure C57: Sediment and sediment sub-cells

involving large sections of the coast. In these cells, sand and shingle movements are largely self-contained. Cells are normally separated by major headlands or dramatic changes to the coastline trend. Within each large sediment cell, sand and shingle can move more freely between smaller sub-cells. Eleven sediment cells are identified along the coast of England and Wales, with eight along the Scottish coastline (Figure C57).

Shoreline Management Plans, Cost-Benefit Analysis and Environmental Impact Assessment

These sediment cells have formed the basis for an integrated management project for England and Wales known as Shoreline Management Plans (SMP). Unfortunately to date, the management of Northern Ireland's coast has not been addressed in this way and so decisions are made locally by whatever government department is most directly concerned.

Shoreline Management Plans were defined as:

> "a document which sets out a strategy for coastal defence for a specified length of coast taking account of natural processes and human and other environmental… needs."

These management plans are created by local authorities and other interested parties (stakeholders) to provide an overview for a region within which local authorities can undertake schemes that fit in with the aims of the strategic plan.

SMPs themselves are concerned with the policy to be applied to each section of coast and not to the methods or techniques; they are developed on the basis of one of these four options:

1. No active intervention – take no action but monitor change on the coastline.
2. Managed realignment – setting up a new line further inland.
3. Hold the existing defence line – maintain the present line of coastal defence.
4. Advance the existing defence line – build forward of the present line (a rare decision).

The first SMPs were used in the 1990s but the second generation, known as SMP2, were implemented from 2005. Plans for the next century were made at three timescales: the next 20 years (2005–2025), the following 30 years (2025–2055) and 50 years after that (2055–2105). It is stated that on the longer timescale the majority of plans should be either: 1) No active intervention or 2) Managed realignment.

For any section of coastline the following tests are used to evaluate the most appropriate option selected:

- **A Technical Feasibility Study**

  This concerns the effectiveness of the technical aspects of a proposed option. Given the specific factors and processes, will the approach accomplish the goals for which it was designed?

- **A Cost-Benefit Analysis (CBA)**

  CBA seeks to find the net balance between the cost of the construction (capital) and up-keep (maintenance) of any proposed coastal defence option against the value and income from the property, employment and land that is being protected. This is normally stated as a ratio, with the benefits divided by costs. Finding accurate up-to-date figures for CBA is difficult; for example, property values constantly change and what is the monetary value of business confidence over a ten year period?

- **An Environmental Impact Assessment (EIA)**

  The EIA evaluates the scale and nature of a proposed option's impact. Environment is interpreted as both the natural environment, such as the threat to plant and animal habitats and the built environment, constructed features including the loss of sites of heritage such as castles and churches. EIAs are designed to reflect both negative and potentially positive impacts.

Figure C58 is part of a matrix used in the decision making process to select a 'Hold the existing defence line' policy, for a coastal town in Yorkshire.

Figure C58: A decision making matrix. Outcome: 'Hold the existing defence line'.

OPTION / TEST	No active intervention	Managed realignment	Hold the existing defence line	Advance the existing defence line
Technical feasibility	✓	✕	✓	✓
Cost-Benefit Analysis	?	✕	✓	✕
Environmental Impact (built)	✕	✓	✓	✓
Environmental Impact (natural)	✕	✕	✓	✕
Sustainability	✕	?	?	✕

✓ = Meets objectives   ✕ = Conflicts with objectives   ? = Insufficient data

Coastal management techniques

Hard engineering

As the variety and scale of demand made on coastlines has grown, so the need to manage these environments has increased. In the past this management was accomplished, almost exclusively, by hard engineering. Hard engineering involves the construction of structures, often large-scale and intrusive, to control or prevent natural processes that threaten property, harbours and tourist amenities.

Hard engineering strategy	Outline drawing	Nature and operation	Limitations and common issues
Sea walls	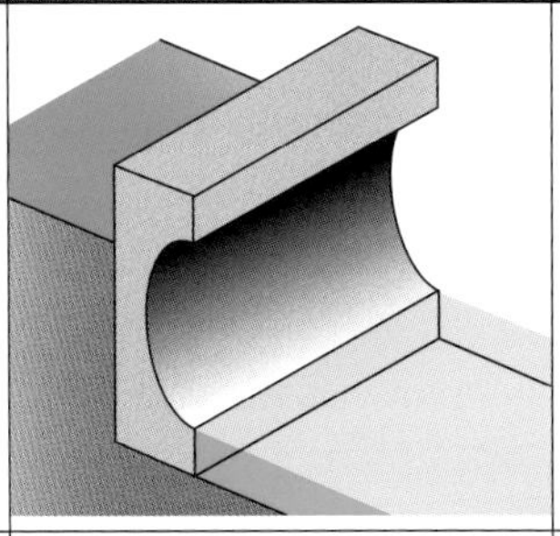	Solid walls separating land and sea. They support the land while holding back the sea. They can be designed to absorb and deflect wave energy. Common along promenades and at harbours (also see Figures C60A and C66A).	Often expensive structures (£6000 per metre) and require deep foundations. Poorly designed sea walls can deflect wave energy downwards scouring the beach of sediment and undermining the wall itself.
Rock armouring or rip-rap	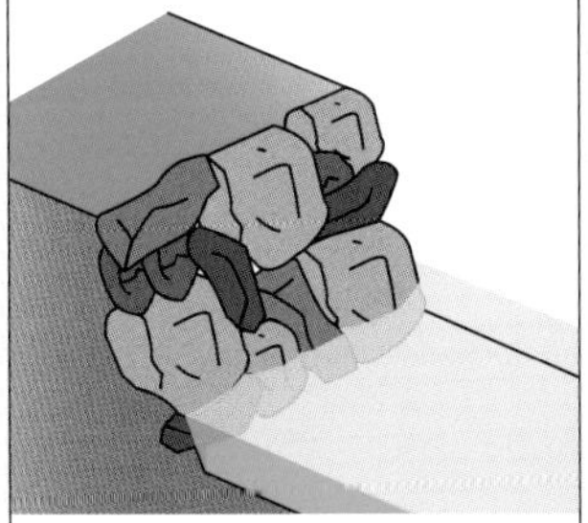	Large boulders used as an alternative to a sea wall. Being permeable they can absorb wave energy and have a more natural appearance (also see Figures C60A and C76B).	Boulders may move or be undermined if placed on sand. Can be unattractive and relatively expensive.
Gabions	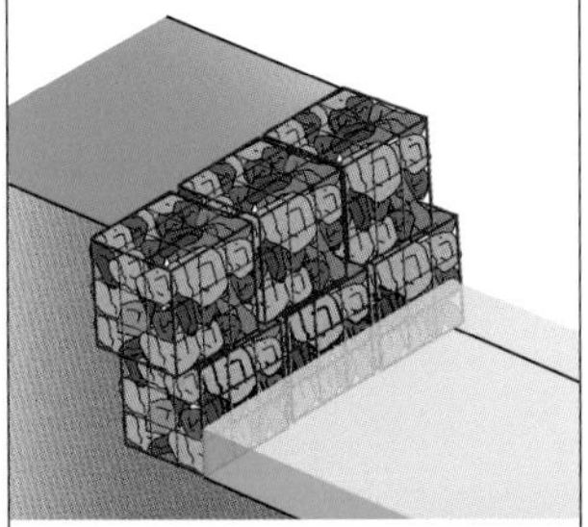	Metal cages filled with rocks used to construct sea walls or laid as a mattress under beach sediment. They can be constructed rapidly and wave energy is absorbed as water percolates around within cages (also see Figures C66B and D).	Visually unattractive and if the cages split over time the rocks can be used to erode the shore. Storms can knock over gabion walls.
Groynes	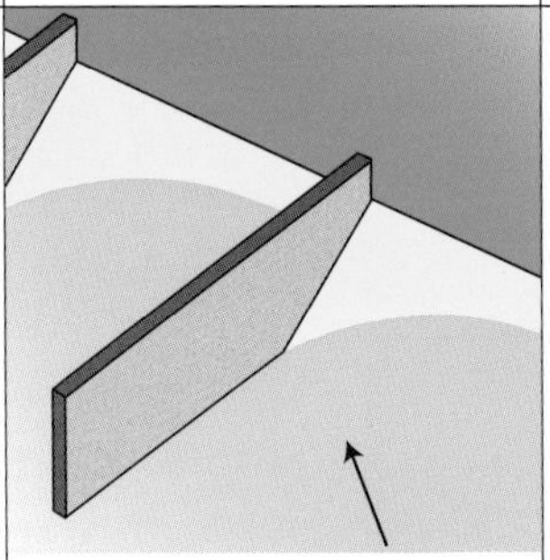	Wooden, concrete or rock barriers built out perpendicular to the shore to trap sediment carried by longshore drift. They are usually build in sets called groyne fields (also see Figures C33A and C76A). Groynes are often combined with revetments or sea walls for full coastal protection (also see Figure C60A).	If too efficient they trap sediment, starving places further down the beach. Groynes need maintenance and replacement. They are visually obtrusive.
Revetments	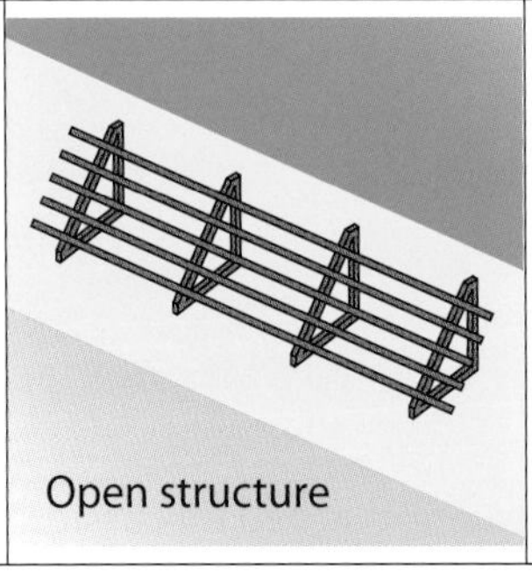 Open structure	Revetments are armoured slopes that may be permeable or solid in nature. Made of timber, concrete, rocks or asphalt they are designed to absorb wave energy (also see Figures C33B and C60B).	Visually intrusive, they can be undermined and can damage beach and shore ecosystems.

Figure C59: Hard engineering schemes used in coastal protection

Early examples of hard engineering followed the rise of seaside tourism in Victorian Britain. During the nineteenth century the coast became the preferred destination for the earliest mass tourism. The advent of the railways had opened up the possibility of families holidaying away from home. Within reach of all the industrial urban centres, seaside resorts developed. Purpose built coastline walkways called promenades stretched for miles along the shore and entertainment piers ran out to sea. Sea walls were constructed to protect these coastline developments from winter storms and, where beaches were not wide enough or where erosion moved the precious sand away, fields of groynes were built. These wooden walls were constructed at regular intervals across the beach at right angles to the shore. Some groyne fields consisted of dozens of individual barriers (Figure C29). The aim was to trap sediment on the 'upstream' side of the barrier, preventing the loss of sand. These were successful in creating wide beaches for recreation and also helped protect promenades from storm waves. Groynes needed to be maintained and eventually replaced so, while effective, groyne based beach management was not cheap.

Figure C60: Hard engineering schemes

A) Restoring the sea wall and rip-rap at Newcastle, Co Down

B) Damage and coastal erosion of a timber revetment at Lower Largo, Fife

The concept of coastal sediment cells states that the stores and flows of sediment along coasts are in a state of dynamic equilibrium, so any interference is likely to have consequences. Sea walls and beach groynes had unintended impacts. In many cases groyne fields that retained sand on the pleasure beaches of Victorian seaside resorts also caused rapid beach and shoreline erosion further along the coast. Sand and pebbles trapped by groynes reduced the sediment carried by longshore drift and starved the beaches beyond the groyne field. In other cases poorly designed sea walls directed the energy of storm waves down onto the beach, undermining their own foundations and causing collapse. Often the answer to such issues was simply to build more structures, higher and stronger or with variations such as rip-rap or revetments (Figure C60). Coastlines became increasingly artificial in both their nature and appearance.

Soft engineering

The expense and failure of many hard engineering strategies around the coast encouraged discussion of alternative approaches, in particular soft engineering. A soft engineering approach involves schemes that use and work with natural processes to achieve the desired outcome. Environmentalists have encouraged planners to develop such solutions, if not to replace, then at least to reduce the impact of hard solutions. Figure C61 illustrates a range of soft engineering schemes used in coastal protection.

Figure C61: Soft engineering schemes used in coastal protection

Strategy	Nature and operation	Limitations and issues
Beach nourishment (recycling)	Sediment, sand or shingle is added to beaches to enhance their ability to protect the shore from erosion. The sediment may be sourced offshore and dumped onto the beach or brought overland from quarries or other sources. (Beach recycling involves transferring sand or shingle from a local sink area in the same sediment cell back onto a beach.) A broad expanse of beach sand protects the shore, as wave energy is dissipated by friction and the transport of the beach sediment.	Effective nourishment needs to match the sediment size to the environment. Sediment must be sourced from a location, often inland, where it does not create environmental issues.
Cliff drainage	Pipes are installed to drain water from the cliff face to reduce saturation and the risk of land slips.	These systems are only effective with certain types of rock.
Dune and cliff stabilisation by vegetation planting	This involves the planting of vegetation, such as marram grass and/or the use fences or matting to protect the area by encouraging the retention and trapping of sediment.	Careful management is needed in such fragile environments and it works best where public access is restricted.

Figure C62: Soft engineering strategies

A) Beach nourishment at Lyme Regis, Dorset with shingle added in the background and sand on the beach in the foreground

B) Concrete pipes, part of the cliff drainage scheme near West Bay, Dorset

Until recently the debate over coastal protection concerned the choice between using hard or soft engineering, now the issue has shifted to a more fundamental question – 'Should we protect the coast at all'?

Three factors are responsible for this new debate over how coasts should be managed:

1. Rising global sea levels will continue for the foreseeable future.
2. Any engineering schemes to retain current coastlines are very expensive and will become more costly in the future.
3. The many negative environmental impacts of coastal schemes mean they are seen as both unsustainable and unacceptable.

Today, partly from the use of Cost-Benefit Analysis and Environmental Assessments, a new concept has emerged, 'do nothing' (no active intervention). In other words, let nature take its course and through natural processes the coast will find a new equilibrium and balance. A slight modification to this view is termed managed retreat. Under this approach any existing coastal defences would be gradually removed allowing the sea to change the morphology of the shore. Some engineering strategies might be used to slow down the rate of change. One example of the new thinking is illustrated by Norfolk County council. In the light of Norfolk's rapidly eroding coastline, the council proposes to establish a setback line some 75 m inland from the present shore and to ban the building of new developments on the coast. This means no new houses, roads or other construction can be located within that distance of today's shoreline.

Nationally, the UK government, faced with an estimated bill of over £5 billion to stop coastal erosion by future rising sea levels, has adopted a plan to stop maintaining coastal defences, except where flooding threatens settlements.

CASE STUDY: South Devon and Dorset, a regional scale study of coastal management

The geographical setting

The complex geology and the variable orientation of the shore along the south coast of England creates a wide diversity of environments, habitats and landforms. Part of this coast is the newly designated SMP2 cell of South Devon and Dorset, stretching from Durlston Head in the east to Rame Head in the west, a distance of over 300 km. The coastal environments in this region include sea cliffs and slopes; estuaries; sand dune systems; spits; and both fresh and salt water lagoons. Much of this coastline is highly valued for its distinctive rocks, including rich fossil deposits, and its historic role in the development of the science of geology. A large section of the shore is now protected as England's first natural UNESCO World Heritage Site – the Jurassic Coast.

While landforms formed by both erosion and deposition are found in this region, the long-term pattern of change is slow coastal retreat, called transgression. One suggested rate, calculated for the last 2000 years, is an average retreat of 1 mm annually. Climate change, producing more severe storms and a rising global sea level, is set to continue and accelerate this process of erosion with serious consequences for the future. In many coastline cells sediment is produced, moved and deposited by natural processes. In Devon and Dorset many of the deposition features, including the shingle beaches and bars, are now understood to be relict features. This means that they were formed from material left, possibly at the end of the last Ice Age, but are no longer being actively formed. This long-term sequence of change can be disrupted by short-term events. In recent decades storm events have not only damaged the local communities but in places caused the equivalent of a century's worth of erosion in one night. Add to this scenario the impact of people, both in their attempts to defend the coast and their other activities, and a complex picture emerges. At best, human action may slow down the erosion and retreat of the shore; at worst it may accelerate the natural change. People make high demands on the coast both from land and sea based resources.

One consequence of the many demands made on this coastline is that, along some sections, it is heavily defended. In low-lying areas the defence is to prevent flooding, whereas along cliffs it is designed to reduce or prevent erosion. The most common defence structures are linear sea walls and groynes. In the long-term, if the sea walls were retained, as the unprotected areas eroded landward, then these sea walls would form promontories along the areas of coast highly exposed to waves in deep water. In short, given a future of eroding shorelines, managed retreat in all but a few key locations is the only sustainable option. The story goes that almost one thousand years ago, Cnut, King of England, commanded the tide to stop in order to demonstrate to his subjects that he was not all powerful. Perhaps the long-term and sustainable future of our coastline requires the modern day decision makers, the engineers and planners, to take a similarly radical position?

The planning framework and the proposed Shoreline Management Plan

Under the current policy of Shoreline Management Plans (SMP2) coastline planning has four options:

1. Hold the existing defence line
2. Advance the existing defence line
3. Managed realignment
4. No active intervention

Figure C63: Map of the South Devon and Dorset Shoreline Management Plan region

The procedure also requires that the plan addresses the future at three timescales: short-term (next 20 years), medium-term (20–50 years) and long-term (50–100 years). The South Devon and Dorset SMP2 initially divides the coast into 17 sub-cells, these

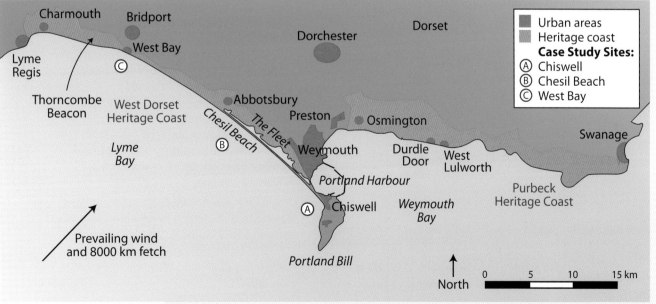

are further divided so that proposals are stated for 190 sections of coast (management units). For each of these, the preferred policy for each timescale is stated. The SMP2 was implemented from 2010. Finally, it should be remembered that SMPs are drawn up as guidelines for the regions and that numerous groups are involved in the decision making process for any one scheme or management unit.

Management of the Dorset and East Devon coast

The section of the Dorset shoreline between Portland Bill and Thorncombe Beacon includes 13 of the region's 190 coastal management units. Facing south west this coastline is open to a potential wave fetch over 8000 km, stretching from the Caribbean. Indeed, as the prevailing winds are from the south west this is clearly an example of a high energy coast. High cliffs are found at Portland Bill and West Bay but the dominant feature is Chesil Beach. This narrow bar of shingle defines and protects the freshwater lagoon called The Fleet and as a tombolo connects the Isle of Portland to the mainland. The Isle of Portland is a small but steep island made of Portland stone which has been used for many important buildings including Westminster Palace and St Paul's cathedral in London as well as Belfast's City Hall. At the northern end of this stretch of coast is the dramatic red East Cliff at West Bay made famous by the ITV detective series 'Broadchurch' (Figure C70).

Figure C64: The SMP2 for the Portland Bill to Thorncombe Beacon coast in Dorset (SE to NW)

Figure C64 outlines the Shoreline Management Plan (SMP2) for these 13 units of Dorset's Heritage Coast.

Policy name and number	Short-term option to 2025	Medium-term option to 2055	Long-term option to 2105	Additional information
6a01 Portland Bill	No active intervention	No active intervention	No active intervention	Undefended cliffs and steeply sloping coast. To be allowed to continue to evolve naturally.
6a02 **A** Chiswell to Chesil Beach	Hold the line	Hold the line	Hold the line	Large number of properties defended by hard engineering from flooding and erosion (Example A in text).
6a03 **A** Chesil Beach	Managed realignment	Managed realignment	Managed realignment	Not artificially defended but the beach protects the road link from Portland to Weymouth so after storms the beach would be restored (Example A in text).
6a04-10 **B** Chesil Beach, The Fleet to East Cliff	No active intervention	No active intervention	No active intervention	Undefended and allowed to evolve naturally – shingle beach is expected to roll back inland (Example B in text 6a04 to 6a08).
6a11 **C** West Bay (east)	Hold the line	Hold the line	Managed realignment	Maintain defences in the short and medium-term to protect the town from flooding. In the long-term a new set-back defence line with beach material created (Example C in text).
6a12 **C** West Bay (west)	Hold the line	Hold the line	Hold the line	Maintain hard engineering scheme at West Bay Harbour including breakwaters to prevent erosion and flooding (Example C in text).
6a13 West Cliff to Thorncombe	No active intervention	No active intervention	No active intervention	Cliffs to be allowed to continue to evolve naturally.

Since the implementation of the SMP2 in 2006 this coastline has been impacted by some of the severest storms on record, in particular during the winter of 2013–2014. These not only tested the existing defences but also the planned responses along the various sections of the coastline

Three examples of SMP2 Management Units on the Dorset and East Devon coast (Figure C62)

Example A: Chiswell village and south Chisel Beach (6a02-03)

At the southern end of Chesil Beach on the edge of Portland Bill lies the small low-lying fishing village of Chiswell (Figures C63, C64 and C65). Here the threat of flooding has been met by a series of hard engineering structures (Figure C66). These include a 300 m long sea wall with a recurved upper edge constructed in 1959. This was modified in the 1980s with steel piles driven into the foundation to prevent undermining by storm waves. Steel gabions filled with pebbles were used to form a 550 m long mattress under the beach to prevent flooding. Behind these defensive features is a 900 m long drainage channel designed to remove wave water breaking over the defences during storms. The total capital cost of these defensive structures was £5 m. At the time of construction these schemes met with opposition from environmentalists who were concerned with both its visual impact and interference with the natural processes of the beach.

Figure C65: The village of Chiswell, Chesil Beach and The Fleet

Weymouth

The Fleet – the lagoon behind the shingle beach

The A354 – the road link to Weymouth protected by Chesil Beach

Beach and hard engineering defences at Chiswell

Chiswell

A series of storms between December 2013 and March 2014 were the worst recorded for 60 years. Huge Atlantic breakers removed 150,000 m³ of the shingle from the beach in front of the built sea defences at Chiswell. The height of the beach was reduced by 3 m and its width by 6 m. In places the base of the sea wall was exposed and gabion cages in the mattress were ripped open and their pebbles scattered.

Several times storm waves breached the beach causing the A354 Portland Beach Road, which links Chiswell and the Isle of Portland to Weymouth and the mainland, to be closed. Nevertheless, the existing defences reduced the potential damage with only 6 of Chiswell's 110 properties reporting severe flooding.

As the SMP2 policy (Figure C64) indicates this section of coast has a 'hold the line' policy over all three time periods. Consequently repair work was undertaken immediately after the storms and completed by October 2014 before the next winter season. Concrete repairs were made to the damaged wall, the gabion castle and mattress were replaced and rebuilt, and the flood drainage system improved. At the same time, using soft engineering methods, shingle was restored to the shore by beach recycling and the shingle beach slope was re-profiled ready for any future storms.

The section of Chesil Beach to the north of Chiswell (6a03) is designated as a section for 'managed retreat'. Here, intervention will only take place when flooding impacts on the A354 between Portland to Weymouth, to re-establish this vital commercial and domestic road link.

Figure C66: The hard engineering strategies at Chiswell village

A) Recurved sea wall looking south to Portland Bill

B) Gabions

Gabion castle built where the sea wall meets the gabion mattress defence

C) Chiswell Fishing village

D) Sea defences

Sea wall

The gabion mattress

Figure C67: Chesil Beach

Example B: Chesil Beach, The Fleet to East Cliff

Chesil Beach is a world famous shingle beach that stretches 29 km from West Bay in the north west to the Isle of Portland to the south east. The beach has a steep storm beach profile and the shingle is graded in size with coarser stones nearer to Portland. Local fishermen claim to be able to tell their location on the beach from pebble size alone (Figure C35).

The tombolo section of Chesil Beach connects the Isle of Portland, a limestone island in the English Channel to Abbotsbury and forms a lagoon behind it, The Fleet. The shingle beach itself continues north westwards against the cliff to West Bay. The small settlements of West Bay in the north and Chiswell in the south currently have coastal protection schemes that will be maintained for the next 50–100 years. However, the plan for almost the entire shingle beach between these two settlements is to allow the expected coastline retreat due to locally sinking land and rising eustatic sea levels.

Figure C68: The Fleet and Chesil Beach near Abbotsbury looking south west

Chesil Beach itself is therefore the coastal protection along this shoreline and it is expected that natural processes will continue to push the beach eastwards and inland. As a result The Fleet lagoon is likely to become narrower over time and it is probable that storms will overtop the beach itself more often. In the longer-term (100 years) there are threats to some car parks at the beach, a caravan park, the swannery at Abbotsbury and one listed monument (St Peter's Abbey), as well as potential habitat loss. Nevertheless the SMP2 policy, short, medium and long-term, is 'no active intervention'.

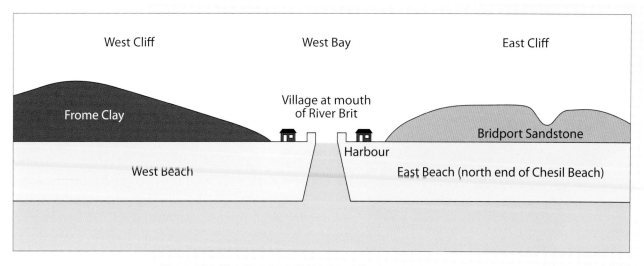

Figure C69: The situation of West Bay village

Figure C70: West Bay's West and East Cliffs

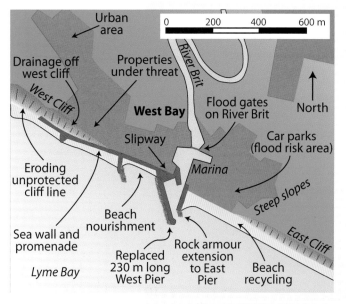

Figure C71: Map of the coastal defences constructed at West Bay, Dorset

Example C: The town, harbour and tourist amenity at West Bay

The harbour at West Bay lies at the mouth of the River Brit and in the centre of the Jurassic heritage coast. To the south east lies the start of Chesil Beach, dramatically backed by the East Cliff, a layered wall of vertical orange brown sandstone. To the north west the geology of West Cliff is very different and the highly faulted and weak clay cliffs are in constant danger of slump and collapse.

As Figure C71 shows, a wide range of hard and soft management strategies have been implemented at West Bay village. These were designed to address a range of management issues including the need to:

- prevent flooding by storm waves of the low-lying land to the east of the harbour.
- deal with erosion rates averaging 0.5 m per year that threaten houses on top of West Cliff.
- prevent river flooding by storm waves flow causing the River Brit to back-up and flood the town.
- maintain a sheltered harbour for fishing and pleasure craft.
- conserve protected land and marine habitats.
- maintain the aesthetic appearance of the coast for the residents and the tourist industry.

Figure C72: Fishing and tourism form the basis of West Bay's economy

West Bay is part of the town of Bridport which lies 1.5 miles inland. While Bridport is home to 13,000 people only 1000 live in West Bay and economically it depends on fishing and, increasingly, tourism (Figure C72). Beach and boat based activities in the summer months have grown, in part encouraged by the filming of the TV drama 'Broadchurch', since 2013. The settlement has over 60 small businesses that depend on the tourists, from ice cream and fast food stalls to hotels and up-market restaurants.

In 2002 a major review of the defence structures at West Bay concluded there was a 50% chance that the existing sea walls and the ancient piers at the mouth of the harbour would fail within five years. A £15 million new defence scheme was constructed by March 2005 designed to address the different issues faced along this section of coast.

The West Cliff is nearly vertical and rock falls onto the beach are common. Consequently, as the cliff recedes the cliff-top walkway is periodically moved inland.

East Beach, the short stretch of shingle beach between the harbour and the edge of East Cliff is the start of Chesil Beach itself and is designated as a Site of Special Scientific Interest (SSSI). This is why no hard engineering structure

Figure C73: Recent rock fall along East Cliff

has been constructed there even though the village area behind the beach is very low-lying and prone to flooding. Instead, since 1986 the area has been protected by a purpose-built shingle ridge. Constructed by the Environment Agency this barrier was 7.5 m high and the shingle was sourced from Burton Bradstock, 3 km to the east along Chesil Beach. This is an example of beach recycling. As the material was added the beach was re-profiled to improve its resistance to storm events. In this high energy environment shingle is rapidly transported and as it appears that nature no longer provides new beach material to this section, the shingle ridge has to be replenished every 5 years. The cost of an alternative hard defence scheme is estimated at £2m but the beach's SSSI status precludes this approach.

Figure C74: Images of the shingle ridge soft engineering beach recycling at East Beach

In the centre of West Bay village the ancient stone piers of the town harbour faced directly into the most common direction of storms and storm waves. This made boat access so hazardous that, on average, it could be used on only 200 days a year. A second issue was that twin piers tend to cause sediment to gather at their entrance. Annually 300 tonnes of sediment had to be removed to maintain a deep water channel for boats. The 2005 scheme strengthened the East Pier with concrete rock armour and boulders, and extended the West Pier (now named Jurassic Pier) to 230 m, realigning it to shelter the entrance. At the same time a steel flood barrier was installed across the river near the harbour to be closed when there is a risk of high tide or storm flooding.

Figure C75: Images of the realigned, extended and reinforced harbour piers and river flood gates

To the west of the town harbour the small West Beach was backed by a sea wall and promenade, and both structures had been severely undermined by erosion, including the loss of steel piling at the wall's foundation. The 2005 scheme addressed these issues creating a new wall fronted with rip-rap rock armour and a single stone groyne designed to trap sediment on the 120 m long West Beach. Beach nourishment ensured that there was sand on West Beach to protect. The only defence measure taken along part of West Cliff was cliff drainage.

Figure C76: Coastal defence at West Beach, West Bay

A) Groyne and beach nourishment at West Beach

B) Rip-rap rock armour and sea wall at West Cliff

Future planning at West Bay (SMP2)

As the region's Shoreline Management Plan (Figure C64) suggests, the strategy for the East and West Cliff sections on each side of West Bay village is for 'No active intervention'. Nevertheless these cliffs are expected to retreat over time and consequently the harbour and village may be left more prominent and exposed to coastal erosion.

Figure C77: SMP2 plans for West Bay village

In the short and medium-term (until 2055) the defences in the town will be retained. Beach recycling and re-profiling will continue on the East Beach and if necessary beach nourishment with material from Freshwater Beach, 6 km along the coast, will be undertaken. Maintenance will continue for the harbour piers, the sea wall, promenade, flood gates, drainage and rock groyne, and in addition beach replenishment of

Section/ Timescale	West Bay east (6a11)	West Bay west (6a12)
Short 2005–2025	**Hold the line** Maintain beach recycling and re-profiling of the shingle ridge at East Beach. Possible additional material needed for replenishment.	**Hold the line** All hard engineering structures that protect from river and coastal flooding (constructed 2004) to be maintained.
Medium to 2055	**Hold the line** Maintain beach recycling and re-profiling of the shingle ridge at East Beach with additional material needed for replenishment. Possible defence realignment required sooner than planned.	**Hold the line** All hard engineering structures that protect from river and coastal flooding (constructed 2004) to be maintained. Sea walls may be raised and beach replenishment undertaken.
Long to 2105	**Managed realignment** New inland line of flood defence will be needed.	**Hold the line** All hard engineering structures that protect from river and coastal flooding will need to be improved, possibly rebuilt, with additional control structures constructed. Retreat of West Cliff may require additional defence to protect loss of property and assets on the cliff top.

Figure C78: West Cliff properties under potential threat in the long-term

West Beach as required. However in the longer-term (2055–2105) is will be necessary to retreat back from the present position of the East Beach and construct a new flood defence line. To the west of the town the existing defences will also need to be raised and reinforced in response to sea level rise and erosion (Figure C77). The primary reasoning for the 'hold the line' policy is the threat to the existing and developing facilities in West Bay. The harbour, car parks, beach access, housing and tourist amenities ensure that there is a favourable cost-benefit to maintain the current defensive structures for the foreseeable future.

Exam Questions

1. Explain the use of any two of the following in relation to coastal management:
    - Environmental Impact Assessment (EIA)
    - Cost-Benefit Analysis (CBA)
    - Shoreline Management Plans (SMP) [10]

2. With the aid of a diagram, describe coastal sediment cells and explain the role they can play in coastal management. [8]

3. With reference to a regional case study of coastal management, evaluate the sustainability of both hard and soft engineering strategies implemented to defend the coast. [18]

References

Geofile:
'Coastal systems: waves, tides, sediments and sediment cells', *Geofile* 575, series 27, 2008–2009
'A comparison of coastal management schemes' (Lyme Regis/Pevensey Bay), *Geofile* 701, series 33, 2014–2005
'Coastal defences: Hard or Soft engineering? A decision-making exercise', *Geofile* 632, series 29, 2011–2012
'Human impact on the Dorset coastline – A decision-making exercise', *Geofile* 420, series 19, 2002–2003

Geo Factsheet:
'An update on coastal management Issues at Barton-on-Sea', *Geo Factsheet* 207, Curriculum Press
'Erosion and coastal management at Hengistbury Head, Dorset', *Geo Factsheet* 269, Curriculum Press

Dorset Coast plan:
http://www.sdadcag.org/SMP.html
https://www.dorsetforyou.gov.uk/article/408546/West-Bay-Coastal-Defence-Scheme-Case-Study
http://www.sdadcag.org/docs/SMP/Policy_Statements/09.pdf
also */10.pdf, /11.pdf* and */12.pdf*

Images and historic storms:
http://www.southampton.ac.uk/~imw/chestorm.htm

2014 storm footage:
https://www.youtube.com/watch?v=rRYbDtqusX4

OPTION D
Climate Change – Past and Present

1. NATURAL CLIMATE CHANGE PROCESSES

Case studies

General reference to places for illustration purposes

When are we?

Geologically we live in the era known as the Cenozoic, from 65 million years ago (mya); this is sometimes called the mammal era. The Cenozoic is subdivided into the Tertiary (third) Period, 65–2.6 mya and the Quaternary (fourth) Period, from 2.6 mya to the present. The Quaternary is divided into the Pleistocene Epoch (or Ice Age), from 2.6 mya to 12,000 years ago, followed by the Holocene Epoch (the post-glacial period), the last 12,000 years.

We are therefore living in the Holocene Epoch, during the Quaternary Period of the Cenozoic Era.

Perhaps the greatest threat to life, including ourselves, on planet Earth in the twenty-first century is global warming. Predictions of the speed and effect of this climate change vary widely but across a broad array of science disciplines it is agreed that it is happening. The climate of the Earth is not fixed; research has revealed that in the distant past the planet has repeatedly been plunged into cold eras (Ice House Periods)

Figure D1: The changing temperature of the Earth during the last one billion years

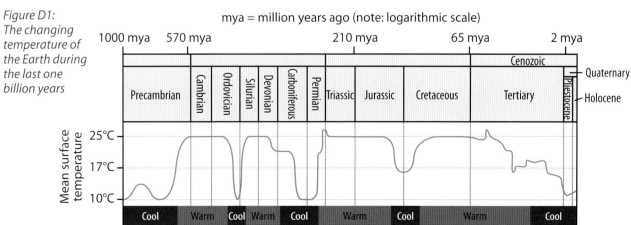

with at least one, described as 'Snowball Earth', covering the planet in ice. At other times, such as the Jurassic geological era, when the dinosaurs dominated life on the planet, the Earth was hot and no ice sheets existed at the poles (a Greenhouse Period).

Timescales

The Earth is around 4.55 billion years old, that is 4,550,000,000, and it is helpful when examining climate change to use three different timescales – short, medium and long-term. Short-term or recent climate change refers to decades and centuries and will be the key theme for parts 3 and 4 of this option. Medium-term relates to climate changes over thousands of years while long-term change covers geological eras, hundreds of thousands to millions of years (Figure D1).

The study of the Earth's past climate conditions is known as paleoclimatology and the evidence for the research is concerned with stratigraphy. Stratigraphy is the layer on layer deposition of material that records environmental change – rocks; ice cores; lake and ocean floor sediment; tree rings (dendrochronology); and pollen analysis in soils such as peat bogs. Normally in such deposits the layers go back in time with depth from the present surface, for example Figure D2 shows how common rock types beneath Irish soils indicate previous climatic conditions.

A note on dates:

Geologists, paleo climatologists and archaeologists use many different methods to state the date or age of features, landforms and periods. Examples are BP (Before Present) where present is 1950 or BCE (Before Christian Era). Some are technical dates, for instance the use of radio-carbon years. In this option, dates will be given as years before the present using the base year 2000 and will be stated as ya (years ago), mya (million years ago) and (bya billion years ago).

Figure D2: A geological cross-section illustrating how geology reflects past climatic conditions

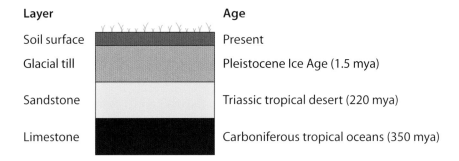

Layer	Age
Soil surface	Present
Glacial till	Pleistocene Ice Age (1.5 mya)
Sandstone	Triassic tropical desert (220 mya)
Limestone	Carboniferous tropical oceans (350 mya)

In the case of sedimentary rocks the chemistry, grain shape, pattern of deposition and the type of fossils present can indicate the nature of the environment under which their original deposition took place.

The evidence for climate change
Ice-cores

Ice is formed by the repeated build-up of layers of snow until the sheer weight compresses the snow into dense ice. Over the last two million years these accumulations of snow have formed deep ice sheets at the poles, in Greenland and Antarctica. It is possible to drill into these ice sheets to recover ice cores in which the youngest ice will be at the top and the oldest at the base of the sample. The longest is a 3200 m core from the East Antarctic Ice Sheet, with layers from the last 800,000 years. In tiny bubbles of air the ice preserves a record of the chemical gases in the atmosphere, in particular the balance of different oxygen isotopes, namely oxygen-16 and oxygen-18, and carbon dioxide (CO_2) – the key greenhouse gas. From this record it is possible to plot the medium to long-term temperature climate change. Figure D3 reveals that there has been about eight separate cold or glacial eras, one roughly every 100,000 years, during the last 0.8 million years.

Figure D3: Temperature variation based on CO_2 levels recorded in the East Antarctica ice core

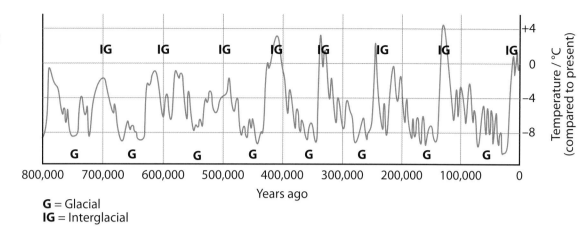

G = Glacial
IG = Interglacial

Figure D4: Ice core extracted from a Peruvian glacier

Source: U.S. Geological Survey / photo by Lonnie G Thompson, Byrd Polar Research Center, The Ohio State University

Videos explaining the use of Ice Cores are available at: https://www.tubeid.co/search/videos/science-and-technology.html

These ice core records show that natural CO_2 levels in the air varied between 180 and 280 parts per million but in 2007 the level was 383 parts per million showing that current greenhouse gas values are much higher than at any time in the past 800,000 years. In 2013 plans to drill an even deeper core in Antarctica were announced. The aim is to push the climate record back to 1.5 million years before the present. The dating of layers in ice cores uses isotope changes for carbon, lead, silicon and argon, and also the record of dust and acidic layers associated with known major volcanic events.

Pollen analysis

Plant pollen is readily preserved in waterlogged environments and each flowering plant species has a distinctive shape of pollen. Annually sediment carried by rivers into lakes and dying plants on peat bogs will accumulate into layers forming a long historical record of change. As with ice cores, lake bed and peat bog sediment is drilled and studied. The pollen grains contained in each layer can be identified and counted, re-creating a picture of the vegetation and therefore the climate of each past environment. By using radio-carbon and dendrochronology analysis these previous environments can be very accurately dated and the temperature and rainfall conditions recreated. In the short-term these studies have shown how the environment changed as conditions improved after the last ice age ended – the present Holocene era. While long, continuous pollen records back from the present are rare, the UK and Ireland have examples that stretch back 10,000 years. Such records of pollen have been used to track the re-emergence of vegetation across Europe and North America as the great ice-sheets retreated from 12,000 years ago. As the climate conditions improved this was reflected by the invasion and succession of different plant communities and ultimately deciduous forests, the climatic climax vegetation. The same pollen analysis technique can identify the vegetation range and climate of much older periods where suitable material has been preserved. Examples include the study of interglacial period vegetation, 100,000 years ago in Co Cork.

Radio-carbon dating

All living organisms are based on carbon. When one dies its carbon content starts to switch from one isotope of carbon (C-14) to another (C-12) at a known rate. If a piece of dead organic material, such as a bone or log, is chemically analysed the proportions of the different carbon isotopes it contains can give a date when death occurred. With some adjustments made for the changing levels of atmospheric CO_2 a very precise date can be found. Carbon dating can be applied with accuracy to the last 62,000 years and allows biological or organic material to be dated and by context any surrounding deposits.

Dendrochronology – tree ring dating

Trees are sensitive to annual changes in climatic conditions – sunlight, temperature and rainfall. These will determine the colour and thickness of a tree's annual growth rings and so distinctive patterns of rings form. By using long-lived trees, such as the Bristlecone Pine, that can live over 4000 years, or overlapping old trees with ancient pieces of timber, records of climate pattern for thousands of years can be constructed. For example, if a Roman Era wooden coffin is unearthed its age can be calculated by matching its tree growth ring pattern to its place in the known sequence. The precision of such dating – to the year a tree was felled – has allowed for accurate re-calibration of radio-carbon dating to ensure its high level of accuracy. The application of such tree ring records is confined to local areas but some of the best and longest have been developed in Europe, for the last 10,000 years in Germany and over 7000 years in the UK and Ireland (Figure D5).

Figure D5: Tree growth ring patterns used to date wooden objects and their context by dendrochronology

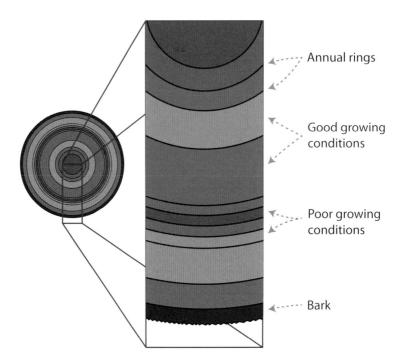

Annual rings

Good growing conditions

Poor growing conditions

Bark

Ocean-floor deposits

Annually rivers, ice and winds carry sediment into the oceans where it slowly accumulates in the ocean basin. This sediment and any organic material it may carry reflect the nature of the physical environment surrounding the ocean, including its climate. Organic, fossil remains can be studied to reveal the past sea surface temperature among other environmental characteristics, and the inorganic sediment can hold clues to the humidity of nearby continents. In common with ice cores, sediment extracted from ocean basins can be analysed for changes in oxygen isotopes and CO_2 content, both of which help to construct past temperature values. Ocean sediment deposits have been used to reconstruct paleoclimate changes over both medium to long-term periods. Sediment on ocean floors can reflect local changes due to continental drift: the floor of the Mediterranean Sea has many deep deposits of evaporates, salt rocks left when the sea basin was cut off from the Atlantic and the basin gradually dried out under desert conditions.

These stratified deposits have helped us to construct the climate changes during the Earth's long, turbulent history but what are the processes behind such change? Are these changes cyclical and predictable? And what role will the presence of 7.5 billion inhabitants have on these changes?

The causes of climate change

There are many mechanisms that influence the climate of Earth: some are internal to the planet's system, others are external (Figure D6). Some of these factors have an important influence on the climate experienced locally or over the short-term while others are the main drivers (or forcing) of natural climate change, in particular:

- astronomic forcing – the variation in the Earth's orbit and the Sun.
- solar forcing – the variation in the Sun's output and therefore the Earth's input of energy.
- atmospheric chemistry – forcing by CO_2 and other greenhouse gases.
- volcanic eruption and emissions.
- continental drift.

Around 100 years ago a Serbian geophysicist, Milutin Milankovitch, proposed the theory that the Earth's surface temperature changes over time because its orbit around the Sun and the angle of its axis vary with time. These variations change the amount and the distribution of solar radiation received by the Earth. Milankovitch identified three patterns or cycles of change: the first had a 26,000 year period, the second a 41,000 year period and the third a 100,000 year period. Firstly, the Earth's orbit of the Sun varies from circular to elliptical over a 100,000 year cycle, the second and third

Figure D6: The main factors that influence the climate of the Earth

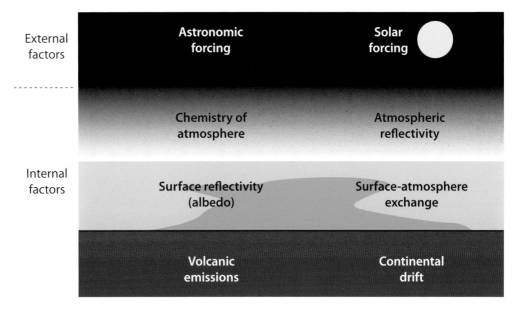

cycles concern changes in the angle of the Earth's axis and therefore the way the Earth is presented to the Sun. Paleoclimate evidence gathered in recent decades suggests that the 41,000 year cycle matches well to the pattern of glacial and interglacial up to one mya. However, it is the 100,000 year cycle, as we have seen (Figure D3), that best fits the warm and cold phases in the last one million year of the Pleistocene Era.

The impact of the Milankovitch cycles is most prominent when their influences overlap, that is when each one produces the maximum (or minimum) amount of solar radiation arriving at the Earth's surface. Even then the total variation does not appear to be enough to cause the significant swings in climate that have produced the glacial and interglacial periods of the last two million years. A temperature change of about +/− 5°C is needed but the cycles by themselves only produce a +/− 0.5°C change. Many researchers agree that the Milankovitch cycles are the trigger mechanism for climate change and that feedback systems then increase the swings in temperature. Such feedback mechanisms act in two different ways:

1. When an initial change takes place and the system adjusts to reduce this change, this is negative feedback. For example, if air temperature increases then evaporation increases, this in turn increases cloud cover but more cloud cover reflects solar insolation away so reducing air temperature – a negative or dampening down feedback.

2. If an initial change works through a system to reinforce the change then this is positive feedback. If a small cooling of the atmosphere takes place, more precipitation falls as snow. White snow reflects away solar insolation and temperatures fall further, this is one mechanism that might explain how a 0.5°C temperature fall due to Milankovitch astronomic cycles might cause a 5° decline in temperature and initiate a glacial ice age.

Solar forcing (insolation)

If the amount of energy emitted by the Sun changed even by a small percentage the impact on the Earth's energy balance would be enormous. It appears that the Sun's output, called the solar constant, has been very consistent for many millions of years. However, intense magnetic storms on the Sun's surface, known as sunspots, do alter its energy output. Their pattern fits a number of cycles including an 11 year cycle. The greater the sunspot activity the more energy is released and the current cycle, the 24th to be monitored, ends with low activity in 2019 and the 25th cycle is due to peak in 2025. But again this variation is small, equating to only 0.1% of the solar constant and therefore is not enough to explain the Earth's climate variation. Historically longer sunspot cycles have been linked to the short-term climate changes. The observed period of low sunspot activity between 1645 and 1715 (the Maunder Minimum) has been associated with the cold period known, rather inaccurately, as the Little Ice Age.

Atmospheric chemistry (greenhouse gas forcing)

This is the best-known factor of climate change as it is the one that is said to be responsible for the current phase of global warming. The trapping by the greenhouse gases of the heat energy radiated by the Earth ensures that the planet has an average surface temperature of 15°C. Without these gases and their greenhouse effect it is estimated that the surface temperature would be −18°C, that is 33°C colder, a very different world. While some dispute the factors behind current climate change less controversial is the evidence, from ice cores and geological sources, that higher levels of atmospheric CO_2, methane and other greenhouse gases have been associated with warmer periods in the Earth's history over millions and tens of millions of years. The atmosphere during the Jurassic Era (201–145 mya), when the dinosaurs dominated the Earth, is estimated to have had CO_2 levels five times greater than today. There were no ice caps at the poles and hot tropical climates existed across regions that are temperate today. Analysis of deep ocean floor sediment shows that during the last one million years of the Pleistocene Period there was a close correlation between atmospheric CO_2 levels and global temperature. In the cold glacial periods CO_2 levels were 30% lower than in the warmer interglacial periods. One explanation of these changes depends on the role of the oceans in the storing and release of CO_2. Warming oceans release CO_2 whereas cooling oceans absorb more of the gas from the atmosphere. Minor cooling of the oceans initiated by Milankovitch cycles would allow the ocean to absorb and store more atmospheric CO_2, so reducing the greenhouse effect. Through this positive feedback further cooling occurs and a glacial period is initiated. Under the 100,000 year Milankovitch cycle of Earth's eccentric orbit, a period of increased solar energy input would later warm the oceans and the reverse positive feedback would commence. Warmer oceans release more CO_2 into the atmosphere, enhancing the greenhouse effect, causing the planet to be warmed into an interglacial period (Figure D7).

Figure D7: The possible link between astronomic forcing and greenhouse gas forcing in the initiation of glacial periods

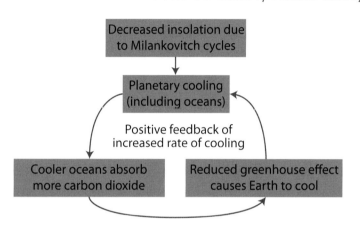

Volcanic eruptions and emissions

Dust thrown high into the atmosphere by major volcanic eruptions has the potential to block solar insolation and so reduce global temperatures. Research has shown that the release of sulphur dioxide (SO_2) gas by volcanic activity has a longer lasting impact. This gas reacts with water vapour in the stratosphere forming a bright haze layer that reflects solar insolation back out to space. Following large historic eruptions including the 1783–1784 Laki fissure eruption in Iceland, Mt Tambora, Indonesia in 1815 and Mt Pinatubo, Philippines in 1991 severe cooling of large parts of the Earth's surface was recorded for up to three years after the event. Significant as this is, it represents very short-term climate change. Unless continuous activity or a series of very large volcanic events coincided and initiated a positive feedback loop of cooling, it is unlikely that medium or long-term changes are the consequence of volcanic action. Similar cooling effects would follow a major asteroid strike as the debris thrown into the air would blanket the planet blocking out insolation. The death of the land and marine dinosaurs and around 75% of all living species on Earth 65 mya is believed to be the result of a huge asteroid impact off Mexico's Yucatan Peninsula. This event, known as the KT boundary, marks the break between the Cretaceous and Tertiary geological Eras.

Continental drift

The rocks of continental plates are ancient in comparison to those of the ocean basins. While the ocean floors form 70% of the Earth's crust they are comparatively young, less than 250 million years old. The theory of plate tectonics involves the continuous movement and relocation of these ancient continents and as they move, especially across latitudes, they are subject to different climates (Figures A7 and A12, pages 9 and 11). The base rocks of the Indian sub-continent retain evidence of having been buried by ice in an ancient glaciation around 300 mya near the South Pole before the plate travelled across the Tropics and the Equator to its present position in the northern hemisphere (Figure A25, page 20). While this process helps explain why individual places show evidence of past climates, because plates have changed location, there is another process that links plate tectonics to worldwide climate change. During the Cretaceous Era (144–66 mya) rapid plate tectonic activity caused the break-up of the supercontinent Pangaea and created new shallow ocean basins. Shallower basins hold less water so global sea levels rose covering more of the Earth's land surface. These shallow warm oceans released more greenhouse gas so warming the atmosphere. Estimates suggest that during the Late Cretaceous Era the Earth's climate was up to 10°C warmer than today.

The end of the last glacial period

The Pleistocene Epoch is the most recent of Earth's ice ages but an ice age is not a single event. As Figure D3 shows there are a series of cold and warm periods known as glacials and interglacials. The most recent of these glacial periods, known in the UK as the Devensian and in Ireland as the Midlandian, started around 115,000 ya, reached its peak 22,000 ya and ended 11,700 ya. Since then the current period, the Holocene (11,700 ya to the present) is in fact an interglacial period. The interglacial period before the Devensian/Midlandian ice age is known as the Ipswichian/Eemian (Figure D8). Glacial and interglacial events last for tens of thousands of years but shorter warm or cold periods, lasting up to a thousand years, during a glacial or interglacial period are termed stadials and interstadials.

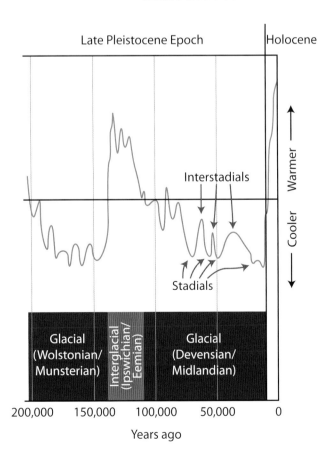

Figure D8: The chronology of the late Pleistocene

Almost 200 years ago a Swiss geologist, Louis Agassiz proposed the idea that much of Europe had been previously covered by ice. He based this on his study of glacier activity high in the European Alps and the many similar landforms and features he recognised across areas no longer affected by ice. This theory helped to explain many landscape features as well as the spread and progress of humanity. The reconstruction of past climates is a rich vein for research and our concern over the outcome of the current rapid global warming only makes the need for better understanding of natural climate change all the more urgent.

There have been several glacial periods with ice sheets covering the Northern Hemisphere continents in the last half million years. In the Southern Hemisphere, apart from the Antarctic continent itself, there has been much less land impacted by these glaciations. Across North America, Europe and Asia the annual accumulation of snow during cold glacial periods has created ice sheets extending south into the hearts of each continent. Ice sheets do not just cover the land, they flow over it lifting material and grinding it across the landscape. By their nature each new glacial period destroys the landscape evidence of the previous event, meaning that today's landscape owes much of its nature to the last glaciation.

Figure D9: The extent of ice sheets at the Last Glacial Maximum (LGM) of the Devensian/ Midlandian glaciation viewed from a North Pole centred map

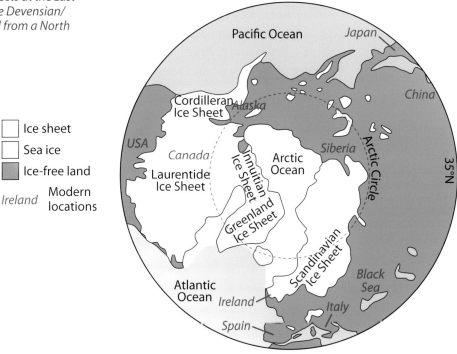

It should be remembered that while parts of the world were repeatedly covered by ice, the lower latitudes including the tropics also underwent climate change. Wet phases are noted in parts of what is now the Sahara Desert and while they survived, the tropical forests of South America and Africa were less extensive. The Laurentide, Scandinavia and Siberian Ice Sheets covered much of North America, Europe and Asia while the sea areas between them would have been frozen pack ice. The landscape impacts of this last glacial period will be examined in the next section but here we are concerned with the climatic change.

Figure D10: The Last Glacial Maximum in Europe

The most extensive ice cover of the last glacial period, the Devensian/ Midlandian, was around 22,000 ya, although this peak timing varies in different parts of the world. Known as the Last Glacial Maximum (LGM) the most southern and western extent of this ice sheet in Ireland and the UK is shown in Figure D10. This ice extended well beyond the present west coast of Ireland and recent research has identified seabed deposits marking the edge of the ice in this area. From this time to the end of the glaciation, 22,000–12,000 ya, is the period of deglaciation, during which the ice sheet melted and its edge retreated. It should be remembered that as an ice sheet melts the ice is either still moving forward or may be stationary (stagnant) but it does not physically retreat, it melts away. Importantly it is clear that this 10,000 year retreat was not continuous; several short stadial (cold) and interstadial (warm) episodes, perhaps millennia (1000 year) long, interrupted the process. Not only does this make the study of the landscape changes complex, it also sheds light on how future climate change for us may take place.

Figures D11 and D12 show that during the final phase of the last glaciation the mean annual temperature in the Northern Hemisphere varied significantly over both short and longer time scales.

Figure D11: Temperature change based on Greenland Ice cores 22,000–8000 ya

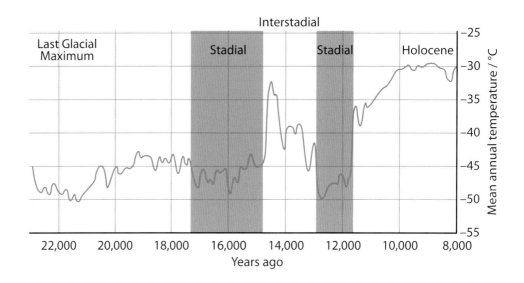

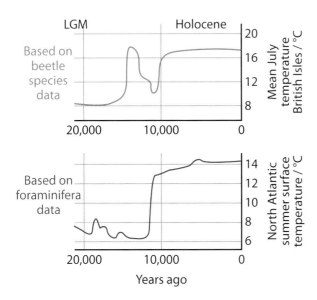

Figure D12: Alternative sources of temperature change between the LGM and the Holocene. The top graph uses different species of beetle, the bottom foraminifera which are tiny shelled sea organisms. In both cases, specific species of each can be linked to an environmental temperature range under which they thrive.

Given the current rate of our global warming, periods in which temperatures rose or fell by over 10°C in less than 100 years are of particular interest.

One theory is that the rapid shifts in temperature were the result of the cutting-off and later restoration of the Gulf Stream, a warm ocean current in the North Atlantic. Today, this ocean current ensures that Western Europe enjoys much milder winter temperatures and remains ice free, unlike many places with similar high latitudes. At least twice in the deglaciation of the Midlandian glaciation this conveyer of warm water was blocked initiating cold stadial conditions in Ireland, the UK and beyond. It is suggested that warming air temperatures in the Arctic caused melting and calving (shedding icebergs) from North America's Laurentide Ice Sheet. This large scale deluge of cold water and ice into the Atlantic then blocked the normal shift of warm water: a pattern named as a Heinrich event.

Figure D13: The contrasting North Atlantic surface ocean currents, today (left) and in the last glaciation (right)

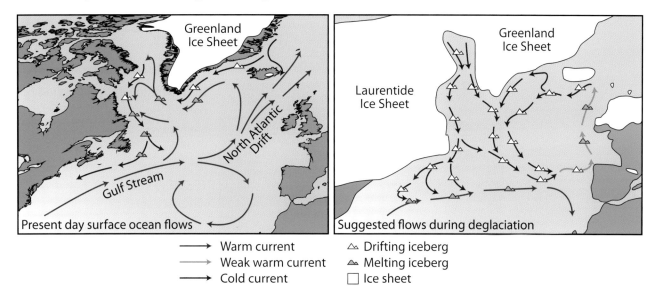

Figure D14: Generalised view of the location and flow of ice sheets in Ireland and the Irish Sea during the last phase of the glaciation

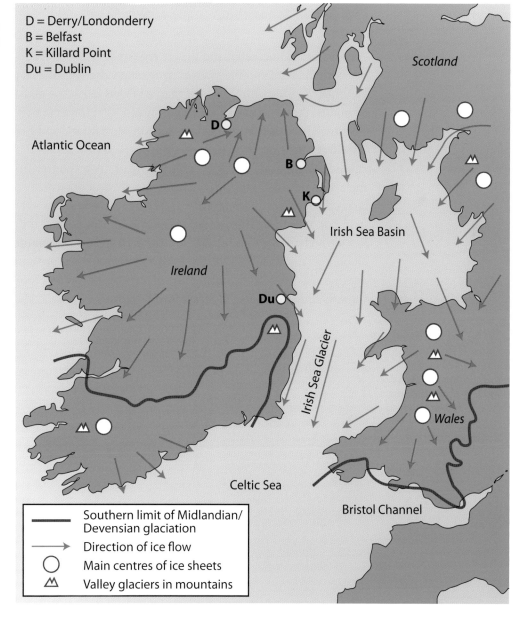

Figure D15: Ice smoothed bedrock beneath a cliff face composed of fluvioglacial sediments formed during the last glacial advance (Benderg Bay, Co Down)

The Last Glacial Termination

In Ireland the last cold period is named the Killard Point Stadial after the section of coast in Co Down where its impact is readily seen. This cooling around 17,000 ya caused the last advance of the ice sheet across the lowlands of north Ireland. This has been designated the Last Glacial Termination in Northern Ireland and being the last it has left the freshest glacial and fluvioglacial landforms and deposits in our landscape.

As the climate fluctuated and the ice repeatedly advanced and retreated the relationship between the land and the sea was in constant change. Glacial periods tie up significant volumes of water with the result that sea levels fall at the global scale. At the LGM it is estimated that world sea level was around 130 m lower than it is today – this is worldwide or eustatic change (see section on 'Eustatic and isostatic change', page 136). However, the water 'missing' from the ocean is now ice on the land and its weight will cause the land to sink down – a local or isostatic response. During deglaciation land ice melts and returns to the sea raising its height and potentially flooding the coast. Then again the land will also start to rise having lost its burden of ice, potentially lifting the land out of the sea. This isostatic response continues even today, 12,000 years after the last ice melted away in Ireland. The north of Ireland has landforms that illustrate these changing relationships well. Raised or fossil shorelines are common along the east and north coasts while at the same time former peat bogs and forests can be found beneath the sea along the shores of Strangford Lough.

Figure D16: A simplified view of the change in relative sea level from the Last Glacial Maximum to the present for the Co Down coast

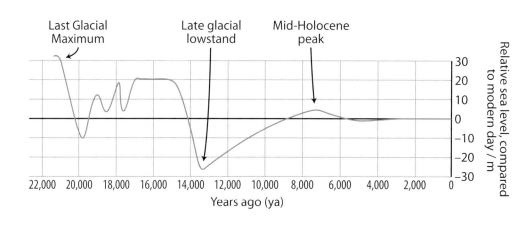

Figure D17:
Reconstructed maps
of global vegetation
distribution at the Last
Glacial Maximum, the
start of the Holocene
and today

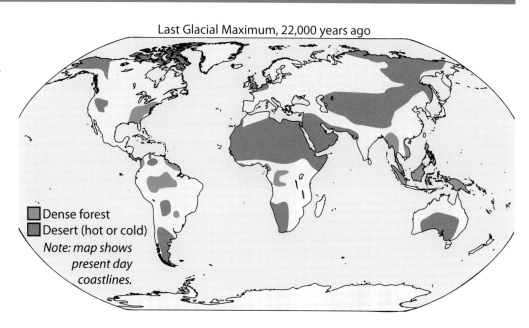

Last Glacial Maximum, 22,000 years ago

Dense forest
Desert (hot or cold)
Note: map shows
present day
coastlines.

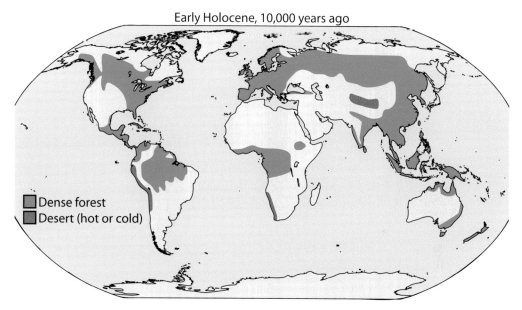

Early Holocene, 10,000 years ago

Dense forest
Desert (hot or cold)

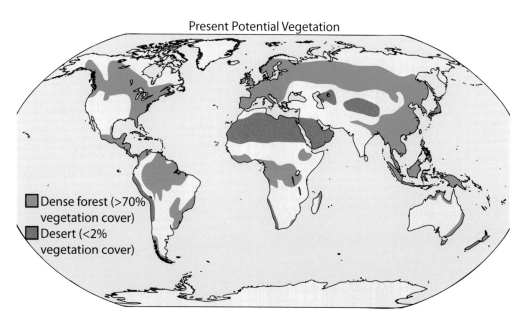

Present Potential Vegetation

Dense forest (>70%
vegetation cover)
Desert (<2%
vegetation cover)

The Ice Age, the Pleistocene, is not over: the current warm phase, the Holocene (11,700 ya to the present) is viewed as another interglacial between a series of glacial periods. The last five glacial periods lasted, on average, between 70,000 and 90,000 years with the interglacials separating them lasting between 10,000 and 15,000 years. If this were to continue in future we might expect a glacial period to commence within the next few thousand years. Previous interglacial warm periods allowed plants, animals and Neanderthal people to occupy parts of Europe including areas of what is Great Britain today. However, the Holocene is the first time we have evidence of people reaching Ireland. By 9000 ya *Homo sapiens* had arrived with a number of scattered camps of hunter gatherers having been found, including an early site on the River Bann at Mount Sandel near Coleraine. Globally, the Holocene is the era in which the advent of farming, permanent settlement, metal working, writing, mechanised industry and human civilisation took place. Due to these profound changes some scientists are suggesting a new name for this geological era; the Anthropocene (Human age).

Exam Questions

1. Explain how any two of the following mechanisms can cause climate change in the long or medium-term:

   - astronomic

   - solar

   - continental drift

   - volcanic [8]

2. What is the Holocene? Describe the end of the last phase of global glaciation. [8]

3. With general reference to places for illustration purposes, describe and explain the evidence for long and medium-term climate change. [18]

References

Geofile articles:
'Climate change over the past 21,000 years', *Geofile* 593, series 27, 2008–2009

Global Climate Change:
http://www.global-climate-change.org.uk/index.php

2. LOWLAND GLACIAL LANDSCAPES

Case studies

Regional scale
lowland
post-glacial
environment:
South East Ulster

Students should be able to:

(i) demonstrate knowledge and understanding of the formation of glacial ice sheets and associated glacial and fluvioglacial processes of erosion, transportation and deposition

(ii) demonstrate knowledge and understanding of glacial and fluvioglacial landforms – till, drumlins, eskers, erratics, outwash plains and moraines, including ribbed moraines

(iii) demonstrate knowledge and understanding of the benefits and problems of socio-economic development in lowland post-glacial environments

Glaciers are bodies of ice formed by the gradual accumulation of snow that are thick enough to flow or deform under their own weight. On land where the winter snowfall does not all melt during the following summer, snow will build up layer on layer and eventually the lower layers will be compressed into glacial ice. The size of a glacier depends on the balance between this accumulation of snowfall and the loss of ice by melting or the calving of icebergs. This total loss is known as ablation. Glaciers come in many forms; small versions, known as cirque or corrie glaciers are confined to hollows in mountainsides, while medium-sized ice caps (less than 50,000 km² in area) cover mountain regions and the largest of all, ice sheets, are now confined to Antarctica and Greenland. During the last glacial period much of North America was covered by the enormous Laurentide Ice Sheet and Northern Europe by the Scandinavian or Fennoscandinavia Ice Sheet.

Figure D18: Snow covered mountains and valley glaciers in Newfoundland, Canada

Perhaps the most obvious place to look for glaciated landforms is in high mountains and such Alpine glacial environments produce distinctive landscapes. Figure D19 shows some of the common erosional landforms found in mountain environments following a period of glaciation. The diagram illustrates how the erosion of moving cirque and valley glaciers (rivers of ice) 'armed' with rocks and boulders can carve out broad 'U' shaped valleys and rock basins later occupied by lakes. After the ice melts smaller tributary glacier valleys are left hanging with steep waterfalls and mountain peaks (horns) and ridges (arêtes) are left sharp-edged and craggy.

Figure D19: Typical landforms of glaciated mountain regions

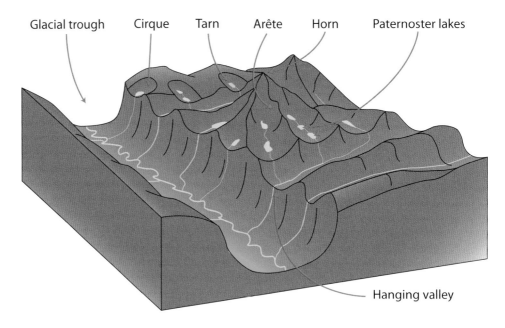

The high mountains of Ireland, Wales, Scotland and England no longer retain ice cover but examples of many of these distinctive landforms can be identified within them.

However, our focus is on the action of past glaciations on lowland landscapes and it is here that ice has had a more subtle but no less significant impact. Ice sheets do not necessarily originate in mountainous areas. During much of the last glaciation the north of Ireland was dominated by an ice sheet centred on the area now occupied by Lough Neagh. Figure D20 shows a cross-section of the ice sheet that covers Greenland today. While the vertical scale is exaggerated, the domed shape is typical of ice sheets. The figure shows that ice flow originates from the deep central zone of accumulation out towards the ablation zones on the edge of the ice sheet. This flow pattern is often likened to honey flowing outwards when poured on a table.

Figure D20: Cross-section across Greenland's Ice Sheet

Also shown by Figure D20 is how the weight of ice (in the case of Greenland nearly 3 km thick) depresses the underlying land down below sea level – isostatic depression. One of the greatest puzzles with the dynamics of ice sheets

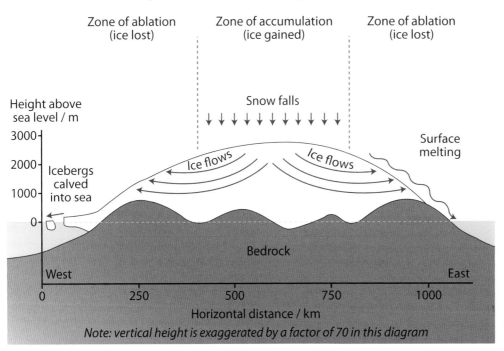

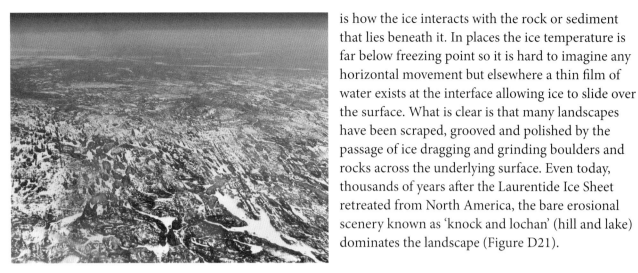

Figure D21: 'Knock and Lochan' scenery, Northern Canada

is how the ice interacts with the rock or sediment that lies beneath it. In places the ice temperature is far below freezing point so it is hard to imagine any horizontal movement but elsewhere a thin film of water exists at the interface allowing ice to slide over the surface. What is clear is that many landscapes have been scraped, grooved and polished by the passage of ice dragging and grinding boulders and rocks across the underlying surface. Even today, thousands of years after the Laurentide Ice Sheet retreated from North America, the bare erosional scenery known as 'knock and lochan' (hill and lake) dominates the landscape (Figure D21).

The glacial and fluvioglacial processes of erosion, transportation and deposition

The post-glacial lowland landscape is usually a complex one, reflecting periods of ice advance and retreat and ultimately the end of a glaciation when ice sheets finally relinquish their grip – releasing ice, meltwater and sediment in vast quantities over the surface. In common with rivers and waves, ice sheets erode, entrain (pick up), transport and deposit material. Landforms are created both where material is removed and where it is deposited. Erosion by ice is termed glacial erosion but with meltwater involved it is fluvioglacial erosion. Ice alone does not erode solid rock but abrasion is a powerful process of glacial erosion. This involves the scratching and polishing of bedrock surfaces by fragments of rock held in the ice. Larger particles leave long grooves or striations on

Figure D22: Ice polished bedrock in Central Park, New York

rocks while the ice uses finer particles to 'polish' the bedrock (Figure D22). Much of the sediment debris left by glaciers is a fine mixture of clay and silt sized particles known as rock-flour. In general the faster the ice moves the more effective the abrasion process. Meltwater erosion is similar to river or fluvial erosion, using hydraulic pressure and abrasion to wear away rock. Chemical or solution erosion by meltwater is also significant, as glacial meltwater can be relatively acidic and the freshly exposed rock surfaces beneath ice react readily.

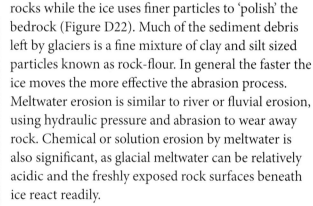

The striations found on this polished rock surface show how ice dragged its entrained load over the bedrock. They help to determine the direction of past ice flow in the region.

The entrainment of sediment into glaciers either comes from above (supraglacial) or below (sub-glacial) sources. Supraglacial material consists of:

- fragments washed or blown onto the ice sheet from the surrounding environment and
- fallout from the air including volcanic ash and industrial pollutants.

Sub-glacial material has either been:

- eroded from the bed of the glacier

or

- carried in by meltwater glacial streams.

Figure D23: Ash from a recent volcanic eruption on the surface of a valley glacier, Iceland

In ice sheets sub-glacial sources are more common and this is where most material is transported by ice and/or water. One of the most distinctive features of material deposited directly by melting ice, without significant water flow, is the variety of grain size found within it. Such sediment is known as glacial till but is often described as boulder clay, reflecting the diversity of its particle size. Most post-glacial lowland landscapes will be dominated by products of deposition processes or the re-working of these by meltwater flows. Deposition from ice sheets takes several forms:

- Under slow flowing ice sub-glacial debris is stuck onto the bed by friction, a process called lodgement.
- Static melting ice can release its debris onto the surface lying below.
- Meltwater deposit material – fluvioglacial deposition.

These processes interact to create a wide array of landforms. Despite almost two centuries of research many of these landforms are not yet fully understood, partly because these processes operate at the contact zone between ice and the rock or sediment beneath, a very challenging environment to observe or record. Recent global warming has caused the retreat of existing glaciers and aided our understanding of the deglaciation processes.

Figure D24: Glacial till: a variety of angular rock particles (clasts) in a fine clay matrix, Co Kerry, Ireland

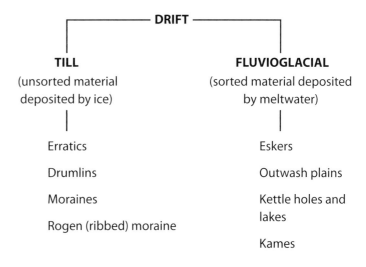

Figure D25: Glacial erratic of Triassic sandstone on Slieve na Calliagh, Co Meath, Ireland

Glacial and fluvioglacial landforms

Drift is the collective term used to describe both types of deposit: glacial till and fluvioglacial. Till is a mixture of unsorted sediment: rocks, sand and clay transported either on, in or under the ice (Figure D24). Lodgement till is material deposited under ice as it moves, while ablation till is deposited at the leading edge of an ice sheet such as a terminal moraine. Large angular blocks of rock may be moved many miles by ice, from one geological region to another and then dumped when it melts. These 'out of place' features are called erratics (Figure D25).

Figure D26: Glacial drift deposits and landforms

	DRIFT	
TILL (unsorted material deposited by ice)		**FLUVIOGLACIAL** (sorted material deposited by meltwater)
Erratics		Eskers
Drumlins		Outwash plains
Moraines		Kettle holes and lakes
Rogen (ribbed) moraine		Kames

Drumlins and Rogen (ribbed) moraines

Drumlins, from the Irish word *druim* (rounded hill) are perhaps the best-known feature of lowland post-glacial environments. Described as smooth, oval-shaped hills, drumlins are normally found in large groups or swarms. The formation of drumlins is a hotly debated issue as these landforms vary widely in shape and composition. The term 'basket of eggs' (or 'basket of potatoes') topography suggests the rolling shape of drumlin dominated areas. As Figure D27 shows, drumlins are commonly illustrated as elongated in the direction of ice flow, with a steep slope facing the ice source and a gentler tapered slope on the 'downstream' side. This may be true for many but others are more rounded in form. While drumlins can be up to 1.5 km long and 100 m high, most are smaller.

The most common material found in drumlins is unsorted glacial till suggesting they were formed by fast flowing ice lodging and shaping sediment at its base. However, some drumlins have a solid rock core while the material in others is both rounded and sorted suggesting a role for meltwater deposition. The truth may be that drumlin features may be formed in several ways. The recent emergence of drumlins from under a retreating ice cap in Iceland provides clear evidence of their sub-glacial origin.

Figure D27: The suggested shape and form of drumlins

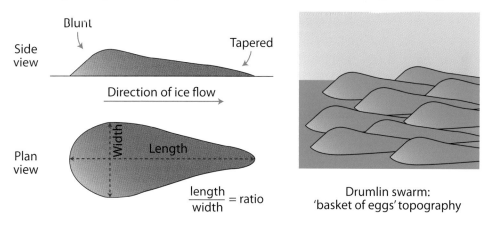

Drumlin swarm: 'basket of eggs' topography

Figure D28: Article on the discovery of newly revealed drumlins

Newly discovered drumlin field provides answers about glaciation and climate, October 2010

Source: 'Newly discovered drumlin field provides answers about glaciation and climate', University of Gothenburg, 21 October 2017, http://science.gu.se/english/News/News_detail/newly-discovered-drumlin-field-provides-answers-about-glaciation-and-climate.cid959019

It appears that drumlins, landforms associated with ice advance during the last Ice Age, can also be produced by glaciers today. On the edge of the retreating Múlajökull glacier in Iceland recently formed drumlins have been revealed. This discovery was made by researchers from the University of Gothenburg.

"Until now, scientists have been divided on how drumlins were created," says Mark Johnson from Gothenburg's Department of Earth Sciences. "Because they are formed under the ice, it's not an observable process. Drumlins are common almost everywhere the Ice Age ice sheets existed, but they're almost unknown with modern-day glaciers. Now, though, we've found a new drumlin field by the Múlajökull glacier on Iceland." The melting of glaciers as a result of climate change has presented researchers with unique opportunities to study their structure. One of the drumlins found was studied layer by layer, and it was clear that it had been built recently. In other words, "…the glacier has not just revealed old drumlins, but is continuing to create new ones." There are currently multiple theories about the origins of drumlins.

Figure D29: Sand ripples on a modern beach form transverse to the current – a pattern comparable to Rogen moraines.

Often closely associated with drumlin swarms are longer ridge landforms that are aligned perpendicular to the length of drumlins, that is across the direction of ice flow. These winding ridges, called Rogen or ribbed moraines, occur in closely spaced parallel lines. They have been described as mega ripples across former glaciated lowland regions. Recently developed mapping techniques, such as Lidar, have helped to reveal that Rogen moraines are more common that previously thought and are widely found across the north of Ireland. Like most drumlins, Rogen moraines are composed of unsorted glacial till and other than being associated with a sub-glacial environment their formation process, again like drumlins, is debated.

Moraines

Moraine is unconsolidated glacial debris gathered, carried and deposited by ice. Many moraines are ridges of sediment or a series of small mounds that run across glacial areas. One common type is a terminal or end moraine. Terminal moraines mark the former leading edge of a glacier where material was bulldozed and/or dropped by the ice front. They are frequently crescentic in form, steep sided, especially on the ice-contact side, and up to 50–60m high. Made of unsorted material dropped as ablation occurred and the glacier retreated, they mark the maximum advance line of any given glacier. Because glaciers do not retreat evenly it is common for ridges similar to terminal moraines to be found in parallel but further back. These are recessional moraines that mark locations where the ice stopped and if it re-advanced small push moraines may be left. Areas covered with irregular small hills and mounds of glacial debris are described as hummocky moraine (Figure D31).

Figure D30: Glacial and fluvioglacial depositional landforms

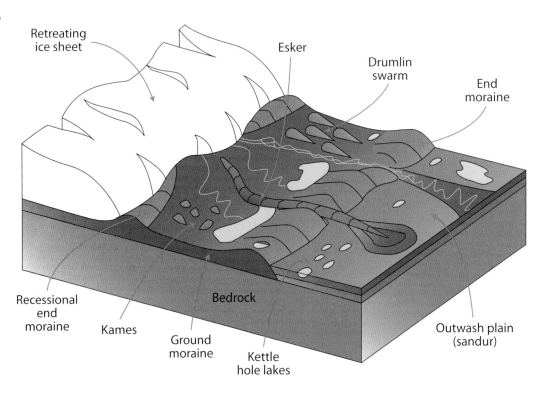

Figure D31: Hummocky moraine (foreground) on the Isle of Mull, Scotland

Figure D32: A small active outwash plain in Iceland. Rounding and sorting of materials can be seen across the area

Figure D33: A kettle hole formation sequence

1. Blocks of dead ice detached as ice sheet retreats.

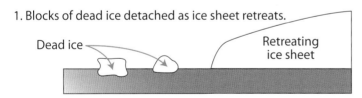

2. Blocks buried by outwash plain deposits.

3. Ice melts to form kettle holes and lakes in the outwash plain.

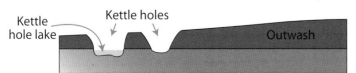

Outwash plains

An outwash plain (sandur) describes the low-lying area that extends beyond a terminal moraine. The plain is formed of sediment carried from the ice by meltwater; these are described as fluvioglacial (or glaciofluvial) deposits. The zone beyond the edge of the ice sheet is termed the pro-glacial area. Meltwater rivers sort their sediment load over the outwash plain (Figure D32); larger boulders are deposited near the terminal moraine, gravels and sand further away and the finer sediment may be carried for many kilometres. Ablation during summer months would produce the highest flows of water and sediment with multiple braided streams spreading out from the leading edge of the glacier. The lowland plain of Northern Europe is a large example of a former sandur, including much of North Germany and the Netherlands, where meltwaters carried glacially eroded debris from the retreating Scandinavian Ice Sheet. Fluvioglacial deposits are generally smaller, more rounded and better sorted than glacial sediment due to the transport and erosional processes of river action. A range of features that owe their origin to fluvioglacial processes are identified, including kames and kettle holes.

Kames and kettle holes

Kames are mounds of sediment deposited by meltwater at the edge of the ice, often in lakes. Some are river deltas that collapse when the supporting ice edge melts away; others are the remains of ice crevasses filled with debris by meltwater streams. As ice sheets melt, large blocks of 'dead ice' become detached and buried by sediment. When these melt small hollows are left and many fill with water to form lakes – these are kettle holes and kettle hole lakes (Figures D33 and D34).

Figure D34: Images of recently formed kettle holes near a glacier snout, South Iceland

Esker

The name Esker comes from *eiscir*, an Irish word meaning ridge. They mark the course of rivers that previously flowed over, in or under the ice. Eskers can be up to 30 m high and several kilometres long. While they are sinuous in form they are generally orientated parallel to the flow of the glacier as opposed to moraines that are aligned across the flow. Esker ridges are made of sands and gravels and many have been exploited as quarries for these materials. Some eskers represent the bed of rivers that flowed underneath an ice sheet (sub-glacial), others were channels within the ice (englacial) where bed material would fall to the ground as ice retreated (Figure D35). Eskers formed in this second way are broader with more chaotic sediment patterns. Esker formation is thought to be associated with the last phase of deglaciation when streams become choked with debris and there is a lack of meltwater to carry material away. Eskers are common features across the previously glaciated regions of the UK and Ireland, though many have been degraded or removed by natural erosional processes or human activity. The Boyne River valley north west of Dublin contains several extensive eskers, some up to 90 m high and one, the Trim esker, can be traced over a distance of 14 km.

Figure D35: Esker formation

1. Stream flows beneath ice.

2. Esker remains after ice has retreated.

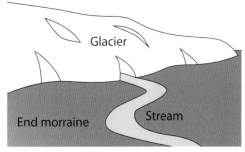
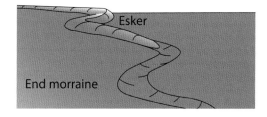

The pro-glacial environment

During deglaciation periods huge quantities of water is released by the ice sheets into the pro-glacial environment. As well as creating extensive outwash plains, moraine ridges and the edge of ice sheets have formed barriers holding back water in pro-glacial lakes. Many of these were temporary, draining away when further ice melting took

Figure D36: The Kaims Esker in the Borders region, Scotland

Source: Dr L Proudfoot

place but some persisted for hundreds or even thousands of years. Former glacial lake bed deposits are commonly found in post-glacial landscapes. Lake Agassiz is the name given to an enormous expanse of glacial meltwater that covered the centre of Canada about 13,000 years ago. It was larger than the present Great Lakes of North America. The UK and Ireland also had pro-glacial lakes; some of the clays beneath Greater Belfast are lake bed sediments formed by former glacial Lake Lagan. Lake bed deposits, defined as glaciolacustrine sediments, have alternating fine layers of mud and sand. These layers or varves have been used in the dating of glacial activity periods. Many pro-glacial lakes eventually drained away to the sea and broad valleys called glacial spillways were created. Today such spillways are occupied by streams far too small to create their huge valleys and so they are called misfit streams. The Dundonald Gap to the east of Belfast was cut by a large river and drained Lake Lagan from the Belfast basin to the sea near present day Comber.

The impact of glaciation and later deglaciation spreads far beyond the areas directly impacted by ice. During glaciation, land beyond the ice front is subjected to frozen ground processes called periglaciation and tundra like conditions extended still further. Global sea level changes between glacial and interglacial eras affected coastlines across the planet. Deglaciation, as noted, brings water and water borne sediment across outwash plains for hundreds of kilometres. The very finest glacial sediment, rock-flour has been lifted by wind and deposited across the prairie grasslands of mid-west America, the central plains of China and onto the lowlands of East Anglia. This fine material, named loess is a common parent material for the fertile black earth soils (mollisols or chernozems) of the central continental grasslands.

The benefits and problems of socio-economic development in lowland post-glacial environments

In the immediate aftermath of ice sheet retreat, the tundra environment would present many challenges for life. However, when the late Midlandian glaciation ended, 10,000–12,000 years ago, the invasion of plants and animals from the warmer regions of Southern Europe was rapid. By 10,000 years ago most of Britain and Ireland was forested with deciduous oak and beech woodlands in the south and pine woods in the Scottish north. By 9000 ya people, albeit in small numbers, had arrived, including hunter gatherers in a site overlooking the River Bann near Coleraine (Mount Sandel).

Figure D37: Reconstruction of the changing coastline of North West Europe during deglaciation

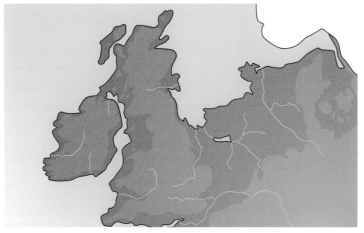

These are Mesolithic (middle stone age) people. By this time Europe was as warm as it is today but global sea levels were continuing to rise. Ireland became an island detached from Great Britain, which later separated from continental Europe (Figures D37 and C43, page 138).

The arrival of people into Western Europe by 9000 years ago illustrates that is was an attractive environment with the potential to support a highly resource dependent, hunting gathering community. At Mount Sandel a lack of a native red deer population was compensated for by the availability of trout and salmon from the Bann. By 7000 ya the Neolithic Revolution (new stone age) had arrived and people began to take control of their own food supply, domesticating animals and planting seeds. This new idea rapidly swept through the islands bringing new forms of stone tool, distinctive pottery and most significantly a new economic model – farming. But just how did the physical nature of the post-glacial lowlands impact on these revolutionary changes? And what impact, if any, do they retain today?

Agriculture

Glaciation largely removed any previous soil or sediment from the rock beneath only to replace this with a thick layer of glacial and fluvioglacial material on which the new, young post-glacial soils had to form. Some of these deposits promote good drainage and fertile soil development; others with deep clay layers inhibit drainage and limit the soil forming conditions. Post-glacial lowland scenery while relatively low in elevation does create many varied environments including:

- well-drained but exposed summits.
- steep slopes with thin soils.
- waterlogged land in poorly-drained hollows, which may form frost pockets in winter.

The outwash plains created by meltwater streams, in the pro-glacial zone beyond the ice sheet, tend to be less fertile as the finer materials were carried away leaving coarser sands and gravels. On the North European Plain these form heathlands of limited agricultural potential, though some are used for commercial forestry, such as the Lüneburg Heath, Germany. On the other hand, as noted earlier, the finest wind-blown loess material promotes deep, fertile grassland soils in continental interiors.

Water supply and drainage

In central counties of Ireland groundwater is the primary source of drinking water and here the porous glacial sands and gravels are an important source of clean and easily extracted water. Also a layer of glacial till can act as an effective filtering system, protecting groundwater supplies from pollution. On the other hand landscapes dominated by glacial deposition are noted for their complex drainage patterns. Kettle hole lakes, transverse moraines and drumlin swarms create a complex, rolling landscape where small ponds, lakes and marshes occupy inter-drumlin hollows. Natural drainage systems often need to be modified to ensure farmland is not regularly inundated or waterlogged. The lakes and ponds do provide water but are also potential hazards for livestock.

Building and engineering

Glacial till is generally a sound material for constructing building foundations upon but the complex sedimentation sequence of fluvioglacial deposits often makes them difficult to use. The summits of drumlins may be strategic sites for defensive structures but their south east facing slopes provide warmer, more sheltered locations for farm houses or homes. Glacial geology and geomorphology still play critical roles in the siting of roads, buildings and other major engineering structures.

Transport routes

Across marshy landscapes sinuous esker ridges can provide drier, safer access routes for people and livestock. Famously in central Ireland, the Esker Riada, known in early Celtic times as 'An Slí Mór' (The Great Highway) linked the east and west of the island. Later the esker formed part of a pilgrim route across the floodplain of the River Shannon to the important ecclesiastical centre at Clonmacnoise. Even today, the N6 Dublin–Galway motorway follows this glacial feature for some of its route. Drumlin landscapes are associated with transport routes that either wind around or roll over the drumlins, or a mixture of both. Today because drumlins, eskers and moraines are fairly easy to cut through using modern earth-moving machinery, flatter and straighter routes are readily created.

Resources, including building material

Glacial deposits are a rich source of building materials estimated to be worth £100 million to the Irish economy annually. In particular, sand and gravels are often extracted from eskers: the formation of eskers as river bed deposits in energetic environments means that finer silts and clays were removed leaving well sorted gravels and sands. As these sands and gravels were laid down by fresh water, they do not need the salt-removing processes required when using materials dredged from marine or coastal environments. A high salt content makes sand and gravel unsuitable for use in cement, concrete or concrete blocks. Each year in Northern Ireland up to 5 million tonnes of glacial sand and gravels are extracted, depending on the health of the local construction industry. In places where extensive esker quarrying has taken place sand pits and quarries have been subsequently used as land fill sites for waste. The suitability of such sites depends on how permeable the underlying material is; a thick clay layer may retain any leachate, protecting groundwater sources, whereas porous sands or gravels would allow potentially dangerous pollutants to percolate into the water table.

Many of the small lakes and ponds left after the retreat of ice have undergone primary succession and peat has formed. These raised bogs are not only distinctive habitats but they are also cut as a traditional domestic fuel (turf – dried peat) and more recently as a substrate in commercial horticulture.

Figure D38: Quarry in an esker, Attiflynn, Co Galway, Ireland

Figure D39: Sand and gravel works on an esker, Attiflynn, Co Galway, Ireland

Figure D40: Drumlin swarm and the Mourne Mountains, Co Down

Scenic quality

For many people the distinctive 'basket of eggs topography' of drumlin scenery is attractive. When asked for his idea of paradise, the Belfast born writer, C S Lewis said, "Heaven is Oxford lifted and placed in the middle of County Down". Many believe his description of the mythical land of Narnia in part reflects the many years he spent walking in the county. Drumlin and esker landscapes are often used as the basis for golf courses: they provide natural and challenging slopes and contours, hidden greens, sand and water hazards.

CASE STUDY: South East Ulster, the counties of Armagh, Down and Monaghan, a regional scale study of a lowland post-glacial environment

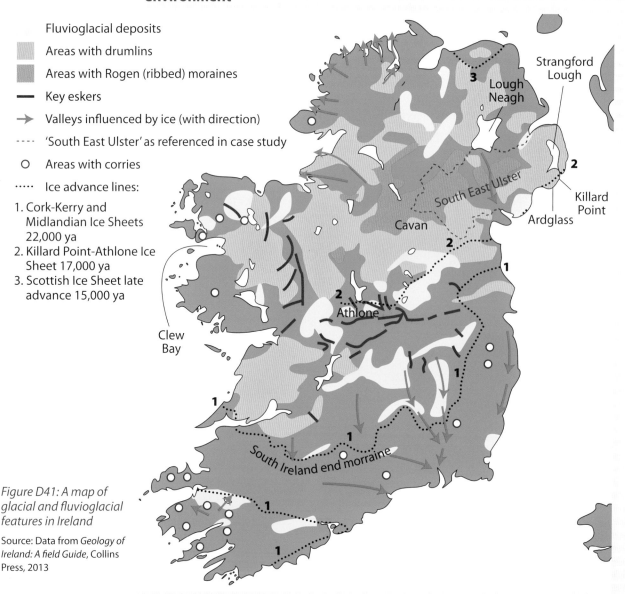

Fluvioglacial deposits

Areas with drumlins

Areas with Rogen (ribbed) moraines

— Key eskers

→ Valleys influenced by ice (with direction)

---- 'South East Ulster' as referenced in case study

O   Areas with corries

····· Ice advance lines:

1. Cork-Kerry and Midlandian Ice Sheets 22,000 ya
2. Killard Point-Athlone Ice Sheet 17,000 ya
3. Scottish Ice Sheet late advance 15,000 ya

Figure D41: A map of glacial and fluvioglacial features in Ireland

Source: Data from *Geology of Ireland: A field Guide*, Collins Press, 2013

Landscapes are rarely confined by administrative boundaries but these three counties of South East Ulster contain excellent examples of many glacial and fluvioglacial landforms. As Figure D41 shows, much of the region is covered by extensive glacial deposits (Rogen moraines and drumlins) or fluvioglacial deposits (outwash plains and lacustrine – lake bed).

The drumlin swarms that dominate much of counties Armagh and Down, including the Strangford Peninsula, are part of the huge arc of these features that extend to Ireland's west coast, to and into Clew Bay in Co Mayo. The 4000 drumlins of north Down were the focus of study in the nineteenth century when these features were first recognised as having a glacial origin. Drowned drumlins are a feature of Strangford Lough, forming many islands some of which are linked by causeways. More recently, digital landscape mapping tools have revealed

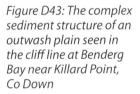

Figure D42: Variable agricultural land quality in drumlin country, near Downpatrick, Co Down

that drumlin forms are often superimposed onto the transverse Rogen (ribbed) moraine features, such as the large region covering up to 7000 km² south of Lough Neagh as far as Co Cavan.

During the deglaciation phase of the last glacial, between 22,000 and 12,000 years ago, the Irish Ice Sheet reduced until it was centred in the Lough Neagh Basin of Ulster. About 17,000 years ago a 'Heinich' event in the North Atlantic produced one last ice sheet advance, which reshaped the sub-glacial sediment and created new moraine ridges close to the coast of present day Co Down. Known as the Killard Point Stadial, after the location of the terminal moraine, it also links to nearby drumlins,

Figure D43: The complex sediment structure of an outwash plain seen in the cliff line at Benderg Bay near Killard Point, Co Down

streamlined in a south east direction. The cliff line between Killard Point and Ardglass comprises of sediments up to 20 m high from fluvioglacial and marine origin, as the area was sequentially subject to pro-glacial and seabed conditions (Figure D15, D43 and D44). As Figure D43 illustrates, modern erosion at the coast reveals a wide variety of sediment deposited in a pro-glacial outwash plain environment as the Irish Ice Sheet advanced to a point nearby. Later, as the ice sheet retreated for the final time, the area was inundated by the sea (marine transgression) before isostatic rebound lifted it above the sea once again. The cross-section shown in Figure D44 shows the terminal moraine and outwash plain associated with the Killard Point ice re-advance around 17000 ya, when most of the drumlins of Ulster were created beneath fast flowing ice.

Figure D44: Cross-section of the terminal moraine and pro-glacial outwash plain near Killard Point, Ardglass, Co Down

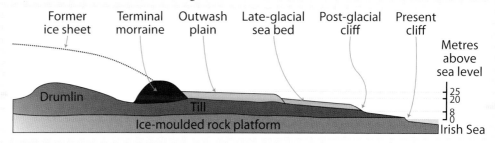

Terminal and recessional moraines associated with this final period of drumlin formation in Ireland can also be seen as a series of arcuate ridges in the extreme south east corner of Co Down at Cranfield Point. Here, in a triangular piece of land to the south east of the Mourne Mountains, outwash plain fluvioglacial and till deposits form the coastal cliff line and numerous commercial gravel pits pock mark the land surface (Figure D45).

Figure D45: A map outlining the major glacial features in South East Ulster

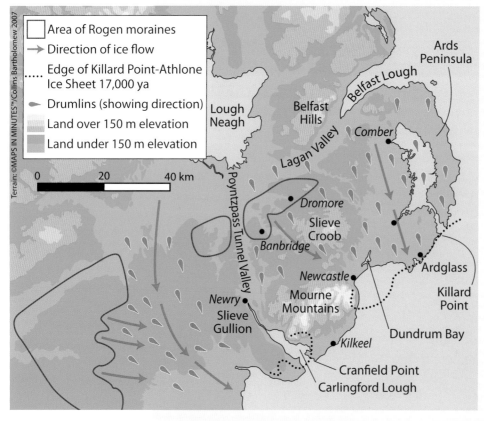

Other glacial landforms that can be observed in the region include small eskers, near Lisburn and Dundonald, the glaciolacustrine sediments on the floor of the Lagan valley at Dunmurry and Malone and kettle hole lakes around the shores of Lough Neagh. The Poyntzpass Tunnel Valley is an example of a melt water cut valley beneath an ice sheet. During deglaciation, at one point Belfast Lough was blocked by ice to the east and by Lough Neagh ice still occupying the area to the west. One drainage route for the overflow from glacial Lake Lagan was south through Poyntzpass to the sea at Carlingford Lough.

Glacial deposits cover 95% of this whole region (below a height of 350 m) and without this veneer of glacial and fluvioglacial sediment much of it would be below present day sea level. The surface area of Lough Neagh would be more than twice its size and the Ards Peninsula would virtually disappear becoming a series of island hills. Most of today's coastline is formed of glacially deposited materials that are gradually being eroded. One of the largest post-glacial depositional landforms in the region is the sand dune complex at Murlough Nature Reserve on Dundrum Bay. While this was created by the action of waves and wind in the last few thousand years, the source of its sand was off-shore in the bay where it had been deposited during glaciation by ice and by meltwater streams during deglaciation. Recent concerns about the loss of the sand beach at Newcastle have been linked to a lack of new off-shore sands as the glacial deposits are depleted.

Figure D46: Map and images of active and disused sand and gravel pits in the Kilkeel area

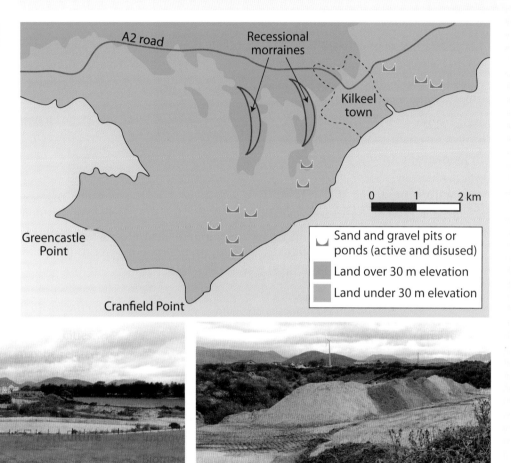

Abandoned quarry near Kilkeel   Active quarrying near Kilkeel

Settlement and the economy across South East Ulster is dominated by farming. A mixed farming environment has been the centuries old pattern over the widespread drumlin and Rogen (ribbed) moraine landscape. Most arable cropping takes place on the drier drumlin slopes to provide fodder crops for livestock. Most land is planted in grassland pasture with inter-drumlin hollows used for rough grazing. One or two specialist areas exist within the general use of the land for pastoral, sheep and cattle. The drier and milder conditions around Comber and the Ards Peninsula have encouraged arable farming of potatoes, oilseed rape and cereals including winter wheat and barley. To the south of Lough Neagh the distinctive landscape is associated with the Armagh apple orchard economy. This is one of the most northernly apple producing regions in Western Europe and the frost avoiding slopes of drumlins have helped this industry survive. Sources of industrial supplies of glacial sand and gravel include quarries in Downpatrick, Newry, Dromore and Banbridge, some of which produce concrete and concrete blocks, as well as sorted gravels and sands for the construction industry. A large concentration of such sand and gravel open quarries are located in the Kilkeel area of South East Co Down (Figure D46).

Figure D47: The first fareway overlooking Strangford at Mahee Golf Club, Co Down

Recreationally, South East Ulster has many attractions including the Mourne Mountains and the sandy beaches of the Co Down coast. Some of these attractions can be linked to the glacial history of the landscape including the use of drumlins for scenic and challenging golf courses (Figure D47). Many of the larger inter-drumlin hollow lakes are used for angling, boating and even water skiing. Strangford Lough itself has a dozen sailing clubs along its shore and annually international cycling events including the Gran Fondo traverse the drumlins of Co Down.

Exam Questions

1. Explain fluvioglacial erosion, transport and deposition processes. [8]

2. With the aid of a diagram(s), illustrate the formation of **any two** of the following landforms associated with lowland glacial landscapes:
   - drumlins
   - eskers
   - erratics
   - outwash plains [8]

3. With reference to a case study of a lowland post-glacial environment:

   either

   (i) Describe with examples the formation and nature of **any three** glacial or fluvioglacial landforms found in the region

   or

   (ii) Explain the benefits and problems of socio-economic development in this region. [18]

References

Geofile:
'Glacier systems: comparative case studies', *Geofile* 745, series 34, 2015–2016
'Glaciers as systems', *Geofile* 622, series 29, 2010–2011
'Glacier and fluvioglacial deposition: case study in Iceland', *Geofile* 573, series 27, 2008–2009
'Climate change over the past 21,000 years', *Geofile* 593, series 27, 2008–2009
'Fluvioglacial activity in Eastern Yorkshire', *Geofile* 533, series 25, 2006–2007
'Glacier fieldwork and coursework', *Geofile* 486, series 23, 2004–2005
'Glacial erosion in lowland areas', *Geofile* 459, series 22, 2003–2004

Geo Factsheet:
'Quaternary glacial landscapes of the UK', *Geo Factsheet* 299, Curriculum Press

Landscape character areas in Northern Ireland:
Armagh drumlins – *https://www.daera-ni.gov.uk/publications/armagh-drumlins-lca*
Environmental landscape report – http://www.habitas.org.uk/escr/site.asp?Item=489

Aspects of the Ice Age in Ireland:
http://www.talamhireland.ie/PDF/Aspects_of_the_last_Ice_Age_in_Ireland_Part_2.pdf

3. CURRENT GLOBAL CLIMATE CHANGE: HUMAN CAUSES AND IMPACTS

Case studies

General reference to places in both MEDCs and LEDCs for illustration purposes

Students should be able to:

(i) demonstrate knowledge and understanding of the evidence for short-term climate change and links to air pollution (enhanced greenhouse effect).

(ii) demonstrate knowledge and understanding of the present and potential impacts of climate change.

The evidence for short-term climate change

The evidence for change in climate over the short-term (decades and centuries) includes: tree-ring data, pollen and ice-core analysis (all mentioned earlier, pages 166–168) and more recently, historical records. All these are indirect or proxy sources of evidence.

Agricultural change is an example of indirect historical records. In medieval times:

- vineyards were found as far north as Yorkshire.
- grain was regularly grown in Iceland.
- arable farming in Scottish mountains was at a higher altitude.

The best-known of recent historic climate changes in Europe is the 'Little Ice Age'. This was the coolest period since the end of the last Ice Age 10,000 years ago and it lasted from 1400 to 1850. At one point, the failure of farming in upland Scotland encouraged a mass migration of Scottish farmers to the richer lowlands found in East Ulster. Between 1607 and 1814 frost fairs were regular winter events on the frozen River Thames at London.

We also have access to direct sources of evidence for climate change. Since about 1850, direct observation of the climate has developed through the use of objective instrumentation including thermometers, barometers and rain gauges. It should be noted that widespread and global coverage for such evidence is much more recent. Both indirect and direct sources are used in the construction of climate change graphs such as Figure D48.

Figure D48: The reconstructed pattern of temperature change in Europe between 900 and 2000 AD

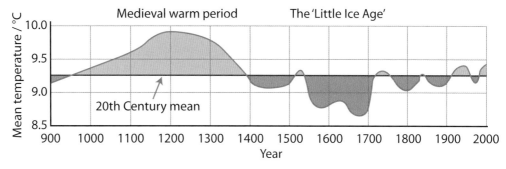

There are two things to note when using this graph:

1. The mid-line along the graph is the average temperature for the twentieth century, that is, the recorded mean European temperatures between 1900 and 2000 AD.

2. The variation in mean temperatures at any point during this 1100 year period appears relatively small: never more than 0.7°C above or below the mid-line.

The recent trend in global climate change

A graph published in 1990 by the Intergovernmental Panel on Climate Change (IPPC) was used to illustrate the most recent phase in global climate change – the sudden twentieth century rise in mean world temperatures. Referred to as the 'hockey stick' (as in ice hockey), it was designed to show the abrupt nature of this recent warming phase (Figure D49).

Figure D49: The IPCC graph of recent global temperature change

The graph is based on data from ice cores, tree rings, historic sources and thermometer records

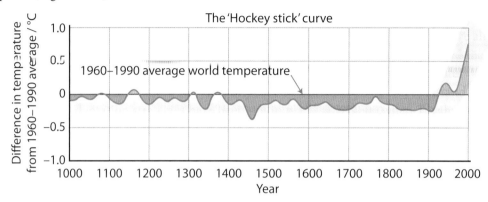

The graph suggests a period of significant warming from 1900 to the present, accelerating from 1970, at a rate and scale unseen at any point in written history. Evidence for this change comes directly from thermometer recordings of temperature at many weather stations. However, most of these are land based and world coverage was patchy until the last few decades. Fifty years of satellite technology, using around 80 weather monitoring satellites, has produced a worldwide cover of temperature data. The net change recorded is warming – a rise of 0.74°C between 1900 and 2000. Over the same timescale, other satellites and ground-based instruments have also recorded significant rises in world ocean levels. By 2000, sea level was rising by over 3 mm a year. Most of this is the result of thermal expansion; that is as the sea warms it expands upwards. This pattern of warming has been recorded at the ocean surface and as deep as 3000 m.

Figure D50: The Pasterze Glacier in the Grossglockner Pass in Austria. Pictured in 2007 the snout of this glacier has been retreating since 1850, currently at an average rate of 18 m each year.

Another source of directly measured evidence is melting ice. Firstly, the World Glacier Monitoring Service has stated that most of the world's land based valley glaciers in all mountain regions have been in retreat since around 1850. Some, like the Pasterze Glacier in the Eastern Alps, have lost 50% of their mass (Figure D50). Secondly, the annual sea ice cover in the Arctic Ocean has been monitored by NASA satellites since 1979 and the average change is a loss of 8.5% per decade. Thirdly, the greatest stores of ice are the ice sheets of Antarctica and Greenland. Changes in these ice sheets are complex but the rate of melting of the Greenland Ice Sheet has increased by over 16% in the last 40 years. Melting of such land ice is of particular concern, as the meltwater will cause a further rise in sea level unlike melting sea ice.

Other evidence of climate change can be seen in the numerous environmental impacts from the acidification of sea water and the bleaching of coral on tropical atolls in the Indian Ocean (page 143) to the increased rate of coastline erosion and fewer clear sky days (increased cloud cover) recorded in Ireland.

The cause of global warming

The evidence shows that global warming is a reality but why is the atmosphere (the thin layer of gases surrounding the planet) getting warmer? Logic suggests we look at the chemistry of the atmosphere itself to see what has changed. One minor atmospheric gas has seen a remarkable change over the last 250 years. As Figure D51 illustrates, carbon dioxide has increased its atmospheric concentration from 275 parts per million (ppm) in 1750 to 406 ppm in 2017. So carbon dioxide rose from 0.0275% to 0.0406% of the atmosphere. In percentage terms this seems insignificant but it is what the gas does in the atmosphere that is critical.

Figure D51:
The changing concentration of carbon dioxide in the atmosphere

Source: Figures are based on ice core research and from 1957 direct observation from the observatory at Mauna Loa, Hawaii

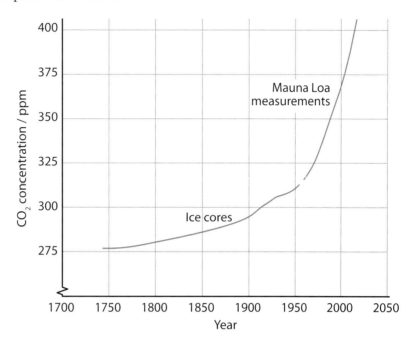

Carbon dioxide is the most significant gas of a group in the atmosphere known as the greenhouse gases (GHG). Together these gases produce a natural phenomenon known as the greenhouse effect. In simple terms, without these gases the Earth's average surface temperature, which is 15°C, would be 20–33°C colder and life on Earth would be very different. The Earth's surface is more or less heated directly by short-wave radiation from the Sun. The surface then radiates this energy back into the atmosphere as long-wave

Figure D52: The operation of the greenhouse effect

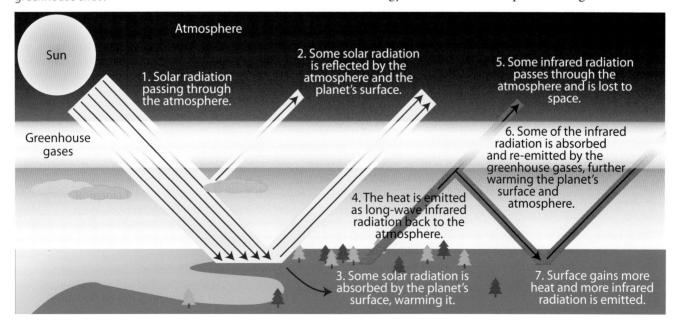

radiation, which these greenhouse gases are then able to absorb, so warming the air. Ultimately the energy gained from the Sun by the Earth and its atmosphere is balanced by the energy lost back to space.

If the quantity of greenhouse gases, including carbon dioxide and methane, increases they will absorb more of the energy from the surface, warming the atmosphere and ending the energy balance. Less energy will escape to space and the Earth-atmosphere system will then warm. This is an enhanced greenhouse effect and is the process that accounts for current global warming.

While the concentration of carbon dioxide in the atmosphere can and does change under natural conditions, this present rapid increase has been explained as the result of human activity in the last 200 years. Directly and indirectly the explosive growth of the world's population, from two billion in 1925 to a projected eight billion in 2025, 100 years later, has altered the atmosphere's chemistry through air pollution. The industrial revolution has released huge quantities of carbon from stored sources into the atmosphere. The fossil fuels are energy sources stored as the remains of life forms from the ancient past: coal from fossilised forests and oil and gas from fossilised sea organisms. Burning these in the vast quantities needed to fuel industry, transport and heating has poured carbon dioxide into the air. But nature also extracts carbon dioxide from the atmosphere. The process of photosynthesis by plants on land and sea uses and stores carbon in the living organisms themselves. However, one major effect of population growth and industrialisation has been the clearance of natural vegetation on an unprecedented scale. Less land covered by vegetation means less carbon dioxide is being extracted from the atmosphere by photosynthesis and the carbon dioxide level rises as illustrated by the graph in Figure D51.

The second most significant greenhouse gas, methane, has doubled its concentration in the atmosphere since 1800. Wetlands and marshes are natural sources of methane but the increased concentration is primarily due to human activity. Leaking gas and oil pipelines, wet rice cultivation, cattle rearing, decay in landfill sites, and wood and peat burning are all significant sources of atmospheric methane.

The present and potential impacts of climate change

The scale and complexity of the Earth's interrelated physical systems makes it difficult to identify all the potential changes that global warming may bring. There is a risk that any extreme event or change may be attributed to global warming though the links may not be understood. However, in a diverse range of study areas researchers have identified changes that can be best explained in light of global warming and therefore they can point to the nature and scale of future changes. Every five years, under current legislation, the UK government publishes the 'UK climate change risk assessment'. The structure of the 2017 report reveals the range of potential climate change threats that this Western MEDC recognises. These are the five chapter headings, with one exemplar from each area:

1. *Natural environment and natural assets* – risks to wildlife from drought and flooding.
2. *Infrastructure* – risks from coastal flooding and erosion.
3. *People and the built environment* – risks to public health from high temperatures.
4. *Business and industry* – risks to business sites from flooding.
5. *International dimensions* – weather-related shock to global food production and trade.

The pattern of current temperature change varies across the world. It is already clear that the Polar Regions, in particular the Arctic, have recorded temperature rises that are much more rapid than the global average. The reported global average warming is 0.9°C from 1880 to 2017; in the Arctic the figure for the same time period is 3°C (Figure D53). Current estimates suggest the next 80 years will see a global average temperature increase of between 1.5 and 3.8°C, depending on which model is used and what action is taken. It is widely agreed that anything above a 2°C increase will have profound impacts on both the natural and human worlds.

Figure D53: Predicted temperature change 1990–2050

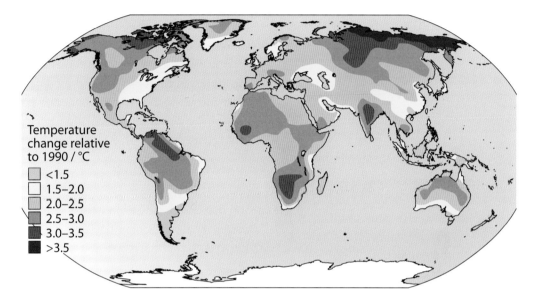

Another alarming possibility is that this Arctic warming may trigger a 'Heinrich-like' event (as noted earlier, pages 174–175). The release of huge quantities of melting ice into the Atlantic Ocean blocking the warm ocean current, the North Atlantic Drift, from reaching Western Europe. This might cause temperatures to fall rather than rise in that region, including Ireland and the UK. Global warming also impacts other elements of climate, especially precipitation and storm severity. It is predicted that shifting climate belts may intensify droughts in arid regions but bring increased rainfall to others (Figure D54).

Figure D54: Predicted twenty-first century change in global precipitation patterns

Source: Data from the IPCC

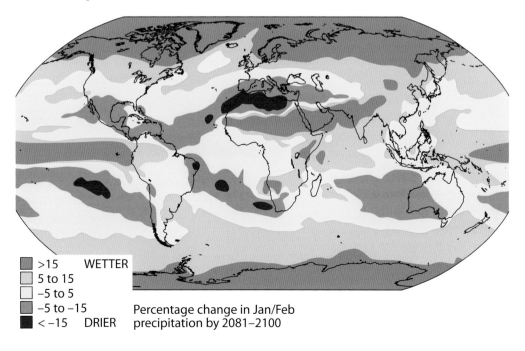

Extreme climate events

A Royal Society report, 'Climate Change: Evidence and Causes, 2014', states, "Attributing extreme climate events to climate change is challenging because these events are by definition rare and therefore hard to evaluate reliably, and are affected by patterns of natural climate variability." The periodic features of El Niño and La Niña, when Pacific Ocean water currents and air flows are modified, produce weather extremes. On land La Niña tends to create drought while El Niño increases precipitation. These are not due to climate change. However, global warming means that energy levels in the lower atmosphere are higher, suggesting that storm winds will be stronger and rainfall totals higher. Weather monitoring in North America and Europe has recorded more extreme conditions, more often in recent decades. One possibility with climate change concerns the concept of a 'tipping point', when change becomes inevitable and irreversible. Scientists estimate that an atmospheric content of carbon dioxide of 450 ppm and/or a global temperature increase greater than 2°C represent environmental tipping points. A visible tipping point would be the loss of the Greenland Ice Sheet or the blocking of the warm North Atlantic Drift Ocean current. These have been suggested as possible events in the coming 80 years.

Sea level change

One natural phenomenon that has already been well-documented is a global or eustatic rise in sea level. Having risen by over 20 cm in the last 130 years, sea level is currently rising at 3 mm a year, due to both thermal expansion and the ablation of land-based ice.

Figure D55: The reduced volume of land-based glaciers and ice sheets, Patagonia

Source: top image ©Archivo Museo Salesiano bottom image: ©Greenpeace/Daniel Beltra

The implications of this process are enormous. Islands and low-lying coastal zones are most vulnerable. Coastal erosion and periodic flooding could impact around 25% of the world's population who live within 100 km of a coast and less than 100 m above sea level. In a world of rising sea levels and increasingly volatile storms, including tropical cyclones, such areas, where tens of millions live, would be at high risk of disaster. In LEDCs such as Thailand, Vietnam and Bangladesh, fertile deltaic land and river floodplains are attractive to subsistence farming and fishing economies (Figure D56). Internationally, the income of over half a billion people depends on fishing. Some scientists suggest overfishing of declining stocks will cause collapse of this industry by 2050. The greatest impact of this will be in LEDCs, where fishing supplies vital protein to almost half of the population. The Sunderbans, a chain of islands along the Ganges coast of India and Bangladesh, are home to most of the endangered Royal Bengal tiger population and they contain the world's largest single mangrove area – a major carbon sink. It is predicted that sea level rise during the twenty-first century will remove both the mangrove vegetation and 96% of the tiger habitat.

MEDCs are also under threat. Both the eastern seaboard of the USA and Great Britain's eastern coast are vulnerable. The economic cost of protecting the present coastline is already regarded as too expensive in the UK and a managed retreat of the coast is its long-term management goal. Today, all forms of flood damage costs the UK around £1 billion a year. This has already been increasing and estimates suggest it could rise to £12 billion by 2080, as a consequence of climate change.

Figure D56: Lowland regions vulnerable to climate change include river floodplains such as that of the Chao Phraya in Bangkok, Thailand

Freshwater supplies

Regions where precipitation may decline, such as the Mediterranean nations of Southern Europe and North Africa or Mexico and the southern USA, will face increased pressure concerning domestic, agricultural and industrial demand. These are also sensitive boundary regions between MEDCs and LEDCs, where the large-scale migration of people, both legal and illegal, is already a major social and economic issue. Even where rainfall is not in decline, rising sea levels may cause saltwater incursions into the fresh groundwater stores making the supplies unsuitable for drinking or irrigation. This problem is already seen along the coasts of Bangladesh and Egypt. In many Middle Eastern nations, water is more expensive than oil. It is also worth noting that even where precipitation levels are predicted to increase, rising temperatures and therefore higher evaporation rates, and growing populations may still mean that the demand for water outstrips the supply available.

Ecosystem impacts

The polar bear adrift on a melting ice flow has become a 'go to' image for the impact of climate change on the polar environment (Figure D57). In the tropics the equivalent headline is the issue of coral bleaching (see page 143). Both these examples present valid current concerns over the loss of habitat and thereby functioning ecosystems. Other potential ecosystem impacts include: stress on tree growth in forests, the extinction of marine species as oceans become more acidic and a reduction in the world's biodiversity. Any habitat change, in this case the abiotic control of weather and climate, will alter the survival potential of species. This means new or exotic species of plant and animal may be able to survive in areas previously beyond their

Figure D57: Loss of sea ice threatens the polar bear, the Arctic's top predator

natural distribution. In turn they may provide a new food supply or alternatively become an additional predator in the ecosystem. Habitat change may of course help farmers; it is estimated that the area of Canada's prairie land climatically suitable for wheat growing could double in the next 50 years. Perhaps the increase of vineyards seen in Southern England in the last 20 years will eventually return commercial grape growing to Yorkshire, as in medieval times. Migration of birds is highly sensitive to habitat change and many species that spend the summer in Ireland and the UK are losing numbers as the timing of food supply with nest building, egg-laying and incubation has altered. Numbers of Pied flycatchers, a bird that winters in West Africa, has now declined by 90% in some European nations. Such changes will cascade through an ecosystem and while some may be positive, most changes will certainly be to the detriment of the natural balance. Added to the direct climate impacts, flooding of rivers and coasts will alter ecosystems such as sand dunes, tropical mangroves and salt marshes. Estimates suggest that within 100 years, 30% of all existing plant and animal species might become extinct: the first global mass extinction directly attributable to human activity (see also 'Development and change in the Arctic tundra biome' *Geography for CCEA AS Level*, Colourpoint Educational, pages 62–73).

Human health

Potentially human health could be impacted in many ways:

- Vectors are living carriers of infection such as insects. The distribution of these will change, for example the malaria and dengue fever mosquito, potentially introducing these tropical conditions into non-tropical regions.

- As farming and food supplies are threatened the risk of malnutrition and similar poverty related illnesses could significantly increase for children and other vulnerable groups.

Figure D58: Potential impact of climate change on human health

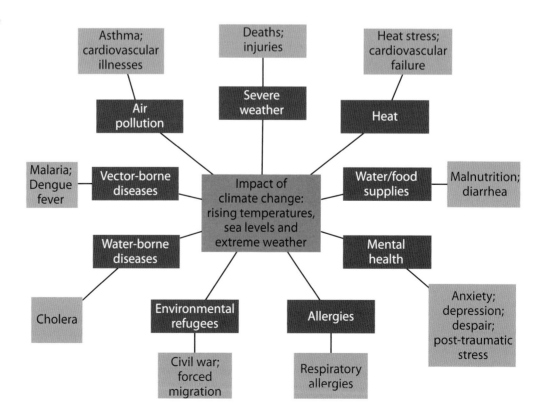

- Extreme events may increase mortality rate, floods, storms, forest fires and heatwaves especially in urban areas. On the other hand, winter mortality rates may decline as hypothermia due to severe cold becomes less common.

Economy

The Stern Review of 2006 (a report commissioned by the UK government) estimated that climate change would reduce world wealth production by 5% of its GDP annually. On the tenth anniversary of his report Stern suggested he had underestimated the impact of climate change on global wealth. Some countries face potential financial disaster (India, Bangladesh and Saudi Arabia) while others might see wealth increase (the UK and Ireland along with most of Western Europe). Food production and tourism are two important areas of the economy that may be positively or negatively impacted by climate change.

Migration and resettlement

The net impact of coastal and floodplain flooding, extreme weather events and long-term climate droughts may well be the redistribution of the population. Tens of millions of Asians and Africans have made their way to more developed nations in Europe and North America. Many more economic migrants, along with millions of environmental refugees, are predicted to leave Africa, Asia, Latin America and the island nations of Oceania to seek a more secure future for themselves and their families.

Figures D59 and D60 illustrate the potential environmental, social and economic impacts of climate change, positive or negative, in African LEDCs and European MEDCs.

Figure D59: Some projected impacts of climate change in Africa during the twenty-first century

North Africa
- Increased aridity producing a shorter growing season will potentially reduce food production across North Africa.
- Water shortages may become a cause of conflict over resource distribution.

East Africa
- Increased rainfall totals are projected in East Africa. Good news for the growing population though also brings an increased flood risk.
- There is a threat of a decline in fish stocks in East African Rift valley lakes.
- Coastal tropical reefs under threat of coral bleaching.

West and Central Africa
- Reduced agricultural productivity could cause a fall in GDP of 4-5% for West African nations.
- Large West African coastal city populations could be severely impacted by sea level rise – including Lagos (Nigeria) and Banjul (The Gambia).
- Loss of coastal ecosystems such as mangroves has negative impacts on the fishing and tourist industries.

Southern Africa
- Malaria transmission zones extend southwards.
- Loss of semi-arid ecosystem in Namibia and species extinction in other ecosystems due to modification of local climates.
- Southern African rainfall becomes less reliable with greater annual variation.
- Food insecurity increases as a consequence of the increased variability of seasonal rains.

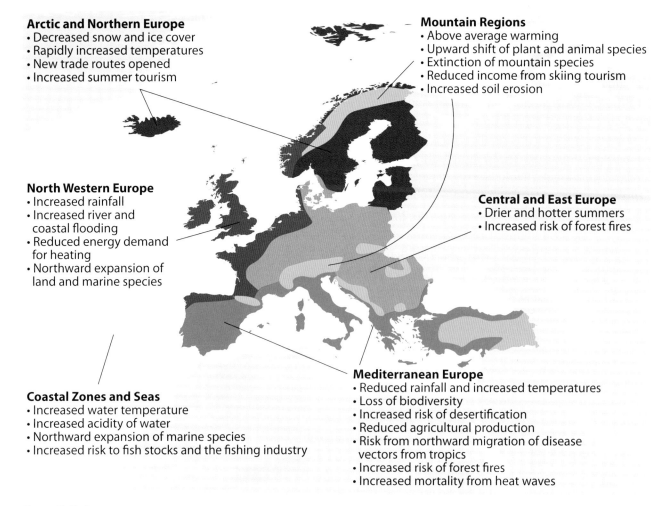

Arctic and Northern Europe
• Decreased snow and ice cover
• Rapidly increased temperatures
• New trade routes opened
• Increased summer tourism

Mountain Regions
• Above average warming
• Upward shift of plant and animal species
• Extinction of mountain species
• Reduced income from skiing tourism
• Increased soil erosion

North Western Europe
• Increased rainfall
• Increased river and coastal flooding
• Reduced energy demand for heating
• Northward expansion of land and marine species

Central and East Europe
• Drier and hotter summers
• Increased risk of forest fires

Coastal Zones and Seas
• Increased water temperature
• Increased acidity of water
• Northward expansion of marine species
• Increased risk to fish stocks and the fishing industry

Mediterranean Europe
• Reduced rainfall and increased temperatures
• Loss of biodiversity
• Increased risk of desertification
• Reduced agricultural production
• Risk from northward migration of disease vectors from tropics
• Increased risk of forest fires
• Increased mortality from heat waves

Figure D60: Some projected impacts of climate change in Europe during the twenty-first century

Exam Questions

1. With reference to places, describe the evidence for the short-term climate change known as global warming. [8]

2. With the aid of a diagram, explain the 'enhanced greenhouse effect'. [8]

3. Study Resource A, which shows the potential impact of climate change in both North and Latin America. Describe the potential environmental and social impacts of different levels of climate change in these MEDC and LEDC regions. [9]

Resource A: The potential impacts of different degrees of global warming
Source: Data from IPCC

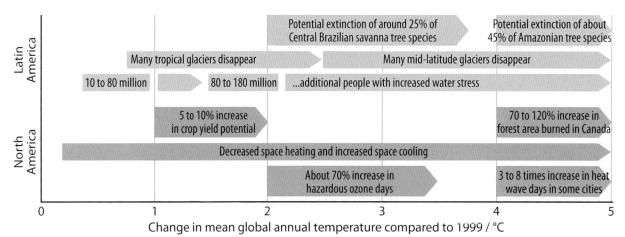

4. With reference to both MEDCs and LEDCs, describe the present and potential impacts of climate change. [18]

References

Geofile:
'The concept of a 'Tipping Point' in climate change', *Geofile* 669, series 31, 2012–2013
'Current global warming realities at extreme latitudes and altitudes', *Geofile* 630, series 29, 2010–2011
'Global warming: hopes and Imperatives', *Geofile* 597, series 27, 2009–2010

Geoactive:
'Recent evidence of a warming world', *Geoactive*, series 20, 2009

GeoFactsheet:
'The Maldives: on the frontline of climate change', *GeoFactsheet,* 296, Curriculum Press
'The impact of climate warming', *Geo Factsheet,* 2017–2018, Curriculum Press

Useful websites:
'Climate Change: Evidence and Causes' – *https://royalsociety.org/~/media/Royal_Society_Content/policy/projects/climate-evidence-causes/climate-change-evidence-causes.pdf*
'Climate changes effects plunder the planet' – *https://www.edf.org/climate/climate-changes-effects-plunder-planet*
'Changing Climate – geography explained fact sheet' – *https://www.rgs.org/NR/rdonlyres/CDC8210C-2BD9-4BC4-AEDB-6C43AA3929AA/0/KS3_Climate_Factsheet.pdf*

4. MANAGING GLOBAL CLIMATE CHANGE

Case studies

General reference to places at an international scale

Students should be able to:

(i) demonstrate knowledge and understanding of attempts to address global climate change through mitigation (carbon capture and reducing greenhouse gas emissions) and adaptation (reducing vulnerability) to global climate change

(ii) evaluate the progress of international action on climate change, including the Kyoto Protocol and the role of the Intergovernmental Panel on Climate Change (IPCC)

Addressing climate change: mitigation and adaptation

The history of human (anthropogenic) impact on climate by air pollution is a story of disaster and response. Large modern cities have suffered the negative impact of pollution on their local atmosphere. Examples include the 'pea-souper' fogs of industrial Victorian London and the toxic brown haze or photochemical smog of Los Angeles. In December 1952 a toxic London smog (a mixture of smoke and fog) caused the death of 1200 residents. Most of these deaths were of elderly people or others with pre-existing respiratory problems. In response to this, the worst peacetime incident in the modern nation's history, a pioneering piece of anti-pollution legislation was drawn up. The Clean Air Act of 1956 started a process that helped clear the atmosphere, not only in London but all the major UK cities, by establishing urban smokeless zones. By 1970, at a wider regional scale including Western Europe, reports of dead lakes, dying forests and human illness were linked with increased acidity of the environment associated with acid rainfall. Some people suggested this was due to the increasing release of sulphur dioxide (SO_2) gas from burning fossil fuels in power stations. Eventually, scientific research proved this link and filters were fitted to power station chimneys and flues for the extraction of SO_2 at source. In some regions at least this proved effective.

Air pollution, first seen as a local, urban issue grew to the national or regional level and finally reached global scale in the 1980s. The British Antarctic Survey (BAS) reported a significant change in the chemistry of the Earth's higher atmosphere. The natural concentration of ozone (O_3) at the tropopause (the upper boundary of the layer above the Earth's surface) was missing over part of the Antarctic (and also in the Arctic). The so-called hole in the ozone layer was important because the presence of ozone at that level prevents life threatening UV (ultraviolet) radiation from the Sun reaching the Earth's surface. The cause of the damage was identified as a group of recently developed artificial chemicals known as chlorofluorocarbons (CFCs). Ironically these CFCs were developed to replace other dangerous gases used as propellants in aerosols and in fridges and freezers. Within a short period of time, an international agreement banning the production and use of these gases, the 1987 Montreal Protocol, was agreed. This action addressed the global ozone issue and the problem, if not resolved, is now improving. This short history of the response to air pollution reveals two key lessons:

1. Air pollution due to human activity has negative impacts on atmospheric conditions and therefore weather and climate at the local, regional and worldwide scales.

2. Management can reduce the impact and potentially solve the problem at each of these scales if legislation is used and commitment given.

The management technique employed in these cases is known as mitigation. Mitigation means tackling the underlying cause of the issue: smoke and hydrocarbons for smog and photochemical smog; sulphur dioxide from power plants for acid rain; and CFCs in the case of ozone. Similarly, the task of tackling climate change will involve mitigation – reducing the emissions of greenhouse gases (GHG) – and also adaptation – dealing in the short-term with the current and future consequences of climate change. Adaptation means adjusting lifestyles and behaviour to cope with warmer and drier, or in some places wetter, conditions.

Mitigation technologies

Mitigation: An Anthropogenic intervention to reduce the sources or enhance the sinks of greenhouse gases.

Source: 'IPCC Third Assessment Report: Climate Change 2001 (TAR)', Working Group III: Mitigation, Glossary, page 716

The current position is that the atmosphere has already warmed by 0.9°C since 1900 and that unprecedented and hazardous impacts will follow unless warming is limited to only 2°C. The projected warming by 2100 is around 4°C.

There are two types of mitigation strategy:

1. Reduce the release of GHG.

   - Reduce the use of fossil fuels for energy generation by increasing efficiency or switching to renewable sources.
   - Reduce land clearance and deforestation.
   - Change agricultural practice and waste disposal (landfill) to reduce methane production.

2. Remove GHG from the atmosphere.

   - Store carbon dioxide in carbon sinks – increase afforestation.
   - Collect gases at the release point – traps on landfill sites and filters on flues.
   - Sequestration – capture and store GHG by engineering methods.

Figure D61: Average emissions of CO_2 for different energy sources

Source of energy	Rate of CO_2 production (grams per kilowatt hour)
Coal	950
Oil	900
Gas	600
Nuclear	3–5
Renewables (average)	11

The scale of the problem requires a global intervention effort. The latest is the Paris Agreement, ratified in spring 2016. All 195 United Nations countries agreed to seek to reduce their GHG emissions. Emissions would be externally reviewed every five years and the developed nations (MEDCs) would create a fund to help less developed nations (LEDCs) move directly to the use of renewable energy sources as they grow and develop, and so avoid the use of polluting fossil fuels. Figure D61 shows how switching fuel sources for power generation can radically reduce the CO_2 output.

In the UK the annual release of CO_2 between 1990 and 2015 fell from 900 million tonnes to 500 million tonnes. Most of this reduction was the result of switching from coal to gas fuelled electrical power stations as well as increased efficiency in the use of fossil fuels in the transport sector. The controversial development of the new Hinkley Point nuclear power plant in England is part of the plan for the reduced dependency on fossil fuels. Encouragingly, on a bright late May day in 2017 the UK managed to produce a power output equal to its daily demand for electricity from its renewable wind and solar farms. Normally the proportion was closer to 15%.

By 2030 India will be the world's largest country by population, with around 1.4 billion people. The Indian government plans to reduce its use of polluting energy fuels by developing renewable sources. Currently only 8% comes from renewables, mainly wind power, but India's tropical location means it receives abundant solar energy, on average 3000 hours of sunlight a year. Theoretically this could meet the total national energy demand for 2030 but the cost of imported silicon for making solar cell panels is still too high. However, on the ground solar charged lights are being widely used to extend daylight and business hours for workers. India has also adopted measures to mitigate climate change through storing GHG. In the Himalayan foothills of Uttarakhand state in North India, large areas of forest degraded by clearance for agriculture have been reforested. This newly afforested land is now expected to capture and store, through photosynthesis, the equivalent of 200,000 tonnes of CO_2 over the next 30 years.

Figure D62: Renewable energy systems

Pioneering tidal power renewable energy technology, Strangford Lough

Danish company Dong assembles wind turbines in Belfast Harbour for off-shore wind farms

Meanwhile the Scottish devolved administration has set targets for GHG reduction of 42% by 2020 and 80% by 2050. They also aim to generate, from renewable sources, the equivalent to all their electricity needs in 2020 and 11% of their heating needs by that date. Scotland has significant potential for renewable energy production from HEP,

Figure D63: How Carbon Capture and Storage (CCS) works
Source: IPCC

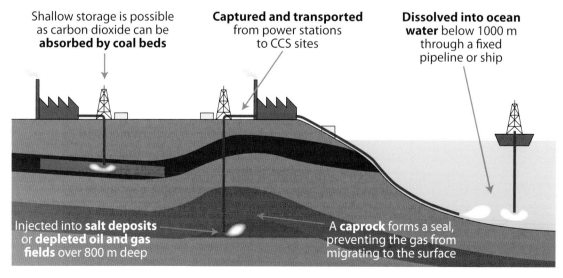

Shallow storage is possible as carbon dioxide can be **absorbed by coal beds**

Captured and transported from power stations to CCS sites

Dissolved into ocean water below 1000 m through a fixed pipeline or ship

Injected into **salt deposits** or **depleted oil and gas fields** over 800 m deep

A **caprock** forms a seal, preventing the gas from migrating to the surface wind and wave/tidal technologies. Carbon Capture and Storage (CCS) by engineering involves recovering CO_2 from power station chimneys and storing it, usually underground in depleted oil, gas or coal fields. Sequestration is similar although it involves extracting CO_2 directly from the atmosphere before storage. Currently there are examples of carbon storage taking place in Norway, Canada and the USA.

Figure D64: Mitigation technologies by sector

Sector	Available mitigation technologies and practice
Energy supply	• Renewable energy sources – hydropower, wind, solar, biomass, geothermal • Switch of fuel source from coal to gas • Nuclear power • Carbon Capture from natural gas
Transport	• More fuel efficient engines • Biofuels • Electric and hybrid vehicles – battery development • Switch to mass public transport systems
Buildings	• Increased efficiency for lighting and heating/cooling systems • Intelligent metering of energy use • Solar photo-voltaic panels integrated in buildings
Industry	• Heat and fuel recovery systems • Recycling of materials
Agriculture	• Livestock and manure management to reduce methane emissions • Improved use of nitrogen based fertilisers • Biomass energy crops grown to replace fossil fuel use • Soil management to increase carbon storage
Forests and forestry	• Reduced deforestation rates • Afforestation and reforestation to increase carbon storage in biomass • Biomass energy sources to replace fossil fuel use
Waste management	• Recovery of methane from landfill sites • Energy recovery from waste incineration • Recycling and waste minimisation policies

Adaptation strategies

> **Adaptation:** Adjustment in natural or human systems in response to actual or expected climatic *stimuli* or their effects, which moderates harm or exploits beneficial opportunities.
>
> Source: 'IPCC Third Assessment Report: Climate Change 2001 (TAR)', Working Group II: Impacts, Adaptation and Vulnerability, Glossary page 982

These adaptations will be local in scale, addressing issues as they arise including water supply, building design, agriculture, coastal flooding and drought.

In a 2013 UK report on adapting to climate change, five areas were identified: agriculture and forestry; business, industries and services; health and well-being; natural environment; and buildings and infrastructure. This alone shows the broad impact that global warming is projected to have on our collective future. The UK strategy was reviewed in 2017 and will be every five years while the European Union's Adaptation Strategy is evaluated in 2018. Government at every level and all public and private organisations are considering how to modify and adapt to the impact that climate change has brought and will continue to bring in the twenty-first century.

Inevitably, the focus of adaptation is on dealing with the problems brought by climate change but, as the definition above states, it will also provide 'beneficial opportunities' for those who can adapt to take them.

There are many approaches to adaptation. For example, if the issue is reduced rainfall and therefore a potential water shortage for agriculture, then potential approaches would be to:

- Share the cost – government provides financial aid for farmers.
- Prevent the problem – by developing drip-irrigation and reducing the water demand.
- Research technological solutions – such as developing drought tolerant crops.
- Educate people – in water conservation techniques.
- Abandon the area – for a less marginal location, if available.

Figure D65: Adaptation strategies, policies and outcomes

Sector	Adaptation strategies	Policy	Issues* and opportunities * Issues are in *italics*
Water: Shortage and drought	• Rainwater collection and storage • Conservation education • Water reuse • Desalinisation	• National integrated water resource management	• *Investment cost* • Integrated and efficient water use
Agriculture	• Change planting dates • Change crop variety • Improve control of soil erosion	• Plant research • Land tenure reform and subsidies	• *Cost and technical barriers* • Longer growing season • Income from new crop varieties
Infrastructure and settlement: Flood risk to settlement, farmland and coasts	• Construction of seawalls, storm surge barriers • Dune reinforcement • Creation of marshlands or wetlands as buffers against sea level rise and flooding	• Building codes – design with future climate change impacts in mind • Land use policies • Insurance	• *Cost and technical barriers* • *Availability of relocation space* • Integrated policies and management • Sustainable development goals

Human health: Heat stroke, new disease vectors and polluted water	• Action plans dealing with heat issues • Disease monitoring and control • Safe water and improved sanitation	• Public health recognise climate risks • Regional and international cooperation	• *Risks to vulnerable groups* • Improved health service • Improved life quality
Tourism: Seasonal change, drought and reduced snowfall	• Diversify attractions • Ski slopes on higher mountains or glaciers • Artificial snow-making	• Integrated planning and incentives	• *Cost and promotion of the new attractions* • Revenue from new attractions
Transport: Warmer, drier or wetter conditions for roads and rail	• New design standards for transport routes	• National transport policy that integrates climate change	• *Cost and technical barriers* • Improved integration of transport system
Energy: Damage to overhead power lines, storms and underground drought	• Strengthen overhead and underground cabling for utilities • Use renewable energy • Reduce dependence on single energy sources	• National energy policy that incorporates climate change in design standards	• *Access to viable alternatives* • *Cost and technical barriers* • *Acceptance of new technologies* • Stimulation of new technologies • Use of local resources

Global examples of adaptation initiatives

Faced with the threat of drought, the East African nation of Sudan has proposed a series of strategies including existing and new technologies. Traditional methods of rainwater gathering and conservation are to be expanded, along with the planting of shelter belts and wind-breaks to reduce the erosion of top soil as it dries out. The density of animals grazing land and the rate of deforestation are to be carefully monitored to avoid land degrading or desertification.

The Canadian government has addressed, among other issues, the potential melting of permafrost in its Arctic territory and the risk of extremely high temperature events (heat health alerts) in its southern cities. Inuit hunting practices will need to change, including permission to hunt a broader range of species. In Toronto during heat health alerts, designated 'cooling centres' will open at public locations to distribute bottled water and advice. These will have trained medical staff and an emergency service vehicle. Fears of widespread drought have prompted the Mexican government to encourage farmers to change their traditional crop planting dates and to include drought-resistant species such as aloe and agave in their crop rotations.

In Europe, concern over the economically vital winter ski tourist industry in parts of Austria and Switzerland has led to research into adaptation strategies. The building of new ski lifts and tows into the higher Alps to access more reliable snow and glacier skiing works alongside the production of artificial snow on carefully groomed slopes. In places, glaciers have been covered in white plastic to reduce rates of melting. As the winter ski season gets shorter, a longer term approach is to diversify the nature of tourism in these regions to make the resorts year round tourist destinations. In the UK, the decision has been taken, initially by DEFRA (Department for Environment, Food and Rural Affairs), to reduce the amount of coastline protected from erosion.

In recognition of rising sea levels and increased storm strength, it has been recognised that the 'hold the line' policy (see page 149) is in many places practically, economically and environmentally unsustainable.

SIDS (Small Island Developing States) is the group of over 50 nations in the Pacific and Indian Oceans. As islands they are particularly at risk from rising sea levels and in many cases they are already suffering from this outcome of climate change. Tuvalu, in a remote part of the Pacific, is typical of these states. Small but densely populated by just 10,000 people, it relies on farming, fishing and foreign aid. Tuvalu's nine islands are all less than 5 m above sea level. High tide flooding and severe storms have increased the rate of coastal erosion and caused the incursion of salt water into the groundwater stores. This in turn has reduced the yield of pulaka, a tuberous plant and the islander's staple crop. Adaptation strategies have been put in place since 2000 when Tuvalu joined the United Nations in an attempt to encourage the world to introduce mitigation strategies. Salt-tolerant plants have been introduced to improve the food supply and removal of sand or coral from beaches has been banned. Many Tuvaluans are leaving the islands and migrating to New Zealand, some under the (as yet unrecognised) status of 'environmental refugees'.

International action on climate change

The first indication that the global community was addressing climate change issues emerged at the 1992 United Nations Earth Summit in Rio de Janeiro. The 'United Nations Framework Convention on Climate Change (UNFCCC)' was signed by 160 nations. Among a number of agreed principles were four that addressed international action:

1. *The Precautionary Principle* – this is the concept that remedial action is taken now even if the severity of climate change is not yet known.
2. *The Principle of Sustainable Development* – present development should not put at risk future development and progress.
3. *The Polluter Pays Principle* – the people or nations responsible for causing climate change should be the ones that pay the costs and fund the search for the solution.
4. *The Principle of Equity* – all nations have a right to develop sustainably and all should work to reduce global poverty and disparity.

Following these principles the first international agreement was drawn up after a UN conference in the Japanese city of Kyoto in 1997. Known as the Kyoto Protocol it made clear proposals for a worldwide effort to address the threat of climate change:

- Wealthier nations agree to reduce Greenhouse Gas (GHG) emissions by 6–12% by 2012.
- All countries had a quota of gases, for MEDCs this was a reduction as they caused the issue.
- Quotas for LEDCs were higher than their current output: to allow for their development of industry, power production etc.
- Countries would work together, with MEDCs helping LEDCs develop sustainable energy sources, such as wind or solar power.
- A controversial idea was Emissions or Carbon Trading: any unused emissions quotas, most likely in an LEDC, could be bought by MEDCs allowing them to increase their own quota of GHG emissions.

While most MEDCs signed and ratified the agreement, the USA, then the largest producer of greenhouse gases, did not.

Progress on the Kyoto Protocol

In 2009, at the UN climate summit in Copenhagen many said Kyoto was a failure because global emissions continued to grow. However, there are a number of positive elements that can be identified even as the world moves to replace Kyoto with a new up-dated version and agenda.

- Kyoto, though not the first, was a rare international agreement.
- The EU and Japan did meet their reduction targets (Figure D66). Even the USA while not active in the Kyoto Protocol has seen reduced emissions, largely thanks to a switch from coal to shale gas.
- One mechanism of Kyoto was the transfer of funding from MEDCs to LEDCs to help them cut carbon output through windfarms and solar power. By 2010 over $200 billion was raised for such development in the world's poorer nations.
- The key to the successful progress in the EU was a scheme (called the ETS – Emissions Trading System scheme, see below) using carbon trading.

The ETS scheme has 31 member nations and targets emissions from 11,000 sites, power stations and industrial plants, and also the airlines that operate between the countries. A total emissions cap is imposed, and lowered over time to ensure total emissions will fall. Each business is awarded an emissions allowance and they can also buy spare allowances from one another. If the company reduces emissions it can keep or sell their spare allowances on to another company. If its emissions are greater than its target allowance heavy fines are imposed. The EU ETS is a success story; it is the world's largest international emissions trading system and it controls three-quarters of the global carbon trading market. A further phase of this system runs from 2013–2020 and aims to reduce EU emissions by 21% compared to 2005.

Figure D66: Kyoto success or failure?

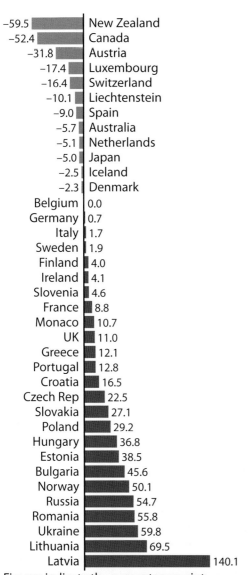

–59.5	New Zealand
–52.4	Canada
–31.8	Austria
–17.4	Luxembourg
–16.4	Switzerland
–10.1	Liechtenstein
–9.0	Spain
–5.7	Australia
–5.1	Netherlands
–5.0	Japan
–2.5	Iceland
–2.3	Denmark
Belgium	0.0
Germany	0.7
Italy	1.7
Sweden	1.9
Finland	4.0
Ireland	4.1
Slovenia	4.6
France	8.8
Monaco	10.7
UK	11.0
Greece	12.1
Portugal	12.8
Croatia	16.5
Czech Rep	22.5
Slovakia	27.1
Poland	29.2
Hungary	36.8
Estonia	38.5
Bulgaria	45.6
Norway	50.1
Russia	54.7
Romania	55.8
Ukraine	59.8
Lithuania	69.5
Latvia	140.1

Figures indicate the percentage point difference between the target percentage reduction and actual percentage reduction by 2012, relative to 1990.

The first commitment period under Kyoto 1997 involved countries reducing their carbon emissions to their lower levels of 1990 and achieving this by 2008–2012. The graph shows the degree to which nations achieved or failed to achieve their target by 2012. *Kyoto successes are shown in purple, with the failures in orange.*

The role of the Intergovernmental Panel on Climate Change (IPCC)

The IPCC is an intergovernmental scientific body of the United Nations. It was set up in 1988 and tasked to provide the world with an objective, scientific view of climate change and its political and economic impacts. The IPCC produces reports for the United Nations Framework Convention on Climate Change, whose aim is to "stabilize greenhouse gas concentrations in the atmosphere at a level that would prevent dangerous anthropogenic (human-induced) interference with the climate system". The first five IPCC reports were published between 1990 and 2014, each one increasing the range of data published and asserting more anxiously the threat posed by climate change. IPCC reports are based on published literature, with thousands of experts voluntarily contributing by writing and reviewing them. The 46th session of the IPCC took place in Montreal in September 2017 and the 6th IPCC report will be published in 2022, when a global review will assess the progress made towards the current goal of keeping global warming to well below 2°C.

The Paris Agreement or the International Climate Change Agreement (ICCA)

After a decade of talks, a new international agreement was signed in 2015 in Paris. It came into action in November 2016, ratified by 195 countries including all the key contributing nations. The general secretary of the UN at the time, Ban Ki-moon, cautioned that there was, "…no plan B because there is no planet B". The key elements of the agreement are:

- Setting the goal of limiting global temperature increase to well below 2°C, while urging a limit of 1.5°C.
- Binding commitments by all parties to make "Nationally Determined Contributions" (NDCs), and to pursue domestic measures aimed at achieving them.
- All countries to report regularly the progress made in achieving their NDCs and these are to be reviewed internationally (stocktaking).
- All countries to submit new NDCs every 5 years, and these will "represent progression" from previous ones (ratcheting).
- Reaffirm the binding obligations of developed countries (MEDCS) under the UNFCCC to support the efforts of LEDCs, now also encouraging voluntary contributions by LEDCs too.
- Extend the goal to release $100 billion a year by 2020–2025, with a new, higher goal to be set after 2025.
- A call for a new mechanism, like the 'Emissions/Carbon Trading' of the Kyoto Protocol, enabling emission reductions in one country to be counted toward another country's NDC.

Information adapted from 'Paris Agreement', UNFCCC, https://unfccc.int/files/meetings/paris_nov_2015/application/pdf/paris_agreement_english_.pdf

The agreement does not neglect the need for adaptation measures, encouraging the need to avoid and minimise losses and damage by climate change. International cooperation on early warning systems, integrated emergency services and risk insurance are all promoted.

The concepts of 'stocktaking' and 'ratcheting' as outlined above are the route by which countries continuously reduce their emissions in a progressive and meaningful way.

The first stocktake is proposed for 2023/24 and every 5 years thereafter. The setting of new, lower and more ambitious targets may be every 5 or 10 years. The agreement does not impose targets but rather individual nations (by ratifying the agreement) will set their own targets for emissions on the principle that these will be lowering over time.

Criticism of the ICCA agreement

Many scientists and politicians believe the voluntary basis of the ICCA agreement is a serious weakness. There are no fines imposed on nations that do not meet their own determined emissions targets. Will the planet's leading polluting nations (China, USA, Indonesia, Australia and the BRIC countries), who together produce most of the world's GHG emissions, self-regulate their self-determined targets? This remains to be seen.

Within eight months of the agreement coming into force, the USA (under a newly elected American president and self-proclaimed climate change sceptic Donald J Trump) has withdrawn support for the process.

Figure D67: The position of the global warming sceptic

- **The atmosphere isn't warming**
  and if it is then
- **it is probably due to natural variation**
  and if it is not due to natural variation, then
- **the amount of warming is insignificant**
  and if it becomes significant, then
- **the benefits will outweigh the problems**
  and even if they don't
- **technology will come to the rescue**
  and even if it doesn't…

Conclusion

We should not destroy the economy to fix the problem when many parts of the science are uncertain.

Despite the scientific evidence, both for global warming and that atmospheric pollution from human activity is a significant contributor to this warming process, some people, including decision makers, are sceptical about making changes. Figure D67 outlines some of the debate over recent decades.

The conclusion in Figure D67 ignores the Precautionary Principle, discussed earlier (page 212), that the sooner action is taken – both in mitigation and adaptation – the greater the chance of avoiding the negative impacts of climate changes.

In addition, most of the changes proposed to address climate change are in themselves more sustainable in the long-term and so will benefit people, the economy and the environment.

Finally, the argument for curtailing or not curtailing economic development in the face of climate change seems a simple one at first. But it is neither realistic nor practical. It is the nature of future development that is most significant. The development of non-polluting energy sources – firstly, to reduce the emission of GHG using mitigation technologies and secondly, to adapt our behaviour to the changes – is critical. In short, what is needed is sustainable development in both LEDCs and MEDCs including the development and use of low-carbon, non-polluting technologies for transport and energy generation.

Exam Questions

1. With respect to climate change:

    (i) Define what is meant by mitigation and adaptation strategies.

    (ii) Describe examples of both strategies with reference to places at an international scale. [18]

2. Explain the role of the following in managing global climate change:

    - Kyoto Protocol and
    - Intergovernmental Panel on Climate Change (IPCC) [8]

3. Study Resource A, which describes changes in the McDonald's fast food business. Using the resource to help you, explain how mitigation strategies can be employed **both** to reduce greenhouse gas emissions **and also** remove them from the atmosphere. [18]

Resource A: McDonald's Goes Green

The fast food chain McDonald's has developed a 'greener' version of its food outlets. Initially opened in Chicago in 2008, a number of these outlets are now found in Canada, France, Germany and Brazil. Regionally, used cooking oil is recycled to make a bio-fuel for the company's delivery vans. The buildings are energy saving in design. Roof skylights are used to provide more natural light and gutters drain rainwater into storage barrels. Inside all cardboard and suitable plastic waste is sent for recycling and LED lighting for signage reduces electricity costs. Some of the internal furniture is made from recycled waste including table tops made from old milk cartons. The saving in terms of utility costs is around 25% compared to traditional restaurants. Globally, with over 35,000 outlets, the company could make huge savings if all were to follow the 'green route'.

Even the McDonald's products have potential, with food waste being used as fuel in Sheffield or as potential compost for local farms in rural Dorset.

References

Geofile:
'Responses to climate change', *Geofile* 700, series 32, 2013–2014

Geoactive:
'Climate change – adaptation and mitigation' *GeoActive,* series 28, 2017

Geo Factsheet:
'Managing short-term climate change – a post Kyoto update', *Geo Factsheet* 177, Curriculum Press
'Global warming mitigation Pt1 – Dealing with energy emissions', *Geo Factsheet* 241, Curriculum Press
'Global warming mitigation Pt2 –Removing carbon from the atmosphere', *Geo Factsheet* 244, Curriculum Press

National Geographic Magazine:
'Cool it: The Climate issue', *National Geographic Magazine,* November 2015

Unit A2 2:
Processes and Issues in Human Geography

1. CULTURAL GEOGRAPHY

Case studies

General reference to places for illustration purposes only

Students should be able to:

(i) understand and explain:
- why cultural groups exist
- the differences between cultural groups
- the expression of cultural nationalism

(ii) understand and explain social inequalities (social exclusion and discrimination) in relation to ethnicity, gender, race, religion, sexuality and social class

(iii) understand and explain social constructions of nature and landscape – landscapes as human systems, natural and cultural landscapes

The word 'culture' is often associated with going to the theatre or opera, listening to classical music and reading great works of literature, the activities of somebody who is 'cultured'. However, the word can be applied to any shared sets of meanings, values and activities. It is a particular way of life. It is how a person behaves, what they do (known as practice) as a member of a group. Culture incorporates language, religion and beliefs; it is affected by gender, age, ethnicity and race, religion, sexuality and social class, all of which impact on practice. A firm will have its corporate culture; there is gang culture and teenage culture. There is popular culture, often linked to music, television and other entertainment; material culture, which considers possessions and buildings; there is agriculture. Culture varies over space and time, and different aspects of culture overlap. A person might belong to more than one cultural group, combining to make up their own particular identity. Geography provides the setting and the space where cultural practices take place. This can be physical space, at scales from the national to the individual and increasingly practices are expressed over virtual space. There is a Facebook culture (how a person operates and behaves on Facebook) amongst its two billion monthly users, whilst Facebook itself has changed other aspects of culture.

Cultural groups

Culture is readily apparent at the national scale. Consider Japan. Few other nations are as culturally distinct or racially homogenous, owing to its geographical isolation as an island nation being reinforced by *sakoku*, when Japan cut itself off from the outside world. From the 1630s until the 1860s foreigners were forbidden to enter and nationals were not allowed to leave. In Japan almost everyone is of Japanese ethnicity and speaks Japanese,

Figure A1: A room in a traditional Japanese apartment

Figure A2: A Japanese wedding

Figure A3: Sumo wrestling in Japan

Note the traditional dress worn by the referee

which has its own script. Behaviour is distinct from that of Europeans, being more formal and constrained. Public displays of affection are unusual; handshakes are rare. Instead people bow at each other in ways that denote respect and consciousness of a social hierarchy. Shop assistants bow to customers; ATM screens display cartoon figures, which bow as the customer takes the money. The use of first names is restricted; people of both genders are given the honorific -san after their family name. Colleagues of Sota Yamamoto would call him Yamamoto-san. Japanese rarely visit each other's houses, instead they go out for meals. In the restaurant they usually sit on the floor at low tables, perhaps with a foot well. Food is communal and is eaten with chopsticks. The bill is divided equally amongst the guests. If the party is male or mixed, the youngest man is presented with the bill and has to collect the cash from his fellow-diners. Traditional housing units are small, with sliding paper doors and tatami mats on the floor. There is little furniture except low tables. There might not be chairs and there are no beds; people sleep on futons (thin mattresses) on the floor. People also sit and eat on the floor. Traditional toilets do not have seats. In Figure A1 the futons were in the cupboard, clean futon covers in the bag.

Colonialisation, migration and globalisation have eroded the distinctiveness of national cultures. Now even Japan has a hybrid culture, mixing elements from local and outside. Traditional Japanese costumes (kimonos and yukatas) are now largely reserved for formal occasions such as weddings (Figure A2). Most Japanese hotels have western style rooms; fewer Japanese live their lives on the floor than in the past; seated toilets are now widespread. Japanese sport has become more global, baseball is popular, but traditional pastimes remain, especially sumo wrestling, which, with its strict rules of etiquette and dress, is quintessentially Japanese (Figure A3).

Globalisation has witnessed the spread of American-origin food outlets such as McDonalds, KFC and Starbucks. This process has been called 'Coca-Colonisation' or 'McDonaldisation'. It has affected national cultures (Figure A4), but there are local variations. For example, Big Macs in India do not contain beef, because some groups would object to this, but chicken: the Chicken Maharaja Mac.

Isolation provides conditions in which distinct cultural attributes including language can develop, although not all countries have their own language. Colonialism may have imposed an imported language, such as English and French on North America. In other places no one language became dominant – Switzerland has four national languages: German, Italian, French and Romansch. Arabic is the official language of 28 states in North Africa and the Middle East. By contrast New Guinea has over 850 distinct languages, which developed largely in isolation from each other given the island's

Figure A4: A McDonald's restaurant in Tokyo. The only concession to the locality is the price in Yen (¥)

rugged terrain. Language is a cultural marker and reflects local needs and conditions. Famously, languages spoken in the Arctic can describe many different types of snow.

Religion is an important aspect of culture, dictating practices from frequency and type of worship through to perhaps food preparation and attitudes towards contraception. There are many different religions with numbers of followers ranging from handfuls to three with over a billion: Christianity, Islam and Hinduism (though each is divided into sub-groups). The history and geography of religious development and conversions is related to colonialism, which was associated with the spread of Christianity especially. More recently, international migration has helped to spread other religions. In England and Wales, at the 2011 census 59.3% identified themselves as Christian, with Muslims at 4.8%, then Hindus at 1.5%, these latter two groups associated with post-World War II migration from Asia.

Often countries have a national religion or an established church. There may also be cultural regions within a country with distinct religious adherence. Utah in the USA is dominated by Mormons and Bali is Hindu within the otherwise Muslim nation of Indonesia. Many disputes and wars have been ascribed to religious disagreements, although often religious labels are just convenient shorthand for wider issues.

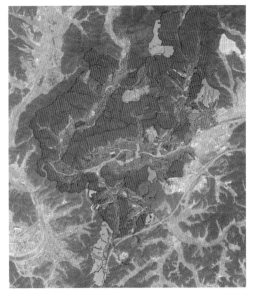

Figure A5: Landholdings in Darsil village, Korea, 1910s. All the holdings shaded in red were owned by people whose surname was Kwon. Many of the other plots were occupied by Kwon relatives, if with different surnames.

Source: Wonseob Song (2017) 'Localised Modernities: Modernization, Genealogy and Landscape Change in South Korea', Unpublished PhD thesis Queen's University Belfast

At a smaller scale than national cultures are sub-groups based on matters such as shared interests, gender, age or kinship. Kinship might be expressed through extended families, such as in Scottish clans. In Korea there are some 'surname villages' where most people have the same surname, as they share descent from common ancestors. For example, a village called Darsil is occupied by people called Kwon (Figure A5). Kinship gives such villages social stability, thus traditionally there were fewer disputes over access to water in surname villages than others. Indigenous tribes might be seen as extended kinship groups, with shared collective loyalty.

Gangs can duplicate some elements of kinship and family groups, particularly the sense of belonging and the shared identity. The following lyrics from the Jets' song in the musical *West Side Story*, which is about gangs, show this:

"You're never alone,
You're never disconnected!"

Culture is associated with gender, since boys and girls tend to behave differently. Gender differences can become formal, for example in the coming of age ceremonies for Jewish children: *bar mitzvah* for boys and *bat mitzvah* for girls. Age is also important, thus young people listen to 'their' music, which differentiates their culture from that of their parents' generation. In the connected world, youth culture may spread beyond national boundaries. A young person may have more in common, in some ways, with people of their own age from another continent who share a liking for a particular type of music than with co-nationals of a different generation. Globalisation spreads the message and images of popular culture round the world.

Exercise

1. Identify two aspects of the cultural group to which you belong and show how these are expressed in behaviour and in space.

Cultural nationalism

Figure A6: Saint-Pierre et Miquelon comprises small islands off Newfoundland, Canada

'Terre de France' (Land of France)

Saint-Pierre island

'Nationalism' is a word with unsavoury associations; the Nazis were nationalists in Germany in the 1930s and 1940s, adopting Aryan racial purity at tragic cost to Germans of a different heritage. 'Cultural nationalism' is more benign, describing a nation celebrating its shared culture, history and experiences. France is diverse ethnically but celebrates being French, rejoicing in, and being protective of, its language and culture. It has tried for decades to protect itself against the Americanisation of its language, food and entertainment. France still has island possessions round the world. These are officially an integral part of France in a way that Britain's remaining colonies are not considered part of the UK (Figure A6). Islamists also strive to protect the purity and centrality of Islamic precepts, although this has been associated with violence in the Middle East, Iraq, Syria etc (see 'Cultural conflicts', pages 343–344).

Countries and unions that do not share culture amongst their populations struggle to celebrate cultural nationalism. Consider two European countries that have broken up since the end of the Cold War. They were artificial creations within a boundary proposed by outside powers. Czechoslovakia was created in 1918 from two places with their own distinct – though related – languages and cultures. They separated in 1993 into the Czech Republic and Slovakia following the end of the Cold War. Yugoslavia was similar, political ties that had held it together since 1918 proved to be weaker than the cultural differences which pulled it apart. Yugoslavia broke up into seven states between 1991 and 2008, a process that saw much bloodshed (see 'Nationality', page 317).

Belgium is split into distinct language regions. In the north people speak Flemish, a form of Dutch, whilst to the south in Wallonia they speak French. There is a small German-speaking district in the east. Belgium often seems to be on the brink of breaking up, given its lack of shared culture and it is joked that the only functional national institutions are its monarchy and football team. Perhaps that is why Belgium threw itself enthusiastically into a larger political grouping, the European Union. The EU itself has struggled to find a shared cultural identity – hardly surprising since Europe's history saw its nations often at war.

Figure A7: A llama in Santiago

Cultural nationalism celebrates what is special to its citizens, so in Santiago, the capital of Chile, a man can wander the streets leading a llama, an animal indigenous to South America (Figure A7). Cultural nationalism is in national holidays, national museums and galleries, and in certain events. The Last Night of the Proms concert energises many English people with the singing of the patriotic *Land of Hope and Glory* amidst much flag waving. The Edinburgh Tattoo festival, with its skirl of bagpipes, would be a Scottish equivalent. Ireland has St Patrick's Day, with the accompanying celebrations. There might be a coming together of citizens during international sports tournaments, if less so during the Eurovision Song Contest. Cultural nationalism can be deepened by an event. When President Nelson Mandela presented the trophy to

Figure A8: Dignitaries arrive for the opening of the new parliament in Malta, 4 May 2015

the victorious South African captain at the 1995 Rugby World Cup he wore a Springboks jersey. Rugby had been the sport of the white elite during Apartheid; by wearing the South African shirt, Mandela made it a sport for all, helping to bring the country closer together.

Cultural nationalism has a physical presence, too. It is in the national parliaments, so the new parliamentary building of Malta was opened in Valletta in 2015 with an elaborate ceremony (Figure A8). It is the preservation of historic buildings and landscapes; it is in the work of the UK's National Trust and Ireland's An Taisce. There are war memorials; England has the National Memorial Arboretum as the centre of remembrance with 300 separate memorials (Figure A9).

Figure A9: The National Memorial Arboretum, England

Individual people, national heroes, are remembered, too. Every country has statues, sometimes of people well-known internationally who came from that country; sometimes they commemorate people famous only within the state – cultural nationalism relates to a nation after all (Figure A10).

Kagoshima, Japan: Ōkubo Toshimichi	Valletta, Malta: Jean Parisot de Valette	Bastia, Corsica, France: Napoleon Bonaparte	Cape Town, South Africa: Nelson Mandela	Vilnius, Lithuania: Tzemakh (Zemach) Shabad

Dublin, Ireland: James Joyce

Exercise

1. Select three (or more) of the statues shown in Figure A10, including at least one person not known to you.

    (a) State (or find out) why each person deserved to be memorialised.

    (b) What does this tell you about cultural nationalism?

2. What makes places and people culturally distinct?

Figure A10: Heroes and other people's heroes

Social inequalities, exclusion and discrimination

Social inequality occurs in a situation where goods, resources, perhaps even respect, are distributed unequally, usually because of discrimination against the 'Other', a group perceived as fundamentally different and by implication inferior. During *sakoku*, the period of exclusion in Japan, non-Japanese people were regarded as foreign barbarians – they were the 'Other' to the Japanese. Ethnicity, gender, race, religion, sexuality and social class are all factors in discrimination. Discrimination is the process of treating people differently, not because of their individual qualities but because they are members of a particular group. Discrimination can be positive but is more often used negatively. Social exclusion results from negative discrimination, when people and groups are denied access to resources and opportunities available to others. Social exclusion is usually related to things like housing, employment or voting, but has wider application. For example, only in 2017 did Muirfield Golf Club in Scotland allow women to become full members. That they could only play as guests or visitors for the first 126 years of the course's history was social exclusion, discrimination against women.

Ethnicity

An ethnic group refers to a community of individuals who share inherited cultural traditions, values, national identity, patterns of behaviour and language. Ethnicity refers to the personal traits which make up an individual's ethnic identity (see 'The Definition of Ethnicity', pages 316–319). People who share a racial group might have different ethnicities. There might be a hierarchy of esteem for various ethnic groups within a country and perhaps attempts to bring them closer together, though sometimes in a way that belittled the Other.

In nineteenth century Wales, some schools used a stick on a string called the 'Welsh not'. It was placed round the neck of a pupil heard to speak Welsh and passed on to another if they too spoke the language in class. The bearer at the end of the day was punished. The purpose was to enforce the notion that only through English could education and thus advancement be achieved.

Figure A11: The approach (top) and entrance (bottom) to Auschwitz concentration camp, Poland. 'Arbeit Macht Frei', means 'work sets you free', a cruel untruth for those taken through those gates.

Source: Nick Perrone (top)

Discrimination against ethnic groups might reach extreme proportions. In the Middle Ages, Jewish people were often confined to ghettos, closed areas, in European cities to keep them apart. In the nineteenth century most ghettos were dismantled, but the system was revived by the Nazis, where Jewish people could be held until transportation to concentration camps (Figure A11).

Gender

Social inequality with regard to gender really considers discrimination against women, the Other of men. Even language treats women as second class. Wives still usually take the husband's surname and only recently has it become usual to seek an alternative way of expressing what used to be called 'Mankind'. Women remain an under privileged group in many cultures. For example, in Saudi Arabia women were not permitted to drive until September 2017 and could not vote until 2015. Even then voting was restricted to municipal (local) elections and only about 130,000 women registered to vote compared to 1.35 million men. Under Taliban rule in Afghanistan women were not allowed to be educated and their freedom of movement was greatly curtailed. Historically, women were unable to vote in Britain until 1918 and 1920 in America.

Despite the 1970 Equal Pay Act in the UK, women still earn less than men, with a gender pay gap of around 18% in 2016, and there are still some social prejudices against women in certain occupations. 'The glass ceiling' is a phrase used to indicate that women are stopped from rising. In 2017, women made up just 6% of CEOs in the world's 500 top companies. There have been only two female British prime ministers, only one Canadian. There has never been a woman President of the USA or Taoiseach of Ireland, although two women have been President of Ireland. The Fawcett Society, named for Millicent Fawcett who worked for women's rights, has as a strapline: 'Equality. It's about time'.

Too often women are subjected to harassment, even in public spaces. In India, this practice is known, rather too light-heartedly, as 'Eve-teasing'. From 2013–2014 there were 31,000 reported crimes against women in Delhi. The city has a Commissioner for Women to press for change and Delhi Metro, like some other Indian railways, reserves carriages for the exclusive use of women. There are similar arrangements in other Asian railways (Figure A12). In cities throughout the world it is advisable for women to avoid certain types of space at night, such as parks. So, solely because of gender, women's behaviour is restricted, social exclusion indeed. Issues over gender are complicated by social class (page 226) and, of course, it is the wealthier groups who tend to be less affected. Over time, as women have become better educated and more assertive regarding control of their bodies, changes are taking place. Better education and life chances for women also lead to a lowering of the birth rate.

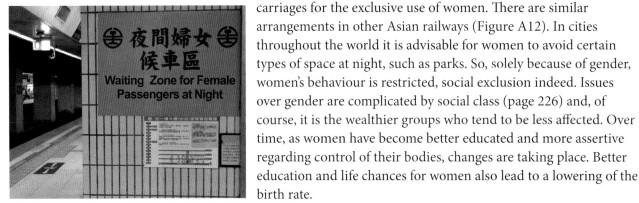

Figure A12: Gender issues shown at a railway station in Taipei, Taiwan

Race

It is generally accepted that humankind is split into different races. However, there is no biological logic as to how many groups there are or how differences should be measured. We are all *Homo sapiens*; it is simply a social construct that, for example, people with dark skin (known as, but not really being, Black) are a different race from those with pale skin (known as, but not really being, White). This has not stopped perceived racial differences being the most significant factors in social inequality, exclusion and discrimination. Throughout the world, people seen as a different race to that of the majority or dominant society face these problems. Racism is not confined to any particular group; all races have members who indulge in belittling their Other.

The most prominent example of racial discrimination and social exclusion applied to race was the Apartheid system of South Africa. The area that became South Africa was taken by Bantu groups moving from the north and Europeans, principally Dutch and British, moving in from the coast. The aboriginal peoples, Khoisan, were pushed aside. After a complex and often violent political history, the Whites entered the post-World War II period as dominant economically and politically but not numerically. To preserve their power and privilege the Apartheid (separateness) system was established. Key pieces of legislation were the Population Registration Act of 1950, which assigned people to racial categories, and the Group Areas Act, also of 1950, under which different racial groups were allocated space for their settlement. Many who inhabited an area now 'belonging' to a different group were relocated, often forcibly. This was 'grand apartheid'; 'petty apartheid' was the separate provision of services from education and health to buses, park benches, even areas on the beaches. Separate did not mean equal and those classified as White enjoyed the best facilities. Such an openly racist system was not sustainable and, after protests and embargos from inside and outside South Africa, Apartheid was withdrawn. Nelson Mandela, a leader of the African National Congress who had been imprisoned for 27 years, mostly on Robben Island (Figure A13), was released and became South Africa's first black president in 1994. The legacy of Apartheid remains and white South Africans, whilst no longer in political control, still form the wealthiest group.

Figure A13: Petty apartheid (left) and Nelson Mandela's cell on Robben Island (right)

Racial discrimination has also had a profound impact on the history of the USA. Its history includes ethnic cleansing of First Nations, slavery, 'Indian' wars and segregation. There are many black Americans who remember the struggle for civil rights in the 1960s and there is still much contestation today. In 2013, the Black Lives Matter pressure group was established after several shootings of black people by white police officers. In Canada, from 1883–1998, aboriginal children were removed from their families for education in residential schools with the express aim of assimilating them into European Canadian society. The school system was harsh and thousands of students died while in attendance, many due to mistreatment or neglect.

In most cities with a racial mix, their social geography displays racial segregation. This may be related to class and income (migrant communities tend to be poorer), but there are also cases where segregation is imposed, the group not being welcome elsewhere. Another factor is that members of the group may desire to live amongst people with whom they share culture, including religion.

Religion

Religion often provides a code of behaviour that makes its followers instantly recognisable. Religious adherence may reflect ethnic or racial differences. Immigrants from a distant location may bring a different religion; the significance of Islam and Hinduism in England and Wales has been noted (page 220). There are situations where religion has been a factor in discrimination, or at least has served as a label for wider social differences. One example is Northern Ireland, where institutional discrimination against the minority Catholic population led to the Civil Rights movement in the late 1960s. This gave way to the violence of 'the troubles', with a wider agenda about competing sovereignties.

Other countries have issues with religious discrimination, even persecution. The Nazi persecution of the Jews has already been mentioned (pages 221, 223 and see also page 330). Disputes as this is being written include the on-going conflict in the Middle East between (Jewish) Israel and her Muslim neighbours (see Israel case study, pages 355–364), Coptic Christians in Egypt versus the majority Muslim population, Muslim Rohingyas in Myanmar versus the majority Buddhists, and Muslim Uighurs in Xinjiang versus the Han Chinese.

Sexuality

Just as the section on gender discussed women as the Other to men, so sexuality focuses on the LGBT community* as the Other to straight society.

*Lesbian, Gay, Bisexual and Transgender, sometimes called LGBT+ to acknowledge other groups.

Historically, in many MEDC countries homosexuality was illegal: think of Oscar Wilde who famously served time in Reading Jail and the celebrated World War II code breaker Alan Turing, who was prosecuted for 'gross indecency' in 1952. It is a mark of how attitudes have changed that in 2009 Prime Minister Gordon Brown apologised for the 'appalling' way Turing was treated and he was given a posthumous pardon in 2013.

In most MEDC cities now, including Belfast, LGBT organisations and nightlife can be found and are openly advertised. There are gay pride marches, where LGBT people celebrate their sexuality and Belfast Pride is Ireland's biggest LGBT festival. However, prejudice still remains, from bullying and name calling to acts of violence.

In over 70 countries worldwide, such as Uganda, India and Pakistan, homosexual activity is a crime. In some, such as Iran and Saudi Arabia, it is punishable by death. In 2017, in Chechnya, there were reports of gay men being persecuted, even tortured and killed, which led to official protests from the British Government.

Social class

Social class is the division of society into different groups based on occupation, wealth and status, but carrying with it other baggage relating to things like attitudes and behaviour. The Office for National Statistics divides the British population into six social groups, known as social grades, based on occupations (Figure A14). These grades are useful for advertisers, allowing them to aim their marketing campaigns at particular social groups. Products will be advertised in the newspapers and television programmes most likely to be read or viewed by the target audience. This is on the assumption that social class is associated with behaviour and attitudes as much as it is with wealth.

Figure A14: The division of society into social groups
Social grades at the 2011 Census, UK

Source: National Readership Survey, http://www.nrs.co.uk

Social grade*	Description	% Adult population, 2011
AB	Higher & intermediate managerial, administrative, professional occupations	22.17
C1	Supervisory, clerical & junior managerial, administrative, professional occupations	30.84
C2	Skilled manual occupations	20.94
DE	Semi-skilled & unskilled manual occupations, unemployed and lowest grade occupations	26.05

In recent decades, the revolution in employment – mechanisation, computerisation and even globalisation affecting the range and type of jobs on offer – has blurred the sharp class boundaries once based on occupation. However, simple distinctions between 'middle class' and 'working class' people remain and are widely understood in society. Class distinctions remain from minor behavioural differences, such as which newspapers are read, to more significant matters such as place of residence, quality of education and life chances. The wealthier, higher classes have most opportunities, can afford good housing and private education and health care of a quality superior to that provided in the public sector. Take South Africa as an example, where there is a major crime problem. Wealthy South Africans, not now all white since the end of Apartheid, reduce their exposure to crime by living behind fences and in gated compounds, often with security firms on call (Figure A15). Poor South Africans, still largely black, have no such protection.

Figure A15: A middle class house in Pretoria, South Africa protected by walls and fences (left) and security signs (right)

Worldwide, those without wealth often occupy poor quality living space in urban and rural areas alike. Such areas may have fewer public services than wealthier areas. Children may find themselves in poorer school facilities, where they are less likely to obtain good qualifications. This will make it more difficult for them to secure well paid jobs in adulthood and reduce their opportunities for economic and social advancement. This cycle of poverty is then passed on to the next generation (see 'Social and Economic Deprivation', *Geography for CCEA AS Level 2nd Edition,* Colourpoint Educational, page 193). Investing in neighbourhood renewal in these areas and tackling employment issues have been seen as policies that could help break this cycle.

The ultimate form of social exclusion is imprisonment. A far greater proportion of people from lower classes are incarcerated than from middles classes. Poor education, a lack of opportunity to obtain well-paid employment and poverty are causes. Further, the types of crime typically committed, such as burglary and robbery are a police priority. Race, age and gender also affect imprisonment with young, lower class males from minority ethnic groups being the most likely to be confined.

Social constructions of nature and landscape

The development of cultural geography was led by Carl Sauer of the University of California Berkeley from the 1920s. Sauer saw 'landscape' as the basic unit of geographical study and taught that cultures develop *because* of the landscape but in turn *affect* that landscape. Nature and the landscape are affected directly, physically, by human actions: clearing forests, building houses etc. Social construction goes further by recognising that people's attitude to nature and how they interact with it depends upon their perception – they participate in creating their reality. A tree is a collection of carbon molecules, part of a habitat that sustains life, perhaps a source of food, raw material for furniture and building, and a source of energy. How people respond to that tree, from cherishing it to cultivating it to chopping it down is a social construction, with impacts upon the development and use of nature and the landscape.

Landscapes as human systems

Carl Sauer thought that interaction between the 'natural' landscape and human communities created the 'cultural landscape'. He wrote: "culture is the agent, the natural area is the medium, the cultural landscape the result" (Figure A16).

Figure A16: Carl Sauer's cultural landscape

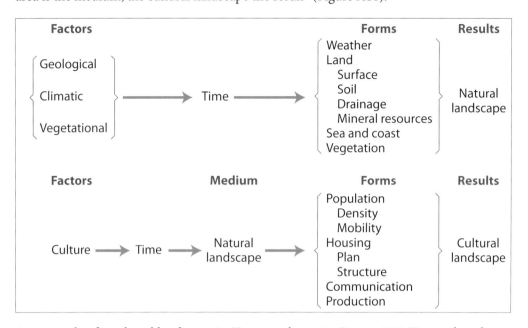

An example of a cultural landscape in Kenya is shown in Figure A17. Here cultural processes (the Maasai people of the area are cattle herders) have resulted in a particular settlement form built on the natural landscape. The thorny brambles and branches placed round the village provide protection and the arrangement of the houses leaves space for pens for the cattle which are brought in at night for safety and easy observation. Great cities are much further away from a natural landscape.

Figure A17: A typical Maasai village in Kenya

In 1955, there was a notable conference in Princeton, New Jersey of 70 international scholars. They were selected for their curiosity about what humans were doing to, and with, their habitat. The subsequent publication of a book entitled *Man's role in changing the face of the earth* in 1956 was very influential. Landscapes that had been thought to be natural might be shown to be cultural features. For example, the Norfolk Broads, a network of lakes and rivers in East Anglia, were demonstrated by geographers in the 1960s to be medieval peat workings, which had become flooded. Now there is recognition of human influence on global warming and climate change and that we are now in the Anthropocene geological epoch, the era of human impact upon the planet and its ecosystems.

Natural landscapes

It might be questioned if any completely natural landscapes remain. The concept of 'wilderness' suggests that there are, but social constructionism comes into play here. Europeans colonising Australia or moving across the 'frontier' in North America saw untouched wilderness, whereas the landscapes were already inhabited and managed by indigenous peoples. Where the indigenes showed themselves they were often cleared away or, in some cases, exterminated. However, there was recognition in the USA that some areas encountered were so special – nature's spiritual value – that they deserved to be cherished. The first National Park was declared in the Yosemite Valley as early as 1864, to protect it against development. Wilderness areas generally are under threat from tourists who like to visit, perhaps not realising that this causes harm; the only true eco-tourists are those that stay at home.

Perhaps there are no entirely natural landscapes but some places, such as remote uninhabited islands, forests or mountainous regions, have been less changed by humans than other areas. The effect of climate change and pollution means nowhere is completely unspoilt, but Henderson Island in the Pacific comes as close as anywhere. It is a raised coral reef of 37 sq km (14 square miles) with poor soil, little fresh water and is unsuitable for settlement, although Polynesians lived there between the twelfth and fifteenth centuries. Occasionally there have been shipwrecks and skeletons have been found, but human impact has been light and the island retains a rich ecosystem, with many of its plants and all its land birds being endemic (found nowhere else). In the early 1980s a wealthy American wanted to build an airstrip so he could live there and he obtained permission from Pitcairn Island, the nearby British colony which administers Henderson. However, the British government vetoed the proposal on environmental grounds. Henderson was made a World Heritage Site in 1988, being "of Outstanding Universal Value due to the comparatively low level of disturbance" (UNESCO). The only regular visits are from the tiny Pitcairn Island community who take wood for carving curios from trees that are not native to the island. However, in May 2017, a study led by the Royal Society for the Protection of Birds estimated that there were 38 million pieces of plastic littering the island's beaches.

Exercise

1. Using the Internet, research 'untouched wilderness'.

    (i) Make a list of some of the places marketed online under that description.

    (ii) Take two or more of these places and describe the factors that make them 'untouched'. Are they and can they remain 'natural landscapes'?

Cultural landscapes

In line with Sauer, it might be proposed that a cultural landscape results from complex interactions between humans (with their own practices, preference, values and aspirations) and the natural environment. Any cultural landscape can change over time, especially with the introduction of an outside culture. Then a new cultural landscape might be superimposed on top of the previous one. Colonialism is one obvious example and this process (or practice) changed landscapes across the globe. Some places became settler colonies and the introduction of migrants transformed landscapes by the building of settlements, from farms to cities to the introduction of alien species. Australia is a prime example. Its British colonial masters declared it to be *terra nullius*, nobody's land, which was open for the taking. This denied the existence of the aboriginal peoples who had been there for thousands of years. Their cultural landscape was overwhelmed by that developed by the migrants. Agriculture, industry and everything that accompanies settlement transformed the landscapes directly. There was also an impact from introduced species, which have severely damaged Australian ecosystems. They include rabbits, introduced originally as a food supply in 1788, and the poisonous cane toad from Hawaii, deliberately released in 1935 to eat cane beetles which damaged sugar crops. This the toads did not do, but predated on insects, birds' eggs and native frogs. There are perhaps 200 million toads now, a real pest.

Cultural landscapes reflect the practices, the way of life, of their residents, also their history. The Berlin Wall, which divided that city's capitalist and communist parts for almost 30 years, has gone, but redevelopment has left its place marked, as a memorial (Resource A). Buildings used for worship differ between religions, from small and plain to large and ornate (Figure A18). There are differing architectural styles which developed in response to climatic conditions. In the Eastern Mediterranean and Middle East buildings have flat roofs where people might sleep on hot nights (Figure A19); in Northern Ireland buildings have pitched roofs to shed rainwater. There are different types of sports grounds dependent upon local traditions. Where groups have mixed through migration and/or colonialism, a hybrid cultural landscape will result.

Figure A18: A village temple in the Penghu Islands, Taiwan

Figure A19: Flat roofed buildings in Nicosia, Cyprus

Exercise

1. With reference to examples, discuss how place shapes culture and how culture shapes place.

Exam Questions

1. Study Resource A and explain why the attitude to the former Berlin Wall in present day Berlin is an example of cultural nationalism.

Resource A: The Berlin Wall

After its defeat in World War II, Germany was divided into sectors controlled by America, Britain, France and the Soviet Union (dominated by Russia). Within a short time, these divisions saw the establishment of the Federal Republic of Germany (West Germany, the British, American and French sectors) and the German Democratic Republic (East Germany, the Soviet sector). This division was mirrored in Berlin, which was split into

West Berlin and East Berlin, the city itself lying within East Germany. Germany was reunited in 1990 at the end of the Cold War.

In Berlin, the political division was marked by the Berlin Wall, which was erected in 1961 to stop East Germans fleeing into the west. The dismantling of the Berlin Wall from 1989 was a symbolic and actual marker of the re-unification of Germany and Berlin.

Line of the former Berlin Wall   Surviving slabs of the Berlin Wall

The former line of the Berlin Wall is marked in the streets of Berlin today and the few remaining slabs of the wall are preserved and are tourist attractions.

References

Information on cultural nationalism:
'Nelson Mandela seized the opportunity of the Rugby World Cup in 1995', *www.telegraph.co.uk*, 6 December 2013
The National Trust for Ireland – *www.antaisce.org*
The National Trust – *www.nationaltrust.org.uk*
The National Memorial Arboretum – *www.thenma.org*
Department for Culture, Media and Sport – *www.culture.gov.uk*

Information on social inequalities, exclusion and discrimination:
UN Women Watch – *http://womenwatch.unwomen.org*
The Fawcett Society – *www.fawcettsociety.org.uk*
Black Lives Matter – *http://blacklivesmatter.com*
Social groups and crime – *http://www.historylearningsite.co.uk/sociology/crime-and-deviance/*
Social groups – *https://ukgeographics.co.uk/blog/social-grade-a-b-c1-c2-d-e*

Information on social constructions of nature and landscape:
The Sierra Club – *www.sierraclub.org*
Henderson Island – *whc.unesco.org/en/list/487* and *www.winthrop.dk/hender.html*
There is a documentary on Cane toads in Australia available on YouTube –
'Cane toads: an unnatural history 1988', www.youtube.com

2. MIGRATION

Students should be able to:

(i) explain push and pull factors in migration – economic, social, political, cultural and environmental factors, and barriers to migration

(ii) demonstrate knowledge and understanding of the implications of migration for service provision, economic activity and social stability

(iii) distinguish between voluntary and forced migration and describe migration processes, including those adopted by undocumented migrants

(iv) discuss immigration (documented and undocumented) as a political issue and governments' responses to it

Migration is defined as a permanent change in place of residence for at least one year. Migration is internal when migrants move from one region to another within their own country or international when the movement involves crossing an international border. About 9% of the world's people are international migrants, living in a country other than that of their birth.

Unless the migration is forced, where the individual has little or no choice, decision making involved in migration is complex. For most, migration is a life-changing experience and the decision to move involves an assessment of those factors that promote migration balanced against those that discourage it. These are called push and pull factors.

Push and pull factors

Push factors are the negative aspects of the potential migrant's current place of residence – things that make them want to get away. Push factors are subjective, based on each decision maker's perception. What one person may regard as a negative factor might have no significance to another.

Working in conjunction with push factors are pull factors – the perceived attractions of the potential destination. These might include the availability of employment for migrants of working age or a pleasant climate for retirees. Perceptions can be based on information acquired from previous migrants, media reports, advertising campaigns or advice from people and agencies facilitating migration. Migrants move because they believe that the circumstances in which they currently live will be improved. Further, this improvement must be sufficient to overcome the barriers to migration (see pages 234–235), the cost and rigours of the actual journey. For many that journey just involves the inconvenience of moving house; for others it can involve risk of death.

Economic

Economic factors are common considerations in migration decision making. Lack of suitable jobs, low wages or an uncertain future are possible push factors. Deindustrialisation has removed employment opportunities in some places. In rural areas, restructuring and mechanisation in farming have reduced the number of job opportunities, prompting people to move elsewhere, especially to cities, in search of work. This rural-urban migration is common in LEDCs.

Eastern European migration to the UK is an example of economic motivations for migration. When Poland became part of the European Union (EU) in 2004, its unemployment rate was 18% overall and 40% in the rural areas. Unemployment in the UK was about 5% and its GDP per capita was over twice that of Poland. So many Poles – and other Eastern Europeans – moved to the UK, which they had the right to do under EU regulations about freedom of movement (this was before Brexit). The British government anticipated 13,000 people would migrate from Poland, but comparison between the 2001 and 2011 census shows an increase of 520,000 Poles in the UK.

Movement of educated individuals from LEDCs to MEDCs in search of better opportunities in, say, the health service, is also an example of economic factors in operation. Within countries, government economic policies might stimulate migration to places receiving investment.

Social

The desire to join family members who have already made a successful move is an important social factor in migration. Often male members of a family make the initial decision to migrate, usually for economic reasons, and after they have become established, the rest of the family moves to join them. West Indian migration to the UK in the 1950s and 1960s generally followed this pattern. Following family members – or people from the same area – like this is called chain migration.

Students often move away to go to university and this initial, temporary move frequently becomes permanent as students form new social ties. Many students leave Northern Ireland for university in Great Britain and never return.

In rural areas, especially where the population is ageing, there might be not only inadequate educational and economic prospects for young people, but also insufficient leisure and recreational opportunities. Having 'nothing to do' – an unrewarding social life – can push young people towards the bright lights of urban areas. Rural areas and islands throughout Europe provide examples of this.

Political

Migration has always responded to political decisions. Slavery, which involved the forced migration of millions of people from Sub-Saharan Africa to North and South America in the eighteenth and nineteenth centuries, was a political act. It ceased only when government policies changed. There are national migration policies under which countries boost or restrict migration in response to economic needs. Politics expressed through warfare and civil strife can see increased migration rates as a response. From 2011–2016 about 11 million Syrians were displaced because of the political situation there. The EU permits freedom of movement of people throughout its area, which has seen major migration streams from the poorer south and east to the wealthier nations of the north. Polish migration to the UK would not have happened without that EU policy. The ageing populations of nations such as Germany has also seen immigration of non-EU citizens, including undocumented migrants from Africa and the Middle East to fill labour needs. This has been welcomed by the German Chancellor, Angela Merkel, if not always by some German citizens. Distaste for foreign migration became a major political issue in the 2010s and was a factor in two significant events in 2016, namely Brexit, the referendum which saw the UK vote to leave the EU, and the election of Donald Trump as US president.

Cultural

Lack of religious or cultural freedom has often promoted migration; not being permitted to use one's first language has also been a push factor. Migrants may leave voluntarily or be driven away by dominant forces from another religion. The Pilgrim Fathers, early migrants in 1620 to what became the USA, were seeking freedom to practice their Calvinist faith without the persecution they had faced at home. Sadly, there are still many cases of discrimination against people of a minority religion. In Egypt, minority Coptic Christians have been persecuted and some have migrated internally or left the country. In Myanmar (Burma), the minority Rohingyas, a Muslim group in Rakhine State, have been persecuted by Buddhists and many have fled to Bangladesh, Thailand or Pakistan. Scores of thousands live in camps for internally displaced persons.

A desire to live amongst co-religionists or people with a similar culture has been a pull factor directing migration streams to particular cities or districts within cities. When Uganda's Asians were driven from the country in 1972 by its dictator, Idi Amin, Leicester City Council put a notice in the *Uganda Argus* newspaper advising Asians not to move there. In block capitals they were told "IN YOUR OWN INTERESTS AND THOSE OF YOUR FAMILY YOU SHOULD ACCEPT THE ADVICE OF THE UGANDA RESETTLEMENT BOARD AND NOT COME TO LEICESTER". The reasons stated were that housing, education, social and health services were already stressed by earlier settlers, although there have been accusations that the real motive was racism. Many Ugandan Asians were not dissuaded, choosing Leicester precisely because the city contained people who shared their culture. In 2012 Sundip Meghani, a councillor in what he called the "rich, diverse and harmonious city", said that was why his family moved from Uganda to Leicester: "with only the clothes on their backs and very few possessions they felt coming to Leicester would provide a support network".

Environmental

Environmental factors have long pushed migrants to leave. Vikings moved to Britain in the ninth and tenth centuries for lack of good farming land in Denmark. The 'Okies' were farmers pushed from their land on the Great Plains of the USA by drought in the 1920s and 1930s, their plight immortalised in John Steinbeck's famous 1939 novel, *Grapes of Wrath*. Droughts, floods and volcanic eruptions have all caused temporary or permanent migration. Desertification and rising sea levels caused by global warming are encouraging migration or at least seeing migration preparations. Kiribati is a Pacific Ocean nation of 100,000 people whose land consists of atolls and islands, only one of which is higher than two metres. Its government has established a 'migration with dignity' policy and has purchased land in Fiji to which its people can migrate in the event of sea level rise making their islands uninhabitable. Rising sea levels might also affect densely populated continental coastal regions, with devastating impacts upon their habitability and consequently the need for mass migration of an unimaginable scale.

Barriers to migration

Having decided to migrate, a potential migrant must overcome a number of real and perceived obstacles before embarking on the journey, never mind reaching their destination. Barriers can be legal, some reception countries impose quotas or have favoured migrants from some places over others (see case study of Canada, pages 253–258). One consideration is the cost of the journey. Also, a potential migrant may have property to dispose of and acquire at either end of the process. Unless they are joining family members who will support them, there is a need to have sufficient funds to tide migrants over until they secure employment. This is not a barrier for migrants who are moving to a new job. Migration involves severing or at least stretching family and friendship ties and this hardship has to be factored in. There is also the potential challenge of the lifestyle at the destination if migrants are moving to an area with differences in culture or language.

In the case of international migration, government policies can be a barrier. Countries that seek migrants usually employ selection procedures and can also dictate the areas migrants may go to. In 2017, the then new USA president, Donald Trump, tried to enact legislation forbidding immigration entirely from certain countries, a strong barrier indeed.

Barriers so far discussed have applied mainly to voluntary migrants, people moving following legal procedures. However, much international migration is 'undocumented', involving people who are desperately fleeing danger or despair and whose imperative is just to get away, perhaps no matter what challenges they face. Migration streams from the Middle East and Africa are examples. The strife in Syria, which started in 2011, has seen about 11 million Syrians displaced inside Syria or to neighbouring countries, where they usually reside in refugee camps, although some have reached Europe and further afield.

Those migrating without documentation have often placed themselves in the hands of people traffickers, who, for a relatively large fee, facilitate migration journeys. Many migrants subsequently have found themselves crowded onto unseaworthy craft sailing, for example, from North Africa across the Mediterranean Sea to Europe. Their boats may reach their destination or be intercepted by the authorities and the passengers rescued, but thousands have drowned (Figure A20). One would have thought that a high likelihood of dying on a migration journey would be an insurmountable barrier: that this is not so is an indication of the pressures these migrants face at their origins.

Figure A20: Recorded deaths in the Mediterranean Sea by migrants' region of origin, 2016

Source: Data from missingmigrants.iom.int

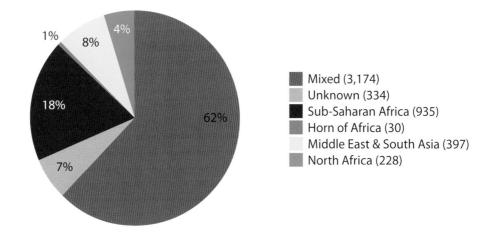

Mixed (3,174)
Unknown (334)
Sub-Saharan Africa (935)
Horn of Africa (30)
Middle East & South Asia (397)
North Africa (228)

Implications of migration

Migration has significant impacts both on the area of out-migration and on the area of in-migration. Where substantial numbers of people relocate, there are repercussions for service provision, economic activity and social stability.

Areas of in-migration

A large influx of migrants puts immediate demands on services such as education, health and housing provision. However well-intentioned, it will take even an MEDC country/region some time to provide the extra capacity needed in schools and other areas of social provision. The migrant population might help itself and provide services for its own community (Figure A21). Sometimes these might become mainstream to serve the wider host community. One excellent example is the rise of Indian restaurants in the UK. Chicken tikka masala has become a British national dish despite its exoticness in a country where takeaway was largely restricted to fish and chips. There are claims that this Indian dish may have originated in Glasgow. A number of services, including shops and restaurants, have opened in Belfast in recent years to serve the Polish (Figure A22) and various other communities (see Figure C10, page 327). Some migrant groups have established their own schools in parts of the UK.

Figure A21: The Chinese Welfare Association, Belfast

Figure A22: Polish shop and restaurant in Belfast

In LEDCs matters might be more problematic. Certainly migrants find it difficult to access decent housing and many live illegally in informal settlements. In South Africa, the ending of Apartheid saw the instigation of government policies designed to improve the housing of the black people who had been discriminated against. However, the relative strength of the South African economy has seen recent immigration, much of it undocumented, from elsewhere in Africa and these migrants often occupy shanties – areas of self-built housing – and South Africa still has major housing problems (Figure A23).

The problem is much worse, of course, if the migrants are refugees. For example, countries near South Sudan, such as Chad, have been forced to accommodate many migrants from the conflict there and they already struggled to provide acceptable living conditions for their own citizens.

Migrants often make a positive economic contribution to their host countries, especially if they fill labour shortages. Examples include West Indian migrants to the

Figure A23: Shanty housing of recent international migrants to Cape Town, South Africa. This is on the Cape Flats behind Table Mountain. Note that although the housing is poor, many have satellite dishes.

UK after World War II and Turkish migrants to Germany in the same period. The Turks were called *gastarbeiter*, 'guest workers', and played a vital role in rebuilding post-war Germany. The 'guest' element of their label shows that they were expected to return home, but many stayed and Germany has over four million people of Turkish descent. By working for low wages, migrants help to keep wage inflation low, but critics say they depress wages to the detriment of local workers. Migrants also spend money and pay taxes, and will often take jobs that members of the host society no longer want, such as harvesting and fruit picking.

The negative implications of migration include the fact that many send a large proportion of their earnings home, so this money is lost to the local economy. Migrants in MEDCs have been accused of taking locals' jobs. This may well not be true given local reluctance to carry out some of the tasks migrants do, but the perception alone can cause resentment and impact social stability.

Regarding social stability, migrants can be seen as threatening to some, especially if they are numerous, visibly different to their host community and/or do not speak its language or share its religion and culture. That migrants often live in segregated groups rather than being dispersed works against chances of social integration (see 'Residential concentration', page 321). The local community may react by withdrawing from an area where migrants have congregated, further increasing segregation. Policies to try and encourage integration have not always been successful.

Then there is outright prejudice and racism, ugly signs of social instability. Even in Northern Ireland, which suffered so much from sectarian hatreds during the troubles, there are problems of racism. Migrant households in Northern Ireland have been subject to racist abuse and attack.

Areas of out-migration

If migrants leave because of overpopulation, pressure on existing services will be eased and those remaining may have better access to services. However, this may be only a short-term benefit because as more people move, service provision deteriorates as demand falls. In an area suffering out-migration of the economically active, primary schools are affected, as their pupils and potential pupils leave with the parents. Falling numbers might necessitate amalgamations and school closures. For families that remain, their children may have further to travel to school, which could in itself be another push factor. Health provision, post offices and banking, retailing and public transport might be similarly affected.

Economic activity might also enjoy short-term relief, as out-migration releases jobs and reduces unemployment. However, as migration can be selective of the better trained, educated and skilled, who have most to gain from taking their talents elsewhere, the jobs freed up might not be easily filled by those who remain. Regarding international migration, while the new country profits from this gained talent, the home country receives no further benefit from the training it invested in its residents. The movement of qualified nurses from Asian countries to work in MEDCs is a case in point. In Northern Ireland, for example, most hospital wards in the South Eastern Health and Social Care Trust employ nurses from Asia. The Trust has also visited the Philippines to recruit staff.

Some migrants remit much of their earnings, which aids the out-migration area. Further, international migrants who return once they have retired or otherwise

Follow up

The Royal Geographical Society (RGS) is running a field research programme called 'Migrants on the Margins'. It "focuses on the vulnerability and opportunities of migrants in some of the world's most pressured cities" in Sri Lanka, Bangladesh, Zimbabwe and Somaliland. Its activities can be followed through the RGS website (www.rgs.org) and a blog (https://migrantsonthemargins.tumblr.com).

finished work in the foreign country may bring investment and new ideas, which contribute to the development and modernisation of their original home. Tourism from migrants and their families is another benefit.

In cases of mass emigration associated with warfare, services may break down altogether for those people who remain and considerable social instability would result. Even peaceful areas undergoing emigration can suffer social instability if the economy becomes unbalanced and services decline as the birth rate falls and the population ages. This could start a cycle or spiral of decline and encourage further emigration. Such decline of rural areas, including small islands, has become common in the British Isles and elsewhere.

Exercise

1. Use Resources A, B and C to help you explain why there has been much out-migration from the Irish islands.

Resource A: Irish island statistics

Source: An analysis based on Ordnance Survey maps and census returns

Irish Islands[1]	1841	1901	1961	2011
Total number of island residents	36,532	26,348	15,265	8,835
Number of populated Irish islands	155	136	74	54
Proportion of islands with a fixed link[2]	10.3%	12.5%	17.6%	29.6%

Notes

[1] In the 26 counties that became the Republic of Ireland. Offshore islands only, discounting those in institutional use such as lighthouses or prisons.

[2] A fixed link is a bridge, causeway or other structure linking the island to the mainland, which reduces its isolation, one of the major push factors behind island emigration.

Resource B: A cycle of rural decline established for the Irish islands

Source: Government of Ireland, *Report of the Interdepartmental Co-ordinating Committee on Island Development*, 1996

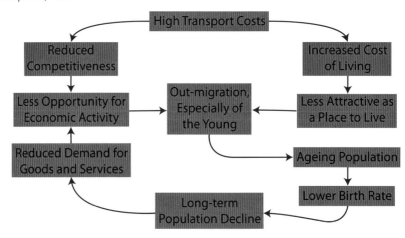

Resource C: Heir Island (Hare, Inishdriscol), Co Cork

Note: The bridge is within the island; there is no fixed link to the mainland.

Population	
1841	358
1901	317
1961	94
2011	29

2. Using the material in Resource D, relating to changing patterns of migration from Albania, identify and describe the push/pull processes and barriers to migration in operation.

Question adapted from A2 1 Human Interactions and Global Issues,
January 2012, © CCEA 2017

Resource D: Changing patterns of migration from Albania

Source: Adapted from R King and J Vullnetari, 'The intersections of gender and generation in Albanian migration', *Geografiska Annaler: Series B, Human Geography*, Vol 91, Issue 1, 2009

When Albania was part of the Ottoman Empire, Albanians traditionally migrated within Eastern Europe. This mobility, known as *kurbet*, reflected the poverty of their mountainous, agro-pastoral homeland and the lack of alternative employment options. *Kurbet* was a male phenomenon, summed up by an old Albanian proverb: "a man becomes a man out in the world [ie by migrating in search of work], a woman becomes a woman rocking the cradle".

When the interior of the United States of America was opened up for settlement during the late nineteenth and early twentieth centuries, significant numbers of Albanians migrated there instead.

However, from the 1940s to the early 1990s, during the period of communist government in Albania, emigration was regarded as treason, punishable by imprisonment or death for those who tried to leave.

In the 1990s the communist regime collapsed, a dramatic political event which saw massive migration amongst the liberated people, especially given the long-term background of economic stagnation in rural areas where most Albanians lived. Three major migratory episodes occurred:

- It is estimated that 200,000 people left during the chaos that followed the fall of communism (1991–1992).
- In 1997 violence erupted after a series of financial scandals, which bankrupted a large number of households and many people left the country.
- In 1999 unrest in former Yugoslavia destabilised northern Albania. Boatloads of migrants arrived on the Italian coast during 'the exodus', as it was portrayed in the international media, but even more migrations took place across the mountainous border with Greece.

Migration took place at a steadier rate between these emigration pulses and continues to do so.

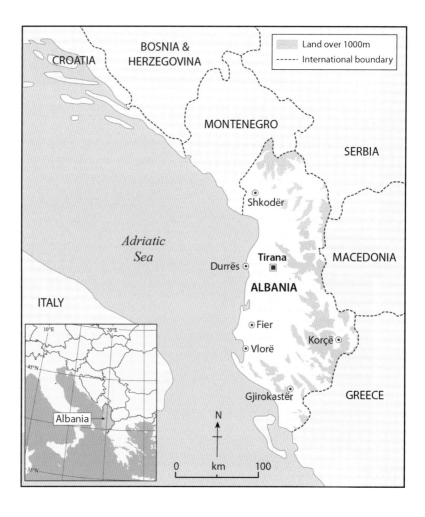

3. Visit the Migration Watch website: https://www.migrationwatchuk.org/ statistics-net-migration-statistics. Create two (or more) graphs from the options given and describe and explain the patterns of migration revealed.

CASE STUDY: Barra and Vatersay, a small-scale study of the implications of out-migration

Barra and Vatersay are islands at the south of the chain of the Outer Hebrides, off the west coast of Scotland (Figure A24). In the 2011 census they had a combined total population of 1264, slightly up on 2001's 1172, but well down on the 1879 of 1951 (Figures A25 and A26). In 1831 Barra had 2363 people. In the Outer Hebrides as a whole, the population declined from 35,591 in 1951 to 27,684 in 2011, with the lowest total being 26,502 in 2001.

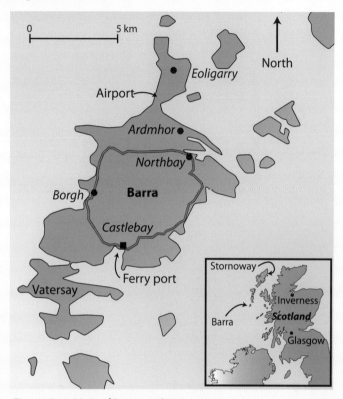

Figure A24: Map of Barra and Vatersay

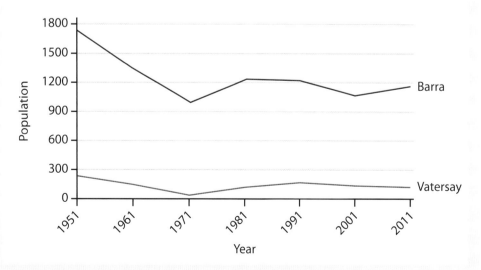

Figure A25: Population change on Barra and Vatersay, 1951–2011

Source: Data from UK Census 1951–2011, Office for National Statistics, www.ons.gov.uk
Contains public sector information licensed under the Open Government Licence v3.0.

Figure A26: Abandoned housing on Barra

Source: All photographs of Barra courtesy of Sarah MacKinnon

Barra is the larger island. It has a mountainous centre (Figure A27) and most settlements are on the coast. In the west and north there is a low-lying area with sand dunes. The airport is here, its 'runway' being the beach (Figure A28). There are two flights to Glasgow per day but services to other parts of the Outer Hebrides have been stopped.

Figure A27: Barra

Figure A28: The beach 'runway' on Barra

Within the islands there is just one main road, the A888, which circles Barra. There are ferry services to Oban on the Scottish mainland, five hours away, and to Eriskay, 40 minutes away, which is connected to South Uist further up the chain of islands. Ferry services to the Scottish isles are run by a nationalised company, Caledonian MacBrayne, with which there is an annual battle over services and timetabling. Islanders have also had disputes with the council over the bus services, which have been cut. In short, travel and transport on, to and from the islands is difficult. Even though transport services are vital to the community, the absolute level of demand is low and has fallen.

One improvement has been the causeway built to link Vatersay to Barra in 1991. Before that Vatersay was facing total depopulation, its population had dropped to 65 in 1988. Since the causeway was built it has recovered and stabilised at 94 in 2001 and 90 in 2011. Life for Vatersay people is now little different from those on Barra.

Because of the small and, over the long period, declining population, service provision is limited on Barra. Most services are concentrated in the largest settlement, Castlebay (Figure A29), where there is the only bank, petrol station and secondary school,

Castlebay Community School, and one of two primary schools (there is another at Eoligarry). The secondary school also houses the library, gym and swimming pool, which are open to the community outside school hours (until 8 pm). There are not enough people for separate provision of such facilities. The largest shop is run by the Co-operative chain, which is the major retailer in the Scottish islands. Retailing has been changed in Barra, as elsewhere, by online shopping.

Figure A29: Castlebay, Barra with its petrol station and bank

There are GP and dental services and a tiny GP-run clinic on Barra. Access to the Uist and Barra Hospital on Benbecula, an island further north, has been made difficult by the ending of flights within the Western Isles. There are plans for new facilities on the island, but presently patients usually access hospital services in Glasgow. Flights and overnight stays are arranged through the NHS. In an emergency, patients can be sent to Glasgow by helicopter, a 40 minute journey. Out-patient services, including physiotherapy and ante-natal care, are provided by specialists travelling down periodically from Stornoway. Other services provided through visiting facilities include driving tests and a mobile cinema. Services are limited in Castlebay and on Barra, but there are more here than would be provided for a mainland village because Barra is an isolated island. A mainland village would be unlikely to have a secondary school, a petrol station or a bank, never mind an airport.

Employment opportunities on Barra are limited. There is a fish factory and a community co-operative (not to be confused with the Co-op shop), which was set up in 1981 to support economic development. There are some seasonal jobs in small hotels and guesthouses and employment with the council, schools, care sector and emergency services. Transport and health and social care provide the greatest number of jobs, the latter related to the needs of the ageing population, typical of an area of emigration. In Barra and Vatersay 21% of the population were 65 or over in 2011, against 17% for Scotland as a whole (and 13.6% for Peterborough, see page 245). Traditional sectors such as fishing and crofting employ ever-decreasing numbers, just 5.6% of the workforce in 2011. Unemployment rates in Barra and Vatersay at the 2011 census were 6.5% for men and 3.7% for women, not high, but 6.5% of men and 30.1% of the women worked part-time, the highest rates in the Outer Hebrides. Wages tend to be low, 12% lower than in the rest of Scotland in the early 2000s, and that, matched against high food, fuel and transport costs are push factors behind emigration.

Nearly all young people leave Barra and Vatersay when they finish school. Those who stay and seek work tend to have the fewest qualifications. Many boys go to the

Figure A30: Population pyramid, Barra and Vatersay, 2011

Source: Data from UK Census 2011, Office for National Statistics, www.ons.gov.uk
Contains public sector information licensed under the Open Government Licence v3.0.

Shetland School for Nautical Studies to train for the merchant navy or the oil industry; girls tend to go to Glasgow to train for professions such as teaching or nursing. There is now a policy to train more people on-island: degrees can be taken by distance learning through the Stornoway branch of the University of the Highlands and Islands. Further, the council is trialling 'e-sgoil' (e-school in English) where subjects not offered at Barra Community School can be taken over distance at other schools in Scotland. This is aimed at retaining sixth formers. However, one report from Barra said that even if more courses were offered locally, most young people would still leave to experience the world 'outside'. Further, Barra and Vatersay cannot offer the type of work ambitious young people want. One policy initiative has been to provide high quality Internet access. In 2017 the entire island was upgraded. This means that it is increasingly viable for people on Barra to work remotely in some employment sectors for national-level salaries.

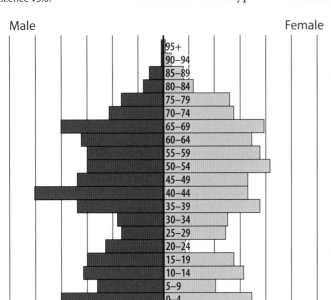

The population structure from the 2011 census for Barra and Vatersay (Figure A30) highlights the islands' problems. The indent in the pyramid for the working population indicates the effects of out-migration. This will impact Barra's future population growth. The European Commission regards a population threshold of four or five thousand as necessary for an island to be sustainable. Islands with lower totals are likely to continue to experience net out-migration, ageing populations and struggle to provide adequate facilities and services.

However, it should be noted that for Barra and Vatersay, as with Scottish (and Irish) islands generally, the population total rose between 2001 and 2011. The proportion of old people grew, while that of young adults fell still. What changed is that there were more people in early middle age, in their forties, many of whom had small children. These tended to be returning islanders and others coming to Barra because it is a safe and satisfying place to raise children. Another report from the Isle of Arran made the same point. Primary school numbers are at their highest in many years. If a person can just secure fulfilling employment, the positives of island life can be enjoyed. As one Barra islander put it, there is: "A sense of community, and knowing (all) one's neighbours is such a rare thing in the modern, mobile world it gives one the sense of belonging and home".

Exercise

1. Discuss possible reasons for continued out-migration from Barra and the policies designed to alleviate the problem.

2. Explain the implications of sustained out-migration for service provision, economic activity and social stability on Barra.

References

2011 Census statistics, Barra and Vatersay:
http://www.cne-siar.gov.uk/factfile/population/documents/Barra%20and%20Vatersay%20Profile.pdf

CASE STUDY: Peterborough, an urban study of the implications of in-migration

Peterborough, a provincial city in Cambridgeshire in the east of England, has had a long tradition of in-migration. It was a Saxon foundation and became a market town specialising in wool production in the Middle Ages. Later it became noted for brickmaking, which continues. Other industries are farm machinery, mechanical and electrical engineering. Peterborough lies within one of Britain's most prosperous agricultural regions, the Fens. The land in the area is flat and fertile, which together with an appropriate climate makes it suitable for arable farming. In addition, with its excellent road and rail communications, and proximity to Cambridge, Peterborough has been able to participate in the development of a hi-tech region, 'Silicon Fen'.

In 1967 Peterborough's population was about 80,000, when it was designated as a New Town, with a plan to double its population. New areas of housing were erected and population grew rapidly in the 1970s and 1980s. In 2011 Peterborough had 183,631 people, and an estimated 194,000 by 2015. The population is young: only 13.6% were aged over 65 in 2011 (compared to 21% for Barra and Vatersay).

Generations of seasonal workers have been employed on farms and food processing plants in and around Peterborough. In addition, after World War II there was an influx of Italians to work in the brick industry. Commonwealth Asian immigrants, mainly from Pakistan, arrived in the 1970s and 1980s, many working in transportation and catering. More recently, there has been migration from Eastern Europe after EU expansion in 2004, as well as migrants from Portugal, many working in agriculture and food processing. The local newspaper, the *Peterborough Telegraph*, reported in 2012 that 17,000 migrants came between 2004 and 2009. A study showed that many had Peterborough social connections: 42% had family living there, while 27% had friends. At the 2011 census 14,134 people were from Eastern and Central Europe, 4206 from Africa and 11,332 from the Middle East and Asia, together making up 11.2% of Peterborough's population. Most were aged between 20 and 44. The city's 2011 age structure (Figure A31) has a characteristic bulge in the young adult cohorts, indicative of in-migration.

Figure A31: Age structure for Peterborough, 2011

Source: Data from UK Census 2011, Office for National Statistics, www.ons.gov.uk Contains public sector information licensed under the Open Government Licence v3.0.

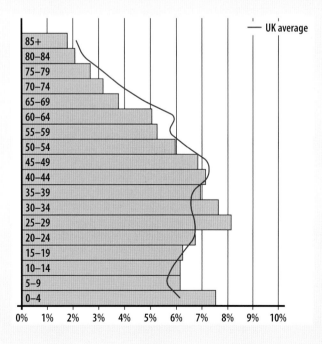

Peterborough had always coped with growth, but the immigration of the twenty-first century has been controversial. In 2012 Peterborough's mayor was positive because the young adult migrants "are the people who work and make money for the city", including through payment of council tax. He said: "Let's not just assume migration is a bad thing. The only bad thing is if you can't deal with it". However, the local Conservative MP thought: "Most people see immigration as a cause for concern … We want people with good skills and earning good salaries contributing to the economy but … we have not been able to choose who comes into the country. The problem is it affects the delivery of public services". For example, the young adult migrants' family size is often larger than that of local people and Peterborough's birth rate in 2011 was the fourth highest in the UK outside London. This sees a need for more school places. Similarly there are pressures on medical services; one GP's register rose from 2000 to 8000 patients from 2004–2006.

Demand for housing in both the private rental and pubic housing sectors has risen, leading to overcrowding. Some unscrupulous landlords charge high rents for poor quality, even unsafe, accommodation. It is clear that better supervision of the private-rented sector is required. Some locals feel that their chances of securing housing have been affected by migration. This might not be true, but perceptions can influence attitudes towards migrants and fuel resentment. One woman interviewed in the *Guardian* stated that her granddaughter has to live with her mother, as she had been priced out of the rental market because landlords make greater returns from renting to multiple families.

Because most migrants are from low income countries, they are prepared to accept low wages and some unscrupulous employers manage to secure workers without paying them the minimum wage. If undocumented, migrants are not in a strong position to complain. Employment might be arranged from the migrant's home country, which means that the job was never open to local applications.

Peterborough is a small city and the impact on its social stability from migration has been evident. This includes tensions between different migrant communities, sometimes a continuation of historical animosities from the migrants' home areas. Many migrants do not have English as their first language – 55 languages are now spoken in Peterborough – and the council has to employ interpreters to help in the schools. Cambridgeshire police spent over £800,000 on translators in 2005–2006. One study showed that 34% of migrants had been provided with an interpreter during their contact with authorities and 25% used family or friends to interpret. It recommended better provision of English language courses. Lack of English language skills is a barrier for migrant workers, affecting their choice of jobs, making them vulnerable in dealings with people such as landlords, and contributing to tension with – and isolation from – the wider community. The woman interviewed in the *Guardian* worried that British culture, including its traditional tolerance, was undermined by other communities with different values: "It is extremely intimidating on this street now. We don't understand each other."

Local people feel that the character of Peterborough has been changed. This is particularly true of the inner city where the migrants have congregated, often in property in multiple-occupation. However, on streets such as Lincoln Road (Figure A32), investment has seen new ventures such as Polish supermarkets and Turkish clothes shops. Peterborough's mayor said that Lincoln Road used to be dead with no businesses and boarded up houses, whereas "Today you have thriving businesses … you have people living there … and it's alive. Doesn't mean it doesn't have its issues, but it's alive."

A study of Peterborough recommended that "there is a need to consult with existing residents in receiving neighbourhoods to explore what some of the issues are from the perspective of local residents" and that "more resources are needed to promote initiatives which increase social interactions between different communities". Meanwhile, in the 2016 Brexit referendum, which was dominated by the subject of migration, Peterborough voted 60.8% in favour of leaving the EU, considerably more than the national proportion of 51.9%.

Figure A32: Lincoln Road, Peterborough

Source: Lovelylight / Alamy Stock Photo

References

'Peterborough braces for new EU arrivals', *The Guardian*, 26 December 2013: *https://www.theguardian.com/uk-news/2013/dec/26/peterborough-romania-bulgaria*

A study of migrant workers in Peterborough: *usir.salford.ac.uk/10113*

2011 census shows highest levels of migration to Peterborough in seven decades: *http://www.peterboroughtoday.co.uk/news/2011-census-show-highest-migration-levels-to-peterborough-in-seven-decades-1-4576279*

Exercise

1. With reference to your case studies of both out-migration and in-migration, explain the impacts of migration on service provision, economic activity and social stability.

Voluntary and forced migration

There is a distinction made between migrants who move of their own free will (voluntary) and others who are compelled to move (forced). In some ways this distinction is too sharp, for rather than their being mutually exclusive, there is a continuum between the voluntary and forced. Some people certainly have to move because of a genuine fear that staying would bring them serious problems, even death. However, others might unconsciously (or consciously) exaggerate threats and move anyway. Some forced migrants have the time and funds to be able to plan their journey and chose where to go, so act more like volunteers. Desperation is a reality, but many who respond to their reality and migrate might be seen by the authorities in their new homeland as being voluntary migrants seeking economic gain. Economic migrants are not guaranteed to receive protection from the government of the receiving nation.

Indisputably forced migrants are asylum seekers and refugees, as defined by the terms of the United Nations ('Geneva Convention') Convention Relating to the Status of Refugees (1951) and the ('New York') Protocol Relating to the Status of Refugees (1967).

Asylum seekers

Asylum seekers are people who have entered a new country having fled persecution and ask permission to remain on the basis that they will face torture or death if they return. There are international agreements about asylum seekers and their treatment, and whilst many applications for asylum are genuine, some are not. The number of asylum seekers has risen in recent years and authorities in receiving countries try to distinguish between genuine claimants and those seeking entry for economic reasons. People in the latter category can be refused permission to remain and be deported.

Refugees

Refugees are defined by the United Nations as "people unable to live safely in their home country". They generally have had limited choice either in their decision to leave or in their ultimate destination. Natural disasters such as floods, volcanoes, famine and drought all cause refugee movement, as do human activities: war and religious, political and/or ethnic discrimination. In 2017 the United Nations High Commission for Refugees (UNHCR, set up in 1950 in the aftermath of the World War II) stated that there were 21.3 million refugees worldwide (including 5.2 million Palestinians). Many refugees had come from the countries of Somalia, Afghanistan and Syria. The UNHCR submits persons for settlement in various states according to their category of need (Figure A33), and counts as 'departures' those who are accepted for settlement (Figure A34). Asylum seekers who are granted permission to stay in a new country might then be reclassified as 'refugees', a different if related use of this term.

Figure A33: UNHCR categories of resettlement needs, January–March 2017

Source: Data from 'Resettlement data', http://www.unhcr.org/uk/

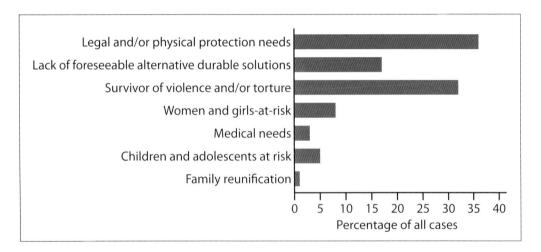

Figure A34: UNHCR submissions and departures, 2013–2016

Source: Data from 'Resettlement data', http://www.unhcr.org/uk/

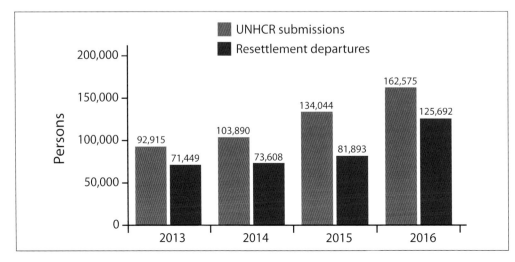

Migration processes, including undocumented migrants

Most migration journeys, particularly regarding internal migration, are straightforward. Processes involved in commonplace migration usually involve engaging estate agents to buy and sell property, removal companies to transfer possessions and transport providers to travel from origin to destination. There might be necessary ancillary processes such as enrolling children in school or choosing a care home. Moving house is stressful, but most migrants readily undergo this stress to start a new job or because they are entering a different life cycle stage, for example:

- Children normally move with their parent(s).
- Students usually move when they go to college or university, many never returning.
- People often migrate upon marriage or union.
- Adults of working age migrate for work reasons.
- Some couples downsize after their children leave home.
- Some migrate upon retirement (sometimes with international destinations).
- Maybe there is a final move into a care home.

Sudden events can lead to migration at any stage, perhaps from the loss of a partner through death or relationship breakdown or unforeseen economic changes, such as unemployment.

Exercise

1. Consider the effect of age and life cycle stage upon migration rates, with reference to Resource A.

Resource A: Migration intensity (rates) and age

Source: Based on A Bernard, M Bell and E Charles-Edwards, 'Life-course transitions and the age profile of internal migration', *Population and Development Review*, 2014, Vol 40 No 2, pages 213–239

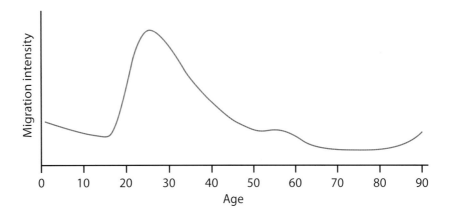

International migrations are more complex, even where this is through official channels for voluntary migrants. Unless moving inside an international bloc such as the EU, within which citizens have right of movement and settlement, migrants have to apply to, and receive permission from, the host country before undertaking their migration journey. The USA operates its well-known 'green card' system. The card is an identity document that attests to its holder's right of permanent residence in the USA. There are three main categories to which application can be made: through family ties, through obtaining employment and through refugee or asylum seeker status. There are other ways to obtain green cards, for example through investing in the USA or via the Diversity Immigrant Visa programme, commonly known as the 'green card lottery'. Most categories of green card are subject to annual quotas. The process for application is cumbersome and time consuming, usually taking several years.

Once the necessary documentation has been acquired, the actual processes – journeys, disposing and acquiring accommodation, etc – is similar to the internal voluntary migrant, if inevitably more complex (and stressful) given the international dimension.

Many people fleeing strife or desperation, be they voluntary or forced migrants, cannot get or cannot wait for official accreditation and move anyway as undocumented migrants. The term 'illegal migrants' was sometimes used for such people, but this had negative connotations, dehumanising migrants and labelling them as criminals. Thus, the term 'undocumented' was adopted instead, if not always by the media or politicians seeking to demonise such migrants for their own purposes. 'Unauthorised migration' is another common term.

The migration processes for undocumented people can be complicated and problematic. Things have been especially difficult in the twenty-first century, which has seen greater restrictions imposed on cross border movement. This has resulted in an increase in migrants having to resort to covert measures to reach their destinations, often involving people traffickers. The traffickers are often unscrupulous and there are many sad cases of African migrants drowning in the Mediterranean Sea when overcrowded boats capsize or sink. There were at least 5000 deaths in 2016, probably many more for authorities count only the bodies that are found. The lucky ones reach land or get rescued by coastguard or naval patrols operated by the European authorities. Once in Europe the migrants then face a struggle to stay. Many have tried to travel onwards in the hope of reaching Britain. The activities of some migrants in northern France trying to get onto or under lorries crossing the Channel have been well documented by the media.

As an example of migration processes of undocumented people, let us consider one man's journey to Northern Ireland.[1] Jafar (not his real name) fled his home country of Sudan because of political aggravation. He went first to Libya, where he spent two years working and saving money before journeying onward to Europe. He crossed the Mediterranean on a small boat from Libya, having bought passage from a people trafficker, and he was lucky enough both for the boat not to sink and for it to remain undetected by coastal border patrols before it reached Sicily. Here Jafar arranged to meet a friend from his home village who had previously claimed asylum in Italy. Jafar was given shelter and took advice from other Sudanese men, who told him not to remain in Italy because of its inadequate social support for asylum seekers. The UK was seen as his best destination since Jafar spoke English. Other pull factors were access to financial assistance (state benefits) and the potential to integrate within British society. Furthermore, his friend provided details of a Sudanese man living in Belfast who would support him. Air travel to Dublin from Italy was made possible by using a falsified refugee travel document provided by one of the Sudanese men. If unchallenged, this would get Jafar into Ireland, if not the UK directly. Jafar was not stopped at the airports and from Dublin telephoned his contact in Belfast who advised him to travel north by

1 Adapted from an unpublished study of migration to Northern Ireland and used with permission from the author.

bus. Jafar then reached Belfast, where he claimed asylum in the UK. Had he been stopped by immigration control in either Sicily or Dublin he would have had to claim asylum there and his plan to enter the UK would have been thwarted. Jafar considers himself to have been lucky.

An unknown number of undocumented migrants never interact with the authorities and remain in legal limbo, presumably working in the black economy. However, many, like Jafar, claim asylum. Regarding the UK, application cannot be made from outside the country, but must be done upon or soon after arrival. Once application has been made, the person cannot be deported until their claim has been processed by the UK Border Agency. Travelling on false documents may harm their case. The agency tries to make decisions within a few weeks, better than in the recent past where claims could drag on for a long time. Some time after an initial interview, a 'substantive interview' takes place when the applicant gets the opportunity to detail their circumstances. The Border Agency keeps tabs on all applicants; some, including those whose application has been rejected, may be held in detention centres, of which there are 11 in the UK, including one in Antrim. Some centres have a chequered record and have been subject to criticism for the way detainees have been treated, especially Yarl's Wood in Bedfordshire. The Border Agency's decision is based upon an assessment on whether the applicant truly faces persecution and whether they could find safety anywhere in their home country. Successful applicants are allowed leave to remain for five years under Refugee status. They can be required to return during that time if the circumstances in their home country ease. If there is still no prospect of safety for them after five years they can apply for Indefinite Leave to Remain (ILR) status. Once granted Refugee status, migrants can seek work, claim benefits and bring over their spouse and children under 18. Asylum seekers are not allowed to work, but might get financial assistance and help with accommodation. If a claim is refused, applicants can appeal but once finally rejected the asylum seeker must return to their home country; if they do not, repatriation can be enforced.

Undocumented migrants are vulnerable. They might well have been exploited and cheated on their migration journey. After arrival, those who remain undocumented might be exploited by gang masters within the black economy. Others might have been unable to pay the traffickers their full account and have to work to pay off their debts. Such work may be unsavoury, including prostitution. One notable event involving undocumented migrants was the death in 2004 of 21 Chinese migrants, who were drowned when picking cockles in dangerous tidal conditions in Morcambe Bay. Within weeks more undocumented migrants were apprehended whilst engaged in the same activity.

Immigration as a political issue

Documented migrants should be welcomed to their new country, as they have been accepted. Early in his presidency, Donald Trump announced a ban on all movement to the USA from seven countries. One reason why the initial policy was controversial was that green card holders from those countries were to be refused entry. Within a few days that aspect of the policy had to be abandoned.

Documented migrants arrive in response to the host country's migration policy; they are wanted, even needed. Sometimes migrants can come anyway, without necessarily being wanted, because they have the right to move to their new country. One example of this is the European Union, whose member countries have to abide by 'four freedoms': the free movement of goods, capital, services and people. This free movement of people has caused problems in the EU. It has seen much migration from poorer counties in Eastern and Southern Europe to wealthier northern nations, although there were some restrictions placed on free movement in the early years after the accession of Eastern European nations.

Migrants often carry out needed jobs (the Polish plumber in the UK became a well-known character) but some locals feel overwhelmed, at least in their perception if not in reality. Resentment against this migration wave, despite its legal basis, became a political issue, especially in the UK. In 2011 David Cameron, the then prime minister, pledged to reduce immigration to tens of thousands annually. This target was never reached; net migration (immigrants minus emigrants) to the UK remained much higher (Figure A35). At the time of writing, reducing net migration to tens of thousands annually remains an aspiration of the British government and it may be easier to achieve once the UK has left the EU. Presumably free movement will then end (Brexit negotiations have not been concluded as this is written).

Figure A35: British migration statistics, year ending September 2016

Source: Data from migrationwatchuk.org

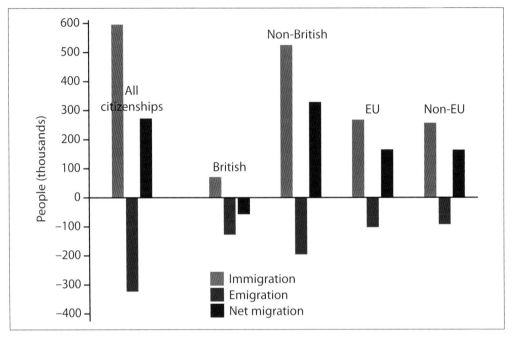

Other European countries are more welcoming of migrants. In 2015 there was a considerable movement of undocumented migrants into Europe, particularly from Syria and the Middle East, a stream which flowed through Turkey, into Greece and north-west further into the EU. The flow was interrupted and diverted by various national governments, some of whom put up fences to stop migrants entering their territory. Germany, by contrast, was welcoming, a political decision based on its need for young labour given its ageing population. About 1.1 million migrants entered Germany in 2015, compared to 475,000 asylum seekers who had done so the previous year. Accepting such a large influx was controversial, particularly after an incident in Cologne on New Year's Day 2016, when there were reports of dozens of women being attacked by 'migrants'.

In other cases, President Trump wants to build a wall to stop Mexicans and others entering the USA across the southern border and pledged to deport undocumented migrants, over 11 million of whom are thought to reside in the US. Australia has used Pacific islands such as Nauru to house undocumented migrants seeking to enter its territory.

CASE STUDY: Canada, a national study of government response to immigration

Figure A36: Map of Canada

Canada is a vast country (Figure A36), slightly larger than the USA, although much of it lies in the Arctic and cannot sustain a dense population. The national population total is only 36 million. There is a rich resource base for industry and plentiful power supplies. The southern part of the country, especially the Prairie Provinces, has rich agricultural land. Most of the population live in cities quite close to the American border.

Canada has a long tradition of migration dating back to European colonisation when its distinction between Anglophones and Francophones (mainly in Quebec and the eastern, Maritime Provinces) began. Immigration has been a central component of nation building in Canada, establishing the pace of demographic and economic growth since the end of the nineteenth century (Figure A37). Canada has always operated a selective migration system through the operation of various policies, which have changed over time to meet the prevailing economic and social needs.

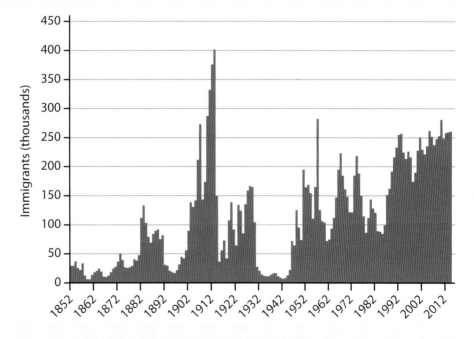

Figure A37: Annual number of immigrants to Canada, 1852–2012

Source: Statistics Canada

The Open Door Policy, 1870–1918

The main economic need during this period was the development of communications, especially the building of the rail network and the development of industry and agriculture. Migration was welcome, the Immigration Act of 1910 encouraged migrants from farmers to domestic servants: the 'Open Door' policy, so-called because there was no restriction on numbers. However, there was a restriction regarding the source of migrants, who were to be from the UK, USA and North-West Europe, in order to keep out "those belonging to nationalities unlikely to assimilate and … prevent the building up of a united nation of people of similar customs and ideals". This political policy to control the racial mix of Canada continued until 1960. The railway companies were unable to attract sufficient migrants from the list of acceptable countries with a white population and had to import Chinese labour. As a result, they had to pay a head tax on each of them.

Preferred/non-preferred countries, 1919–1929

During this phase immigration became more selective. Prospective migrants had to pass a literacy test. The government also separated them into those from 'preferred' as opposed to 'non-preferred' countries. The former included the UK, USA, Australia, New Zealand and South Africa, whose citizens were given financial assistance to aid their move to, and settlement in, Canada. The Empire Settlement Act of 1922 subsidised travel costs of British migrants willing to settle in western Canadian farms. 'Non-preferred' countries included those in Eastern Europe. Their citizens would only be admitted in times of need for the lowest paid jobs and they faced a variety of restrictions. The 'non-preferred' countries also had a 'non-acceptable' category, people from 'visible minorities'. Further, Chinese migrants were forbidden to bring in family members under the Exclusion Order of 1923.

> "It may be very right indeed to separate a man by law from his wife and family if he belongs to a race whose increase in the country would be disastrous to those already in occupation of it, especially if such intruding race be very prolific and very difficult to assimilate and by reason of a more meagre standard of living capable of undoing the masses of those to whom such a country belongs. But aside from all that, the Chinese cannot be rightly said to be separated by any Canadian law from their wives and children in China. They are free to go back to their wives and children at any time, and God speed them!"
>
> Source: Tom MacInnes in *Oriental occupation of British Columbia*, 1927, pages 12–13

The Canadian government exercised tight control over migrant numbers, allowing in more in times of labour shortage. The destination of the new migrants was also controlled, again according to economic need.

The Closed Door Policy, 1930–1945

At this period of depression and war the government stopped all immigration, except for family reunion migrants from Britain and the USA. These family dependents were not allowed to work.

1946–1960

Migration was relaxed in the post-war period, but selection became even more stringent. Some migration was permitted from Eastern Europe, particularly of those fleeing Communist regimes during this Cold War era. However, renewed immigration was not to be allowed to alter Canada's population composition: ethnic selection was still imposed, a policy which was clearly racist. Under the Immigration Act of 1952, unwanted groups or people could be excluded for the following reasons:

- Nationality, citizenship, ethnic group, occupation, class or geographical area of origin.
- Peculiar customs, habits, modes of life, or methods of holding property.
- Unsuitability having regard to climatic, economic and social [conditions].
- Probable inability to become readily assimilated or to assume the duties or responsibilities of citizenship.

1960–1986

This era marked a turning point for Canada's immigration policy. Racist undertones were removed with attention focussed instead on skills offered by potential migrants. Indeed, it became unlawful to discriminate against anybody on the grounds of race, national or ethnic origin, colour, religion or gender. The preferred/non-preferred system was replaced by a points system, designed to be a fairer method of selecting migrants based on economic requirements. Points were awarded objectively based on education, age, language (proficiency in French or English) and skills. This mix of points could be altered as economic conditions changed and numbers could be controlled; an economic downturn in the 1980s saw migration reduced.

1986–1993

Canadian migration policy changed once more, as there was a recognition that Canada now had an ageing population, its fertility levels being close to the replacement rate by the mid-1980s. This led the government to introduce another element into a policy hitherto based on short-term economic need, namely long-term demographic necessity. Immigrants were needed to boost population growth in this under-populated country whilst adjusting the overall age structure of the population. To achieve these aims, migrants were allowed to enter Canada without having arranged work beforehand and their numbers increased from 85,000 in 1985 to almost 250,000 in 1993. There was still selection based on skills and entrepreneurship.

1993 onwards

The Canadian government continues to view migration as an essential requirement for the demographic stability of the country and its policy encourages selected people to immigrate and become citizens. People with Permanent Residence status can apply for Canadian citizenship if they have been in Canada for 1460 days during the six years immediately before the date of application.

There are several main categories of migrant, each with its own regulations. The French-speaking province of Quebec has a target migration of 29,000 in 2017, largely through its **Quebec Skilled Worker Scheme**. Another regional programme is the **Atlantic Pilot Scheme**, under which the four eastern provinces of New Brunswick, Newfoundland and Labrador, Nova Scotia and Prince Edward Island – which have weak economies – encourage migrants who have a job offer from a designated employer in the region. Further, all Canadian Provinces and Territories* (except Quebec) operate **Provincial Nominee Programmes** for their own migrants, who also have to go through the federal government processes.

* Canada is a federation with provinces and territories responsible for certain matters, with the national, federal, government in Ottawa.

Business applicants can go through the **Immigrant Investor Venture Capital Pilot Program**, limited to persons able to show they have at least C$10m of net worth (which must have been legally acquired), discounting their primary residence or inherited wealth. New applicants were not being accepted in 2017. **Self-employed** people can apply if they demonstrate relevant experience in cultural activities, athletics, or farm management, the last if they intend to buy and manage a farm in Canada. **Start-up Visas** may be available for migrants who demonstrate they have the skills and potential to build businesses in Canada.

The **Family Class Scheme** permits Canadians to sponsor their close relatives to come to join them. It is a mark of the needs of its ageing populations that Canada has established a substantial **Caregivers** category for people who come to care for children, the elderly or those with disabilities. It is also a mark of the modern world that Canada hosts asylum seekers and refugees. There is the **Refugee and Humanitarian Resettlement Program** for people brought to Canada under the auspices of the UN High Commission for Refugees. People outside Canada cannot apply themselves to join this program. Others can be sponsored privately. All resettled people are checked for security, criminality and health issues before acceptance. Asylum seekers who have reached Canada can apply under the **In-Canada Asylum Program** for refugee status in the usual way. Government assistance (private in the case of sponsored refugees) is available. This includes language training. Quebec operates its own refugee system.

Figure A38: Six selection factors for Federal Skilled Workers, 2008 and 2017

Source: Canada Immigration and Citizenship, http://www.cic.gc.ca

Despite these humanitarian aspects, the greater part of Canadian migration remains tied to economic needs. There are now three major programs, which qualify for **Express Entry**: the **Federal Skilled Worker** and **Federal Skilled Trades Programs** (suitably qualified people with relevant work experience or tradespeople with an offer of employment) and the **Canadian Experience Class** (for people who have worked in Canada before application). These form what used to be the 'Independent class' and comprise skilled workers and professionals necessary for economic and/or cultural development. A list of required skills and occupations, known as the National Occupation Classification, has been produced. Numbers, though large, are capped and ranking schemes score potential migrants so only the better

Category	Points 2008	Points 2017	Notes
Language Skills	24	28	In English or French. Scores for speaking, reading, listening and writing. Applicants below a minimum standard cannot apply.
Education	25	25	From 5 points for High School to 25 points for a PhD.
Experience	21	15	From 9 points for 1 year's relevant work experience to 15 points for 6 or more years.
Age	10	12	Under 18 0; 18–35 12, dropping by 1 point per year to 47 and older, 0 points.
Arranged employment in Canada	10	10	10 points or 0 if no employment has been arranged.
Adaptability	10	10	Scores for a spouse or partner's language level, applicant's or spouse/partner's past study or work experience in Canada, or having relatives in Canada.
Total	100	100	
Minimum score necessary	67	67	

qualified are accepted. The scores can be adapted over time as circumstances dictate. Between 2008 and 2017 language and age were given greater weight and experience less (Figure A38). Migrants can be directed to reside in areas of Canada most in need of new people, but such direction is not always successful.

The number of migrants under each category is targeted each year. Numbers can exceed the targets by only a limited amount. In 2016 the maximum number was 305,000; in 2017, 320,000, though in both years the actual target was 300,000, made up of migrants in the different categories discussed in Figure A39.

Figure A39: Canada: Immigration targets by category, 2017

Source: Immigration Plan 2017, CIC news, cicnews. com, archive for October 2016

Category	Program	2017 target
Economic programs	Federal skilled worker, Federal skilled trades and Canadian experience class	71,700
	Atlantic Pilot	2000
	Caregivers	18,000
	Business	500
	Provincial Nominees	51,000
	Quebec	29,300
	All economic	172,500
Family class	Spouses, partners, dependent children	64,000
	Parents and grandparents	20,000
	All family class	84,000
Refugees and protected Persons	Government-assisted refugees	7500
	Privately sponsored refugees	16,000
	Blended visa office referred	1500
	Protected persons in Canada and dependents abroad	15,000
	All refugees and protected persons	40,000
Humanitarian and other		3500
Total		**300,000**

Evaluation of the government response to immigration

- National insurance contributions paid by immigrants supports the state pension fund and health care for the elderly.
- Immigrants contribute to the domestic market demand for Canadian goods.
- Migration has always been controlled to reflect perceived economic or demographic needs.
- Earlier policies were blatantly racist, as were migration policies elsewhere at that time, including the White Australia policy.

- Canada had to compete with other settler nations, such as Australia for 'preferred' migrants.

- More enlightened policies have operated since the 1960s with the introduction of the points system.

- Canada has become more globalised and outward facing as a result of this change in policy.

- Migration has always been adjusted to the needs of Canada.

- Attempts to direct migration to less well-developed parts of the country have not always been successful and most have ended up in the large cities. In the south east of Vancouver 40% of residents are of Chinese ethnicity.

- The family reunion system allowed close family members to join their kin in Canada even during periods of economic recession.

- Canada operates a more generous policy towards asylum seekers and refugees than many MEDCs; even so, this is not an open door policy and migrants are scrutinised before acceptance.

- Some new migrants have been unable to find employment that matches their skills and experience.

- In recent years immigration has accounted for most of Canada's population growth, but its age-sex pyramid still shows evidence of population ageing (Figure A40).

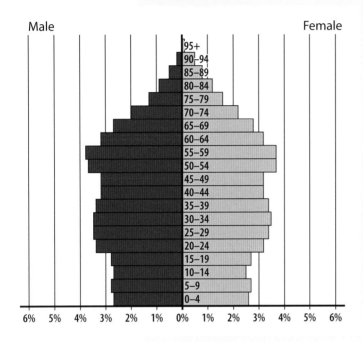

Figure A40: Population pyramid, Canada 2017

Exercise

1. Discuss the way in which political issues have contributed towards Canada's changing migration policies.

Exam Questions

1. What does 'barrier' mean when used in the context of migration? Give an example. [6]

   Question adapted from A2 1 Human Interactions and Global Issues, May 2010, © CCEA 2017

2. With reference to your two small-scale case studies, explain the implications of migration for economic activity and social stability. [15]

3. Study Resource A about migration and urbanisation in part of the Arab world. Use this information and your small-scale case study to explain some of the implications of in-migration. [15]

   Question adapted from A2 1 Human Interactions and Global Issues, May 2011, © CCEA 2017

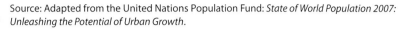
Resource A: Arab states of Western Asia

Source: Adapted from the United Nations Population Fund: *State of World Population 2007: Unleashing the Potential of Urban Growth.*

Doha, capital of Qatar, 2009

Urbanisation levels in the Arab states of western Asia range from very high, such as Qatar, to low. Urban centres dominate the economies of most of these countries, and rural-urban migration is still strong in several of them. Coupled with natural population increase, this generates some high rates of urban growth. Government policies are generally hostile to migration, which helps to limit the supply of housing for the urban poor, who often find themselves in informal settlements. As elsewhere, failure to plan ahead for urban growth increases density and slum formation in these neighbourhoods.

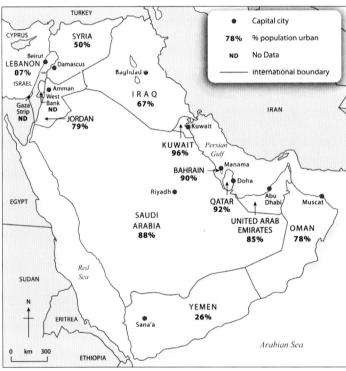

Neither history nor recent experience gives any support to the notion that urban migration can be stopped or even significantly slowed. Opposing migration and refusing to help the urban poor for fear of attracting additional migrants merely increases poverty and environmental degradation.

Data from 'Percentage living in urban areas', Nation Master, http://www.nationmaster.com/country-info/stats/People/Percentage-living-in-urban-areas

References

Information on immigration:
United Nations High Commission for Refugees – *www.unhcr.org*
USA 'green card', Department of Homeland Security – *https://www.uscis.gov/greencard*
'Ugandan Asians advert 'foolish' says Leicester councillor' – *www.bbc.co.uk/news/uk-england-leicestershire-19165216*
'Germany saw 1.1 million migrants in 2015 as debate intensifies', Bloomberg, 6 January 2016

Information on Asylum:
Asylum Aid – *asylumaid.org.uk*
UK government information on asylum – *https://www.gov.uk/browse/visas-immigration/asylum*
Missing Migrants Project – *missingmigrants.iom.int*
Mediterranean sea arrivals and recorded deaths – *http://missingmigrants.iom.int/mediterranean*

Information on immigration in Canada:
Immigration rules and procedures [for Quebec] – *http://www.immigration-quebec.gouv.qc.ca/en/informations/rules-procedures.html*
Canada Immigration and Citizenship – *www.cic.gc.ca/English*
150 years of immigration in Canada – *statcan.gc.ca/pub/11-630-x/11-630-x2016006-eng.htm*

3. THE GEOGRAPHIES OF CYBERSPACE

Case studies

General reference to places for illustration purposes only

Students should be able to:

(i) understand that the development of cyberspace has led to changes in socio-economic activity and has helped to produce international cultures

(ii) recognise that global contrasts remain, brought about by economic, social and political issues

The development of cyberspace

Cyberspace, a term coined from the words 'cybernetics' and 'space' by science fiction writer William Gibson in 1982, is "the online world of computer networks and especially the Internet" according to the online Merriam-Webster dictionary. Or it is the "realm of electronic communication" (Dictionary.com). Or "the electronic medium of computer networks, in which online communication takes place" (The Free Dictionary). These definitions and others can be found in moments in cyberspace itself; looking for definitions no longer requires access to a printed dictionary. More loosely, cyberspace characterises everything associated with the Internet and Internet culture.

The origin of the Internet dates back to 1960s America and attempts to develop more secure communications, largely for military purposes, by connecting up and merging computer networks. Outside the military, it was first widely adopted by universities in the 1980s and became fully commercial from the mid-1990s.

A necessary companion to the Internet is the World Wide Web (www). This is the 'space' where documents and other material is held, identified by their Uniform Resource Locators (URLs). They are accessed via the Internet by users, who employ hyperlinks to navigate between different documents and websites. The web was invented by the British computer scientist, Sir Tim Berners-Lee, who proposed and first implemented the system in 1989. It was made available to the public in 1991 and rapidly expanded after web browsers were developed by 1993. Today, almost half the world's population is connected to the World Wide Web via the Internet. A huge industry, a new employment sector and new technologies, including communications satellites, have grown up around cyberspace and its components. Also, cyberspace has affected human behaviour, especially socio-economic activity.

Changes in socio-economic activity

Thomas Young (1773–1829) was a doctor who proposed theories on the workings of the eye, an experimental physicist, and the Egyptologist who deciphered the Rosetta Stone. He has been called "the last man who knew everything". Since Young's time, the expansion of knowledge denies such a title to anybody else. Now anybody with access to the Internet can be in possession of almost any fact within seconds. They might not possess the knowledge within their brains, but they can find it in cyberspace through the device in their hands. Knowledge is no longer the property of a privileged few but is widely available. This, the democratisation of knowledge, can bring real benefits. For example, in terms of development, many people in LEDCs can share in learning as readily as citizens of MEDCS, provided they have access to the Internet. Advice can be sought, problems solved.

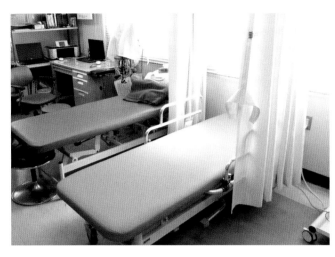

Figure A41: The hospital/clinic on the island of Nakanoshima, Japan

Figure A41 shows the two-bed hospital on the Japanese island of Nakanoshima, population about 160. There is no resident doctor, just a nurse, although in emergencies patients can be evacuated by helicopter. In the ward, as well as the beds the photograph shows two computers. Thus, if needed, the nurse can seek advice, guidance and knowledge on the web or via a video chat consult with a doctor.

Cyberspace has changed the way in which some people work. This includes the growth of working from home or distance. Recall Barra (pages 241–244), the island in the Outer Hebrides, where the council has invested in high-speed broadband to facilitate islanders to work from distance. Working from home reduces travel needs; cutting down the time and money spent commuting to and from work. It reduces emissions from travel, benefiting the environment. It also offers employees more flexibility with childcare arrangements and other commitments. Many companies find it beneficial too, as less workspace is needed and costs such as electricity and heating can be reduced.

There have always been people who, without easy access to the bricks and mortar premises of retailers, have shopped by distance. In the last century, in rural parts of the USA the annual arrival of the Sears or Montgomery Ward catalogue would be eagerly anticipated so goods could be obtained through mail order. Shopping over distance still exists – it is more important than ever – but it no longer requires flipping through a large book (the 1895 Sears catalogue was 532 pages). Instead, it is now almost entirely carried out via e-commerce, activated by clicking computer keys. Catalogues in paper form are still produced by some companies but even then they bear a website address to enable customers to order online as well as through the post. Online shopping has transformed retailing, for both good and ill. People in Barra can now shop as easily as those in Birmingham or Belfast. One report from Barra said, "Online shopping means that there is virtually nothing we can't get here. I actually don't like shopping in cities any more – it seems inefficient and frustrating".

Figure A42: The closed BHS store in central Belfast, March 2017

Online shopping has supported delivery firms, making up for the massive decline in the number of letters posted since the development of cyberspace, but has adversely affected

those bricks and mortar shops. Many famous retailers have closed in recent years as that "inefficient and frustrating" activity of physical shopping has declined. Even groceries and other foods can now be ordered online and it would be perfectly possible to live fully without ever entering a shop. Retailers have had to adjust and establish an online presence. BHS, which closed on the High Street in 2016, now operates online: "Welcome to our new home, the British Home Store. WE'RE EXCITED TO BE BACK" (bhs.com). Those retailers that still have a physical presence also invest in their websites, retailing's cyberspace, seeking market share and recognition – the more the retailer is known about, the greater its chance of attracting customers. One example of successful recognition is the John Lewis department store chain. Its annual Christmas advert, released online since 2007, has become "something of an annual tradition in British popular culture" according to Wikipedia, the free Internet encyclopaedia, itself now an Internet institution.

The Internet has also been of benefit to smaller retailers and craft producers who can establish and operate a company from home, without the expense of business premises. They can reach both the local and global markets by setting up their own website or joining a marketplace site, such as eBay or Amazon, as a virtual 'shop' or seller for a fee. Other websites, such as Gumtree, allow goods and possessions to be sold, exchanged or given away without listing costs.

Other services, industries and activities have been transformed. People book travel and entertainment tickets, arrange holidays, pay bills and taxes, do their banking, all online, usually without having to speak to a living person. Banks, like shops, have lost footfall and many branches have been closed. This is despite the inconvenience to customers, including the elderly and disabled, of having to use alternative banking locations and the social costs of excluding low-income customers from mainstream financial services. These are the groups who are least likely to use e-banking, the rise of which had led to the closure of their bank branch in the first place. That the elderly have, in many cases, not entered cyberspace is a social problem of limited duration, for coming generations will have grown up using it.

Cyberspace has been associated with globalisation, the process of the world becoming more interconnected and interdependent. Goods and services produced in one part of the world are becoming increasingly available in other parts. Companies can seek clients from across the globe, given instant communications via cyberspace and the ability to send documents electronically. One downside of globalisation is competition, and small, local businesses are those most likely to struggle as a result.

Another issue with the increased use of cyberspace is cybercrime. With so much business now conducted through the Internet, criminals and hackers have seen possibilities to profit or make mischief. 'Phishing' is the term given to Internet scams, where victims might be convinced to respond to an email offering rich rewards if they simply send through the details of their accounts. Alternatively, they might be told that there is a problem with their account that requires them to reveal their personal details and passwords. Another concern is 'malware', systems deliberately designed to cause harm to the user's computer, either for the malicious satisfaction of the malware designer or to make money by holding the user's computer to ransom. For example, in May 2017, about 100 countries were affected by the WannaCry 'ransomware' attack, which threatened to shut down systems until a ransom was paid in the Internet currency, Bitcoin. The British National Health Service was particularly affected, perhaps because many of its sections were using systems without recent security updates. Also of growing concern is cyberterrorism – activities designed to damage and disrupt computer systems to achieve political gains through intimidation. It particularly affects national security systems that might be vulnerable to interference from outside forces.

Socially, life has been transformed; people move, travel and interact in different ways than before. Facebook, Twitter and other social media platforms offer myriad opportunities for forming and joining interest groups and new social communities, which can be global in extent. Online games, such as Call of Duty, allow people to chat

Fig A43: Four of the estimated 2.71 billion people in the world who use smartphones

to players worldwide as they play. There are location maps showing where they are supposed to be fighting, often in 'real' war zones, such as Iraq. Role-playing games, such as World of Warcraft, allow people to be submerged in new worlds and new geography, interacting socially with other people who are also role-playing as someone else, all within Cyberspace. Minecraft takes this further, allowing people to create their own new worlds. There are also online interest groups, forums and blogs catering for almost any conceivable interest or hobby. The Internet uses cookies to filter information according to users' interests, providing information and links according to demographic group, location and key words used. All this has increased and broadened people's opportunities and altered their behaviour.

On the downside, people now look at their screens, not at each other. Friends often interact via their smartphones, on social media or private message, rather than physically talking. Cyberbullying is a sad outcome of the wide availability of the Internet. This is when a bully uses the Internet to target their victim via social media, private message or email. Examples include posting unkind or abusive comments on social media, sending threatening messages or sharing photographs or personal details online without permission. A survey showed that over half of young people had observed cyberbullying taking place and this can badly affect some victims.

Exercise

1. When in public, especially on public transport, observe people's behaviour. Are they having conversations or looking at screens? Use your observations to help you explain why and how social behaviour and practice has been influenced by modern technology.

International cultures

Culture is a shared set of norms, behaviours, customs and sometimes beliefs, which operate within a group. There is often an assumption that residents of a nation have a shared culture, although there will be variations within a national population, given the existence of regional and social sub-groupings. International culture refers to the way in which globalisation has spread certain aspects of culture, especially popular culture, widely throughout the world. This is not a recent phenomenon. On 17 February 1945, a British soldier stationed in Accra, in what became Ghana, wrote to his wife in England saying, "I saw a first rate film the other night – *Together Again* with Charles Boyer and Irene Dunne, very funny and well acted". This film had been released in Hollywood on 22 December 1944. So within two months, despite World War II being in progress, it had been screened half a world away. This demonstrates that international cultures did not start with cyberspace. However, cyberspace has broadened and hastened the spread of international culture and in some ways diluted national culture. Streaming media, such as Netflix, Amazon Prime and YouTube, provides easy access to international entertainment to the detriment of national television broadcasting. Even the ritual of watching national news bulletins or reading newspapers has been affected as more and more people turn to the Internet for information.

Important sports events are shown everywhere. Sporting heroes are international celebrities. Certain teams, especially football teams, are marketed worldwide. Manchester United's website can be read in Mandarin, Spanish, French, Japanese and Korean, as well as English. Chelsea has 89 official international supporters' clubs in 49 different countries. Even Birmingham City, a team rarely in the Premiership, has supporters' clubs in 14 countries. Foreign fans, unable to visit the grounds, keep up with their teams on television and online. Football is now part of international culture in a way unimaginable before cyberspace. The 2014 FIFA World Cup final in Brazil attracted an audience of just over one billion people, about one person in seven throughout the globe. Football is just one dimension of international culture; impressive statistics, if not so large, might be found about popular musicians, actors and entertainers.

However, cyberspace has not led to the world having a uniform international culture. Differences in language, traditions, religion and historical experience will always moderate the spread of global culture. English may be the dominant language of the Internet, but it appears to be in decline. In 1996 research estimated that 80% of Internet content was in English. By 2005 this had fallen to 45%. France and French Canada are concerned about the preponderance of English on the Internet and strive to get their citizens to operate through French, sending not an email but *un courriel*. Regional cultural differences will always remain, even if there are shared global events such as the Olympics. Hybrid cultures result, mixing elements of local and international cultures.

Global contrasts: the digital divide

Access to cyberspace is not uniform; there is a 'digital divide' between those who use the Internet and those who don't. The divide exists even in MEDCs, reflecting age, educational and socio-economic differences. Globally the digital divide reflects contrasts between MEDCs and LEDCs. Figure A44 highlights this, each year showing a considerably greater proportion of the population in MEDCs using the Internet than those in LEDCs. It shows growth everywhere, but note the rate of growth in LEDCs is faster, increasing fivefold over the 11-year period – LEDCs are catching up.

Figure A44: Worldwide Internet use, 2005–2016

Source: Data from International Telecommunications Union (ITU), www.itu.int

Use of the Internet	2005	2010	2016
Global users	16%	30%	47%
MEDC users	51%	67%	81%
LEDC users	8%	21%	40%

Economic issues

Information technology advance is everywhere associated with productivity improvement, so the development of the necessary infrastructure should lead to economic growth. Being on the wrong side of the digital divide is an economic issue for LEDCs. Figure A44 shows they are making progress, but there remains a long way to go, particularly for rural areas which have poorer provision. In some ways, the global contrast in the Internet reproduces the LEDC position in infrastructure and other technologies, such as poorer roads, fewer and slower railways and fewer fixed line telephones than MEDCs. For example, in Ghana in 2012 there were only 285,000 landlines, the system was unreliable and was not distributed widely, most lines being

Figure A45: Communications mast, Inishmore, Aran Islands, Co Galway

in and around Accra, the capital city. Ghana was ranked 120th amongst the nations in terms of landline provision. In the same year, Ghana had 25.6 million mobile phones and the country was ranked 42nd. Provided there are satellites in place and phone masts, cyberspace can be accessed through portable devices, so it is much easier to use hand held devices than fixed lines. LEDCs are simply by-passing the technological stage of fixed lines to their economic advantage.

Mention has been made of Barra needing to install fast broadband; the same is true of other islands (Figure A45), rural areas and cities everywhere. The Internet and all that it brings is not just necessary for economic development, it is now simply regarded as a given, much as having a water supply or electricity.

Social issues

The Internet plays such an important role in education, leisure and employment that people without access or the skills to operate it effectively are disadvantaged. LEDCs have less availability than MEDCS but Figure A44 shows that 19% of MEDC populations were without access in 2016. Some were old; others were poor. Education has to strive to bridge this divide for schoolchildren, whilst the provision of computers for public use in places such as libraries helps adults and children alike. Young people without a smartphone are surely cut off from much contemporary social life.

Political issues

The Internet has the potential to lead to healthier democracies. The information available can help people learn about political issues and choices; the communication potential can increase public participation in elections and decision making. Politicians use the tools too, from Barack Obama's then innovative and extensive use of social media in campaigning and organising voters for his first American presidential election in 2008 to President Donald Trump's famous tweets. Another good example was in July 2016, when the Turkish President Recep Tayyip Erdogan, used FaceTime to address his citizens and ask them to take to the streets to end a political coup against him.

However, not all countries or their political leaders necessarily welcome the openness of the Internet. Some politicians fear the scrutiny to which open cyberspace might submit them. It is notable that whilst western democracies generally allow and display wide ranging discussions, even on government websites, other countries do not favour open debate and official sites are less full and frank. There are worries about the democratisation of knowledge and the growth of participatory democracy. Myanmar (formerly Burma), Iran, North Korea, China, Saudi Arabia and the United Arab Emirates have all restricted access to content or systems within the Internet given their sensitivities, especially to political, religious and human rights debate. In China, the search engine Google has had many problems in its operation given interference from the Chinese authorities. Instead Chinese companies, including Baidu and Alibaba, dominate the market. In the closed society of North Korea, the global Internet is accessible only with special permission, usually restricted to foreigners and some government officials. Other people in North Korea have no access to the full Internet, only to a domestic search engine, Kwangmyong, which is officially controlled and censored. In April 2017, Turkey blocked access to the Internet encyclopaedia Wikipedia, having in the past also blocked Twitter, Facebook and YouTube, for a time, as well as sites directly critical of the Turkish government or President Recep Tayyip Erdogan. No official reason was given for the Wikipedia ban, but there has been speculation that it was a political decision to suppress dissent.

Exercise

1. Explain why the impact of cyberspace has been uneven across the world.

Exam Questions

1. Explain how the development of cyberspace has led to changes in socio-economic activity. [8]

   Question from CCEA A2 1 Processes and Issues in Human Geography, Specimen Assessment Materials © CCEA 2017

2. How have political issues brought about global contrasts in the impact of cyberspace? [9]

References

'Bank branch closures', House of Commons Briefing Paper 35, 15 December 2016, *researchbriefings.files.parliament.uk/documents/SN00385/SN00385.pdf*

What is cyber bullying? *www.bullying.co.uk/cyberbullying*

International Politics in the Digital Age: Power Diffusion or Power Concentration? *https://www.academia.edu/14336129/International_Politics_in_the_Digital_Age*

'The digital divide, ICT and broadband Internet', Internetworldstats: *http://www.internetworldstats.com/links10.htm*

'Turkish authorities block Wikipedia without giving reason': *http://www.bbc.co.uk/news/world-europe-39754909*

'English is no longer the language of the web': *https://qz.com/96054/english-is-no-longer-the-language-of-the-web/*

Planning for Sustainable Settlements

1. SUSTAINABLE DEVELOPMENT

Case studies

Sustainability in a city: Leicester

Students should be able to:

(i) explain sustainability with reference to social and environmental considerations

(ii) demonstrate knowledge and understanding of urban ecological and carbon footprints

(iii) understand how sustainability is related to waste management, energy consumption and water supply

The concept of sustainable development became prominent after the 1992 Earth Summit in Rio de Janeiro. It refers to development "that meets the needs of the present without compromising the ability of future generations to meet their own needs" (Bruntland Report, 1987). At the Earth Summit in Rio it was agreed that all nations should adopt a sustainable development strategy for the twenty-first century. This became known as Agenda 21. The UK was one of the first countries to adopt these principles, publishing the 'Sustainable Development Strategy' in 1994, 'A Better Quality of Life, A Strategy for Sustainable Development in the UK' in 1999 and 'Securing the Future: Delivering UK Sustainable Development Strategy' in 2005. UK sustainable development policy now comes under the Department for Environment, Food and Rural Affairs.

As population grows and urbanises, the global economic situation changes and countries like China and India, with large populations, have made dramatic economic progress in recent decades. These recently industrialised nations will make demands on scarce resources and contribute to waste generation. Sustainable development is especially challenging in relation to settlements because they alter the components of the natural environment including drainage basins, forests and water resources. Economic activities in settlements have caused environmental damage to the atmosphere, resulting in global warming and acid rain, pollution of rivers and oceans, and have generated large amounts of waste, much of which is non-biodegradable.

In MEDCs economic development was often based on the exploitation of finite reserves, such as mineral resources and fossil fuels, with little regard for the potential repercussions for the environment or the health of local communities. Then when coal mining declined in Britain whole communities experienced the social and economic difficulties associated with unemployment, along with the environmental consequences of derelict buildings and waste tips. With limited alternative employment opportunities, and lacking the skills required for modern industry, many people became unemployed. Unemployment has a knock-on effect on other sectors of economic activity, for example demand for non-essential items falls. Gradually these areas become economic blackspots and can enter a downward spiral of decline. Personal morale diminishes and a raft of social problems can follow, including family splits, poor educational attainment, social exclusion and criminality. In other words, these settlements built and developed during the boom years of a single industry, such as coal mining or shipbuilding, proved not to be sustainable when economic circumstances altered.

Other settlement issues challenging sustainable development relate to urban sprawl, where new residential, retail and industrial developments encroach onto the rural–urban fringe, resulting in increased pollution from traffic and a reduction in biodiversity. Many inner city areas have become run down as developers seek more attractive greenfield sites for development.

Exercise

1. Study Resources A and B.

    (a) Using the website ninis2.nisra.gov.uk (which is the source of the data in Resource A), research Ballymacarrett, in inner city Belfast, where shipbuilding used to provide much employment and which is the 18th most deprived ward of the 582 wards in Northern Ireland.

    (b) Discuss the evidence that shows that this ward was not developed in a sustainable way.

Resource A: Social and economic data for Ballymacarrett (inner city) and Belfast, 2011

Source: Neighbourhood Statistics (NISRA) Website: www.nisra.gov.uk/ninis licensed under the Open Government Licence v3.0

Indicator	Ballymacarrett	Belfast
% with less than 5 GCSE grade C or equivalent	60.82	41.14
% unemployed	8.09	5.67
% people declaring good or very good health	68.74	75.87
% owner occupied households	30.69	51.66
Mean household size	2.14	2.29

Resource B: The location of Ballymacarrett within Belfast

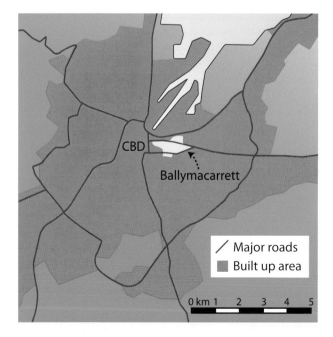

The UK government's sustainable development strategy, developed since 1994, now seeks to monitor sustainability, applying to society, the economy and the environment.

Social considerations

In settlements a sustainable society should aim to incorporate the following guidelines in planning proposals:

- Provision of good quality housing, health and recreational facilities.
- Address poverty and social exclusion in the more deprived areas.
- Improve the local surroundings, especially in areas of industrial decline.
- Ensure that the character of rural areas is maintained.
- Establish partnerships with local organisations to promote community engagement.

Environmental considerations

Environmental concerns are perhaps the most challenging of all the targets for sustainable development. Key areas are:

- Cutting greenhouse gas emissions and improving air quality, especially in urban areas.
- Promoting the development and supply of renewable energy at competitive prices.
- Improving waste management including the promotion of recycling.
- Safeguarding water resources.
- Improving land stewardship, biodiversity and protecting wildlife.
- Working internationally to tackle global challenges such as climate change.

In order to monitor progress on sustainable development the government developed a range of 35 Sustainabile Development Indicators to be measured. A sample of these indicators is given below:

- Economic prosperity
- Knowledge and skills (human capital)
- Social capital (people helping each other; the benefits gained from trust and cooperation within social networks)
- Housing (net additional dwellings and housing energy efficiency)
- Greenhouse gas emissions
- Water (usage and quality)
- Proportion of physically active people
- Air quality (days when air pollution is moderate or higher)
- Renewable energy
- Waste disposal and recycling
- Biodiversity

Information from the Department for Environment, Food and Rural Affairs, *Sustainable Development Indicators, July 2013*. Contains public sector information licensed under the Open Government Licence v3.0

Delivering sustainable development requires financial input and engagement from government. Policies are in place, but the record in the UK has been mixed, especially given the controversial nature of some sustainable development initiatives such as wind farms. The Sustainable Development Commission was established in 2000 to manage national and local sustainable development policies in the UK as well as promoting a global perspective on this issue. However, the Commission was shut down in 2011, and in a closing statement wrote "more than twenty years after the Brundtland Commission, governments still struggle to place sustainable development at the heart of what they do". At the international level the European Commission has produced a fact sheet on their policies. Further, in 2015 the United Nations replaced its Millennium Development Goals with 17 universal Sustainable Development Goals focusing on five key elements: people, planet, peace, prosperity and partnership (see 'The Global Goals for Sustainable Development', *Geography for CCEA AS Level*, Colourpoint Educational, pages 232–235).

Urban ecological and carbon footprints

World population increased dramatically in recent decades with an associated impact on demand for the Earth's resources. The total world population currently stands at 7.4 billion, with about three quarters residing in LEDCs. With increased affluence in MEDCs and the economic rise of other economies such as those of the BRICS (Brazil, Russia, India, China, South Africa) – especially China – the demand for consumer goods has increased, consuming finite resources and increasing waste. In a global society it is possible to import from abroad and cheap airfares enable more international travel, also affecting consumption and pollution. According to the Global Footprint Network it takes the equivalent of 1.5 Earths to provide the resources our world population uses in every day life and to absorb our waste for one year. This means that it takes the Earth one year and six months to produce what we use in one year. If everybody had the consumption patterns of Americans we would need the equivalent of four Earths to support us. Turning resources into waste faster than waste can be turned back into resources threatens global ecosystems, and causes pollution, global climate change and food shortages. Many organisations, including the UN, have been proactive in formulating measures to encourage us to live more sustainably. In particular, the environmental impacts of urban areas are of much concern because approximately 3.9 billion people or 53.9% of the world's population now live in urban areas, especially in large cities. Ecological and carbon footprints are methods used to evaluate sustainability in an area and enable comparisons to be made between regions.

Ecological footprints

The ecological footprint refers to the total number of hectares (global hectares) required to provide an area with all of its needs, including farmland, fuel and water resources, as well as the amount of land required to absorb its carbon dioxide emissions and other waste. The figure is then compared to the actual area of the region. The ecological footprint is really a measurement of the land area required to sustain a population and can be measured at any scale from individual people to the globe. Because cities have high-density populations, industry and high levels of car ownership, their ecological footprints are inevitably larger than their physical areas. In 2009 the World Bank published a study of the ecological footprint for London. Some of the results are summarised in Figures B1 and B2.

Figure B1: Resource use and waste generation in London

- The population of Greater London at the 2011 census was 8.2 million (9.8 million in the Greater London Built-up Area).
- In 2003 Londoners consumed 154,400 GigaWatt hours (GWh) of energy (or 13,276,000 tonnes of oil equivalent), which produced 41 million tonnes of CO_2.

- Londoners consume about 6.7 tonnes of materials per capita each year.

- 26 million tonnes of waste are generated each year.

- 6.9 million tonnes of food are consumed each year.

- In the mid-2000s Londoners were travelling about 64 billion passenger kilometres annually, of which 69% was by car.

- Water consumption reached 876,000,000,000 litres, of which 28% was lost to leakage. Per capita water consumption was 163 litres per day, against a national average of 150 litres per day.

Figure B2: Ecological footprint for London

- The ecological footprint of London was 49 million global hectares (gha) in the mid-2000s, which was 42 times its biocapacity and 293 times its geographical area. This is about twice the area of the UK, and roughly the size of Spain.

- The ecological footprint per London resident was 6.63 gha against a UK average of 6.3 gha and a global average of 2.18 gha.

- The ecological footprint of London's tourists was estimated at 2.4 million gha, which equates to an additional 0.32 gha per Londoner.

- The proposed global average for 2050 is targeted at 1.44 gha per capita. For Londoners to be ecologically sustainable by 2050, a 35% reduction in the ecological footprint by 2020 and an 80% reduction by 2050 will be needed.

Exercise

1. Northern Ireland's ecological footprint is 5.63 gha. What does this figure mean?

2. Study the information relating to Ecological Footprints in the USA and Chad in Resources A–D.

   (a) Describe the relationship between resource demand (ecological footprint) and resource supply (biocapacity*) in both countries.

   (b) Contrast the ecological footprints of Chad and the USA.

Resource A: Resource demand (ecological footprint) per person and resource supply (biocapacity) in Chad 1961–2005

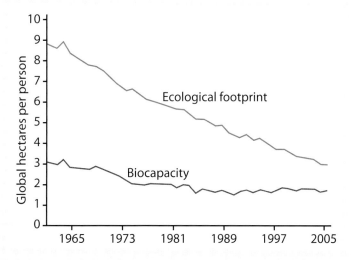

* Biocapacity varies each year with ecosystem management, agricultural practices (such as fertiliser use and irrigation), ecosystem degradation and weather.

Resource B: Components of the ecological footprint per person in Chad 1961–2005

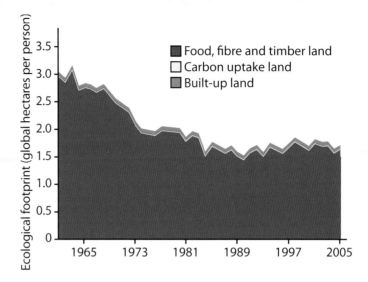

Resource C: Resource demand (ecological footprint) per person and resource supply (biocapacity) in USA 1961–2005.

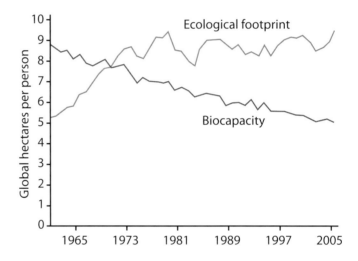

Resource D: Components of the ecological footprint per person in USA 1961–2005

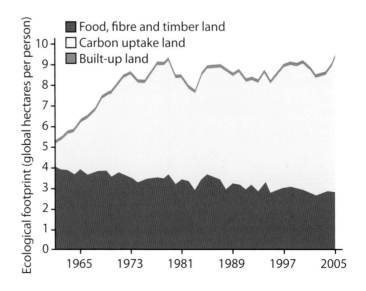

Carbon footprints

A carbon footprint is a sub-set of the ecological footprint. It measures the total amount of carbon dioxide emissions that enters the atmosphere as a result of the electricity and fuel used in everyday life as well as the amount of CO_2 emissions generated by the manufacture of the products bought. There are two types of emissions:

- Direct emissions result from heating and car use.
- Indirect emissions occur from the generation of electricity, the production of goods and services, and the amount of transport required to bring them to the point of sale.

The carbon footprint is measured in tonnes of CO_2. Carbon footprints have been produced at various scales from national to individual. The carbon footprint in the UK peaked at 1296 million tonnes in 2007, falling by 19% by 2013 (DEFRA). You can calculate your household's carbon footprint at www.carbonfootprint.com.

The pie chart in Figure B3 shows the main elements that make up the total of a typical person's carbon footprint in the developed world. The primary footprint (in orange) is a measure of our direct emissions of CO_2 from the burning of fossil fuels, including domestic energy consumption and transportation (such as cars and planes). The secondary footprint (**in purple**) is a measure of the indirect CO_2 emissions from the whole lifecycle of the products we use (those associated with their manufacture and eventual breakdown).

Local councils incorporate both ecological and carbon footprint analysis into the planning of new developments. Increasingly, government and public sector businesses will carry out carbon footprint analysis. Belfast City Council's website (www.belfastcity.gov.uk) has information about how the city plans to reduce its carbon footprint.

Figure B3: Personal carbon footprints in the developed world

Source: Data from http://www.carbonfootprint.com/

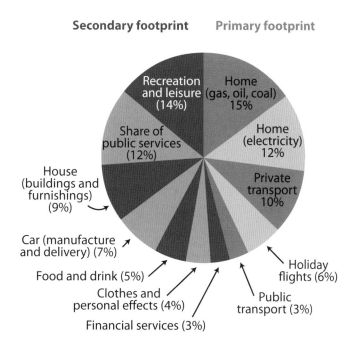

Exercise

1. Using Resource A, as well as other material in this section, explain how sustainable development is related to social, economic and environmental considerations.

2. Discuss how urban ecological and carbon footprint analysis might be incorporated into urban planning.

3. Study Resources B and C and comment on the global patterns of ecological footprints revealed.

Resource A:
Sustainability and
development

Source: Human
Development Report
2015, United Nations
Development Programme,
http://hdr.undp.org

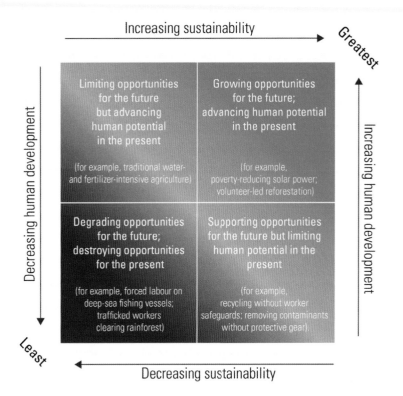

Resource B: Average
ecological footprint
in global hectares per
person per country in
2012

Source: Data from WWF
Living Planet Report, 2016,
www.wwf.org.uk

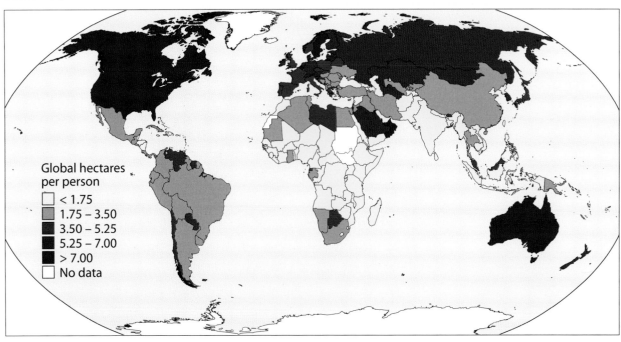

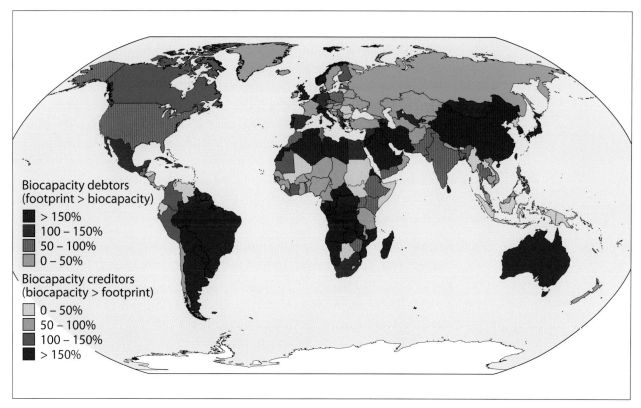

Resource C: The ecological wealth of nations

Source: Data from Global Footprint Network, Annual Report 2012, www.footprintnetwork. org/images/article_ uploads/2012_Annual_ Report.pdf

Waste management

Wherever human beings gather, waste is produced, from piles of bones and shells, botanical waste, bits of broken pot and stone tools found in the waste heaps or 'middens' studied by archaeologists to the more problematic wastes of our own industrial era. Human waste production and disposal is one of the characteristics of the present human-induced geological period, recently dubbed the anthropocene. Waste from human bodies, from excreta to the bodies themselves, is part of the problem. Waste has always had to be managed to enable societies to exist and reproduce. Thus, every society developed a means of disposing of their dead for hygienic reasons, if often as part of a ceremony of honouring the deceased. In the past other wastes were not always handled effectively, dumping of wastes in streets or water bodies being especially noxious. For example, on 12 November 1817 the *Belfast News Letter* wrote that "nuisances [which included parts of animals] cast into and heaped up in May's Dock by the butchers, porters and others are sufficient to spread contagion … stopping up … the tide and obstructing the free passage of the sewers." As societies modernised, increasingly waste disposal became regulated and contained – rules were brought in that no longer allowed Belfast butchers to throw pigs' heads into the dock.

Cities throughout the world at the very least have rubbish 'dumps'. In some LEDC cities dumps are scavenged by local people who make a living from recycling material of some value that has been disposed of there. In more prosperous places, the dumps, properly termed landfill sites, are carefully managed (Figure B4).

Figure B4: Landfill site in central Israel

Some wastes are particularly troublesome, such as asbestos, hospital waste and especially nuclear waste from power stations and these have to be handled with great care, often at considerable expense, to minimise risk to health and life. Otherwise, waste is now seen almost as a resource. For example, in 2015 Birmingham City Council ran a public consultation scheme called 'Waste … it's not all rubbish', part of which sought views on how waste could be made more valuable. Local authorities operate recycling centres, with many also having waste-to-power schemes where combustible waste is burnt to produce electricity. Birmingham runs such a plant at Tyseley, which processes about 350,000 tons of waste annually to produce 25 MW of electricity. Ferrous metals from the waste are recovered and sold. Such plants have been criticised for causing air pollution, whilst environmentalists argue that it would be more sustainable if the waste were not generated in the first place. Hence the familiar 'reduce, reuse, recycle' mantra:

- *Reduce:* Minimising waste is the most important strategy in waste management. People are encouraged to buy less or otherwise act responsibly.

- *Reuse:* Extending the life of a product by using it and reusing it as much as possible. Donating products to charity shops and clothes banks are popular ways of extending a product's life even further.

- *Recycle:* Converting items into new products. Glass, metals and paper are obvious examples. Recycling waste paper rather than making fresh paper not only saves trees and space in landfill but also water (40% less is needed) and energy (70% less is needed).

Energy consumption

Settlements have always consumed energy. People from all eras have required warmth, cooked food, and the manufacture of clothes and utensils. What has changed is the energy source: human and animal power and fires from wood have given way to the varied supplies of our own day, meeting our complex and energy-intensive demands. Nuclear fission provides terrifying weapons but also electricity, an energy mode indispensible to modern life. Electricity is also produced from fossil fuels and increasingly from renewable sources, as we realise the damage of fossil fuel consumption to our environment and climate. Pollution is only one problem. There are fears, too, of energy shortages, from both running out and from being unable to secure supplies. That the Middle East, a region that is unstable politically, is a major source for oil has long been seen as a problem for oil importing nations. The USA's domestic oil production was at its lowest in 2008, but has since more than doubled given investment in the environmentally controversial process of fracking, which produces oil from domestic shale. This has reduced the US dependence on Middle East supplies.

The energy and generating mix can then change over time. It also varies over space; countries have different patterns dependent on local circumstances. For decades, houses in Cyprus have had solar-powered hot water systems on their roofs (Figure B5); not so in cooler Northern Ireland, although both countries are now investing in modern photovoltaic systems to produce electricity directly from sunlight. France relies on nuclear power for over 70% of its energy,

Figure B5: Rooftop water heating in Cyprus

lacking in domestically produced alternatives. The UK has less than 25% nuclear generation (unless and until new power stations are built) and has much more gas and renewable (largely wind) energy than France. China's recent massive industrial growth and modernisation has been powered largely by coal, at a considerable cost to the air quality in its major cities.

There is a growing realisation that energy management has not just to consider availability (supply) but also consumption (demand). Demand management helps reduce expenditure, control pollution and improves a country's strategic position. In addition, the cost of energy can cause problems to low-income households. If a household has to spend more than 10% of its income on fuel, it is said to be in 'fuel poverty'. In 2014, 10.6% of English households, 2.88 million, were in this situation and the number was rising. Whilst fuel poverty obviously relates to income, older and larger buildings and those without cavity walls, modern condensing boilers or mains gas supply are particularly expensive to heat. Policy responses are to encourage energy efficiency in the home: double (or triple) glazing, insulation for walls and lofts, boiler scrappage schemes, and advice to change behaviour such as shutting doors and installing thick curtains.

Water supply

Water is essential for life, from drinking through washing to its use in cooking and manufacture. It takes about 137,000 litres (30,000 gallons) of water to produce a car and 82,000 litres (18,000 gallons) for a pair of jeans – mostly used in growing the cotton. As cities grow, keeping them supplied with water becomes ever more difficult. In Cape Town in South Africa, the population grew from 2.7 million in 2000 to about 3.7 million in 2017. In early 2017, the reservoirs in Cape Town were under one-third full (Figure B6) and on March 29 the *Cape Times* newspaper reported that only 103 days of usable water remained, unless consumption were to be dramatically reduced.

Figure B6: Central Cape Town seen from Table Mountain in April 2017. Note the low water level in the two reservoirs, particularly the more distant one.

There was a public information campaign to encourage voluntary conservation, such as taking shorter showers, and the local authority imposed severe restrictions on water use (Figure B8). Schemes to tap aquifers to boost supply were being considered.

Figure B7: Bowling greens in Newlands, a prosperous area of Cape Town. Note that the club has its own supply of borehole water for irrigation.

Figure B8: Poster displayed in Cape Town hotels in April 2017

For some cities, local supplies of water may not be sufficient and water may have to be brought in from afar. For example, since the 1890s Birmingham's water has come from the Elan Valley in mid-Wales; and Leicester, Nottingham and Derby get supplies from reservoirs in the Derwent Valley in north-east Derbyshire.

Belfast's water now comes from the Silent Valley in the Mournes. Its first piped supply, using wooden pipes, was established in 1678. In 1795, the Belfast Charitable Society set up the Spring Water Commissioners to provide water for the town through a public fountain and water carts supplied from local springs, a dam and a service reservoir in Basin Lane. In 1840, the Belfast Water Commissioners became responsible for supply and new reservoirs were opened. By 1852 there were 24 public fountains, but families also collected rainwater for washing and other purposes. Supplies were increased through the construction of reservoirs close to Belfast but there were still problems over water volume and quality, as demonstrated by a typhoid epidemic in 1898. It was clear that a new, substantial water source was needed for the growing city and after considering a number of different options, including Slieve Croob and Lough Neagh, the Silent Valley was the location chosen. Its water rights were secured by the Belfast Water Act of 1893. At first, water from rivers was pumped up to a storage reservoir at Knockbracken but from 1923–1933 the Silent Valley Reservoir was constructed at a cost of £1.35 million (about £68 million at today's prices). Schemes such as the Silent Valley and Elan Valley sustain life in distant cities, but at the cost of loss and environmental degradation for the areas flooded.

In some coastal cities desalination plants turn seawater to fresh water, especially in dry areas such as the Middle East. For example, all Kuwait's water is desalinated. However, desalinisation is very expensive.

CASE STUDY: Leicester, a study of the sustainability of a city

Leicester is the largest city in the East Midlands, with a population of 329,900 at the 2011 census. The city traditionally focused on the manufacture of textiles, which in the post-World War II period made it attractive to migrants, especially from the Indian sub-continent. Leicester now has a minority of white Britons in its population mix; 45% of respondents to the 2011 census described themselves as white British. It has the smallest proportion of over-65s in the East Midlands and the largest proportion of young people. In 1996, Leicester was the first city in the UK to receive a European Sustainable City Award and the greening of the city was singled out for commendation at the 1992 Earth Summit in Rio. Leicester City Council has invested heavily in devising and implementing policies in line with sustainable development. These include work on sustainable transport and air quality, whilst a number of strategies focus on waste management and energy.

An energy efficiency strategy

Leicester's Home Energy Strategy policy is to reduce consumption of non-renewable energy sources and to reduce fuel poverty: all households should have access to 'affordable warmth'. Further, the council aims to reduce the city's energy use by 50% by 2025:

- 20% of all council buildings will use renewable energy by 2020.
- Residents are encouraged to install solar panels, initially to heat water, now to produce electricity.
- Home energy saving advice and information packs and websites have been produced.
- In 2014, 30% of the city's refuse was used as fuel.
- Working with private sector partners, the council has plans for both social housing tenants and owner occupiers to move to zero carbon generated electricity.

Leicester City Council has a Home Energy Office to tackle fuel poverty and to provide advice to households seeking to make their homes more energy efficient. Under the Energy Vision scheme, interest-free loans are available to householders to pay for energy efficiency improvements managed through the Home Energy Office. There are grants for free insulation and heating measures, and the council registers contractors under the 'Gas Safe' scheme which guarantees good customer care and after-sales support. There is also the Energy Sense scheme under which householders can have a free home visit to draw up an energy audit of their property, together with advice and recommendations on how to make improvements.

Under the Home Energy Conservation Act of 1995, Leicester between 2013–2015 had achieved annual CO_2 savings of almost 30,000 tonnes given the installation of:

- solid wall insulation for 1320 homes.
- solar photovoltaic panels for 680 homes.
- double glazing for a further 9375 homes.
- loft insulation top-ups for 7060 homes.
- cavity wall insulation for a further 3,020 homes.
- condensing boilers in 17,980 homes.
- heating control upgrades in 4420 homes.

Leicester's waste management strategy

- Public awareness campaigns promote efficient waste management.
- Households are issued with large orange plastic bags to be filled with recyclable material such as paper, glass, plastic, tins, cardboard packaging, tetrapaks and aerosols. The orange bags are placed for collection next to the household's black bin, which is for waste items that cannot be recycled. An increasing number of areas have orange communal bins for recycling, replacing the orange bag system.
- The council advises residents to take unwanted clothes and shoes to a charity shop or place them within a clothing bank. Other banks accept cardboard, paper and glass.
- Bin collection is run by a private contractor. Bulky items can be disposed of through a free special collection, with residents advised to donate unwanted furniture free of charge to the Leicestershire and Rutland Reuse Network.
- The council has to deal with about 84 tons of soiled disposable nappies each week; residents are encouraged to use traditional cloth nappies instead and the city employs a 'nappy advisor' to help reinforce this message.
- Homes and schools are entitled to buy a subsidised compost bin. The council website offers advice on composting and supports the Rot-a-Lot home composting club.
- The council operates a garden waste collection service, but this is for an annual fee, rather than being free of charge as in some other cities, including Belfast.
- Leicester has two recycling centres, one of which, Gypsum Close, has a 'reuse shop' where 'pre-loved' items such as crockery, curtains and domestic appliances in good condition/working order can be donated to be sold, with the proceeds going to charity.
- Hazardous waste has to be taken to one of the recycling centres where dedicated containers are provided for its collection. It is then removed for specialist treatment and recycling.
- In the early 2000s Leicester council aimed to recycle 40% of all household waste by 2025; by 2014 43% was being recycled or composted.

Figure B9: Leicester's household waste statistics 2002–2014: recycling, composting and diversion. These rates show how much waste Leicester diverts away from landfill

Year	2002–2003	2003–2004	2004–2005	2005–2006	2006–2007	2007–2008	2008–2009	2009–2010	2010–2011	2011–2012	2012–2013	2013–2014
% Recycling	10.1	12.2	13.6	17.4	16.3	17.0	17.1	17.3	18.1	22.4	24.0	23.1
% Composting	1.4	2.5	4.4	9.7	10.9	16.4	13.6	22.6	22.4	19.5	17.6	19.9
Total	11.5	14.7	18.0	27.1	27.2	33.4	30.7	39.9	40.5	41.9	41.6	43.0
% Refuse Derived Fuel	0	0	8.7	10.7	7.2	8.7	12.4	0.03	5.8	27.6	27.4	30.2
% Diversion	11.5	14.7	26.7	37.8	34.4	42.1	43.1	39.9	46.3	69.5	69.0	73.2

Leicester's water supply

Leicester's primary water supply comes from the Upper Valley of the River Derwent, a deep valley which has three reservoirs providing for cities in the East Midlands and South Yorkshire. Two dams were constructed in the 1900s and 1910s. The third, larger, reservoir lies behind Ladybower Dam, which was built from 1935–1943, then the reservoir took two years to fill. This scheme was controversial as it led to the flooding of two villages. Leicester's supply is provided by Severn Trent Water. At the time of writing, this company is involved in a £2 million project to improve Leicester's water by replacing any remaining lead water pipes with modern pipes.

The River Soar flows through Leicester. Its water quality is constantly monitored by the Environment Agency. Pollution levels are generally low and the water of good quality. However, just downstream of Leicester, discharge from the Wanlip Sewage Treatment Works enters the river leading to a decrease in water quality.

Exam Questions

1. Study Resource A which presents data from the Global Footprint Network on global contrasts regarding the 'built up land footprint'. The Global Footprint Network uses satellite imagery to estimate this 'built-up land footprint', capturing infrastructure for housing, transportation and industrial production as well as reservoirs and hydroelectric dams.

   (i) Use the resource **to help you** explain that urban ecological and carbon footprints vary between different places. [8]

   (ii) Explain why this measure underestimates full urban ecological footprints. [9]

   Questions from CCEA A21 Human Interactions and Global Issues,
   January 2010, © CCEA 2017

Resource A: Built-up land footprints by region

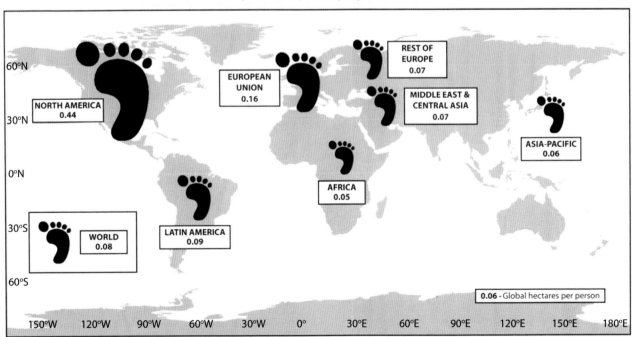

References

Sustainable development:
Department for Environment, Food and Rural Affairs, *Sustainable Development Indicators,* July 2013 – *https://www.gov.uk/government/organisations/department-for-environment-food-rural-affairs/series/ sustainable-development-indicators*

Sustainable Development Commission, *Governing for the Future – The opportunities for mainstreaming sustainable development,* 2011: *http://www.sd-commission.org.uk/publications.php?id=1191*

A fact sheet relating to sustainable development in Europe can be found at: *ec.europa.eu/environment/ pubs/pdf/factsheets/sust_dev.pdf*

The UN's Sustainable Development Goals can be studied at: *www.imf.org/external/np/exr/facts/sdg.htm*

World Bank (2009), City Profiles, London, United Kingdom: *http://siteresources.worldbank.org/INTEAPREGTOPURBDEV/Resources/573631-1233613121646/ london_extop.pdf*

Department for Environment, Food and Rural Affairs, *UK's Carbon Footprint, 1997–2013*: *https://www.gov.uk/government/uploads/system/uploads/attachment_data/file/542558/Consumption_ emissions_May16_Final.pdf*

Birmingham:
Waste: it's not all rubbish – *https://birmingham.dialogue-app.com/waste-its-not-all-rubbish*

Cape Town:
City of Cape Town, Residential water restrictions explained – *www.capetown.gov.za/thinkwater*

Leicester:
The Leicester City Council website – *www.leicester.gov.uk*
www.leicester.gov.uk/media/179571/home-energy-conservation-act-1995-update-progress-report- march-2015.pdf

2. URBAN PLANNING AND DESIGN IN RELATION TO SUSTAINABILITY

Case studies

Urban planning and design in a city: Curitiba

Students should be able to:

(i) explain how urban design, planning and management relates to sustainability in eco-towns or cities

(ii) explain how urban design, planning and management relates to sustainability in:

– residential space such as housing design or defensible space

– greenfield and brownfield development

– the environmental and social consequences of the development of retail parks, including their competition with town centres

– leisure and sports facilities, open space and urban parks

Sustainable development, where planners do not simply focus on short-term gain but consider the long-term social, economic and environmental impacts of any developments, can be applied to settlements. The UK government's policy document, 'Securing the future, delivering UK sustainable development strategy', 2005, identified the following components of sustainable communities:

1. **active, inclusive and safe** – fair, tolerant and cohesive with a strong local culture and other shared community activities.

2. **well run** – with effective and inclusive participation, representation and leadership.

3. **environmentally sensitive** – providing places for people to live that are considerate to the environment.

4. **well designed and built** – featuring a quality built and natural environment.

5. **well connected** – with good transport services and communication linking people to jobs, schools, health and other services.

6. **thriving** – with a flourishing and diverse local economy.

7. **well served** – with public, private, community and voluntary services that are appropriate to people's needs and accessible to all.

8. **fair for everyone** – including those in other communities, now and in the future.

(Contains public sector information licensed under the Open Government Licence v3.0.)

Local councils, under government direction, have been attempting to incorporate such sustainability concepts into their planning and management policies. One example is Arun District Council in Sussex, Southern England. The development of urban planning policies in Arun was influenced by the 2006 regional plan for South East England, which required new housing to be in sustainable locations whilst development generally had to include "health, education, cultural and leisure amenities, necessary to meet the needs of a growing population." Four objectives were identified for the Arun District Council 'Settlement Sustainability Study', July 2007:

1. to provide a description of the demographic characteristics of the district's settlements.

2. to provide an assessment of accessibility to key facilities and services in the district's settlements.

3. to provide an analysis of employment and commuting flows in the district's settlements.

4. to provide an assessment of accessibility to public transport in the settlements within the Arun District.

A quantitative analysis was then carried out using census and other social and economic data to calculate the sustainability ranking of the various settlements in the area, ranging from very good to very poor. Only three of Arun's settlements (Bognor Regis, Littlehampton and Rustington) received all "good" or "very good" scores; smaller settlements tended to score less favourably. These results about sustainability would "help inform decisions on the location of future residential and other development".

Other elements in sustainability that might be included in urban planning relate to:

- energy supply, particularly to renewable energy.
- efficient use of land and other assets, including conservation.
- the reuse of brownfield sites.
- recycling and waste management.
- services would include leisure and recreation facilities, parks and open space.

Eco-towns and garden villages

In 2007 the Labour government unveiled a programme to build 15 eco-towns in Central and Southern England. This radical proposal marked the first new town proposals in the UK since the 1960s. Although designed for contemporary living, the new eco-towns drew on the experience of Ebenezer Howard's Garden City proposals from 1898. Garden cities combined residential, employment, leisure and recreational facilities for all their residents. The proposed eco-towns also incorporated many principles of sustainability, being low-energy and carbon neutral with much recycled material to be used in their construction. Renewable energy systems were to be used in public buildings and many homes. The largest of the developments would provide 15–20,000 homes, 30–40% of which being affordable starter homes aimed at first-time buyers. The new developments would have their own distinct identities, with good links to surrounding towns. There would be a good range of amenities including schools, shops and leisure facilities. High quality public transport would reduce the need for car journeys and the clustering of public services was also designed to minimise transport use. Low speed limits would be imposed within the towns. The towns would have good provision of green space. Each eco-town was to develop plans for community involvement in the new development. Furthermore, each was to have a clear economic strategy for its inhabitants.

Figure B10 shows the location of these proposed eco-towns. Note that they are largely greenfield sites, which was criticised by some environmentalists.

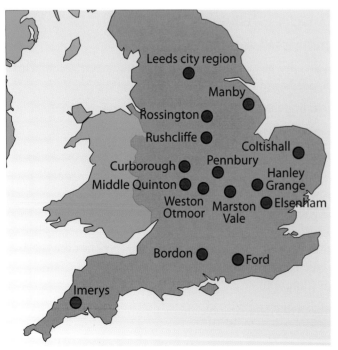

Figure B10: Map of the proposed eco-towns in England

In the event, the eco-town scheme was not that successful. By 2012 the government had approved only four sites, not all from the original list, and none had been completed. NW Bicester is the most advanced. The idea, if not the eco-town scheme itself, was relaunched in March 2016. Under a Conservative government, the Department for Communities and Local Government issued a prospectus for new garden villages and towns, the development of which would receive financial backing. Proposals were invited from local authorities for free-standing developments with 20% starter homes. Whilst schemes involving brownfield sites were especially welcome, there were not the sustainability restrictions of the eco-towns. However, "this prospectus is not looking to support places which merely use 'garden' as a convenient label. Rather, we will support local areas that embed key garden city principles". Further, "It will be important for expressions of interest to demonstrate how the garden village will be well-designed, built to a high quality, and attractive. Use of qualitative and quantitative research on local public opinion will be welcomed on issues around design and community". In January 2017, the government announced that 14 garden villages of 1500–10,000 homes and three garden towns of over 10,000 homes were to be supported. The garden towns are to be near Aylesbury, Taunton and Harlow (which was one of the post-World War II New Towns). Government support was made available to "unlock the full capacity of the sites".

* **Material cycle**

The material cycle starts with raw material which is processed into goods and used. After use, waste material is recycled and (with any necessary additional raw material) used for processing once more and the cycle continues. For example empty bottles are recycled and made into new bottles.

Other countries have also established eco-towns. Japan did so in 1997, with the aim of promoting waste reduction and achieving zero emissions. There were 26 Japanese eco-towns by 2006. Key elements in the policy are:

- promoting a material-cycle* society.
- bringing together industrial clusters to be more sustainable.
- increasing product research and development.
- expanding eco-business markets.
- focusing on environmental technologies.
- focusing on energy conservation, material development and integrated waste management.

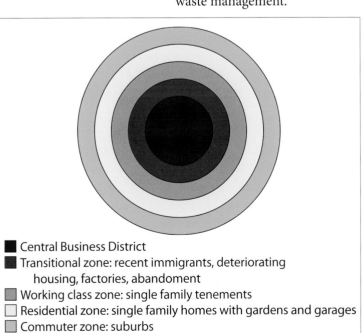

■ Central Business District
■ Transitional zone: recent immigrants, deteriorating housing, factories, abandoment
■ Working class zone: single family tenements
□ Residential zone: single family homes with gardens and garages
■ Commuter zone: suburbs

Figure B11: The Ernest Burgess Concentric Zone Model 1925

Housing design and defensible space

Within many western cities residential areas are segregated on an income basis, which relates to a considerable extent to social class. Better off members of society are able to choose where they live and a person's address is often an indication of wealth and status. The less well off have more limited choice. In western cities this has often resulted in the wealthy occupying the more prestigious suburban locations with the urban poor confined to inner city areas, where once there were industrial jobs. The Ernest Burgess Concentric Zone Model 1925 (Figure B11) of urban land use reflected this distribution, with outer zones being of higher residential status than the inner city 'zone of transition'.

As people became better off they moved further from the city centre, leaving their former neighbourhoods to be taken over by those less wealthy, sometimes immigrants. As deindustrialisation occurred in western cities, the less well off areas, which always had poor housing, became characterised also by high levels of unemployment and associated socio-economic problems (as with Ballymacarrett, discussed on page 268).

Urban planners in the 1960s sought to address this inner city housing issue by replacing the slum housing with high rise flats to accommodate as many people as possible in their original areas, in an affordable manner. Public housing estates, sometimes incorporating high rise blocks, were also built further out to accommodate people who had to be relocated. However, many of these new developments became areas of high unemployment, low educational attainments and high crime rates. Some of the high rise tower blocks were of poor quality and were not maintained properly. In 2017 at least 80 people died when the Grenfell tower block in the London Borough of Kensington and Chelsea caught fire. Enquiries after this tragedy revealed that many other tower blocks also had fire safety risks. In the UK there was also often an ethnic divide, with BME (Black and Minority Ethnic) groups inhabiting poorer areas. It was clear that the urban planners had made fundamental miscalculations about the workings of communities.

In the USA, a study of two housing developments in St Louis, Missouri in the 1960s provided some interesting lessons. Both housing developments were occupied by people from the same socio-economic grouping, with low incomes and high levels of unemployment. However, one development, Pruett-Igoe, was blighted by crime and vandalism while the other, Carr Square Village, was relatively free of crime. This apparent difference in behaviour in the two housing developments prompted planners to question the influence of urban design.

1. Carr Square Village, the crime-free development, consisted of terraced housing, each housing unit occupied by one family with a clear demarcation of the territory it owned or rented. The houses were of uniform design but individual families were able to paint the exterior according to their choice.

2. The Pruett-Igoe scheme consisted of 33 identical 11 storey apartment blocks which were particularly blighted by crime. These were built in the 1960s following the concepts of Le Corbusier, the pioneer of modern architecture. Each apartment block had its ground floor surrounded by communal outdoor space known as 'the river of trees.' Every third floor contained a communal laundry and other facilities, such as waste disposal chutes.

Within a short period of time, Pruett-Igoe showed evidence of vandalism and crime. The open areas were contaminated with litter, the communal areas vandalised and the corridors, halls and staircases were covered with graffiti and became dangerous to walk alone in. Women had to gather in groups to escort children to school or go shopping. The level of vandalism increased in the areas of most intense public use. By contrast, the interiors of the apartments were generally well maintained. Only 60% of the apartments in Pruett-Igoe were ever occupied and in 1972 the entire complex was demolished (Figure B12). Carr Square Village remained fully occupied and trouble free.

*Figure B12:
Pruett-Igoe's
demolition,1972*

Source: U.S. Department
of Housing and Urban
Development

The American planner, Oscar Newman, explained these observations through his theory of defensible space. At its simplest, individuals will claim ownership of, and take responsibility for, territory that can be clearly demarcated by a physical boundary such as a wall, hedge or fence. The two main principles behind defensible space are:

1. A family's claim to territory diminishes as the number of families sharing that space increases.

2. The larger the number of people sharing a communal area, the more difficult it is for people to identify with it or to control the activity taking place within it.

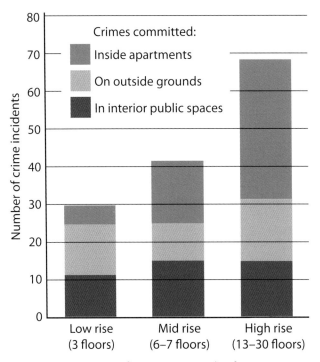

Figure B13: Location of crime in a sample of apartment blocks in St Louis

Source: Data from Oscar Newman, *Creating Defensible Space*

Newman stated that land surrounding a dwelling could be classified as private, semi-private, public or semi-public depending on the degree of privacy and accessibility. In the case of a detached house, the back of the house is private if it can only be accessed from within the house or via a gate. The front garden also belongs to the house owner but being accessible from the street it is only semi-private. In the case of a high rise apartment block, there are areas within and outside the building that are communal and the only private area is the interior of each apartment. Corridors, landings and staircases are at best semi-public and the areas outside the complex are public. In other words as the density of occupation increases, the amount of defensible space tends to decrease.

The importance of this concept of defensible space has been appreciated by urban planners. The spatial pattern of burglaries in British cities has been associated with particular types of built environment. The British Crime Survey found the lack of defensible space in the dimly lit and blind corners of the communal staircases of an inner London estate often provided the breeding grounds for crime, whilst the interlocking walkways linking various blocks allowed the perpetrators of crime to escape from their victims. From the early 1990s an 'official police security initiative', Secured by Design (SBD) was established. Secured By Design 'Homes 2016' report contains many technical details about locks and security fitting whilst encouraging planners to incorporate the concepts of defensible space into their designs:

- "Dwellings should be positioned facing each other to allow neighbours to easily view their surroundings and thus making the potential offender feel vulnerable to detection."

- Entrances to garages "should be easily observed from the street and neighbouring dwellings."

- "Communal areas, such as playgrounds and seating areas, have the potential to generate crime, the fear of crime and anti-social behaviour. They should be designed to allow supervision from nearby dwellings with safe routes for users to come and go. Boundaries between public and private space should be clearly defined and open spaces must have features which prevent unauthorised vehicular access. Communal spaces as described above should not immediately abut residential buildings."

Coal Pit Mews, Batley

One early SBD project was in Batley, Yorkshire, an area of high unemployment as a result of the decline of the textile and manufacturing industries. A new housing area, Coal Pit Mews, was built with the following characteristics:

- Every dwelling entry is overlooked by at least one other property.

- Tall trees and undergrowth were removed. New trees were planted which would have no foliage below 2 m when fully grown.

- Trees were not planted to obscure windows, doors or street lights.

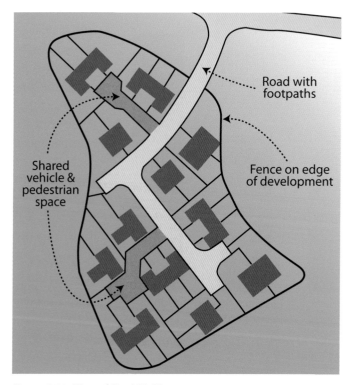

Figure B14: Plan of Coal Pit Mews

- The surface of the roads and pavements in the estate are noticeably different from those beyond the limits of the estate.
- Coal Pit Mews is a cul-de-sac, so non-residents cannot use it as a through route to other destinations.
- Car parking space is provided at the front of each building.
- All houses have clearly identifiable security features.

In November 2016 statistics for Batley recorded 325 crimes, but only two in or near Coal Pit Mews, both being anti-social behaviour. Surveys show that SBD dwellings on the whole tend to have about 26% fewer crime events than non-SBD developments in otherwise comparable areas.

Exercise

1. Define 'defensible space' and explain how it can be used in the management of residential areas to enhance their sustainability.

Greenfield and brownfield development

Greenfield

Greenfields are rural areas that have not been encroached upon by urban development. So in one sense all rural areas are greenfield sites. However, the term is usually more restricted. A useful definition comes from an organisation called Sustainable Build, which has greenfield sites as "areas of land, usually agricultural or amenity land, which are being considered for urban development". Once development has taken place the greenfield site is forever lost and even if it is cleared, the legacy of having been built up will mean that it becomes a brownfield site. Settlements have grown through the ages onto greenfield sites of course, but there is now a realisation that development should be controlled and further greenfield sites taken only when other options are not available. Sustainable Build's article 'Greenfield Sites' lists the issues arising from taking greenfield sites for urban development:

- Once land has been converted to development, it is unlikely to ever be converted back to greenfield use.
- Destruction of the natural habitat of some animal and plant species.
- Loss of agricultural land results in loss of production and loss of employment.
- Reduction of or complete loss of amenity or recreation value.
- Negative effect upon transport and energy use.
- Loss of the greenbelt of agricultural or designated wildlife land.

One notable policy established to protect rural areas around settlements in the UK and elsewhere has been the greenbelt, which designates areas of open land around cities that are not permitted to be taken for development (Figure B15). Designed to limit urban sprawl, which was seen to become a problem in the years between World War I and II, the first greenbelt policies were discussed in the mid-1930s. The significant post-war planning document, the 'Town and Country Planning Act' of 1947, brought the policy itself into being and it is now in force throughout the UK and in many other places; thus about 16% of Northern Ireland is protected by greenbelt designation. Greenbelts have been criticised for being too rigid, for limiting the supply of accessible land, thus pushing up the price of housing. On the other hand they provide urban people with accessible open space for leisure and recreation, improve air quality and biodiversity as well as maintaining open space for agricultural and scenic purposes. Greenbelts are everywhere under threat given the necessities for urban expansion, not least to cope with national housing shortages.

Figure B15: Greenbelts in England

Source: Data from 'Greenbelts: a greener future', the Council for the Preservation of Rural England

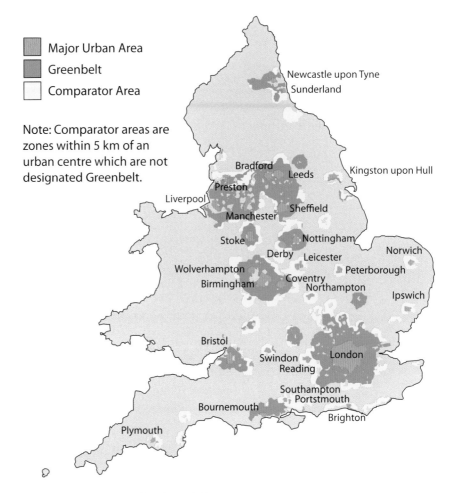

Major Urban Area

Greenbelt

Comparator Area

Note: Comparator areas are zones within 5 km of an urban centre which are not designated Greenbelt.

Brownfields: The reuse of industrial areas

The decline in inner city housing areas often followed on from the decline in industry. Many cities in the British Isles grew rapidly during industrial developments associated with the manufacturing industry in the nineteenth and early twentieth centuries. At that time workers were housed close to their place of work, leading to the development of high density, low income housing in the inner city, which might be in apartment blocks (as in Glasgow) or terraced housing (as in Birmingham and Belfast). From the second half of the twentieth century, a combination of out-dated production methods in western cities and competition from low wage economies abroad in an increasingly globalised world resulted in the decline of much of the UK's manufacturing industry and the urban areas where it was located. During this period, the inner cities also lost much of their residential structures through redevelopment, which often involved building replacement housing in suburban areas. New industries and commercial developments often preferred these more accessible greenfield sites on the edge of the city, where there were better and more efficient road links and cheaper land. The growth in private car ownership and suburbanisation generally meant that many inner city areas became run down and neglected. The sites of former industry were left derelict, being referred to as brownfield sites. After years of neglect, planners turned their attention towards these brownfield sites in the late 1980s. Cities in the UK saw comprehensive regeneration and redevelopment plans focused on the inner cities by Urban Development Corporations such as the Merseyside Development Corporation in Liverpool (1981–1998) and the Laganside Corporation in Belfast (1989–2007).

Reuse of brownfield sites has become a key element of urban land use planning in relation to sustainability. Such redevelopment or regeneration contributes to sustainability in a number of ways. Most of these schemes included a variety of land uses, including industrial, commercial, residential, recreational and transport. Some residents find work in the development, whilst improved public transport should also limit the number of commuter journeys by car. The new buildings usually incorporate many of the principles of sustainability, such as carbon neutral elements in their design. In addition, the reuse of these sites improves the overall environment of the area, often associated with a reduction in crime and at the same time the rural areas at the edge of the city are protected from urban sprawl.

The former shipbuilding area in Belfast is an example of a brownfield site that has undergone substantial regeneration (Figure B16). Whilst Harland and Wolff, with its iconic yellow cranes still exists (though no longer building new ships), much of the extensive shipbuilding complex has been redesigned as the Titanic Quarter (recalling the most famous ship built there), which at 185 ha (457 acres) is one of the world's largest urban waterfront regeneration projects. Titanic Quarter has a number of modern hi-tech industrial units, forming Northern Ireland Science Park, some associated with Queen's University Belfast. There is also a hotel, apartments, restaurants, entertainment facilities, marina, new premises for the Public Records Office of Northern Ireland and Belfast Metropolitan College, and a film studio. The most prominent building is Titanic Belfast (Figure B17), a 'visitor experience' structure erected next to the spot where the *Titanic* was built and which won an award as the world's leading tourist attraction in 2016 (titanicbelfast.com). A million visitors per year come to the Titanic Quarter, which has about 18,000 residents. It is served by public transport and the nearest railway station, once called Bridge End after a local housing area, was renamed Titanic Quarter.

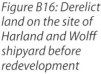

Figure B16: Derelict land on the site of Harland and Wolff shipyard before redevelopment

Figure B17: Titanic Belfast

There are environmental issues regarding reuse of some brownfield sites. Often the land has been contaminated through industrial use and a considerable amount of money is required to clean up such sites. Within Belfast, the former gasworks site, which was in use from 1822–1988, had to be subject to an extensive decontamination process, part-funded by the European Union, before it could be recast by the Laganside Corporation as a business park with a major hotel. The 138 ha (341 acres) North

Foreshore of Belfast Lough was used as a landfill site for waste from 1958–2007. One of the issues associated with landfill sites is the production of methane as the waste decomposes. At this site a network of landfill gas wells and pipe work collect the methane, which is used for local energy needs. Working with the Sufalnet 4EU (Sustainable Use of Former and Abandoned Landfill Network For You) European Union scheme, the area, now dubbed the Giant's Park, provides space for office and industrial buildings, particularly focusing on the 'Green Tech Hub' with renewable energy, solar power, recycling and other environmental technologies. At the time of writing, the northern part of the scheme is being planned for a commercial, leisure led, mixed use development, with the protection of wildlife habitats.

Retail parks and their competition with town centres

We all shop, but where, how, and how often we shop has changed dramatically in the last few decades. Until about the 1960s, shopping was done locally and frequently. Many social and economic changes have occurred since then, including the increased proportion of women in the workforce (most couples of working age now both have jobs), increased car ownership, increased disposable income, improved food storage facilities (refrigerators and later, freezers in the home), online shopping opportunities and globalisation. The retail industry has adapted to these changes in a number of ways.

One of the most significant changes has been the development of large chain stores, often part of multinational companies. There has also been a great increase in the range and quality of items for sale; for example, globalisation has virtually ended the seasonality of foodstuffs, with foods brought in from the other side of the world to ensure continuity of supply. Competition between retailers is intense, a situation complicated by online shopping, and advertising and marketing strategies encourage customers not just to spend more, but to bring their spending to the advertisers' outlets. From the late-1960s an increasing proportion of these outlets are found in out-of-town retail parks, sometimes on brownfield sites, often greenfield developments.

The earliest out-of-town shopping centres provided supermarket facilities for the growing population of the suburbs, but by the 1980s non-food retailing had become important and in the 1990s some very large shopping centres had developed. The Bluewater Retail Park in Kent, built in 1999 on a former quarry, has over 300 shopping units, 60 restaurants, a multi-screen cinema and an adventure park. There are 13,000 car park spaces.

There are many reasons for the development of these large retail centres:

- Land is cheaper at the edge of the city, facilitating the building of large shopping malls and other facilities.
- Greenfield sites are easier to develop than brownfield sites in the inner city.
- It is easy to provide good road transport links, attractive to customers from a wide area.
- Free and plentiful car parking space attracts shoppers with cars.

As these developments were taking place, traditional high street retail areas were losing custom. Customers increasingly used the out-of-town shopping areas to avoid the congestion and high cost of parking in town centres. A number of British cities experienced a downturn in sales, with some of the major chain stores leaving town centres altogether. Belfast suffered, especially as the situation there was compounded by civil unrest and bombings during the troubles. Online shopping was a later development that further impacted traditional retailing and a number of famous high street chains have gone out of business, including Woolworths in 2009 and BHS (formerly British Homes Stores) in 2016 (Figure A42, page 261).

The changes in retailing had more than an economic impact. Although most of the new retail centres were served to some extent by public transport, they were developed with car owners in mind and poorer and/or older people without private cars were disadvantaged. Deindustrialisation was another factor that negatively impacted inner city areas. Suburbanisation and counter-urbanisation had anyway left them populated disproportionately by disadvantaged groups and retail change saw them become even more marginalised and affected with social problems.

The changing pattern of retail also had significant environmental consequences. The use of greenfield sites was a major concern. Whilst the new centres do undergo landscaping, they have been seen as a visual eyesore in what was formerly a rural area. There was much opposition to the effects of the increase in traffic and new road developments associated with these centres. They have long opening hours, including weekends and residents close to them might be concerned about noise, pollution, disturbance, loss of privacy and possibly negative impacts on the value of their properties. Other environmental issues might be litter, a loss of biodiversity and increased greenhouse gas emissions from vehicles and structures.

More recently there has been something of a change of policy in relation to retail, with city centres fighting back, re-energised with new retail developments. In Belfast, the Castle Court development, anchored by Debenhams, was opened in 1990 and the much larger Victoria Square retail centre in 2008. The latter has 68,000 sq m (81,000 sq yd) of retail space, anchored by the 20,000 sq m (24,000 sq yd) House of Fraser store, also 1000 car park spaces, 106 apartments and a multiscreen cinema.

Leisure and sports facilities, open space and urban parks

If urban areas are to be sustainable they need to provide opportunities for all aspects of life including leisure and sporting activities. Local councils throughout the UK provide leisure centres, parks and sports facilities delivering a range of leisure activities for all age groups. Belfast, for example, has 47 parks, 14 leisure centres and 69 sports pitch and playing field areas. There are 13 community gardens (Figure B18) where people can join together to grow fruit and vegetables, and 7 areas of allotments.

Figure B18: Connswater Street Community Garden, East Belfast

Outdoor gym machines are provided in 9 locations in Belfast parks and there are 21 designated walking routes. One example is the Connswater Community Greenway project in East Belfast, which after an investment of £40m provides a 9 km (5.6 mile) linear park from Belfast Lough into the Castlereagh Hills. The project also deals with flooding problems along the rivers in the area (Figure B19). Cities also house private leisure and sporting activities from gyms to professional football stadiums, which can accommodate tens of thousands of spectators.

Urban parks are an important type of open space. They can range from formal landscaped areas such as Botanic Gardens and Lady Dixon Park in Belfast to

Figure B19: The Knock River in Orangefield Park, Belfast, part of the Connswater Community Greenway. The river used to run by the houses to the left before being moved and placed within levées to prevent flooding.

areas left as natural wildernesses. Parks play a vital role in leisure and recreation. In modern western cities an increasing proportion of residents live in apartments with no gardens, and parks provide their only convenient access to green spaces. Additionally, parks can be venues for events, for example in Belfast open air concerts have been held in Botanic Gardens. Parks also have environmental benefits. Their trees and other plants filter out some of the atmospheric pollutants and in hot climates they offer welcome shade; temperatures in parks can be up to two degrees lower than in their urban surroundings. Green spaces also support wildlife and contribute to local biodiversity. Parkland can be used as an environmentally sensitive means of flood defence; water might be diverted onto parkland to prevent it flooding commercial or residential areas.

The UK government set up the Urban Green Spaces Taskforce in 2001 to examine the design, management and maintenance of green spaces and urban parks. Its 2002 report agreed that good quality, well designed parks and green spaces make a critical contribution to our neighbourhoods, towns and cites, and to people's quality of life, playing an important role in creating a sense of place. Quality green spaces have been shown to:

- support the local economy, making neighbourhoods more desirable.
- enhance physical and mental health.
- benefit children and young people.
- reduce crime and fear of crime.
- support social cohesion.
- aid movement between other spaces.
- protect biodiversity and enhance the environment.

CASE STUDY: Curitiba, urban planning and design in relation to sustainability in a city

Curitiba is the capital of Parana, a largely agricultural state in Southern Brazil, and has become a major industrial and commercial centre. Its population growth has been rapid, trebling from about 650,000 in 1970 to 1.9m in 2015. Initially the city planners followed a policy of decentralisation, with new developments located on the edge of the existing city contributing to urban sprawl. However, then there was a significant policy change, with a greater emphasis on sustainability, largely due to the direction of the city's mayor and chief architect, Jaime Lerner. Lerner was involved in drawing up the city's 1968 Master Plan. He also helped to establish the Urban Planning Institute of Curitiba, served three terms as mayor of Curitiba and later as governor of Parana. He was one of *Time* magazine's 'influential thinkers' of 2010.

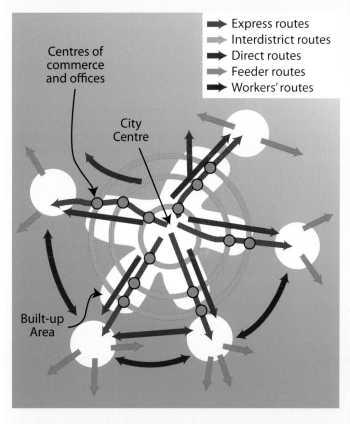

Figure B20: Concept plan for Curitiba's transport system

Transport

Curitiba is a well-known example of a sustainable city and its transport system is one of the key elements of its success. From the outset the planners sought to integrate traffic management, transportation and land-use planning to improve sustainability. The aim was to reduce the number of car journeys from the suburbs and the outlying region into the city centre, which would reduce congestion and pollution. Other cities have resolved this issue by building an underground system. However, the costs and the time needed to construct underground railways ruled this out for Curitiba. Instead, the planners sought to incorporate many of the features of an underground system into the bus network. There are five major arterial routes linking the centre of Curitiba to the suburbs, which cross three ring-roads creating a web-like road pattern. Each arterial route has a two-way lane dedicated to express buses, a local access lane for cars and a lane for mixed traffic use.

There are five different types of buses in Curitiba:

1. **Express buses,** which operate on the dedicated bus lanes.
2. **Bi-articulated buses** ('bendy buses'), which operate on the fast outer lane of the dedicated bus routes. These buses carry 270 passengers and given a frequency of every 30 seconds can transport over 32,000 passengers per hour.
3. **'Rapid' buses**, which operate on all arteries and across the city's ring roads. These buses respond to the level of demand.
4. **'Inter-district' buses**, which bring passengers from the sectors between the arterial roads.
5. **'Feeder' buses,** which carry passengers from outlying districts to transfer stations on the arterial routes.

In addition, all of the major bus routes have tube-shaped bus stops, with the exit at the same level as the doors of the bus to facilitate rapid entry. Buses have a separate exit door which aids passenger flow. These measures reduce the time the bus idles at stops, so journeys are faster and pollution reduced. Further, passengers purchase tickets prior to getting on. The buses are operated by private companies, but tickets purchased from any company can be used across the network. Fares are per journey, so longer journeys, typically taken by poorer people living on the edge of Curitiba, are relatively cheap.

All public utilities such as water services, electricity offices, police stations and hospitals in Curitiba are located close to the arterial routes in areas known as 'citizenship streets'. This means public services are readily accessible by public transport. The density of buildings deceases with distance from the citizenship streets to where the residential areas are located. These are typically low rise developments and divided into neighbourhoods, focused around multi-purpose community centres which provide library and Internet services, mostly for children. These centres called 'Lighthouses of Knowledge' work in collaboration with local schools and provide safe shelter for street children. They are patrolled by the police to ensure their security.

The planners wanted to retain the commercial activity of the city centre while reducing car journeys. For this reason the centre has been pedestrianised. Initially shop owners were concerned that this might lead to a decease in customer numbers, but this did not happen and the strategy has been successful. The streets were redesigned with new lighting, trees and seating areas, and historical buildings were restored. Some streets now have 24 hour shopping.

Economic activity

An essential element of sustainable development in cities is the need to promote economic activity. Curitiba has a strict policy on industrial development. Only non-polluting industries are given planning permission and the city council provides inexpensive courses to train workers in the skills necessary for modern industry. An industrial region, which has provided many thousands of jobs in Brazilian as well as multi-national firms, was Curitiba Industrial City (CIC). The diversified range of jobs here is more sustainable than a highly specialised economic structure, which would be more susceptible to mass unemployment, even deindustrialisation in times of economic recession. CIC was built 10 km south west of Curitiba, so the region's prevailing south easterly winds would blow any pollution away from the central city. Factories were located with reference to the public transport system, limiting the need for commuter journeys by car.

Green space

The World Health Organization recommends that cities should provide 16 m² (19 sq yd) of open, green space per person. Curitiba has more than 28 wooded areas and parks, which provide about 52 m² (62 sq yd) per resident. Developers are offered tax breaks if they incorporate trees and green space in their plans. Some of the green spaces are beside watercourses and act as environmentally friendly flood defences, reducing the need for hard engineering flood control projects. The open areas increase infiltration, trees reduce the amount of surface run off and lakes in the parks serve as temporary storage basins at times of heavy rainfall. Curitiba also pursues policies for the sustainable use of brownfield sites, such as a former landfill site, which has been reclaimed and developed as a botanical garden.

Waste management

Curitiba has an impressive strategy regarding waste management. A 'garbage that's not garbage' programme has seen over 70% of the city's waste being recycled – in Belfast the rate is about 40%. Paper recycling saves about 1200 trees daily; money raised from recycling funds social programmes; and the city employs homeless and people with addiction issues in its waste separation plants. In areas that cannot be reached by the waste collection lorries, families can bring their waste to a recycling centre where it will be exchanged for food or bus tickets. The city's programme has resulted in less waste being dumped in water courses, less disease from polluted water and a better environment.

Immigration

Curitiba, like many LEDC cities, attracts many rural migrants, threatening its development strategies. Many migrants attempted to establish informal settlements on the green spaces whilst their numbers threatened to overwhelm the city's infrastructure. The authorities devised a two-pronged approach to this problem. Potential migrants are intercepted at bus stations and encouraged to return home, whilst in the surrounding rural areas development programmes have been established to attempt to reduce the push factors, which were driving residents to seek a better life in Curitiba. Families who have to build their own houses in Curitiba are given two trees to plant and are entitled to help from an architect.

Evaluation

Overall the strategies employed in Curitiba have been successful and the city has won a number of awards, including the Global Sustainable City Award of 2010. Curitiba's per capita income is above the Brazilian national average, whilst there are also many achievements towards environmental sustainability. The example of Curitiba shows that the twin goals of economic prosperity and green policies are achievable. One of the key reasons for Curitiba's success relates to the policy of partnership and social inclusion, involving local groups in planning. Services have been made accessible to people who did not own a car. Indeed, many of the policies relating to public transport, such as the single journey fares, are advantageous to the poor. The location of essential services in close proximity to public transport reduced the need for car journeys and, although Curitiba has a high rate of car ownership, it has low rates for fuel usage and pollution. Also, attention has been given to creating the skills necessary for modern industry. However, there are some causes of concern over the future of Curitiba. Population growth remains high, recycling rates no longer increase and providing landfill sites has been a problem. The city's authorities need to be constantly alert to ensure that the achievements in Curitiba regarding sustainability are maintained.

Exam Questions

1. "Planning policies should be guided by an emphasis on sustainable development". Examine this statement with regard to your case study of a city. [9]

2. Study Resources A–C which relate to the redevelopment of a former steelworks site in Sydney, Canada. Use this material **to help you** discuss how and why such polluted brownfield sites are redeveloped despite the problems and high costs involved. [18]

Question from A2 1 Human Interactions and Global Issues, May 2014, © CCEA 2017

Resource A: Sydney steelworks in operation, 1988

At Sydney, the main town on Cape Breton Island, Nova Scotia, Canada, a steelworks opened in 1901 utilising coal from mines on the island and iron ore from nearby Newfoundland. The steelworks became a major employer in the region, although there were often labour disputes and there was much pollution.

Resource B: Sydney steelworks site being cleared, 2007

In 2000 the steelworks closed down, as did the coal mines shortly afterwards, with many workers losing their jobs. The steelworks site was cleared, using former workers as labour, with disused machinery and metal being sold to an Indian company. Clearing and cleaning the site was very costly, given its size and the high level of pollution. The Sydney tar ponds, in a tidal estuary that had been used to dump polluted industrial effluent, were thought to be the most polluted areas on Earth. The Syndey Tar Ponds Agency was established to deal specifically with the restoration of the water body.

Resource C: Sydney steelworks site, Focus on the Future, 2012

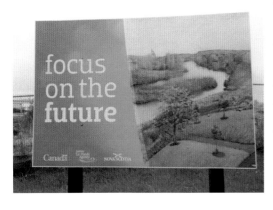

By 2012 most of the site had been cleared, polluted material treated and removed, and the area was being replanted. One Sydney resident commented that the tar ponds, which had cost over £250m to clean up, now "look pretty good, but I wouldn't want to build my house near them." A group of former steelworkers has spent over ten years without success in trying to establish a museum about steelmaking in Sydney. However, a coal mine near Sydney has re-opened as a museum and visitors can take tours underground guided by former miners.

3. Study Resource D about an urban park in Rome. Use it **to help you** evaluate the contribution urban parks make to sustainability. [18]

Question from A2 1 Human Interactions and Global Issues, May 2016, © CCEA 2017

Resource D: Observations in a park in Rome

A geographer visited a small park in central Rome and made these observations. Mature trees surround the park providing shade against the fierce sun. The park contains benches, two small green areas, a large fountain and a place for washing feet and filling water bottles. There is a statue of an Italian author. A sign forbids:

A neighbourhood park in Rome

- children from playing games;
- owners from letting dogs off their leads; and
- picking flowers.

People were sitting on benches, eating, reading, using mobile devices or sleeping. Tourists took a rest or peered at maps. Foreign migrants to Rome of African appearance sat apart. One corner of the park was occupied by an intimidating group of young men; some had dogs, which they allowed to frolic in the fountain and foul the grass. People fed pigeons; friends met by arrangement or chance; children ate ice cream.

A council worker emptied the rubbish bins, separating items for recycling from other waste. The small square surrounding the park contained a tram stop, shops, cafés, a church and apartments.

References

Arun District Council, *Settlement Sustainability Study*, 2007
– *www.arun.gov.uk/download.cfm?doc=docm93jijm4n1575.pdf&ver*

Garden villages:
Department for Communities and Local Government, *Locally led garden villages, towns and cities*
– *https://www.gov.uk/government/uploads/system/uploads/attachment_data/file/508205/Locally-led_garden_villages__towns_and_cities.pdf*

Department for Communities and Local Government, *First ever garden villages named with government support* – *https://www.gov.uk/government/news/first-ever-garden-villages-named-with-government-support*

Eco-towns:
Global Environment Centre Foundation, *Eco-towns in Japan* – *www.unep.or.jp/ietc/Publications/spc/Eco_Towns_in_Japan.pdf*

Defensible space:
Oscar Newman, *Creating Defensible Space*, 1996 – *www.huduser.gov/publications/pdf/def.pdf*
Secured By Design, *Homes 2016*, Version 1, February 2016 –
http://www.securedbydesign.com/wp-content/uploads/2017/06/Secured_by_Design_Homes_2016_V2.pdf

Greenfield sites:
Sustainable Build, Greenfield Sites – *www.sustainablebuild.co.uk/GreenfieldSites.html*

Curitiba:
'Curitiba, the greenest city on earth' –*http://www.theecologist.org/green_green_living/2299325/curitiba_the_greenest_city_on_earth.html*
'Curitiba: an environmental showcase' – *www.huffingtonpost.com/roberta-brandes-gratz/curitiba_b_3713953.html*
'Curitiba: the cradle of bus rapid transport' – *http://www.sibrtonline.org/downloads/built-environment-curitiba-oct19-4db0b5ac230da.pdf*

Green spaces:
Department of Transport, Local Government and the Regions (2002) *Green spaces, better places, final report of the Urban Green Spaces Taskforce* – *www.ocs.polito.it/biblioteca/verde/taskforce/gspaces_.pdf*
National Audit Office, 2006, *Enhancing urban green space* – *https://www.nao.org.uk/report/enhancing-urban-green-space*

3. TRAFFIC AND TRANSPORT

Case studies

Traffic and transport management in a city: Cambridge

Students should be able to:

(i) demonstrate knowledge and understanding of the impact on sustainability of different modes of transport by sea, air and land

(ii) evaluate urban traffic management strategies including public transport, integrated transport networks, restrictions on car usage, car parking and pedestrian and cycling policies

Traffic and transport are two of the most important issues affecting the sustainability of settlements, both in the present and the past (Figure B21).

Transport refers to the movement, the carriage and the conveyance of goods and people. Traffic refers to the volume of vehicles or people using a transport route or network at a given time. Within the UK, 1.5% of journeys are by air, 8% by rail and the rest on the roads. In MEDCs increased affluence has resulted in suburbanisation, even counterurbanisation, as people and industry have decentralised. This has increased the length of commuter journeys. In some big cities, such as London, many commuter journeys are by public transport but nationally the picture is different. In the 2013 'National Travel Survey' for England, it was shown that 44% of people did not use local buses and 42% never got on trains, but only 4% did not use cars with 84% travelling by car at least once a week. The next highest mode of transport used at least weekly was the bus with 27%. Similarly, in many LEDCs development has seen growing car usage with knock on effects on congestion and pollution. This is evident in Asian cities especially where bicycles have largely given way to scooters and cars (Figure B22).

Figure B21: Advertisement for London's Transport Museum

Figure B22: Scooters in Taipei, Taiwan

Modes of transport

Land

Road

The unique flexibility of car transport and the fact that cars are seen by many as a status symbol are two reasons for the increase in car usage. In 1952 Britain's roads had about 2 million cars; in 2012 34.5 million vehicles were licensed for use, 28.7 million (83%) being cars. However, private cars, at least those powered by petrol or diesel, are not a sustainable form of transport.

Congestion is a major issue, especially in inner urban areas where the street layout may reflect transport needs from a period before the car had even been invented. In London horse drawn traffic moved at about 10 mph; motorised traffic in 2003 moved at an average of 8.5 mph. The congestion charge introduced that year led to an increase back to about 10 mph, slightly faster than a chicken can run. The *Economist* (3 November 2014) reported that traffic congestion in 2013 cost the UK as a whole about £200 billion, 0.8% of GDP, due to its waste of fuel and time. In addition, there is an environmental cost from vehicle exhausts. Internal combustion engines are much cleaner than they used to be but such gains are offset by the increased number of vehicles. In the UK, 24% of greenhouse gas emissions came from transportation in 2015 and there had been little change in emissions since 1990, whilst other sectors had shown major declines. Congestion also damages the attractiveness of town centres and may encourage investment in greenfield areas instead. Further, motorists might travel through residential areas to avoid congestion, leading to safety concerns. The development of modern industry, commerce and retailing in purpose built locations in out-of-town areas has promoted increased road transport for commercial vehicles, workers and customers. Over time, the size of commercial and industrial vehicles has increased and this has created more problems.

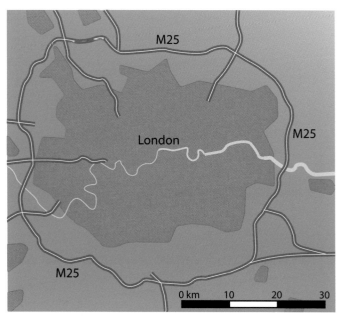

Figure B23: Map of the M25 motorway network

Road building was initially considered the best solution to traffic congestion, but this has raised environmental issues. Between 1980 and 2000 about 550 km (342 miles) of motorway were built in Britain. Inevitably rural land was affected, including protected land; the 188 km (117 mile) M25 orbital motorway around London, completed in 1986, was all built on the greenbelt (Figure B23).

Rail

Trains are more sustainable than cars, given that they can transport hundreds of people at quite high speeds on dedicated tracks. Railways also carry freight. In Britain, the equivalent of 7.6 million lorry loads are taken by rail annually at an estimated saving of £12 billion. Many train services worldwide are now powered by electricity rather than diesel (or the earlier steam), which is efficient and relatively low cost in terms of both expense and environmental impact. The chief problems are achieving a satisfactory administrative structure to run the railways, and meeting demand, especially for commuter services to large cities. In Britain, passenger numbers have doubled in 20 years and 4.5 million journeys are made each day. A transfer of just 2% of road traffic to rail would necessitate a 25% increase in rail capacity in a system that barely copes with present demand.

The development of rail and tracked transport in the UK was very early, associated with industrialisation in the nineteenth century. For example, London's underground railway, the 'Tube', dates back to 1863 and was the first system in the world. Improving, modernising and extending a rail system is expensive: the 118 km (73 mile) Crossrail project across London and neighbouring counties will have taken ten years to construct at a cost of almost £15 billion when it is all opened in 2019. UK railways generally suffer from an ageing infrastructure, which is costly to update, even for a single station. Birmingham's New Street Station was extensively enlarged and modernised in 2015, a necessary investment that cost £550 million. Comprehensive planning is difficult given the privatisation of the British railways, which by 1997 saw them in the hands of different companies. The Strategic Rail Authority, which announced a £56 billion plan for modernisation in 2002, was itself shut down in 2006 and its functions transferred to a number of different agencies. Britain Runs on Rail now acts as an umbrella body and on its website can be found details of the Railway Upgrade Plan, a £50 billion investment scheme for new carriages, electrification and other enhancements, Crossrail, and £7.2 billion towards HS2. HS2 is a planned high speed railway to connect London to Birmingham and on to the northern English cities of Leeds and Manchester, which has a projected budget of £56 billion. This has attracted much controversy because of the damage it would do to the rural areas through which it would run, especially in the Chiltern Hills north of London.

A number of countries have progressed much further than the UK in developing high speed rail. One is Japan, where the *Shinkansen* system (Figure B24), featuring the famous 'bullet trains', began to be developed in 1964 and now connects all four main islands of the country. It runs, often on elevated tracks, at speeds of up to 320 km/h (200 mph) and has reduced the need for internal flights within Japan.

Figure B24: Shinkansen on Kyushu Island, Japan

Sea

The sea is now seen as a barrier, a stretch of water that interrupts land travel and is to be crossed, if at all possible, by flying above it. Before modern land transport or proper roads, the sea was a highway and transport across land was more problematic. Thus, before transcontinental railways, people travelling from Europe to the west of North America would usually choose to sail round Cape Horn rather than expose themselves to a land journey. Things have changed on land and at sea: sail gave way to steam power, then to oil and in some cases nuclear power, and ships have got bigger. What has not changed is that sea transport remains important for moving goods and in some cases people. Cruising is popular and ferries are heavily used for short sea crossings, not least between Ireland and Great Britain. Sea freight is also important in this globalised world and carriage has been transformed in recent decades by containerisation. Standard metal containers, first developed in the 1950s, can easily be taken on and off ships and other modes of transport, and ports throughout the world now have container terminals. About 90% of shipping freight is now containerised, excluding the carriage of bulk goods such as oil and mineral ore.

Transport by sea is relatively slow, but can be efficient both economically and environmentally given the huge loads transported in large ships. However, ship operation is not inexpensive and ship owners minimise costs by employing cheap labour and seeking shorter routes: climate change may make transport through the Northwest Passage north of Canada viable. Ships themselves are a source of pollution:

- The largest ships burn approximately 170,000 litres of fuel daily to power their engines and to generate electricity.

- According to a German environmental group, whose findings were reported in the *Guardian* online 21 May 2016, one medium cruise ship generates as many pollutants as 5 million cars going the same distance.

- According to the environmental group, Friends of the Earth, a cruise ship with 7000 passengers, on a one week cruise produces 4.5 million litres of grey water from sinks, showers, laundries and galleys and 1 million litres of sewage.

Air

The first powered aircraft flight by the Wright brothers was in 1903. In the century and more since then, air transport has been transformed; indeed that first flight covered 37 m, less than half the wingspan of a large modern jet. According to the World Bank, in the 35 years from 1970 to 2015 passengers carried per year increased from 310 million to 3.4 billion and flights of registered carriers from 9.4 million to almost 33 million. Air travel is hardly a daily event, except for crew, and 95% the world's people have never flown, but in many MEDCs air travel has become commonplace. Certainly it has lost its exclusivity and glamour and, given the influence of low cost, low service airlines, it has became a mode of transport to be endured rather than enjoyed. Its benefit is its speed, although this is lessened for short journeys if the time spent at the airports either end of the actual flight is factored in. However, even within fairly small countries, air travel competes with long distance car and train journeys – even Ireland has domestic flights (Dublin to Kerry and Donegal), as does Wales (Cardiff to Anglesey). Many people travel by plane to and from their holiday destinations. The tourism industry in regions like the Mediterranean is heavily dependent upon air travel, indeed it developed largely because of the growth in air travel from the 1950s

Figure B25: Tourists alight at Easter Island after a 3766 km (2340 mile) flight from Santiago, Chile

and 1960s made possible by technical advances such as the jet engine. By facilitating long distance travel (Figure B25), air transport has had a negative influence upon sustainability and one criticism of eco-tourism ventures in places like Central America has been that to get to the log lodges and eat local food, tourists have travelled long distances in a plane.

Aircraft issues include noise and air pollution. Jet engines in flight are quite efficient but emit nitrogen dioxide, which has been seen to damage the stratospheric ozone layer. Ground level pollution is caused by aircraft taxiing, airport operations and also from vehicles travelling to the airports. Efforts are made to improve engine efficiency, which has economic as well as environmental benefits. Air travel is taxed, but financial disincentives have not been fully imposed as an international agreement does not permit aviation fuel to be taxed. Further, the low-cost airlines have made flying cheaper than it has ever been so more journeys are made. One pressure group, Environmental Protection UK, has put forward the following proposals:

- Ensure airlines pay for the pollution they cause, like other transport operators.
- Encourage the development of more fuel-efficient aircraft.
- Help reduce the demand for air travel as other options become more competitive.
- Be consistent with UK pledges to reduce greenhouse gas emissions from airport operations.

Traffic management strategies

In order to attain a sustainable transport policy, planners need to implement strategies that will make public transport more efficient and accessible, therefore challenging the supremacy of private cars, which are the most polluting form of transport. There are a number of options available and most governments use disincentives for motorists and incentives for public transport users.

Road pricing and restrictions on car usage

This policy includes toll roads, where a vehicle is charged to use a specific stretch of road. This adds to the cost of the journey, thus in theory discouraging demand, whilst the toll charges are often used to help meet the costs of providing the road infrastructure. The concept of toll roads dates back centuries, but in the modern era an important policy initiative was the road pricing strategy adopted in Singapore from 1975. Over 60% of morning rush hour traffic on the roads of this city-state switched to other modes of transport or journeys were made outside the peak period over which the toll operated.

Figure B26: Durham charging zone

Another road pricing scheme is the congestion charge. One notable example is central London where vehicles crossing the congestion charge boundary have to pay a fee. The system was first introduced in 2003 and since then it has been extended and refined. At the time of writing there is discussion about diesel vehicles being charged more – the toxicity charge, or T-charge – to discourage their use. At present the charge is £11.50 to enter the zone between 07.00 and 18.00 Monday to Friday, with discounts for some categories of road user including residents, disabled drivers and drivers of low-emission vehicles. The London congestion charge saw about a 10% reduction in vehicle use within the zone after 10 years. About £1.2 billion of the money accrued was spent on infrastructure and the London bus network. Other cities that have introduced a congestion charge system include Milan, Stockholm and Durham, where the charge was introduced to protect the historic centre of the city (Figure B26).

Another policy is a variable road tax, under which larger and/or more polluting vehicles (measured by CO_2 emissions) are charged more for their annual licence than smaller-engined vehicles. Hybrid and electric vehicles can be charged little or are even zero-rated.

Figure B27: Pedestrianisation in Kagoshima, Japan

Pedestrianisation

This strategy, the banning of vehicular traffic from an area for at least some of the time, is used to increase the attractiveness and safety of town centres and also to preserve historic buildings. Much of the centre of Belfast is pedestrianised or at least has vehicular access limited to buses. The attractiveness of pedestrianised areas is often enhanced with landscaping, trees, seating areas and attractive street furniture. They are open and welcoming and play a part in attracting shoppers to the town centre (Figure B27).

Opponents of pedestrianisation polices claim that shoppers can actually be deterred by having to carry their purchases, especially if they have used public transport. This may encourage them to use out-of-town shopping areas instead. Although most pedestrianised areas do permit access for delivery vehicles at certain times, pedestrianisation imposes restrictions on retailers too. Furthermore, pedestrianisation can increase traffic congestion and demand for parking spaces in areas surrounding the zone.

Car parking policies

These operate in a number of ways. In town centres on-street parking is often not permitted in the busiest streets nor, of course, in pedestrianised areas. In other streets it would have been controlled by parking meters, but these have largely been replaced by pay-and-display schemes. These are often time-limited so the parking is suitable only for shoppers, not commuters who would want to stay all day. Multi-storey or underground car parks, where all-day parking is also available, can be found on the edges of main commercial districts and perhaps also within the centre in new developments. One example of this is the 1000 space underground car park, QPark, at the Victoria Square Shopping Centre in Belfast. Car park charges are usually higher in the most central and accessible facilities.

To discourage people from bringing their cars into the centre, many cities operate park-and-ride schemes. These are large car parks on the edge of the city where drivers can leave their vehicles and transfer to the centre by public transport. Belfast has a number of park-and-ride locations, as does Cambridge (see Cambridge case study, pages 307–313). Some cities also have places outside the city where work colleagues gather to share one car for the last leg of their journey to work, leaving the others parked for the day.

Cycling policies

In MEDCs especially, there are now policies in urban areas to encourage the use of bicycles as such machines transport people at low cost without causing pollution. There are also health benefits: bikes are the ultimate form of sustainable transport. Cities often encourage bicycle use by providing cycle lanes on their roads to make journeys safer, as one major problem with cycling is the vulnerability of riders if they are involved in a collision with a vehicle. In LEDC cities, bicycles are seen rather as a necessity for economic reasons. It is notable that as development takes place and some cities become wealthier, as in China, the use of bicycles declines as people purchase cars, perhaps partly as a status symbol. Instead it now tends to be European cities, especially those that are compact with flat terrain, that see most bicycle use for speed and convenience as well as for health, environmental and sustainable policy reasons. Examples are Amsterdam

Figure B28: The morning rush hour in Copenhagen, Denmark

and Copenhagen (Figure B28). In Copenhagen, 37% of commuter journeys are by bike. The city has a network of segregated cycle lanes – the first cycle lane was established in 1910. This enables riders to get across the city without mixing with vehicles, or often without even stopping as traffic light sequences are set to favour cyclists moving at 20 kph, an urban speed which usually exceeds the average for motor vehicles as cars are more likely to get stuck in traffic. In winter, snow is cleared first from cycle lanes and 80% of Copenhagen cyclists make their journeys throughout the year.

Another cycling policy of growing significance is public bicycle sharing schemes, which are now widespread in European cities (Figure B29), including Belfast. There are a number of docking stations throughout a city where people who have joined the scheme can pick up and drop off bikes, paying a small charge for their hire. One of the most notable is the popularly known 'Boris bike' scheme in London, nicknamed for the then mayor, Boris Johnson, who introduced them. Officially now Santander Cycles, after the firm than sponsors them, London has 750 docking stations and 11,000 bikes in circulation. The bikes are serviced and maintained but there are obvious drawbacks: safety concerns if the hirers are not competent cyclists and there is a risk that the bicycles can be abused or stolen. Belfast Bikes, which was launched in April 2015 had had 210 of its 576 bicycles stolen or taken out of service through vandalism by April 2017. That month, a low tide uncovered 10 bikes thrown into the Lagan. A campaigner warned that "Belfast Bikes is a cheap, socially inclusive transport form for everyone in the city, and it's about to be squandered".

Figure B29: 'Villo' bikes in Brussels, Belgium

Public transport

Traffic management strategies aim to reduce the popularity of private car journeys by improving the appeal of public transport by providing a reliable, regular and cost-effective service with high quality buses and trains. Fare concessions for regular users might be provided, in addition to free or subsidised tickets for schoolchildren and the elderly, made available for social welfare reasons. Many cities now have bus lanes on urban roads where private cars are not allowed, to free buses from congestion and make journeys quicker (Figure B30). This gives buses some of the qualities of urban trams or light rail systems, which are powered by electricity, the least polluting power source, and run on dedicated routes (Resource A, page 313).

Large cities may have underground railways such as Glasgow, the 'Tube' in London and the Metro in Paris. These are very expensive to provide and maintain but can make a large contribution to the efficient and relatively environmentally friendly transportation of large numbers of people. The Indian city of Delhi opened the first stage of its Metro in 2002. It now carries about 2.7 million passengers per year, speeding their

Figure B30: Bus lane in Taipei, Taiwan

journeys whilst reducing congestion and carbon emissions in the city, if at a financial cost, since the operation does not make a profit.

All public transport systems struggle to compete with the flexibility and personal comfort provided by the private car. The car goes when and where its driver wants and, although it may be caught up in traffic jams, at least the passengers are comfortable, travel with their friends or family and are able to enjoy their own choice of radio or music. On buses or trains people might be cramped, crowded and forced to jostle up against strangers, whilst their journeys can also be subject to delays.

Integrated transport networks

Public transport can never offer the flexibility of the private car. However, integrated transport networks do go some way to maximise the flexibility and efficiency of public transport. An integrated transport network is one that co-ordinates several forms of public transport in one location, enabling passengers to transfer easily from one mode of transport to another. Timings should be organised so that connections are as seamless as possible, thus the last bus should not leave until the last train has arrived. In London, the main railway stations surrounding the central area have underground stations, bus connections, taxi ranks and bicycle parks. In Zurich, Switzerland the central train station has not only car parks, bicycle parks, a taxi rank, bus and tram services but also a stop on the city's waterbus service, which transports people along Lake Zurich. New developments in and around cities must take transport systems into account.

CASE STUDY: Cambridge, a study of traffic and transport management in a city

Background

The historic city of Cambridge arose on a crossing point of the River Cam, about 80 km (50 miles) north of London, now one hour's travel on the M11 or by rail.

Cambridge is the commercial and administrative centre for the county of Cambridgeshire and houses the famous university, which dates back to 1284. Many of the colleges that make up the university are sited in the centre of the city and are of considerable historic importance and have to be protected by strict conservation regulations. Although Cambridge is a fairly small city (123,900 at the 2011 census, with about 29,000 students), it is growing quickly on its southern fringe and to the north west at Eddington, the University of Cambridge's new district. Further pressures arise from the city being a major tourist destination, about 4.5 million visitors every year (Figure B31).

Cambridge is well served by public transport. There is a good rail service to other parts of East Anglia, including Stansted Airport, as well as to Birmingham and London. However, one problem is the location of the station well outside the city centre. A number of bus companies operate between Cambridge and other urban areas in southern and eastern England, and there is a good bus network within the city. There is an excellent road network surrounding Cambridge.

Figure B31: Tourists outside St John's College, Cambridge

However, the approach roads are under pressure. The M11 from London joins the A14 near Cambridge, which being the major east–west freight route to the port of Felixstowe on the east coast, is often congested. Further, the ring road, the A1134, carries through traffic as well as traffic destined for central Cambridge. Within the historic core problems arise for traffic management:

- The ancient streets of the historic core are narrow with many bends and corners and are not suited for modern traffic.
- Making changes is difficult, if not impossible given the need to conserve the historic buildings.
- The narrow streets lined with substantial buildings impact on the dispersal of pollutants from the heavy traffic.
- One surprising problem is how to deal with bicycles, about one-third of people in Cambridge travel to work by bike, almost the same as travel by car.

A pressure group, Smarter Cambridge Transport, made up of local people working to promote integrated transport has proposed ten policies.

1. Implement Smart Traffic Management in the city.
   - Use proven technology to regulate traffic flow responsively (i.e. in real time).

2. Build travel hubs throughout the region
   - Rural travel hubs would provide shelter, secure cycle parking, live transport information, and some car parking.
   - Park-and-Ride sites would intercept longer distance traffic.

3. Reorganise bus services.
   - Express services to run frequently along radial routes to and from Cambridge, calling only at travel hubs and other major stops en route.
   - Feeder bus services to connect with express services at travel hubs, providing inward and onward connections.

4. Simplify ticketing.
   - Smart ticketing for all public transport, car parking and cycle hire within the region to facilitate multi-modal journeys.

5. Create a journey planner app and website.

6. Create a connected network of segregated cycle ways (protected where possible).

7. Make strategic modifications to the road network.
   - Restrict through access around the inner ring road to promote freer movement of buses around the city centre.
   - Create more home zones without through traffic ('rat runs').

8. Enhance access to rail services.
   - Build new train stations and enhance access to existing ones.

9. Promote city-wide goods delivery services using consolidation depots and collection points.

10. Rationalise car parking.
    - Phase out free parking for commuters on residential roads.
    - Charge employers a workplace parking levy to encourage employees to use alternatives to driving.

Information from *The Smarter Cambridge Transport Plan*, http://www.smartertransport.uk/plan/

Cambridgeshire County Council is responsible for transport planning and management, whilst Cambridge City Council produced a local plan for 2014 which aims to meet the city's needs until 2031. This is under examination by the Planning Inspectorate at the time of writing and is subject to change. The city's approach was to "minimise the distance people need to travel, and … make it easy for everyone to move around the city and access jobs and services by sustainable modes of transport". The following is the list of strategies:

- Delivery of local and strategic transport schemes.
- Promoting greater pedestrian and cycle priority through and to the city centre.
- Promoting sustainable transport and access for all to and from major employers, education and research clusters, hospitals, schools and colleges.
- Aiming for a joined-up, city-wide cycle and pedestrian network by addressing 'pinch-points', barriers and missing links.
- Proposing a city-wide 20 mph zone.
- Easing pressure on the air quality in the city centre.

Delivery would be through:

- ensuring sustainable urban extensions, linked through high quality, frequent public transport routes and cycle ways to the city centre, railway station and main employment centres.
- regenerating Cambridge railway station as a multi-modal transport interchange.
- creating a low speed traffic environment to restore the balance between people and vehicles.

Information from *Cambridge Local Plan 2014: Proposed Submission*, Cambridge City Council

Figure B32: Map of Cambridge

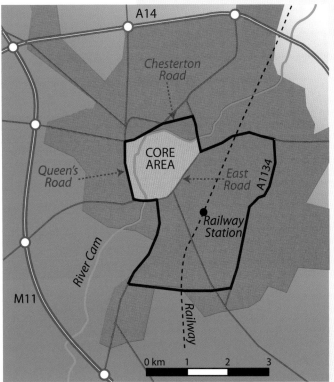

Road restrictions, cycling and pedestrian zones

The historic core of Cambridge is bounded by the inner ring-road and the River Cam (Figure B32). Within this area are eight traffic cells, mostly with just one entry point. One-way systems within the cells ease the flow of traffic. Much of the historic core of the city has been pedestrianised (Figures B31 and B32). These streets have limitations for motorised traffic, with access for deliveries being restricted to early mornings and late afternoons. Rising bollards were used to protect some places from entry by those without permits, but now they are guarded by cameras. Many residential roads are now 20 mph zones (Figure B35).

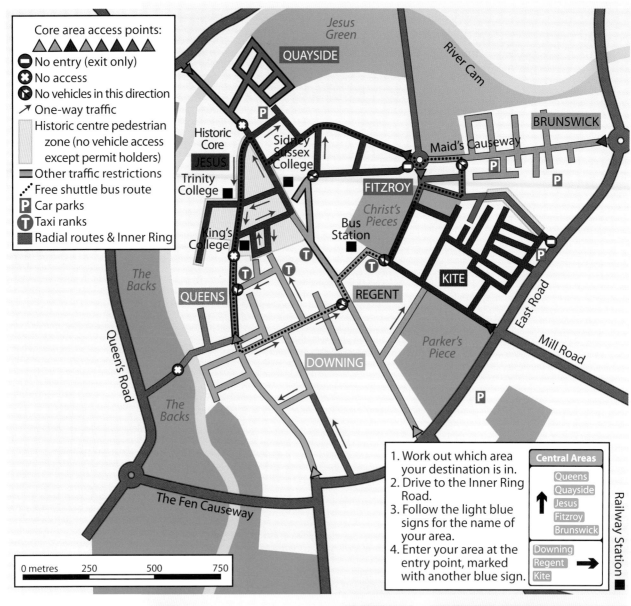

Figure B33: Map of restrictions in Cambridge

Core area access points:
△△△▲▲▲▲▲ △
⊖ No entry (exit only)
⊗ No access
◉ No vehicles in this direction
↗ One-way traffic
▨ Historic centre pedestrian zone (no vehicle access except permit holders)
▬ Other traffic restrictions
⋰ Free shuttle bus route
P Car parks
T Taxi ranks
■ Radial routes & Inner Ring

1. Work out which area your destination is in.
2. Drive to the Inner Ring Road.
3. Follow the light blue signs for the name of your area.
4. Enter your area at the entry point, marked with another blue sign.

Central Areas
↑ Queens
Quayside
Jesus
Fitzroy
Brunswick
→ Downing
Regent
Kite
Railway Station ■

0 metres 250   500   750

Figure B34: Pedestrianisation in central Cambridge

Figure B35: 20 mph restriction in a residential area of Cambridge

Cambridge is a bicycle-friendly place – its narrow streets are difficult for cars and the city and surrounding areas are flat – and it has the highest rate of cycle commuting in the UK. There are cycle lanes, cycle contraflows on some streets,

Figure B36: Bicycle lane in Cambridge

which are otherwise one-way, also numerous bicycle lanes throughout the city (Figure B36). However, bikes can become a nuisance when left on the street and there are restrictions on where bikes can be left. Cyclists also have to dismount and walk along some streets. In the replanning of the area outside Cambridge station, what was once a large site where a jumble of bikes used to be left has been given over to a new space for buses and taxis. A 3000 space indoor bike park has been provided instead (Figure B37).

There have been proposals to impose a London-style congestion charge in Cambridge to further constrain traffic, but they met much opposition and have not yet been implemented.

Figure B37: The former (left) and new (right) bike parking area at Cambridge station

Parking

Parking is prohibited throughout the historic core. Demand is restricted by the colleges not letting their students bring private cars to university. Parking on residential streets is usually restricted to residents only, who have to apply for a permit. The council has provided five pay-on-foot multi-storey car parks close to the centre providing about 3000 places; also three pay-and-display car parks. Car park charges in central Cambridge are set at such a rate that after a short time it would have been cheaper to have used one of the five park-and-ride facilities around the city. Cambridge tourism websites advise visiting motorists to use the park-and-ride sites. These are located on arterial routes, provide over 5000 spaces and attract over 4 million users per year. Parking is cheap in these sites, at £1.00 for up to 18 hours, with the bus journey costing an additional £3.00 before concessions (Figures B38–B40).

Figure B38: Park-and-ride facilities outside Cambridge

Park-and-ride site	Car spaces	Disabled spaces
Babraham Road	1458	10
Madingley Road	930	12
Milton	792	17
Newmarket Road	Front 259/ Back 614	15
Trumpington	1340	24

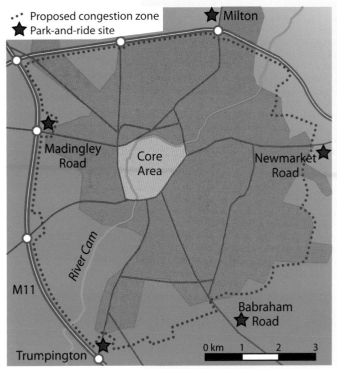

Proposed congestion zone
Park-and-ride site

Figure B40: Cambridge park-and-ride bus service

All Cambridge car parks provide charging points for electric vehicles. The park-and-ride sites are staffed during opening hours and have waiting rooms with snack and drink machines. After the last bus they are secured with barriers but these rise to allow any cars still in the park to leave.

Figure B39: Cambridge park-and-ride locations

Rail transport

Cambridge station is inconveniently sited about 1.6 km (a mile) from the centre. It has to have bus and taxi services from the city centre and also provide space for cars and hundreds of bicycles, many commuters keeping a bike at the station to facilitate the last leg of their journey to work. Until recently the bikes occupied a disorganised, big open space by the station (Figure B37). In 2016, the bicycles were moved to a new 3000 space under-cover bike storage area and the station forecourt was completely redesigned to serve buses and taxis (Figure B41). The station also has bus services to park-and-ride sites. A new railway station, Cambridge North, has just been built close to the Cambridge Science Park. This will connect to the guided busway, local bus services and a park-and-ride hub.

Figure B41: Public transport area at Cambridge station

Buses

Cambridge buses are operated by a private company, which has an obligation to meet environmental standards regarding emissions. Bus stops usually have shelters and also raised kerbs to make boarding the bus easier. They are sited to try to minimise congestion. Different categories of ticket are available to try to encourage as wide a use of the bus as possible. There are a number of bus lanes and since 2014 £60 fines have been issued to any drivers of private cars recorded using them, by new cameras. There used to be three 'bus gates' in the centre protected by rising bollards, which could be lowered only by buses. These too have been replaced by cameras, which capture illegal usage.

Cambridge also has a guided busway, a dedicated track for buses only, which opened in 2011. This runs mainly to the north east of the city to the towns of Huntingdon and St Ives, mostly following disused railway tracks along which the bus is

Figure B42: Cambridge busway system

controlled by guide wheels, not by the driver's steering wheel. It links through Cambridge Science Park, the new Cambridge North station, the city centre, the central bus station, the railway station to the major hospital, Addenbrookes, and Trumpington park-and-ride (Figure B42).

Where the busway runs along regular roads there are bus lanes and bus priority traffic signals. The busway's surface is constructed from shredded car tyres, which is cheaper than tarmac and makes effective use of waste material. The buses produce much less carbon dioxide emissions than ordinary buses. The busway cost £181m to construct, almost three times its original budget, was delayed by several years, was subject to objections from environmental groups and there were a number of court cases involving disputes in its construction.

Exercise

1. To what extent have urban planners in Cambridge incorporated the principles of sustainability in their traffic management strategy?

Exam Questions

1. Study Resources A–C, which show transport policies in Dublin.

   (i) Describe they way in which the concept of integrated transport networks has influenced transport policies and provision in Dublin. [8]

   (ii) Use the resources to help you explain the significance of the role of public transport in traffic management strategies. [9]

   Question adapted from CCEA A22 Processes and Issues in Human Geography, January 2009, © CCEA 2017

Follow up

See the website at
https://www.LUAS.ie

Resource A: The LUAS network

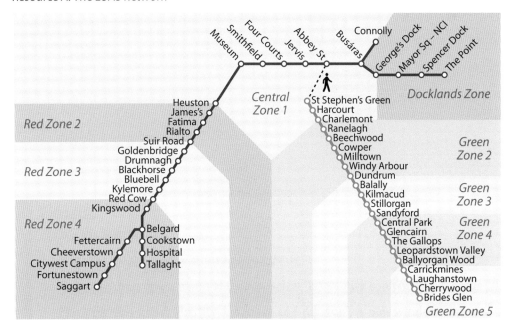

Resource B: The LUAS, Dublin
Source: Adapted from https://www.LUAS.ie

- LUAS (the Irish word for speed) is Dublin's modern tram (light rail) system and opened in 2004.
- The earlier Dublin City Tramways operated between 1872 and 1949, before being replaced by buses.
- LUAS has two lines, Red (14 km) and Green (9 km), with two spurs.
- Building the Red and Green LUAS lines cost €728m (c £620m). There was support from the European Union.
- The tracks run along the road, but are not accessible by other vehicles.
- There are 54 stations and 36.5 km (22.7 miles) of track.
- There are 66 trams in the LUAS system and in 2017 seven more were on order.
- 36.6 million passengers rode LUAS in 2014.
- The Red Line connects Dublin's two main rail terminals, Connolly and Heuston Stations, replacing the need for a bus service to make the journey.
- The original concept had the lines joining at O'Connell Street, but there was only pedestrian access between St Stephen's Green on the Green Line and Abbey Street on the Red Line, the stations closest to each other, until the lines were joined in 2017 at an additional cost of €368 million.
- There are six park-and-ride car parks connected with LUAS. Payment for parking can be made at LUAS ticket machines.
- Most LUAS stops also have a bus stop.
- Bicycles (except for folding bikes in bags) cannot be taken on board.
- Bicycle racks are provided at most stations; over 700 spaces for bikes are provided in total. Several LUAS stops are adjacent to the Dublin public bike hire system, Dublin Bikes.
- All LUAS stations and the trams are accessible to wheelchairs.
- To speed travel, tickets must be purchased before boarding from machines, which take cash or cards.
- LUAS is regarded as a safe form of transport; even so there were four fatal accidents between 2008 and 2016.
- Discounted fares are available for certain groups.

Resource C: LUAS at Heuston Station, Dublin

References

Department for Business, Energy and Industrial Strategy, Final UK greenhouse gas emissions national statistics:
https://www.gov.uk/government/collections/final-uk-greenhouse-gas-emissions-national-statistics

'The cost of traffic jams', *The Economist*, 3 November 2014:
https://www.economist.com/blogs/economist-explains/2014/11/economist-explains-1

Britain Runs on Rail:
www.britainrunsonrail.co.uk

Cruise ship pollution, the problem:
www.beachapedia.org/Cruise_Ship_Pollution

Aviation pollution (under Policy areas, Air quality):
www.environmental-protection.org.uk

Good, better, best: The city of Copenhagen's bicycle strategy, 2011–2025:
kk.sites.itera.dk/apps/kk_pub2/pdf/823_Bg65v7UH2t.pdf

Cambridge growth:
https://www.cambridge.gov.uk/where-cambridge-is-growing
www.nwcambridge.co.uk/news/open-eddington

Cambridge City Council, *Cambridge Local Plan 2014*:
https://www.cambridge.gov.uk/local-plan-core-documents-library

Updates on the Cambridge Local Plan can be followed on the Cambridge City Council website:
cambridge.gov.uk via 'Planning', 'Planning Policy' to 'Local Plan Review'.

Future transport developments in Cambridge:
https://www.greatercambridge.org.uk/

Smarter Cambridge Transport:
www.smartertransport.uk

1. THE DEFINITION OF ETHNICITY

Case studies

General reference
to places for
illustration
purposes only

Students should be able to:

(i)   explain the factors that define ethnicity – race, nationality, language and religion

(ii) explain how role, residential concentration, age and gender influence perceived
      ethnic and social identity

An ethnic group refers to a community of individuals who share inherited cultural
traditions, values, national identity, patterns of behaviour and language. Individual
members recognise themselves as part of a separate group which makes them distinct
from other communities. There is a boundary, which separates 'us' from 'them', and the
distinction would probably be recognised on both sides of that boundary. Ethnic groups
vary in size from the Han Chinese, with over 1.6 billion people, to small numbers of
tribal indigenous groups.

Ethnicity refers to the personal traits which make up an individual's ethnic identity. It is
a multi-faceted phenomenon based on physical appearance, subjective identification,
cultural and religious affiliation, stereotyping and social exclusion. This can be
anything visible, from skin colour and language to dress code. Male Orthodox (Haredi)
Jews have a dress code, which has religious significance. Its recognisable features
include a skull cap, black hat and long black coat. Some have long beards and wear a
curl at the side of their head. Many Muslim women also adhere to a strict dress code,
which includes a head covering such as the hijab (headscarf). Questions on ethnicity
were first included in the 1991 Census in Britain and in Northern Ireland from 2001.
The questions have evolved over time. In 1991, respondents were asked to select from a
small number of pre-defined groups "Which group have you descended from?" By
2001, the question focussed on cultural background and with many more pre-defined
categories. In 2011, an additional question on national identity was included.

The factors that define ethnicity

The definition of an ethnicity is complex but there are a number of factors that can be
used to make broad classifications:

Race

Race is probably the most controversial factor used to define an ethnic group. Race
classifies people according to the colour of their skin, visible facial features or hair type.
Traditionally there were four major races: Caucasian (white or European), Mongoloid
(Asian or Chinese), Negroid (black or African) and Australoid (Aboriginals). Early

studies of these divisions assumed that there was some biological difference between the groups. However, modern studies have proved this to be false. About 99% of the genetic make-up of the human population is common to all ethnic groups. Nevertheless, race has been a divisive factor for centuries. White European colonialists assumed domination over black Africans, taking millions as slaves to the Americas and elsewhere. Military superiority translated to racial superiority. Nineteenth century writers claimed that people from temperate climates had a superior work ethic. People living in tropical climates were deemed inferior and in need of 'civilising' by their white superiors. Slavery and racial discrimination has had a profound impact on the history of the United States of America. Government law leading to the abolition of slavery was one of the main causes of the American Civil War. There are still many black Americans who remember the struggle against segregation and for civil rights in the 1960s.

Racial divisions are a very visible sign of ethnic division but movements of people and intermarriage mean that there is no such thing as a 'pure' race anymore. In America, individuals with any characteristics regarded as 'African' are categorised as 'black' even when the majority are of mixed race. In 2008, America elected Barack Obama as its first black African American President.

Nationality

A strong unifying element for large numbers of people is their country of origin or ancestral home, with all the trappings of national flags and national anthems. Nationality is at once unifying and divisive. The concept of a 'nation state', where political boundaries enclosed territory controlled by people of similar nationality, played a key role in political thought in Europe throughout the 19th century. Italy became a nation state in 1861, having been a group of separate and independent city states. Nationality is a personal and mobile form of ethnicity, even when the group are away from their home country. The examples of the Irish Americans or Hispanic Americans illustrate this point well. Members of an ethnic group identified by nationality present a group image of their national identity to the outside world. The group, although made up of individuals, proclaims its national unity to those who are different and excluded from their group. In the case of Northern Ireland, the Catholic population are often broadly referred to as Nationalist. Nationalist in this context refers to this group's allegiance to Ireland as opposed to the UK. In Northern Ireland there are laws regarding when and where flags may be displayed, the routes of marches and the playing of the national anthem.

Nationalism has increased in Europe since the 1990s. The break-up of the former Soviet Union has resulted in the emergence of a number of independent nations, each with their own identity. The aspirations of an ethnic group, defined by national identity, to break away from their current political rulers have often led to bitter conflict. The disintegration of the former Yugoslavia in the 1990s into ethnic national units (Figure C1) followed ethnic conflict and civil wars.

Figure C1: The partition of Yugoslavia

Yugoslavia 1991

Austria
Hungary
Slovenia
Romania
Croatia
Vojvodina*
Bosnia Herzegovina
Serbia
Kosovo*
Montenegro
Macedonia
Italy
Albania
Greece

*autonomous provinces

Former Yugoslav republics 2017

Austria
Hungary
Republika Srpska*
Romania
Slovenia
Croatia
Vojvodina*
Bosnia and Herzegovina
Serbia
Federation of Bosnia and Herzegovina*
Kosovo
Montenegro
Macedonia
Italy
Albania
Greece

*autonomous provinces

Language

Language unites and divides groups of people. Worldwide there are approximately 5000–6000 different languages. English is the most widely spoken language, reflecting past colonialism. English is spoken by somewhere between a quarter and a third of the global population. Language is often regarded as an outward expression of ethnicity. In Northern Ireland, there are 29 Irish medium schools and street names in predominantly Nationalist parts of Belfast are often written in Irish. Members of Sinn Féin frequently use Irish when delivering speeches in the Northern Ireland Assembly. The party also campaigned for an Irish Language Act during the 2017 election. If granted, this would mean all legal and official political documents would be delivered in Irish as well as English. One reason the Unionist parties object to this is because they see it as an attempt to dilute the 'Britishness' of Northern Ireland. In Sri Lanka, Sinhala (the language of the majority Sinhalese population) was made the official state language in 1956, forcing all ethnic groups to learn it. This was seen as a discriminatory act against the minority Tamil population. In Canada, the province of Quebec maintains its separate identity from the rest of the country by speaking French. In Belgium, the individuality of the two provinces of Flanders (Dutch speaking) and Wallonia (French speaking) is emphasised by the linguistic differences between them. It has been shown that people who are unable to communicate because of language differences are more likely to maintain other differences as well. Some languages are dying out and about half of the world's languages are not spoken by children. Economic factors and globalisation that promote other languages are thought to be the main reasons for this.

Religion

Religion often provides a code of behaviour that makes its followers instantly recognisable. Reference has already been made to Orthodox Jews and Muslims. On a global scale there are six major world religions (Figure C2), with numerous sub-divisions. The members of some religious groups maintain a degree of segregation from others in society through faith schools and sport. Some religions take this segregation to extremes and live in totally segregated communities, such as the Amish in America. However, many people identify with a specific religious group even if they do not regularly attend religious services.

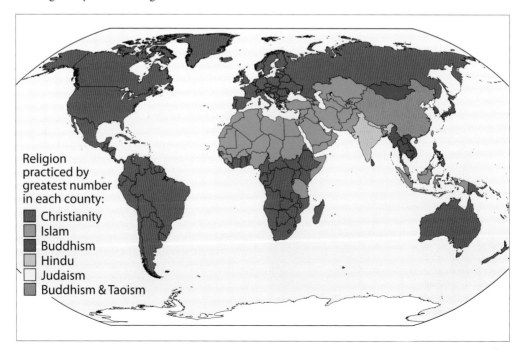

Figure C2: Religions of the world

Some of the worst ethnic conflicts in recent times have involved religious groups. The Holocaust, which resulted in the deaths of six million Jews under Nazi rule during World War II; the on-going conflict in the Middle East between (Jewish) Israel and its Muslim neighbours (see Israel case study, pages 355–364); and the global conflict between Islamic extremists, especially Islamic State (IS) and the western Christian world, are all examples of this. Islamic State has attempted to establish an area defined by Islamic rule, a Caliphate, cutting across current political boundaries in Syria and Iraq.

Perceived ethnic and social identity

Ethnic identity is rarely defined by one factor alone. Increasingly ethnicity is seen as a personal and subjective assessment of how individuals perceive the distinctiveness or uniqueness of their group from that of others in society. This assessment is often made up of a combination of factors, such as race and nationality. Since 2001, the census in England and Wales has divided British identity into a number of components (Figures C3 and C4). Similarly, in Northern Ireland the 2011 census broadened the definition of ethnic identity to include questions on national identity, language and religion. In this way society becomes increasingly diverse and the emphasis in defining ethnicity becomes more complex and subjective. In addition, ethnic identity can also be influenced by place of residence, age, gender, residential concentration and role in society. These operate as an additional filter within society, often in conjunction with one or more of the factors discussed previously. This increasingly complex process is referred to as perceived ethnic and social identity.

Exercise

1. Study Figures C3 and C4 showing ethnic identity information from the 2001 and 2011 censuses in England and Wales.

   (a) Describe the ethnic diversity in England and Wales in 2011 as shown in Figure C3.

   (b) Describe how ethnic identity is defined in the census of 2011 as shown in Figure C4.

   (c) Describe how ethnic diversity has changed between 2001 and 2011 in England and Wales as shown in Figure C4.

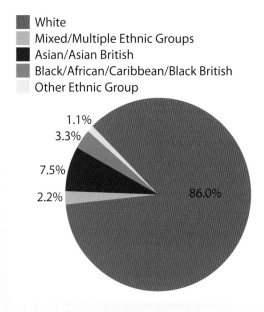

Figure C3: Ethnic groups in England and Wales 2011

Source: Census – Office for National Statistics. Contains public sector information licensed under the Open Government Licence v3.0.

Figure C4: Ethnic Groups in England and Wales 2001–2011 (excluding White British)

Source: Census – Office for National Statistics. Contains public sector information licensed under the Open Government Licence v3.0.

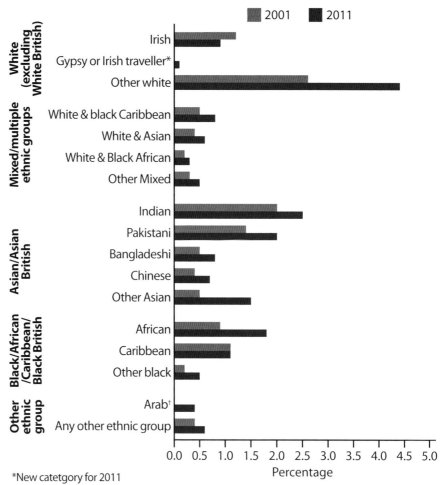

*New catetgory for 2011

†No comparable data exists for this ethnic group in 2001 Census

Role

This refers to a person's occupation or position in society and it has been shown to be a significant element in perceived ethnic identity. Certain individuals are regarded as spokespersons for the ethnicity of particular groups. For example, Imams (Muslim clergy) voice the elements or components of Islam in their community. These individuals have considerable influence and advise Sharia councils on the interpretation of Islam. In Northern Ireland, most political parties are supported by a religious or social group within the country.

All countries display some form of social division and this division has been shown to influence perceived ethnic identity, especially where people of similar social class are grouped together (see 'Residential concentration' section opposite). In the late nineteenth and twentieth centuries, many UK cities experienced rapid industrialisation associated with labour intensive industries such as mining and manufacturing. The residential areas built to house the workers became tight knit communities with strong local identities. These districts had their own churches, schools, shops and recreational amenities. Over time, they developed a strong local working class identity, which was distinct from neighbouring communities. In Belfast, the inner city has several such areas on both sides of the religious divide, including the lower Falls Road (Catholic working class) and lower Shankill Road (Protestant working class). The outward manifestation of perceived ethnic identity is very visible in these districts through wall murals, flags and Irish street names (in Catholic areas only) and contrasts strongly with that of middle class people of similar religion. Middle class professional people tend to live in the suburban mixed areas of the city. Social interactions in these neighbourhoods are carried out across a wider area and with a greater mix of people. In Britain, the Brexit vote in 2016 showed a social class distinction. Working class areas were more likely to vote in favour of leaving the EU than middle class areas. The underlying reasons for this are varied but a desire for a stronger national identity amongst working classes played a part.

In some societies, minority ethnic groups often fit into specific social niches from which it is very difficult to escape. The example of black Americans illustrates this point well. Many black Americans are descended from slaves forcibly brought to America from West and Central Africa. Even after their emancipation they remained a disadvantaged group within American society. They were condemned by poverty and discrimination to the lowest paid jobs, which offered little opportunity for social mobility. It was only in the second half of the twentieth century that the black American population achieved basic civil rights but many still remain a disadvantaged group within American society today. In 2016 and 2017, the controversial shootings of a number of black men by white policemen, in several states, convinced many black Americans that they still do not share equal rights with white Americans.

Residential concentration

People often live in clusters with people of similar ethnicity. This is partly for social and cultural reasons, so that they can avail of places of worship, shops and services, as well as the desire to socialise with those from similar backgrounds. Clusters of ethnic minorities in British cities often reflect the economic ability of the groups to purchase cheap accommodation or to access housing suitable for multiple occupation. The sense of security that comes from living in an ethnically homogeneous area is another major reason for ethnic clustering. Whatever the reason for the clustering, once established, this residential concentration develops, leading to ghettoes or enclaves. These clusters grow in two ways:

- These neighbourhoods are often hostile to those of different ethnicity. This can be achieved through visible displays such as flags and murals. For example, during 'the troubles', Belfast developed clearly defined Republican and Loyalist areas. People of different ethnicity can feel threatened and move away.
- The ethnic neighbourhoods continue to attract more people of similar ethnicity.

These neighbourhoods develop and maintain their unique ethnicity and individuals living there adopt this identity. Many cities in Britain contain communities that are almost completely segregated from each other. The Cantle Report, published in 2001 following ethnic riots in some northern British cities, warned of the dangers of ethnic segregation. The Casey Report, published in December 2016 to detail levels of integration in British cities, showed that little had changed in the interim. Some wards of Blackburn, Birmingham, Burnley and Bradford were 75% Muslim. People living in these areas had little opportunity to develop any strands of mainstream British culture and perceived their identity according to the values of their country of origin.

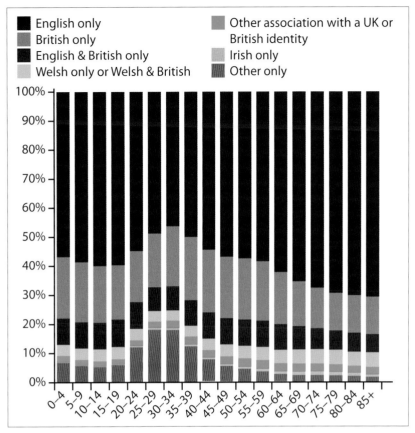

Legend:
■ English only
■ British only
■ English & British only
■ Welsh only or Welsh & British
■ Other association with a UK or British identity
■ Irish only
▓ Other only

Figure C5: National Identity by age in England and Wales 2011 census

Source: '2011 Census: Detailed Characteristics for England and Wales, March 2011', Office for National Statistics licensed under the Open Government Licence v.3.0

The website for the Office for National Statistics provides an interactive version of this graph in its statistical bulletin '2011 Census: Detailed Characteristics for England and Wales, March 2011', https://www.ons.gov.uk/peoplepopulationandcommunity/populationandmigration/populationestimates/bulletins/2011census/2013-05-16#ethnicity

Age

In some societies the elderly population are afforded preferential treatment. This is especially the case in some tribal societies, where the tribal or village leader will be an aged person whose lifetime experience is valued. In MEDCs, increases in life expectancy have meant that the elderly are now a sizeable sector of society. In the case of immigrant populations, the elderly are more likely to hold on to the ethnicity of their ancestral homeland than their children. This is especially the case in the USA, where second and third generation immigrants become more allied to mainstream American culture than their parents. According to figures released from the 2011 census in England and Wales, age played a significant part in determining national identity. Figure C5 shows that the proportion of people identifying as British only decreases with age. In Northern Ireland, the 2011 census revealed that those claiming 'Irish only' as their national identity had a slightly younger age profile than those claiming to be 'British' or 'Northern Irish' (Figure C6). The underlying reasons for these patterns are complex but the important point is that perceived ethnic identity is influenced by age.

Gender

In some male dominated societies, gender plays a significant role in the application of the law. In these countries women occupy a lower niche in society and certain laws apply only to them. Strict laws regarding traditional Islamic dress for women apply across the Arab world. This style of dress is seen an integral part of their culture and many women choose to wear it even when the law is not enforced. In Afghanistan, under Taliban rule, women were not allowed to be educated and their freedom of movement was greatly curtailed. They had to adhere to a very strict dress code, wearing a burka in public. In Somalia in 2008, a teenage girl was sentenced to death by stoning when a local court rejected her claim that she had been raped. In Britain there has been an increase in the number of 'honour killings'. These are the murders of women, usually Muslim, accused of behaving immorally or violating their religious principles, bringing shame to their families. This includes marrying outside of their religion. The murders are often carried out by a family member to preserve the family honour – hence the term 'honour killing'. In several British cities, there are Muslim communities where women live in isolation from the remainder of British society. These women may not leave home without male permission or escort, and do not learn English. In 2016, the British government set up schemes to teach English to Muslim women, hoping to improve community integration.

NATIONAL IDENTITY IN NORTHERN IRELAND

Population

40% identified themselves as British only, 25% as Irish only and 21% as Northern Irish only.

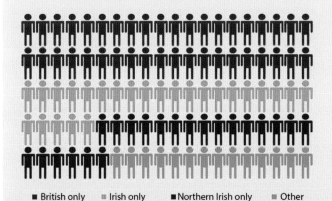

- British only - Irish only - Northern Irish only - Other

Age

Those with an Irish only national identity had a younger age distribution than those with a British only or Northern Irish only identity.

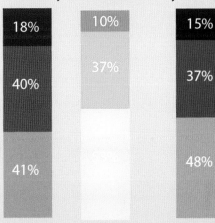

British only	Irish only	Northern Irish only
18%	10%	15%
40%	37%	37%
41%		48%

British only
- Aged 65 and over
- Aged 35-64
- Aged 0-34

Irish only
- Aged 65 and over
- Aged 35-64
- Aged 0-34

Northern Irish only
- Aged 65 and over
- Aged 35-64
- Aged 0-34

Highest Rates for National Identity (LGD 2014)

Causeway Coast and Glens
Mid and East Antrim
Derry and Strabane
Antrim and Newtownabbey
Mid Ulster
North Down and Ards
Belfast
Lisburn and Castlereagh
Fermanagh and Omagh
Armagh, Banbridge and Craigavon
Newry, Mourne and Down

BRITISH ONLY

1. Mid and East Antrim	59%
2. North Down and Ards	58%
3. Lisburn and Castlereagh	53%

IRISH ONLY

1. Derry and Strabane	48%
2. Newry, Mourne and Down	41%
3. Mid Ulster	36%

NORTHERN IRISH ONLY

1. Fermanagh and Omagh	26%
2. Newry, Mourne and Down	25%
3. Mid Ulster	24%

Religion Or Religion Brought Up In

Protestants and other Christians made up the highest proportion of those with a British only identity; Catholics made up the highest proportions of those with an Irish only identity or a Northern Irish only identity.

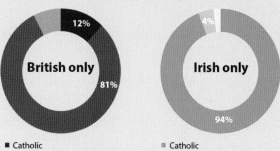

British only — 12%, 81%
- Catholic
- Protestant and other Christian
- Other or none

Irish only — 4%, 94%
- Catholic
- Protestant and other Christian
- Other or none

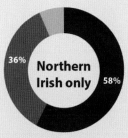

Northern Irish only — 36%, 58%
- Catholic
- Protestant and other Christian
- Other or none

* Figures may not always add up to 100% due to rounding

Northern Ireland Statistics & Research Agency

NINIS

Figure C6: Infographic on National identity in Northern Ireland, 2011

Source: 'Short Story - National Identity', Neighbourhood Statistics (NISRA) Website: www.nisra.gov.uk/ninis, licensed under the Open Government Licence v.3.0

Historically, women were unable to vote in Britain until 1918 and 1920 in the USA. Despite the 1970 Equal Pay Act in the UK, women still earn less than men, with a gender pay gap of around 18% in 2016.

Exam Questions

1. Ethnic minorities often live in clusters within cities. Explain the underlying reasons for this residential concentration. [8]

   Question from CCEA A2 2 Processes and Issues in Human Geography,
   Specimen Assessment Materials, © CCEA 2017

2. "Ethnicity cannot be defined by any one factor. A combination of factors is required." Discuss the extent to which you agree with this statement. You must use examples in your answer. [18]

   Question from A2 1 Human Interactions and Global Issues,
   January 2014, © CCEA 2017

3. Briefly explain how both residential concentration and gender can help define ethnic identity. [8]

   Question adapted from A2 1 Human Interactions and Global Issues,
   May 2012, © CCEA 2017

References

Ethnic identity in Britain:
http://www.ethnicity.ac.uk/medialibrary/briefingsupdated/who-feels-british.pdf

2011 Northern Ireland census form:
http://www.nisra.gov.uk/archive/census/2011/forms/individual.pdf

National identity in Northern Ireland:
www.ninis2.nisra.gov.uk/public/census2011analysis/nationalidentity/index.aspx

2. THE PROCESSES THAT CREATE AND MAINTAIN ETHNIC DIVERSITY

Case studies

Ethnic diversity in one country: the UK

One ethnically diverse city: Jerusalem

Processes that create ethnic diversity

Colonisation

For centuries powerful nations have sought to increase their power by overseas expansion, a process known as colonialism. When addressing the impact on ethnic diversity, attention is focused on the colonial expansion that occurred in the MEDCs from the sixteenth century onwards. There is a distinction between colonialism (see above) and colonisation. Colonisation involves setting up settlements in the new colony. This process results in the migration of people from the ruling country to the new colony. These people came as administrators and they usually established an enclave in a port which ultimately became a leading city, often the capital city. The colonialists needed military personnel to effect control over their newly acquired territory and to fend off rival claims from other aspiring colonial powers. Much of Africa was colonised in this way. The rival European powers sub-divided the continent according to the agreement set out in the Berlin Conference in 1884–1885. An examination of a map of Africa (Figure C7) reveals very regular boundaries between countries, reflecting the arbitrary and almost geometric nature of the sub-division of land. This led to the creation of ethnic diversity in three ways:

Figure C7: Colonial sub-division in Africa c1885

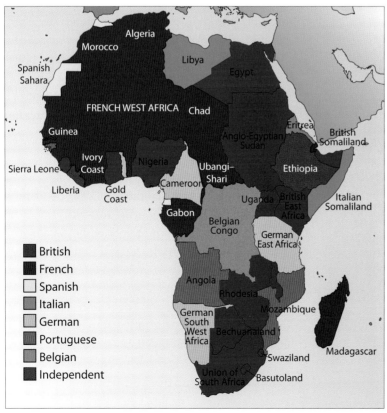

- It established a European layer to the population. The Europeans were distinctive in Africa and Asia by their skin colour, language, nationality, religion, social status, residential concentration, and they were mostly male. They usually established the European way of life in the colony. Everything from language and sport to architecture reflected the colonial rulers' home country. Even in post-colonial days, relics of this Europeanisation remains.

The language of the colonial rulers is still spoken in many former colonies, for example English in India and French in most of former French West Africa. The importance of cricket in former British colonies such as India, Pakistan and the West Indies, is another example of this.

- The sub-division of territory, particularly in Africa, often cut across tribal homelands, leaving formerly united groups in rival countries. The post-colonial period in Africa and in the Indian sub-continent has had many ethnic conflicts as a result of this.

- On occasions, the colonial rulers brought labour from other parts of the Empire to work on specific projects. They were not slaves but were under contract to work for a given period in the new country – so called indentured labour. In this way, Uganda in east Africa had Indian workers brought to work on railways and in a similar move, Indian Tamils were brought to Sri Lanka to work on tea, coffee and rubber plantations.

The colonies gained their independence at various times throughout the twentieth century but most have maintained links with their colonial rulers to some extent. The Commonwealth of Nations (formerly the British Commonwealth), a group of mostly former British colonies, 16 out of 52 of which retain the British Monarch as their Head of State, is an example. Following the end of World War II, European nations attracted migrants from their former colonies to fill the gap in the labour market. Many came to work in the low paid jobs in the inner cities. In Britain, immigrants from the West Indies, India and Pakistan added to the ethnic diversity of many cities. Like the colonialists, they were distinctive by many primary and secondary factors.

One lasting issue that all these immigrants share concerns their second and subsequent generations. Should descendants of former British colonialists in Zimbabwe be regarded as Zimbabwean or British? Should descendants of West Indian immigrants to Britain be regarded as British or West Indian? In the Zimbabwean example, the country's president confiscated land belonging to white farmers, whom he regarded as British even though they were born in Zimbabwe. In Britain, the census documents people who are black British. This is an attempt to accept that being British is not confined to a white population.

Figure C8: Map of Indonesia and East Timor

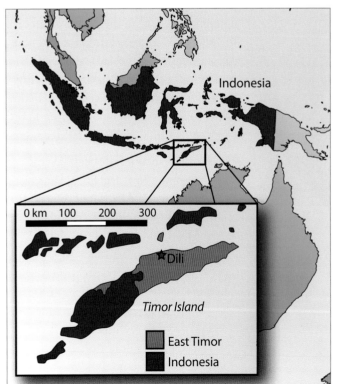

Annexation

Annexation is taking political control of a neighbouring adjacent country. In 1990, Saddam Hussein annexed neighbouring Kuwait as the nineteenth province of Iraq. Indonesia, already in control over West Timor, annexed East Timor in 1975 (Figure C8). Russia annexed Crimea from Ukraine in 2014 (Figure C9). This annexation is recognised only by Russia. The reason given for annexation is usually the unification of separated ethnic minorities but inevitably there will be those who do not wish to become an integral part of another country and most incidences of annexation result in conflict. The first Gulf War in 1991 followed

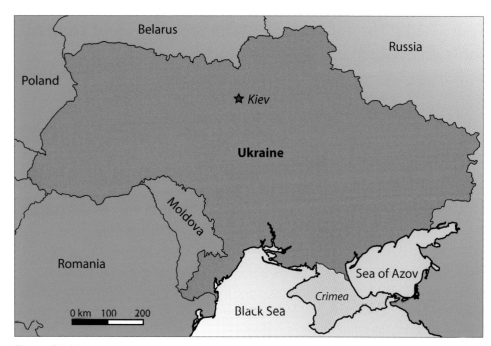

Figure C9: Map of Ukraine and surrounding countries

the annexation of Kuwait by Iraq. Following the annexation of Crimea there has been on-going conflict in Ukraine with those who oppose the annexation. Annexation creates ethnic diversity when the annexed region contains people of a different ethnic group from the annexing country.

International migration

International migration has created and continues to create ethnic diversity on a global scale. The USA, Canada, Australia and New Zealand are populated almost entirely by migrants or their descendants. In Western Europe, there has been unprecedented movement of economic migrants from the former communist countries that are now part of the enlarged European Union, to richer parts of Europe, including the UK. The impact of this recent large scale migration has had far reaching impacts and played a significant part in the Brexit vote in 2016. Until recently, Northern Ireland was not a major destination country for international migrants but it now receives large numbers of emigrants from Poland, Romania, Latvia, Lithuania and Estonia. The following figures were reported for Northern Ireland by Migration Observatory* in 2014:

- The proportion of foreign born people increased from 1.6% to 4.5% between 2001 and 2011.
- The largest group of foreign born people (20,000) came from Poland.
- Belfast, Craigavon and Dungannon had the largest numbers of migrants.

Figure C10: Ethnic shops in Belfast

* Source: Data from Migration Observatory, Northern Ireland Census Profile, June 2014, http://www.migrationobservatory.ox.ac.uk/resources/briefings/northern-ireland-census-profile

CASE STUDY: The UK, a study of the processes that created ethnic diversity in a country

The UK is becoming more ethnically diverse, with rising numbers of people identifying with minority groups in the 2011 census. Figures C3–C4 (pages 319–320) show the ethnic diversity in England and Wales based on the 2011 census. White British make up 80% of the population compared to 91% in 2001 and 94% in 1991. There is no doubt that the UK has become an increasingly ethnically diverse country. Most large cities contain several ethnic groups, none more so than London. In 2014, 58% of all births in London were to foreign mothers compared to 27% for England and Wales. In some boroughs of London, the figure was 70%. The reasons for this ethnic diversity can be explained by looking at the combined effects of colonialism, annexation and international migration.

Since Roman times, Britain has been colonised by various groups but these early colonists made limited impact on the present ethnic composition of the country. The British Isles came together as a political unit through various waves of annexation over a number of centuries, culminating in Ireland. The first wave of immigrants to Britain came in the mid-nineteenth century, when thousands of Irish fled from famine. They settled mainly in the port cities of Liverpool, Glasgow and London. While there are still some ties with Ireland in these cities, second and third generation Irish immigrants have blended seamlessly into British society.

The most significant increase in ethnic diversity in Britain started in the 1950s. During the two world wars, hundreds of thousands of men from across the Empire fought for Britain. India alone provided 1.3 million soldiers. In the interwar years many remained in the UK, forming small ethnic communities in the ports. A number of Jewish immigrants settled in the London area, fleeing from Nazi oppression in Europe. At the end of World War II there were work shortages throughout Europe and Britain began a recruitment drive abroad. Initially, 157,000 Polish immigrants, many of whom had formed ties with Britain during the war years, arrived in the UK in search of work. Italians joined them but there was still a labour shortage and this prompted the search for workers from outside Europe.

On 22 June 1948, *The Empire Windrush* (a ship) brought the first of many West Indian immigrants to Britain. The British Nationality Act of 1948 granted citizenship to people from the Commonwealth, enabling them to live and work in UK. Mass immigration continued from the West Indies throughout the 1950s. In 1956, London Transport, struggling to find workers, advertised in Barbados, Trinidad and Jamaica for bus drivers and conductors. Within 12 years, 4000 Barbadians had been recruited with their fares loaned by London Transport and repaid from their wages. By 1958 some 125,000 West Indians had migrated to the UK in search of a better lifestyle and higher wages than they were receiving at home. In the 1960s they were joined by immigrants from the Indian sub-continent, which had become India, West and East Pakistan following independence from Britain. Mostly the new immigrants went to the London area, filling low paid, unskilled jobs in factories and the service sector. The car and engineering factories in the West Midlands were another focus. The migrants from India and Pakistan worked in the footwear and clothing factories in the East Midlands, as well as in the transport and textile mills of the northern cities in Lancashire and Yorkshire. They frequently established clusters or neighbourhoods in the poorest areas in the inner cities, such as Toxteth in Liverpool, Brixton and Bethnal Green in London. In most cases, the new immigrants eventually established their own places of worship and other ethnic services. These new immigrants were not welcomed easily into British society and there were protests at their arrival. The government reacted by amending the British Nationality Act to make it more difficult for non-white immigrants to bring their family members with them. In spite of this, the numbers of non-white residents continued to grow and by 1970 they numbered 1.5 million; one third of these were children born in the UK.

In 1972, the Ugandan dictator General Idi Amin expelled most of the 50,000 Asian community in Uganda. These were the descendents of indentured Asian workers brought to Uganda by Britain. Approximately 30,000 of these Ugandan Asians arrived in the UK. Others were accepted by the former British colonies of Canada, Kenya and India. Many immigrants ended up in areas of significant social deprivation, as unemployment rose throughout the 1980s. Racial prejudice was quite widespread in the UK and there were racially motivated riots in the 80s. The riots were sparked by claims that ethnic minorities, especially black male youths, were being targeted by the police. Right wing politicians and political parties argued for at least curtailment of the numbers gaining entry. The numbers of new immigrants in the 1980s were much lower than at any time since 1948. However, as most of the immigrants were in the young, economically active sector of the population, there was significant potential for future natural increase.

Since 2004, Britain has received another wave of migrants. This time the migrants are from Eastern Europe, following the demise of communism and the entry of many former communist countries into the European Union in 2004. In 2015, there were approximately 831,000 Poles living in the UK, making them the largest group of first generation migrants in the country. In addition, the growth of asylum seeker applications has contributed to increased ethnic diversity. Figure C11 shows the international migration figures for England and Wales in 2016.

Figure C11: International Migration Statistics England and Wales 2016

Source: Figures taken from Migration Watch UK, complied from 'The International Passenger Survey', Office for National Statistics

	All (000s)	British (000s)	EU (000s)	Non EU (000s)
Immigration	650	77	284	289
Emigration	315	127	95	93
Net Migration	335	−50	189	198

Exercise

Follow the instructions below:

1. Visit the website: www.ninis2.nisra.gov.uk

2. From the drop down menu at the top, select 'Interactive content' and 'Census 2011'.

3. Click on 'Ethnicity, identity, language and religion'. A new window appears.

4. From the 'Data' drop down menu at the top, select 'Country of birth: Other EU: Accession countries 2004 onwards (%)' and '2011'.

5. From the 'Geography' drop down menu at the top, select 'Local Government District 2014'.

6. From the map now displayed, answer the following questions.

    (a) Describe the overall pattern of EU migrants in Northern Ireland. Use the interactive graph for precise figures and the Northern Ireland average figure.

    (b) Name the Local Government Districts (LGDs) with the highest and lowest proportion of EU migrants. Use the interactive map and graph for precise figures.

More detailed information can be obtained by selecting either 'Super Output Area' or 'Ward' from the 'Geography' drop down menu.

Exam Questions

1. With reference to a case study of an ethnically diverse country, discuss the processes that created its ethnic diversity. [18]

    Question from A2 1 Human Interactions and Global Issues, May 2014, © CCEA 2017

2. With reference to your case study, evaluate the roles of colonisation, annexation and international migration in creating an ethnically diverse country. [18]

    Question from A2 1 Human Interactions and Global Issues, May 2016, © CCEA 2017

Processes that maintain ethnic diversity

In ethnically diverse societies there will usually be some degree of interaction between the various groups. While the first generation maintain their ethnic distinctiveness, subsequent generations may become more affiliated with the majority population, a process described as assimilation. This process is most readily observed where the original differences are less visible and where there is a willingness from both the majority and the minority populations for assimilation. There are, however, several processes operating in societies that prevent this 'melting pot' situation occurring.

Segregation

Segregation or residential segregation of ethnic groups takes place in many ways.

- It can be a physical segregation with visible physical barriers such as walls or fences enclosing one group and preventing access by outsiders. An extreme form of segregation occurred in Nazi Germany during the 1930s and 1940s, when Jews in Nazi-controlled states were made to wear yellow ribbons or Stars of David. They were forced to live in ghettoes, in tightly packed areas of cities and their movement outside of these ghettoes was controlled by the Nazis. The Warsaw ghetto was the largest, containing about 400,000 people between 1940 and 1943. Another extreme case of segregation took place in the apartheid era in South Africa. Under this scheme, black South Africans were totally segregated from white South Africans. The segregation process was institutionalised by law and pervaded all aspects of life. Black South Africans were forced to live in homelands or townships and were excluded from all decision making and

Figure C12: Clearly demarcated boundaries in East Belfast

Loyalist mural at 'Freedom Corner'

Security fence separating Catholic and Protestant housing areas in East Belfast

'Cluan Place', a Protestant enclave surrounded by Catholic housing

political life in white areas. In the USA a high level of racial segregation also occurred, especially in the southern states, until the late 1960s. These are extreme cases, where the segregation is enforced by law but residential segregation is still widespread in many ethnically diverse societies.

- Segregation can occur through the use of clearly demarcated boundaries which mark the territory of one group. These boundaries take the form of symbols, which have meaning and significance to a particular group, and include murals to heroes, flags, graffiti and place names. In most cases these symbols will be a deterrent to rival communities. In Belfast some Protestant and Catholic housing areas were separated by Peace Walls for safety reasons during 'the troubles'. Murals and flags were used by both groups to delimit their territory and intimidate the opposing religious group. While attempts are made to establish mixed social housing areas in Belfast, these are often abandoned as the numerically larger group in each case forces the rival group away.

- People often prefer to live with people with whom they share cultural, religious and other similarities. In British cities there are enclaves of ethnic groups with their own services, schools, places of worship and recreation. In some cases there are linguistic and religious barriers, which make social interaction with the majority population very difficult.

- Sometimes segregation is reinforced by social stratification, where each group occupies a particular position in society. After the emancipation of slavery in the USA, the white population often employed black Americans as servants. The black population were no longer slaves but their only contact with the white population was in this subservient role.

Segregation of ethnic groups, irrespective of the underlying reasons for it, maintains ethnic diversity because it minimises the opportunities for social interaction. In 2001, there were race riots in Bradford and Oldham between Asian and white youths. A government report on the riots referred to people "living parallel lives with no meaningful contact between the various groups". In 2016, the Casey Report concluded that little had changed (see 'Residential Concentration', page 321). The segregation of the groups occurred partly for social and economic reasons but also because many white people moved away from neighbourhoods populated by Asians. The net result is that the various groups live separate lives, with little understanding of the cultural norms of other groups. A recent report suggests there is a link between segregation and terrorism (Figure C13).

Figure C13: The link between segregation and terrorism in Britain

Source: Data from Andrew Gilligan and Sian Griffiths, 'Terror map reveals danger of segregation', *The Sunday Times*, 5 March 2017

A report into Britain's 'known Islamist terrorists' (published in 2017) found the following:

- Terrorists are predominantly young and male.
- A clear link exists between poverty and terrorism. 38% of terrorists were unemployed and 76% came from neighbourhoods with above average levels of deprivation.
- Terrorism is most evident in highly segregated neighbourhoods. 14% of British Muslims live in segregated neighbourhoods (over 60% Muslim). Such areas produced 24% of terrorists. For example, Birmingham with its highly segregated Muslim neighbourhoods has produced more terrorists than West Yorkshire, Greater Manchester and Lancashire put together, even though their combined Muslim population is three times that of Birmingham. Alternatively, 50% of British Muslims live in mixed communities. However, only 38% of terrorists originated in these neighbourhoods. The city of Leicester has a well integrated Muslim population and has produced only two terrorists in the last 20 years.

Exam Questions

1. (a) Study Resources A and B relating to ethnic segregation in Britain.

   (i) Resource A claims there is a high degree of residential segregation in London. Describe the evidence for this from both resources.

   (ii) Use Resource A to help you explain the reasons for such segregation. [9]

   Question adapted from A2 1 Human Interactions and Global Issues,
   May 2016, © CCEA 2017

Resource A: Ethnic segregation in Britain

Source: Text adapted from Nicholas Hellen, 'Polite white flight as culture divides us', *The Sunday Times*, 24 November 2013

In 2012, 16% of Britain's population was from an ethnic minority. By 2050 ethnic minorities are expected to make up 38% of the population. Such an increase is likely to have a considerable impact on society. One survey of attitudes towards increasing ethnic diversity found that Britain is becoming more sharply divided along ethnic lines and that London has the highest levels of residential segregation. Figures from the 2011 census show that more than 600,000 white Britons have moved from London to areas that are over 90% white, since 2001. This 'white flight' can lead to further isolation of ethnic minorities. Such areas are often characterised by low levels of inward investment and increased social deprivation.

Even when people from ethically different backgrounds live in close proximity, the Social Integration Commission (SIC) found that social segregation can still exist. For this to end there have to be meaningful social interactions between members of ethnically diverse groups. To be considered 'meaningful', social interactions must go beyond the superficial contact such as travelling on the same bus. Instead, they involve shared activity where participants feel they have equal status, such as regular conversations at the school gates, playing football together, meeting for lunch etc. These 'meaningful' interactions have a significant impact on breaking down stereotypes, reducing prejudice and increasing trust. SIC commissioned a survey of 4000 people and looked at the extent of meaningful interactions in ethnically diverse communities. The survey highlighted varying levels of segregation between groups and between London and Britain as a whole.

Resource B: Results of Social Integration Commission Survey

Source: adapted from data published by the Social Integration Commission, 'How integrated is modern Britain?', socialintegrationcommission.org.uk, July 2014

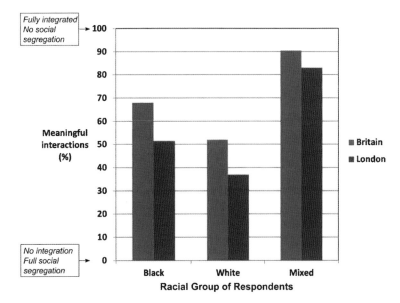

Note:
100% indicates when interactions with people from other groups perfectly reflect the mix of these groups in the area.

Exercise

1. Study Resources I and II relating to ethnic segregation in British cities.

    (a) With reference to both resources, describe how ethnic segregation has changed between 2001 and 2016.

    (b) Use the resources to help you explain why such segregation has occurred.

Resource I: Ethnicity in British cities

Source: Adapted from 'Too white towns are labelled unhealthy', *The Sunday Times*, 22 April 2006, https://www. thetimes.co.uk/article/too-white-towns-are-labelled-unhealthy-wk9902qsdq6

Resource adapted from A2 2 Module 5: Processes and Issues in Human Geography, January 2008, © CCEA 2017

Professor Ted Cantle, who wrote the report on the 2001 riots in Bradford and Oldham, suggested people from ethnic minorities in some parts of the Midlands might not feel "safe and secure" living near predominantly white communities.

Cantle, who has chaired a panel advising ministers on implementing the recommendations of his report, made the remarks in an interview about multiculturalism with a local newspaper last week...

Cantle said he was concerned about the strength of support for the far-right British National party in some parts of the East Midlands…In February the BNP came second in a council by-election in Heanor. A few days later Channel Five dubbed it the "skinhead capital of Britain"…

In his 2001 report on the riots in Bradford, Burnley and Oldham, Cantle identified communities living "parallel lives" and highlighted the polarisation of communities with different schools, estates and social lives. He said schools should change their catchment areas to attract a broader mix.

At the time one in four primary schools in Bradford were more than 70% Asian while half were totally white. Cantle opposed single-faith and "monocultural" schools, but ministers ignored his advice.

[In 2005] Trevor Phillips, chairman of the Commission for Racial Equality, warned that unless steps were taken to promote deeper integration, segregation could reach the levels witnessed in New Orleans. He warned that Britain might be "sleepwalking to segregation".

Cantle's remarks go further by describing parts of the country as "unhealthily" white, a phrase that critics said this weekend appeared to place the blame for ethnic tensions on the white community.

Local people agree Heanor is predominantly white. But they deny they pose a threat to non-white communities. Brian Lucas, a Labour councillor for the nearby area of Cotmanhay, said: "I'm a big believer in people choosing where they live and not being pushed, guided or forced into an area."

Resource II: Selected results from The Casey Review 2016
Source: information from 'The Casey Review', December 2016, licensed under the Open Government Licence v.3.0

- 50% of the British population lives in areas with relatively high migration flows.
- Half of all minority ethnic citizens in Britain live in London, Birmingham and Manchester.
- Similar patterns of urban concentration of ethnic minorities exist in Scotland and Wales.

The 2011 census recorded:

- 24 wards in 12 local authority areas where more than 40% of the population identified themselves as being of Pakistani ethnicity; up from 12 wards in 7 local authorities in 2001.
- 20 wards in 8 local authority areas where more than 40% of the population identified themselves as being of Indian ethnicity; up from 16 wards within 6 local authorities in 2001.
- Blackburn, Birmingham, Burnley and Bradford included wards with between 70% and 85% Muslim populations.

The school age population is even more segregated when compared to residential patterns of living. In 2013, it was reported that more than 50% of ethnic minority students were in schools where ethnic minorities were the majority, and that school segregation was highest among students from Pakistani and Bangladeshi ethnic backgrounds relative to other ethnic groups.

Research examined for the Casey review suggests that concentrations of ethnic communities:

- reduce opportunities for social ties between minority and White British communities; and
- lead to lower identification with Britain and lower levels of trust between ethnic groups, compared to minorities living in more diverse areas.

Multiculturalism

International migration and globalisation have greatly increased the ethnic diversity in most countries. In some UK cities, this increased ethnic diversity has resulted in a situation where no single ethnic group has an overall majority, a situation referred to as ethnic pluralism. There has been much debate about how governments should respond to increasing ethnic diversity. There are those who argue for an integrationist approach. Under this scheme ethnic groups should not display outward manifestations of their ethnicity. In France the government has pursued this approach and banned the wearing of the Muslim headdress, the hijab, or Christian symbols such as crosses in schools. However, some countries, including Britain, have an official policy of multiculturalism. Multiculturalism is a political policy which permits ethnic groups to maintain their separate identities within society. Multiculturalism was adopted as official policy in most MEDCs from the 1960s onward and most large cities are increasingly made up of a mosaic of cultures.

Government multicultural policies include the following:

- Recognition of multiple citizenship. At one stage, citizens of the British Commonwealth were entitled to British citizenship.
- Government support for minority languages.
- Support for minority festivals, holidays and celebrations.
- Acceptance of traditional and religious dress in schools, the military and society in general. Support for music and arts from minority cultures. Programmes to encourage minority representation in politics, education and the work force in general.

There are many examples of this approach. Indonesia is a country made up of many islands spread across a large archipelago and there are many different languages and dialects. Although predominantly Muslim, the country also has large Christian and Hindu populations. Singapore recognises three languages – Mandarin Chinese, Tamil and English – as its official languages, with Malay being the national language. Apart from languages, Singapore also celebrates festivals celebrated by these three ethnic communities. In the UK, multiculturalism is especially evident in cities where ethnic communities have their own places of worship, shops and faith schools. Celebrations and festivals such as the Chinese New Year and the Notting Hill Carnival are outward signs of multiculturalism.

Multiculturalism maintains ethnic diversity where an ethnic group has clearly defined outward manifestation of their culture, such as the Muslim dress code for women or the Sikh turban for men. Due to improvements in communications, many of the recent migrants to the UK maintain links with their home country and as many are temporary migrants, they do not learn the language of their new country. This is especially the case for women. This helps to maintain ethnic diversity and slows down or prevents assimilation taking place.

From the late 1990s multiculturalism became a contentious issue in some European countries, including Britain. Some of the opposition came from extreme right wing groups, such as the British National Party (BNP) but also from concern about the rise of Islamic fundamentalism in Europe. As mentioned earlier (see 'Residential Concentration', page 321), some ethnic communities were living totally separate lives with little or no interaction. In 2016, the UK government launched a scheme to encourage greater integration of ethnic communities, particularly Muslim groups.

Exam Questions

1. Identify and explain how any two processes might operate to maintain ethnic diversity in an urban area. [10]

Question adapted from A2 2 Module 5: Processes and Issues in Human Geography, January 2010, © CCEA 2017

CASE STUDY: Jerusalem, a study of the processes and outcomes of maintaining ethnic diversity in a city

Multiculturalism

Jerusalem is an ethnically diverse city in Israel. Ethnic identity in Jerusalem, as in Israel, is rigidly defined by religion. The population of over 800,000 in 2011 was approximately 62% Jewish, 35% Muslim and a minority 2% were Christian. The city holds a special place for each of these three western religions: Judaism, Islam and Christianity. Christianity is divided into several sects, including Roman Catholic, Orthodox Armenians and Coptic Christians from Ethiopia. The multicultural mix of the population is best illustrated in the walled 'Old City' of Jerusalem (Figure C14), which is a unique mosaic of areas of deep significance to each group. It consists of four clearly defined areas:

- The Jewish Quarter
- The Muslim Quarter
- The Armenian Quarter
- The Christian Quarter

Each quarter has its own unique places of worship, such as the Church of the Holy Sepulchre in the Christian quarter (reputed to contain the site of Christ's crucifixion, burial and resurrection). One site, known as the Temple Mount, is of the utmost significance to the two main religious groups within Jerusalem – Judaism and Islam. The Temple Mount was the site of Jewish temples dating back to 960 BC. These temples have been destroyed, leaving only the Western or Wailing Wall, which has remained a sacred site for Jews throughout history. The Temple Mount is also significant to Muslims who believe it is the site from where Muhammad ascended to heaven. Two mosques – the Dome of the Rock, built on the site of the former Jewish temple, and the nearby Al Aqsa mosque – mark Muslims' claim to this area. There is

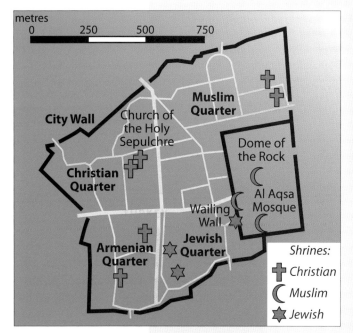

Figure C14: Map showing the religious segregation in the Old City of Jerusalem

a strict territorial demarcation between each quarter on the walls surrounding this Old City. In addition to separate places of worship, each quarter has its own distinctive architecture, religious festivals and dress code.

Figure C15: The Western Wall with Dome of the Rock mosque and a minaret of the Temple Mount in the background. This open plaza had Palestinian housing until 1967.

Segregation 1948–1967

Following World War II and the Holocaust, the United Nations sought to establish a homeland for Jews in Palestine. In 1948 the decision was taken by the UN to partition Palestine into a western Jewish section (Israel) and an Eastern Arab section (Jordan) (Figure C16). Jerusalem straddled the dividing line and, under the initial plan, the city was to be a neutral area administered by the United Nations.

The partition of Palestine was never acceptable to the Arab population in the region and when Israel claimed independence, the neighbouring Arab nations declared war. The Arabs were defeated and part of the Peace Deal saw Jerusalem divided by the 'green line' into an Israeli and Jewish western section and a Jordanian (Muslim) eastern section (Figure C17). The 'green line' was a zone about 100 feet wide and included buildings and even whole streets. Many areas became no man's land, with concrete barriers constructed to protect Jews against sniper attacks. Large numbers of people caught on 'the wrong side' of the divide fled to join their fellow religionists. The residential areas were effectively segregated between east and west Jerusalem but the eastern section contained the Old City and its important Jewish religious sites.

Figure C16: Map of Israel showing the location of Jerusalem

Jordan denied Israelis access to the Western or Wailing Wall and the Hebrew University. At the end of the 1948 war, the Israeli government began to develop the western part of the city, now under Israeli control, but their stated aim was the reunification of Jerusalem. Ben Gurion, the first Israeli prime minister, claimed that

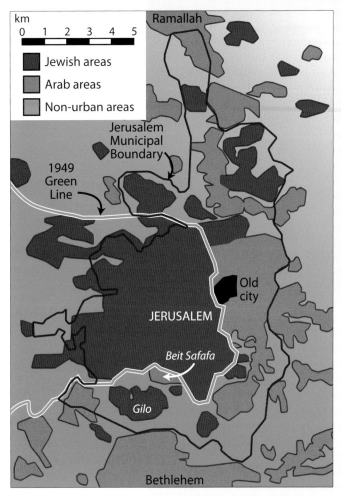

Figure C17: Map of religious segregation in Jerusalem

"Jewish Jerusalem is an organic and inseparable part of the State of Israel". This was the first of many conflicts in the region which are deep rooted in territorial disputes between the Israelis and Palestinians. The importance of Jerusalem to the two major groups in this multicultural state and the historical animosities between the Israelis and Palestinians converge in Jerusalem, and have resulted in a polarised and rigidly segregated city.

In 1967, Israel attacked the surrounding Arab nations in what is known as the Six Day War and annexed a considerable amount of territory from these countries, including the eastern section of Jerusalem. A new city boundary was drawn which included some Palestinian villages into an enlarged East Jerusalem. East Jerusalem still remains under Israeli rule, although it is not ratified by international law. An entire Arab quarter close to the Western Wall was demolished and replaced by an open plaza by Israel (Figure C15).

Segregation after the Six Day War

When Israel annexed East Jerusalem in 1967 the city was already segregated by the 'green line'. Although the physical division has gone, the degree of segregation remains absolute and the city has been described as "groups of people living together separately".

- There are separate business districts, public transport systems and educational and medical facilities. Services administered across the city, such as police and emergency services, are not dispatched according to geographical proximity but according to their ethnic match to the neighbourhood requesting assistance.

- Since 1967, Israel has embarked on a large scale building programme for Jewish settlers in East Jerusalem. This is to achieve their ambition to establish Jerusalem as a Jewish city. The international community has condemned the building of these settlements but they have continued. In January 2017, emboldened by support from the newly-elected American President Trump, Israel announced plans to build a further 600 Jewish settlements in East Jerusalem.

- There has been a massive road building programme aimed to improve links between East Jerusalem and the remainder of Israel. Some of these new roads increased the segregation of Jewish and Palestinian settlements. In the Arab village of Beit Safafa (Figure C17) in southern Jerusalem, regional road building that connects the Jewish Gilo neighbourhood to west Jerusalem has divided the village into four pieces.

- Palestinian settlements have been subjected to a 'green areas' zoning plan. This zoning was to prevent urban sprawl and applied throughout the city. However, it was applied more strictly in Palestinian areas.

- Since 1991, non-Jerusalem Palestinians have been barred from entering the city without a permit issued by the Israeli Authorities. A ring of roadblocks with Israeli military checkpoints acts to deter even those Palestinians who have permits from entering the city. At times of conflict these permits can be rescinded, as in 2016 when Palestinians from outside Jerusalem were denied access to the Mosques in the Old City during Ramadan. Many of the Palestinian refugees who fled to Jordan during earlier conflict have not been allowed to return.

The economic, social and spatial outcomes of ethnic diversity in Jerusalem

Ethnic diversity does not always result in conflict situations as in the case of Jerusalem. Ethnically diverse societies exist peacefully in many parts of the world, such as Australia, Canada and the USA, although the latter has had serious ethnic conflict in the past. Where there is harmony between the various groups, the country will benefit economically and socially. In a society where there is no discrimination, economic advancement and social mobility are determined by ability rather than membership of the ruling elite. In the case of Jerusalem, ethnic diversity has resulted in serious and prolonged conflict that has had a detrimental effect on the city and its inhabitants.

Social outcomes

The impacts of ethnic diversity are greatest in East Jerusalem. Palestinians see East Jerusalem as a future capital city of an independent Palestinian state, while the Israelis see East Jerusalem as an integral part of a Jewish capital city. These very different views have led to serious civil unrest and war on a number of occasions. Prolonged unrest followed two uprisings or Intifada by Palestinian youths from 1987–1993 and from 2000–2005. These uprisings took the form of street riots and suicide bombings by the Palestinians, and met swift and robust Israeli retaliation. The close proximity of religious sites important to both sides has been the cause of much ethnic unrest. In January 2017, a Palestinian drove a lorry into a group of Israeli soldiers close to the Old City, killing four soldiers and injuring 15. Israeli reaction to these attacks sometimes involves demolition of homes belonging to the suspect and the wider family.

There is a marked social divide between Israelis and Palestinians in East Jerusalem. The Palestinians were a disadvantaged group before the Six Day War but under Israeli rule they have become more marginalised. According to a UN Report published in 2013 ('The Palestinian Economy in East Jerusalem: Enduring annexation, isolation and disintegration'), Palestinians have suffered discrimination in all aspects of life as Israel has sought to secure control over the city and the wider area. Israelis justify their actions in the annexed East Jerusalem, on the grounds of defence from attack from Palestinian militants and the belief that this is their 'Promised Land' and that all Jews have a right to live there. Israel needed more land for settlement and following the annexation of East Jerusalem the government began building new neighbourhoods. Palestinians make up 57% of the population of East Jerusalem but they are allocated only 13% of building land. As a consequence, population density is higher in Palestinian areas. The situation is particularly acute in the Old City, where population density is 53 per 1000 m^2 for Palestinians compared with 19 per 1000 m^2

for Israelis. Former Muslim housing areas were cleared close to the Wailing Wall and are now populated by Orthodox or Haredi Jews.

A Human Rights Organisation working in Israel (B'Tselem) claims that Palestinians do not share equal access to health care and education. Although all children have the right to education in Israel, decades of neglect for the Palestinian schools has resulted in poor, run-down buildings and classroom shortages. In addition, access to schools is made difficult by roadblocks and a security wall, known as the West Bank barrier. This barrier separates Israeli and Palestinian settlements and was built following a period of sustained unrest in 2000. As a result, according to the UN, as many as half of all Palestinian children do not attend school. Declining infrastructure, including water supply, is also a major issue in East Jerusalem. In 2010, the UN estimated that 30% of Palestinians in the city were not connected to a piped water supply.

Economic outcomes

Jerusalem has also suffered economically and not just from the cost of the security measures. It is one of Israel's poorest cities, ranked bottom in a survey of quality of life throughout Israel. Job shortages, economic stagnation and poor infrastructure are just some of the problems. The situation is worse in Arab East Jerusalem. There are high rates of unemployment, especially among the Palestinians and about 75% of them live below the poverty line. The 2013 UN report mentioned in 'Social outcomes' (page 339) revealed a bleak economic picture for Palestinians in East Jerusalem. This report found that Palestinians:

- are routinely paid lower wages than Israelis, earning less than half the average monthly wage in Israel as a whole. However, they still have to face the Israeli costs of living.

- work longer hours than Israelis, typically 10 hours per day, are not permitted to form trade unions and have limited job security.

- fill the lowest and least desirable jobs. They account for 35% of the total working population of the city but 44% of the unskilled jobs are carried out by Palestinians.

With its historic sites, Jerusalem has the potential to be a major tourist attraction but the violence over the years has seriously affected this lucrative industry, especially in the Old City (Figure C18). Although Israel claims jurisdiction over all of Jerusalem, the international community has refused to accept this claim. No foreign country has an embassy in Jerusalem, but in 2017 the new American administration suggested relocating its embassy from Tel Aviv to Jerusalem. Since the tightening of controls on the numbers of Palestinians from outside Jerusalem, many Palestinian businesses have lost custom. Investment in all aspects of public services is lower in East Jerusalem. According to B'Tselem, only 10% of government urban spending was directed to East Jerusalem despite the fact that it

Figure C18: Number of Tourists in Jerusalem Hotels (1996–2010)

Source: Data from Palestinian Central Bureau Statistics, published in 'The Palestinian economy of East Jerusalem: Enduring Annexation, Isolation and disintegration'

*Second intifada was a Palestinian uprising from 2000–2005

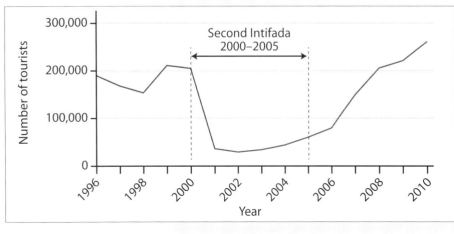

accounts for 37% of Israel's total urban population. The West Bank barrier has added to the economic isolation of the East Jerusalem Palestinians by reducing their trading contacts with neighbouring Jordan.

Spatial outcomes

The years of conflict have had an effect on the overall city environment. The city is divided into clearly demarcated residential areas for Palestinians and Israelis. The flying of Israeli and Palestinian flags, along with murals and graffiti, indicate the territorial limits of each group. The Old City is divided into the various quarters by walls and each sector has its own distinctive architecture. Since 2000, the West Bank barrier (a security wall some 450 km in length with another 250 km planned) has been built, part of which surrounds East Jerusalem. This security wall has increased the land area of East Jerusalem but has also left some Palestinian towns and villages outside Jerusalem.

Figure C19:
West Bank barrier at Abu Dis, a Palestinian settlement now outside East Jerusalem

Source: (left) Justin McIntosh and (right) Amal

Exam Questions

1. With reference to an ethnically diverse city, discuss the economic, social and spatial outcomes that have resulted from its ethnic diversity. [18]

Question adapted from A2 1 Human Interactions and Global Issues,
May 2015, © CCEA 2017

References

East Jerusalem:
https://www.theguardian.com/world/2017/jan/08/truck-rammed-into-pedestrians-jerusalem
http://www.yourmiddleeast.com/opinion/the-israelization-of-east-jerusalem_41999
http://www.bbc.co.uk/news/world-middle-east-36197817

'The Palestinian Economy in East Jerusalem: Enduring annexation, isolation and disintegration',
UNCTAD, UN, 2013 report:
http://www.un.org/depts/dpa/qpal/docs/2014Ankara/P2%20MAHMOUD%20ELKHAFIF%20 gdsapp2012d1_en.pdf

The Israeli Information Center for Human Rights in the Occupied Territories:
http://www.btselem.org

Settlements:
http://www.reuters.com/article/us-mideast-crisis-israel-settlements-idUSKBN1560CZ
http://www.bbc.co.uk/news/world-middle-east-38458884

3. ETHNIC CONFLICT

Case studies

National case study of ethnic conflict: Israel

Students should be able to:

(i) explain the causes of ethnic conflict – territorial disputes, historical animosities, racism, sectarianism, cultural conflicts, human rights abuses and discrimination

(ii) understand the nature of ethnic conflict, including civil disobedience, civil war and terrorism

(iii) demonstrate knowledge and understanding of the outcomes of ethnic conflict – social and economic impacts, territorial division, autonomy, ethnic cleansing, international intervention and peace processes

The causes of ethnic conflict

Conflict between ethnic groups is an unfortunate reality in many parts of the world. The conflict can be anything from a simple protest to a fully fledged war and ethnic conflict occurs across all levels of development. Some of the most serious conflicts in recent times have been ethnically based. At the time of writing there are major ethnic conflicts in the Middle East, in several African countries, including Sudan and the Democratic Republic of Congo, and in Myanmar and China in Asia. UK examples include 'the troubles' in Northern Ireland and the racial riots in some northern British cities in 2001. The causes of these conflicts are complex and they are often due to a combination of a number of factors.

Territorial disputes

Figure C20: Map of Sudan and South Sudan

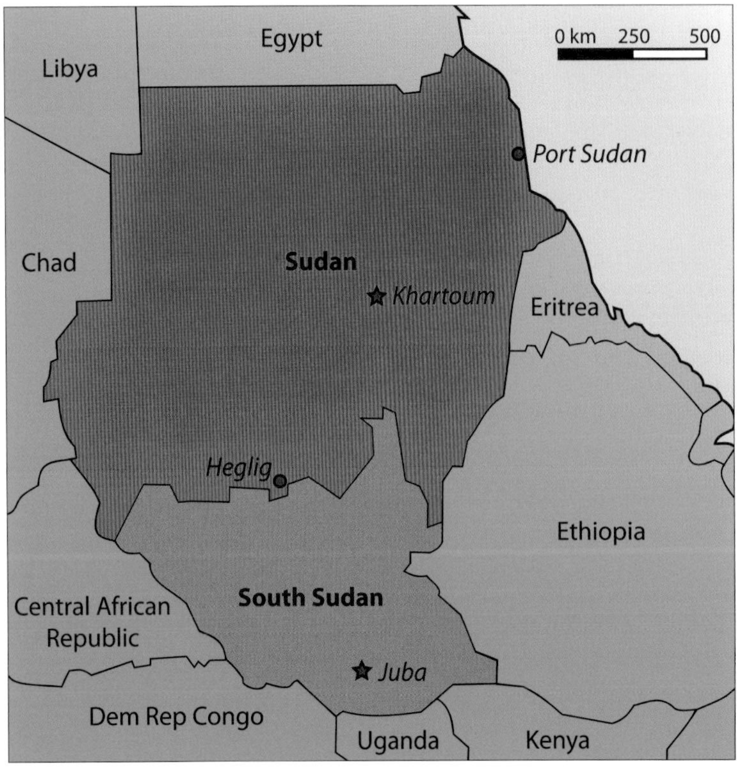

Disputes over territory have been a major source of unrest and conflict in a number of major world regions. The continent of Africa was carved up amongst the European

powers during the colonial period, with little attention given to either tribal or economic regions. Under colonial rule these 'artificial' countries were united against their colonial rulers but following independence old tribal loyalties have re-emerged. People separated from the remainder of their tribe or ethnic group by imposed international boundaries have engaged in territorial disputes with their neighbouring countries. Closer to home, the conflict in Northern Ireland was really a territorial dispute between the Nationalist population, many of whom wanted to unite Ireland, and the Unionist population, who wanted to maintain the division of Ireland and remain part of the United Kingdom.

Territorial disputes between ethnic groups are sometimes based on the economic or strategic value of the territory in question.

The dispute between Israel and Syria over the Golan Heights is partly to do with the important water resources in that region. Border conflicts between Sudan and South Sudan also illustrate this point. South Sudan gained independence from Sudan in 2011. The border between these two countries cuts across oil supplies and disputes over these led to conflict in 2012. At one stage, South Sudan captured and occupied some land around Heglig, in the province of Abyei, from Sudan (Figure C20). An uneasy peace was reached in 2012 and a 10 km demilitarised zone was put in place along the border.

Historical animosities

Disputes between ethnic groups often last for generations and even after the conflict is over historical animosities keep the potential for future conflict very much to the fore. Each new generation grows up with information about past wrong doings of the other group in the country. Such situations are most likely to occur in segregated societies where there is little contact between the various groups. In these circumstances, where there is minimal social contact between the groups, mutual suspicions and animosities develop. Past grievances visited on one group by the other are kept very much alive through cultural differences in literature, music and political organisations. In Northern Ireland, historical animosities between the Catholic and Protestant populations were expressed in the contrasting interpretations of the annual 12th of July Orange marches. For the Protestant population they were a sign of their British identity but for the Catholic population they were a sign of Protestant domination and division. Bitter riots followed some marches that came close to largely Nationalist areas and now a Parades Commission decides the route of contentious marches.

Racism and sectarianism

Prejudice against one section of society, either on racial (racism) or religious (sectarianism) grounds, has been a significant cause of ethnic conflict throughout history. The Holocaust was based on Nazi doctrine of Aryan supremacy and the inferiority of the Jewish population. Under colonial rule, black Africans were regarded as inferior and therefore enslaving them was justified. In South Africa, the apartheid system was a blatantly racist regime which condemned the non-white population to an underclass in society. Sectarian conflicts occurred in Northern Ireland, where the Catholic population were discriminated against in local government and in the allocation of jobs. In Israel the conflict is largely based on sectarianism (see Israel case study, pages 355–364).

Cultural conflicts

Globalisation has facilitated the movement of people and ideas throughout the world. In theory, the mixing of ideas and cultures should be an enriching experience but in some cases cultural conflicts have resulted. Over the last 30 years some Middle Eastern Muslim nations have adopted a fundamentalist Islamic code. Iran was one of the first nations to have an Islamic revolution, which meant a total rejection of all western influences in the country. Following the First Gulf War in 1991, the USA maintained military bases in Saudi Arabia, the ancestral home of Islam. This enraged the growing number of fundamentalist Muslims who regarded western culture as immoral and anti-Muslim. Although from mixed backgrounds, a growing anti-western or anti-American movement has gathered momentum and unified the extremist Muslims. The attacks on New York in 2001 were carried out by Al-Qaeda terrorists as part of a Holy War or Jihad against the west. The subsequent war on global terrorism (the name used in the west to describe the worldwide threat to western countries by Islamic extremists) gave rise to the American and British led invasions of Afghanistan and Iraq. Since 2014, Islamic State (IS), an extremist Islamic group, is attempting to establish an Islamic controlled region (caliphate) across the Middle East and North Africa, and is playing a key role in the on-going conflicts in Syria and Iraq. This cultural conflict has not been confined to Middle Eastern Muslims. The London bombings in July 2005 were carried out by British born Muslims. IS have carried out a number of deadly attacks in western cities including Paris in 2015 and Brussels, Nice and Berlin in 2016. Cultural ideologies are spread through the Internet and a recent worrying development in the UK and elsewhere is the 'radicalisation' of some British Muslims. IS uses this tactic to spread their brand of Sharia Islam and influence or radicalise Muslims, mostly young males. There have been several well documented cases of young British men going to Syria to join IS or carrying out terrorist attacks in Britain. Cultural conflicts can even occur within families. For some Islamic people, arranged marriages are part of traditional culture but many younger Islamic women are now opposed to this practice, particularly those who are living in secular countries. There have been several cases of so-called 'honour killings', where young women have been killed by a family member because they had not complied with the cultural laws of their ethnic group.

Human rights abuses

In many cases, ethnic conflict arises from serious mistreatment of an ethnic group or mistreatment can follow an ethnic conflict. Collectively, these cases are referred to as human rights abuses. The United Nations defines human rights as the "basic rights and freedoms to which all humans are entitled." This includes:

- civil and political rights, such as the right to life and liberty, freedom of expression and equality before the law.
- social, cultural and economic rights, including the right to participate in culture, the right to food, the right to work and the right to education.

Abuse of these human rights can lead to ethnic conflict because it is essentially a form of extreme discrimination. The group of people targeted is likely to mount some form of protest against the government. Palestinians in Israel claim human rights abuses as justification for their attacks on Israelis (see Israel case study, pages 355–364). Some of the worst cases of human rights abuses occur in on-going conflict zones.

On occasions, human rights abuses actually mean death. There have been examples where a government has attempted to kill an entire ethnic group. This is known as genocide. In Rwanda, in 1994, the majority Hutu population killed over 1 million of the minority Tutsi population in a three week period. In 2016, the United Nations accused IS of the attempted genocide of the Yazidi people, a minority group in Northern Iraq. In one incident alone, known as the Sinjar massacre, in August 2014, 5000 Yazidi men from the city of Sinjar were murdered by IS, 40,000 were displaced to the surrounding Sinjar mountains and an estimated 7000 women were taken as sex slaves.

Several conventions or codes of practice have been drawn up to safeguard human rights. The Geneva Conventions, a series of internationally agreed rules governing the protection of human rights in conflict zones, were established between 1864 and 1949. The International Committee of the Red Cross is an independent neutral organisation which delivers emergency humanitarian assistance, including food, water, shelter and medical aid in conflict zones.

Discrimination

In some ethnically diverse situations, the allocation of resources seems to favour the ruling group. In South Africa the apartheid system was a deliberate attempt to keep the black South Africans an underclass and maximise the wealth and resources of the country for the white population. South Africa was ostracised by most western nations and by most of Africa during the apartheid era. In Zimbabwe many white farmers have had their land expropriated by the government and given to supporters of President Mugabe. Denying one section of the population fair access to resources or unfair political practices leads to dissatisfaction and often breeds conflict. When Northern Ireland was first established, local government districts were created in a way that maximised the Unionist representation on the local councils. As the councils controlled the budget for housing and other services, this was seen as an attempt by the Unionist government to discriminate against the minority Nationalist population. Business people were entitled to vote in council elections at their home address as well as at their business address. This meant business people could vote in more than one council area. As most business people were from the Unionist population this was also regarded as an unfair practice. The Civil Rights movement in the late 1960s was formed to protest against these injustices. Local government reform has removed both of these practices.

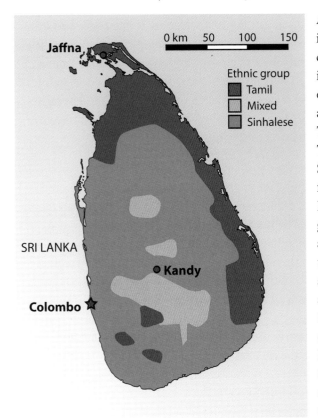

Figure C21: Major ethnic groups in Sri Lanka

As stated earlier, ethnic conflict is usually the result of the interaction of a number of factors. The example of the conflict in Sri Lanka demonstrates this. Sri Lanka is a small island in the Indian Ocean (Figure C21). It has two main ethnic groups: the majority Sinhalese, who speak Sinhala and are Buddhists; and the minority Tamils, who speak Tamil and are Hindu. Under British colonial rule the Tamils became the more prosperous group. When Sri Lanka became independent in 1948, the Sinhalese formed the government. Historical animosities towards Britain were now directed at the Tamil population and the government embarked on a policy of discrimination against the Tamils. Tamils required higher grades to enter university than Sinhalese. Sinhala was made the official state language and all government documentation was available only in Sinhala. Land close to sacred sites of the Hindu Tamils was taken over by the Sinhalese. A bitter ethnic conflict has taken place in Sri Lanka, claiming the lives of over 60,000 people. During the conflict the Sinhalese were accused of human rights abuses. Part of the conflict arose from Tamil demands for a separate state in the north of the island, leading to territorial disputes.

The nature of ethnic conflict

Ethnic conflict has to involve some confrontation between the rival sides in the dispute. In today's world of satellite media and 24 hour news bulletins it is possible to follow events as they unfold. Those involved in any conflict situation will strive to get their viewpoint broadcast sympathetically by reporting journalists. The form of ethnic conflict varies greatly, from protest marches to full scale war.

Civil disobedience

Civil disobedience is the active refusal to obey certain laws or commands of a government. It is a non-violent protest, where the protesting group withdraws its participation in the working of the country. It includes non-payment of rates, taxes, boycotting services or shops owned by the opposition, and mass strikes. To be effective, civil disobedience needs the support of large numbers from the protesting group. If the protesting group are the dominant workforce in one sector of industry, a strike can have a dramatic impact on the country as a whole. The civil rights movement in America, under Martin Luther King, and some of the protests in India against British control, organised by Mahatma Gandhi, constituted civil disobedience. Today the use of social media sites facilitates instant coverage of events. The Arab Spring, a democracy movement that spread across many countries in the Middle East and North Africa from 2010, relied heavily on digital communication to organise mass civil disobedience protests against the ruling elite.

Civil war

At the other end of the scale there is civil war. This describes a situation where there are clearly identified armed forces within the country actively engaged in armed conflict with each other. Civil wars develop for many reasons, including ethnic conflict. In Europe, the civil wars that occurred in the Balkans in the late 1990s, leading to the break-up of the former Yugoslavia, were ethnically based. Africa has many examples of civil wars. The Democratic Republic of Congo was involved in a civil war between the government forces and the minority Tutsi population from 1997–2003. The Democratic Republic of Congo is itself the product of another civil war in neighbouring Rwanda in the early 1990s. The civil war in Syria since 2011 is a conflict between the minority ruling elite, who are a sect of Shia Muslims, and the majority Sunni Muslims.

Terrorism

Many ethnic conflicts do not reach full scale civil war but take the form of a terrorist campaign. Terrorism involves armed conflict but the terrorist is a member of an illegal guerrilla organisation which operates within the community. Terrorism pursues some ideological goal, such as a united Ireland for the IRA or a Tamil homeland for the Tamil Tigers in Sri Lanka. Terrorist groups do not openly display the trappings of a regular army; instead they operate secretively within their community. This form of conflict poses particular problems for the security forces because terrorists can blend unnoticed into the community. The tactics employed by terrorist groups include car bombs and attacks directed at the rival group, destruction of state property and killing members of the opposition. In Northern Ireland, the IRA carried out terrorist attacks against Unionists and the British Army for over 25 years. Terrorism from one side often results in a terrorist response from the opposition, and in Northern Ireland the Ulster Volunteer Force (UVF) carried out terrorist attacks on the Nationalist population. Terrorism reached a new dimension with the Al-Qaeda attacks on New York on 11 September 2001. The term global terrorism is used in the west to describe the worldwide threat to western countries by Islamic extremists. Apart from the USA, other countries targeted as part of global terrorism include: the UK (London 2005 and 2017, and Manchester 2017), Spain (Madrid 2004, Barcelona 2017), India (Mumbai 2008), France (Paris 2015 and Nice 2016), Belgium (Brussels 2016) and Germany (Berlin 2016). Western communities were also targeted in tourist resorts in Turkey on several occasions (most recently in 2017), Ivory Coast (2016), Egypt (2016), Bali (2002 and 2015) and Tunisia (2015).

Outcomes and response to ethnic conflict

Social and economic impacts

Ethnic conflict has far reaching impacts wherever it occurs. Society is always negatively affected by conflict. At the lowest level of impact, communities become more segregated and polarised. Throughout the Northern Ireland conflict, residential segregation increased either because people were forced out of mixed housing areas or people simply decided to move to be with their co-religionists. This type of segregation was always more pronounced in the inner city areas.

Conflicts of any kind can force people to flee from their homes in search of safety. Refugees are a particularly vulnerable sector of society. They are mostly civilians who have no possessions, living in cramped and unsanitary conditions and totally dependent on aid from charities such as the Red Cross. Death rates are high, especially amongst children. The civil war in Syria has caused 7.6 million refugees and internally displaced people to flee their homes to camps within Syria or abroad. Figure C22 shows information on refugees and internally displaced people in 2015.

Worldwide, the number of refugees is increasing. According to the United Nations High Commission for Refugees (UNHCR), about half of the refugees are under 18 and most will spend up to 20 years of their lives as refugees. In addition, most refugees come from the poorest countries and end up in neighbouring poor countries, adding significantly to the existing problems of poverty.

Note:

Internally displaced people are those who have been displaced, but have not crossed an international boundary. Refugees are displaced people who have crossed an international boundary.

Figure C22: Refugees and internally displaced people 2015

Source. Data from 'Figures at a glance', UNHCR, http://www.unhcr.org/uk/figures-at-a-glance.html

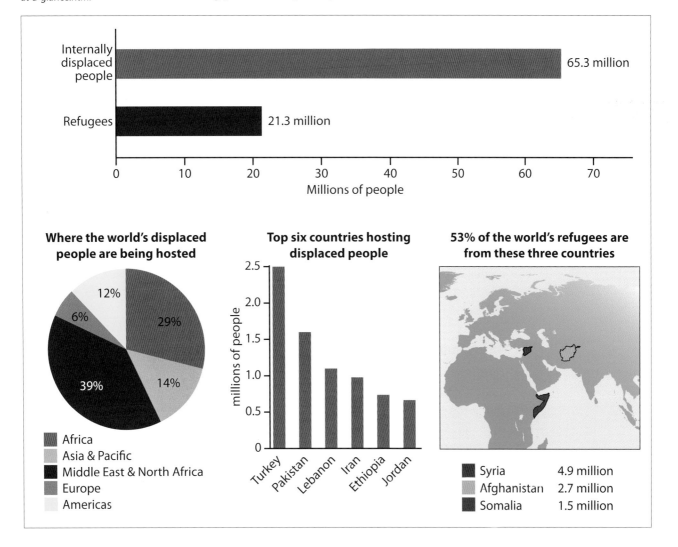

The treatment of female refugees has been widely reported in several ethnic conflicts. In northern Iraq, approximately 7000 Yazidi women and young girls were taken and sold as sex slaves. This incident and others, including the gang rape of Bosnian women in Srebrenica in 1995, has prompted many to call for such actions to be deemed war crimes.

Loss of life and injury have a major impact on society. 'The troubles' in Northern Ireland resulted in over 3000 deaths. The UN estimates about 400,000 deaths from the Syrian civil war. These figures, together with the numbers of displaced people, represent a substantial future loss to the countries concerned.

The economy of a region experiencing ethnic conflict can be affected in several ways. There will inevitably be a direct loss of property and businesses through bombings but in addition, conflict areas present a very negative image to outside investors. Since the end of 'the troubles', Northern Ireland and Belfast in particular has received much investment which would not have occurred if there was still civil unrest. Tourist numbers were greatly reduced following the terrorist attacks in both Tunisia and Sharm El Sheikh (Egypt) in 2015. Following this latter attack, tourist numbers fell from 640,000 in 2015 to 346,000 in 2016. This reduction means a very significant loss of income for a country where tourism is a major source of revenue.

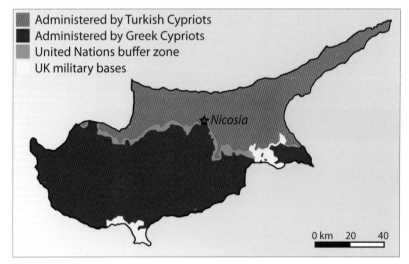

Figure C23: Partition of Cyprus

Territorial division

At some stage the opposing sides in any ethnic conflict will have to attempt a solution. The form that this will take depends on many factors, including the geographical distribution of the various groups involved. If the protesting groups have clearly defined territorial boundaries it may be that territorial division is considered. An example is the sub-division of British India into a Hindu India and a Muslim West Pakistan (now Pakistan) and East Pakistan (now Bangladesh). Ireland was divided into a 26 county Republic of Ireland, while the remaining 6 counties became part of the United Kingdom. The island of Cyprus was partitioned into a northern Turkish Cypriot sector and a southern Greek Cypriot sector (Figure C23). A number of former Soviet republics, including Ukraine and Georgia, have broken away from Russia since the demise of communism. Ethnic identity played a major part in their quest for territorial separation from Russia.

Autonomy

Territorial division can sometimes result in a region gaining some degree of political control while still remaining an integral part of the ruling country. This is known as autonomy. In Sri Lanka, the Tamils were granted autonomy in the Jaffna peninsula but were still part of Sri Lanka. In May 2009 the Sri Lankan army defeated the Tamil Tigers and regained full control of Sri Lanka.

Figure C24: The ethnic cleansing plan in Bosnia

Source: Mark Danner, 'Endgame in Kosovo', *New York Review of Books*, 6 May 1999

1. **Concentration**. Surround the area to be cleansed and after warning the resident Serbs – often they are urged to leave or are at least told to mark their houses with white flags – intimidate the target.
2. **Decapitation**. Execute political leaders and those capable of taking their places: lawyers, judges, public officials, writers, professors.
3. **Separation**. Divide women, children, and old men from men of 'fighting age' – sixteen years to sixty years old.
4. **Evacuation**. Transport women, children, and old men to the border, expelling them into a neighbouring territory or country.
5. **Execute** 'fighting age' men, dispose of bodies.

Ethnic cleansing

The most extreme form of segregation is ethnic cleansing. This is the whole-scale removal of an ethnic group from an area (Figure C24). Ethnic cleansing created more than two million refugees and displaced persons in former Yugoslavia (Figure C1, page 317) during the war in Bosnia (Figure C25). Although the Serbs were by far the most successful 'cleansers', all sides adopted this method in the course of the war. One of the worst atrocities in modern times occurred during this war in Srebrenica, when over 8000 Bosnian Muslims, mostly men, were murdered by the Serbian Army as part of ethnic cleansing in 1995. In Myanmar, the government has been accused of ethnic cleansing and genocide of the minority Rohingya people. The United Nations Human Rights Council has a mandate to investigate such violations. The Security Council hears reports from all organs of the United Nations and can take action over any issue that it feels threatens peace and security, including the treatment of civilians caught up in conflict. However, it has also been criticised, at times, for failing to take action to prevent human rights abuses, such as the massacre of over 8000 Muslims in Srebrenica (Bosnia 1995) and the genocide in Rwanda (1994).

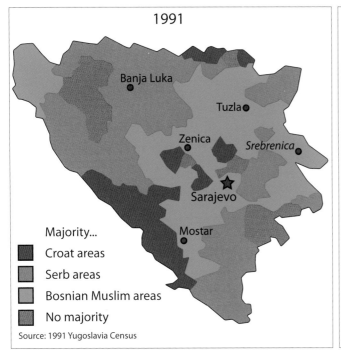

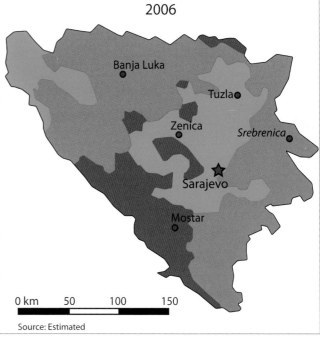

Figure C25: Map of Bosnia before and after ethnic cleansing

Source: 1991 Yugoslavia Census and 2006 estimated

International intervention and peace processes

Sometimes the international community, apart from the United Nations, becomes involved in foreign conflict situations. There are many reasons for this international intervention including:

- Moral concern for the human suffering that ethnic conflict brings, such as the NATO support for the Muslim population of Kosovo (a disputed territory in the former Yugoslavia) in 1999, who were enduring ethnic cleansing and other war crimes by the Serbian army.

- Political or historical links with one of the groups concerned, such as the French interest in its former colony of Chad in central Africa.

- Strategic reasons, such as American support for Israel in the Middle East. This is partly because there is a Jewish population in the USA but also because during the Cold War (a period of political and military tension between USA and Russia between 1947 and 1991) Russia backed some of the Arab countries in the region.

- Security reasons, for example, the American involvement in Iraq and Afghanistan was justified by the perceived threat of global terrorism from these countries.

The effectiveness of international intervention has been mixed. In Northern Ireland the intervention of the USA made a positive contribution to the resolution of conflict. In other parts of the world international intervention has been more confrontational.

International intervention in ethnic conflict usually involves an attempt at conflict resolution and the formulation of a peace process. There have been some successful peace processes, notably the Dayton Agreement, which brought an end to the conflict between Bosnia and Serbia in 1995. Not all peace processes lead to an immediate and permanent cessation of hostilities, as the Northern Ireland example illustrates. The peace process in the Middle East has been on-going since the creation of Israel in 1948 and currently it is overseen by an international quartet of countries or regions – the European Union, USA, Russia and the United Nations.

Exam Questions

1. (a) Ethnic minorities often live in clusters within cities. Explain the underlying reasons for this residential concentration. [8]

   (b) Study Resource A relating to territorial division in Cyprus. 'Territorial division has, according to some observers, brought benefits to Cyprus. However, this is not always the case'. Use the resource to help you evaluate the success of territorial division as an outcome of ethnic conflict.

   (c) With reference to case study material of an ethnically diverse city, evaluate the roles of segregation and multiculturalism in maintaining its ethnic diversity. [18]

   Question from CCEA A2 2 Processes and Issues in Human Geography,
   Specimen Assessment Materials, © CCEA 2017

Resource A: The partition of Cyprus

Source: text adapted from Michael L Grumelli, 'Cyprus: Managing Ethnic Conflict Through Geographic Partitioning' published on the following website: http://handle.dtic.mil/100.2/ ADA430996, © The Air Command and Staff College. Map © CCEA. Photograph SA Royle.

The island of Cyprus in the eastern Mediterranean has had a history of ethnic conflict between the majority Greek Cypriots and the minority

Turkish Cypriots. Following a Turkish invasion in 1974, a 180-kilometre long buffer zone or 'Green Line' has divided the island along ethnic lines. This Green Line runs through the heart of the island's capital, Nicosia, and is patrolled by the UN. The buffer zone varies in width from a few metres to 8 km and is home to 10,000 people. Turkish Cypriots established a separate political entity in the north although this does not have international recognition. The partition of the island resulted in the displacement of thousands of Cypriots who found themselves on the 'wrong side' of the Green Line. Movement between the two parts of the island is strictly controlled to a number of crossing points. Over the years a number of unsuccessful attempts have been made to reunite the island.

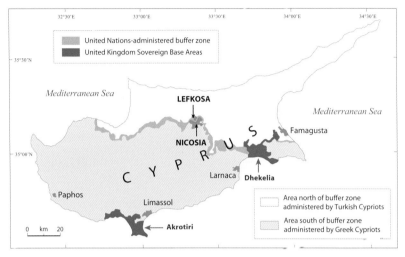

Some believe that a permanent split would perpetuate frictions in the region hindering economic progress (especially northern Cyprus), and requiring greater defence spending. The unnatural division and segregation of the two communities has resulted in a generation of Greek and Turkish Cypriots who do not know each other. Moreover, the division of Cyprus has frustrated attempts by some citizens from both ethnic communities to secure a political solution to the problem. In addition, a partitioned Cyprus remains a continuing irritant in the troubled relations between Greece and Turkey. The persistence of the informal partition of the island has turned Cyprus into one of the most heavily militarised countries in the world.

Abandoned buildings at an interface in Nicosia – Greek and Turkish flags are visible

However, there are those who disagree with this viewpoint. The 1974 Turkish invasion of northern Cyprus followed a ten-year period of escalating violence between the two rival communities. Since partition there has been limited violence on the island. In addition, Cyprus was spared the problem of semi-permanent refugee camps. Turkish refugees who fled to the north were housed through the confiscation of Greek Cypriot homes. The Greek Cypriot refugees who had been forcibly displaced by the Turkish invasion were rapidly housed through a massive construction programme in the south.

2. (a) Study Resource B relating to the autonomous state of Gorkhaland in West Bengal, India.

    (i) Define autonomy in this context and suggest one possible objection to Gorkhaland's autonomy from both:

- some members of the Indian Government; and
- some of the Gorkha people. [8]

    (ii) Use the resource to help you discuss the economic and social impacts of ethnic conflict. [9]

  (b) 'International migration plays a greater role in the creation of ethnically diverse countries than annexation or colonisation'.

With reference to your case study of an ethnically diverse country, discuss the extent to which you agree with this statement. [18]

Question from CCEA A2 2 Processes and Issues in Human Geography, Specimen Assessment Materials, © CCEA 2017

Resource B: India grants autonomy to the Gorkha in West Bengal

In July 2011, the Indian Government agreed a deal to grant autonomy to the Gorkha ethnic group in north-west Bengal. The Gorkha are a distinctive ethnic group in this region and have long accused the Indian Government of unfair treatment. The newly created autonomous state with an area of 7000 km^2 and a population of 3.5 million follows a similar concession made to an ethnic minority in southern India.

The acceptance of autonomy resulted from a compromise on both sides. The Gorkha had campaigned for full independence from India for over one hundred years. At times the campaign was violent especially during the 1980s. Some estimates put the death toll at over 1000. The most recent campaign focussed largely on peaceful protest and civil disobedience. In the months leading up to July 2011, there were several hunger strikes and the Gorkha workers on the Darjeeling tea plantations called an indefinite strike. Darjeeling produces over 9 million kilograms of tea annually, of which 70% is exported. The growing unrest resulted in a 30% drop in tea production. Tourism is the other mainstay of the local economy and part of Gorkhaland is a world heritage site. Some sources claim that thousands of tourists either curtailed their stay or cancelled as a result of the growing uncertainty in the region.

It is hoped that the creation of the autonomous state of Gorkhaland within India will bring peace and stability to the area. However, there are many opponents to the new state both from within the Indian government and within Gorkhaland itself.

3. (a) Study Resource C below relating to ethnic conflict in Syria.

   (i) Identify and describe two causes of ethnic conflict in Syria. [8]

   (ii) Use the Resource to help you explain why ethnic cleansing and territorial division are often outcomes of ethnic conflict. [9]

Question adapted from A2 1 Human Interactions and Global Issues,
January 2014, © CCEA 2017

Resource C: Ethnic Cleansing in Syria

Source: adapted from 'Assad accused of sectarian cleansing', Hugh MacLeod and Annasofie Flamand, *The Sunday Times*, 15 July 2012

The Middle Eastern country of Syria has been under authoritarian rule by the Assad family since 1970. The predominantly Muslim population is divided into the Alawite and Sunni sects. President Assad and most of his ruling regime belong to the minority Alawite sect while the majority of the civilian population are Sunni Muslim. Since taking control of the country, the Assad family has ruled Syria as a one party state. All aspects of life are controlled by the regime. There are no elections, no freedom of speech and any opposition is crushed.

Since the Arab Spring in 2011, Syria, along with other Middle Eastern countries, has experienced serious civil unrest. There are concerns that this uprising has an ethnic dimension. The Assad regime has attempted to defeat the rebels by force and the Syrian authorities have been accused of torture of prisoners, indiscriminate bombings and the massacre of civilians. Following the latest massacre, fears are growing that forces loyal to President Assad are attempting to carve out a breakaway Alawite state. Some observers claim that, if the Assad regime cannot defeat the uprising it will adopt the next best option of partitioning Syria to create an Alawite only area in western Syria. In this region, Sunni enclaves in the cities of Latakia and Tartous have been effectively cleared while the Sunni dominated cities of Homs and Hama have been subjected to sustained attacks by government forces. Tens of thousands have been killed and 120,000 have fled to refugee camps in neighbouring Turkey, Jordan and Lebanon. Further deaths occurred throughout the summer of 2012 when remote Sunni villages were cleared by Assad's militia to create a buffer zone between Sunni and Alawite areas. These, and similar incidents, have led some to accuse the Syrian government of ethnic cleansing.

4. Study Resource D below relating to ethnic conflict in Iraq in 2014.

    (i) Identify and briefly outline two causes of this ethnic conflict. [8]

    (ii) Using the resource to help you, explain why ethnic cleansing and territorial division can occur in ethnic conflict situations. [9]

    Question from A2 1 Human Interactions and Global Issues, May 2016, © CCEA 2017

Resource D: Ethnic Issues in Iraq in 2014

Iraq has a complex ethnic structure. Conflict between the highly segregated ethnic groups is not a new occurrence in Iraq but the current conflict between the Shia and Sunni Muslims threatens the break-up of the country along ethnic lines. It may also have repercussions for neighbouring countries.

The majority Shia have held political control since parliamentary elections were first held in 2005. Iraqi Sunni claim they have been marginalised by the government as they were denied devolved regional power and were targeted by the security forces. Ethnic violence escalated in 2014 and the death toll averages 1000 a month.

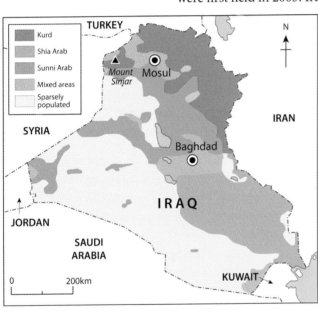

In June 2014, the most militant of the Sunni terrorist organisations, Islamic State (IS), captured large areas in northern Iraq and declared their intention to establish an Islamic state based on Sharia law across northern Iraq and Syria. Those who do not adhere to IS laws have been forcibly removed or executed. The Yazidi, an ancient and distinctive ethnic group were forced from their homes and sought refuge in desperate conditions on Mount Sinjar in northern Iraq. As many as 1.5 million people have been displaced by IS, creating a major humanitarian crisis and claims of genocide. IS continued their attacks in northern Iraq capturing a number of Kurdish cities. Many believe that territorial division of Iraq is an inevitable consequence of on-going ethnic conflict. The Kurds already have some devolved control and are demanding greater independence.

References

Examples of ethnic conflict:
https://www.theguardian.com/global-development/conflict-and-developmenttime.com/4089276/burma-rohingya-genocide-report-documentary/

International Committee of the Red Cross:
https://www.icrc.org/en

United Nations High Commission for Refugees:
www.unhcr.org/uk

CASE STUDY: Israel, a national study of ethnic conflict

Background

In 1947 a homeland for Jewish people was formed in Palestine, an action that initiated an ethnic conflict between Jews and Palestinians which has remained at the centre of the Middle East's political landscape ever since. The conflict is rooted in a territorial dispute between Jews, over land that they claim as their biblical entitlement, and Palestinians who make similar claims. Whilst this conflict mainly concerns territorial disputes, other issues, including historical animosities, sectarianism, human rights abuses and discrimination, have all played a significant role. The conflict has taken the form of civil disobedience, civil war, terrorism and international wars. In terms of outcomes, this conflict has resulted in territorial division, autonomy and ethnic cleansing. All aspects of society and the economy have been negatively affected. There has been considerable international attention to events in the region, at one time becoming a potential threat of conflict between the USA and the Soviet Union in 1956. In addition, a number of peace deals have been brokered by international organisations but to date none has succeeded in achieving a permanent cessation of hostilities.

The present ethnic conflict between Israelis and the Palestinians and the surrounding Arab countries can be traced back to the migration of Jews from Europe throughout the nineteenth and early twentieth centuries. Sectarianism, in the form of anti-Semitism, resulted in widespread discrimination against Jews in Europe and this galvanised the Jewish people into a unified group. Large numbers migrated in successive streams from Europe to what many considered to be their ancestral home in the Middle East – Palestine. These migration streams, referred to as Aliyah, were supported by the growth of Zionism or Jewish Nationalism in Europe during the nineteenth century. The Zionist movement formed institutions such as the Jewish Agency to facilitate Jewish migration to Palestine. The Jewish Agency promoted the Hebrew language and culture, established a Hebrew University in Jerusalem and purchased land in Palestine for future Jewish settlement. It also formed political parties and a Jewish defence organisation. In essence, the Jewish Agency was moulding a unified Jewish nation from people who had lived in many different countries and spoke different languages. All of these institutions laid the foundations for the management of a state, which Jews believed was their entitlement. Anti-Semitism in Europe intensified in the years leading up to World War II, culminating in the mass murder of six million Jews in Nazi Germany during the Holocaust. In the immediate aftermath of World War II, those Jews who had survived the Holocaust made even more strenuous demands for a Jewish homeland in Palestine.

Causes and nature of the conflict

Israel is surrounded by the Arab Islamic countries of Jordan, Lebanon, Syria and Egypt, and in the wider Middle East by Saudi Arabia, Iraq and Iran. Territorial disputes have been at the centre of the ethnic conflict and have shaped the political landscape of the Middle East and beyond since 1947. Major incidences include:

1. The partition of Palestine and the creation of Israel

Figure C26: Map of the proposed partition of Palestine in 1947

Palestine and its mainly Muslim population became a British mandate in 1917. Anxious to gain Jewish support against Germany, Britain backed a plan for a Jewish Homeland in Palestine by signing the Balfour Declaration in 1917. The intention was that this Jewish homeland would live peacefully within an independent Palestine. In fact, Britain supported the idea of Arab nationalism in Palestine and favoured a reduction in the numbers of Jewish migrants to the region. However, Jewish migration gathered momentum from 1945 onwards and there were bitter clashes between Jews and Palestinians. Britain planned to withdraw from Palestine in 1947, leaving a United Nations Commission to decide the future of Palestine. The Commission decided that Palestine should be partitioned into a western Jewish homeland and an eastern Palestinian section of Transjordan, later known as Jordan. The city of Jerusalem was to remain under UN control. The western section was particularly fragmented as Figure C26 shows, but the Jewish population accepted it reluctantly. The Palestinians rejected the partition outright because they resented the loss of territory to the Jews and a sizeable number of Palestinians were trapped in the Jewish state.

The Palestinians' first form of protest against the proposed partition was a general strike in December 1947, which led to inter-communal rioting and eventually a civil war. The civil war lasted for six months and the Jewish Agency declared the territory allocated to the Jews as the new state of Israel on 14 May 1948. The following day Egyptian, Lebanese, Jordanian, Syrian and Iraqi troops attacked Israel in what is known as the First Arab-Israeli war.

Israeli forces defeated the Arab armies and in 1949 a new territorial division of Palestine was agreed and the state of Israel was formally recognised by the United Nations. Israel had increased its territory by about 21% (Figure C27). The Arab nations also took land from Palestine.

Figure C27: Map of Palestine in 1949

Many Palestinians fled from Israel to neighbouring Arab countries during the fighting and became refugees in the hope of returning when peace was restored. Exact numbers are difficult to verify but it is estimated that this war created somewhere between 750,000 and 900,000 Palestinian refugees. Few of the Palestinians were allowed to return and most set up refugee camps close to the Israeli border, where they attempted to unite as a group and called for an independent Palestine. Meanwhile, after the war, Israel encouraged further immigration of Jews to their newly enlarged state. The refugee issue and the increase in Jewish immigration to Israel became and remain major stumbling blocks to lasting peace in this region. However, an immediate concern for Israelis was the division of Jerusalem, which left East Jerusalem (including the Old City with its religious sites) under Jordanian Muslim control. Jordan denied Jews access to their sacred shrines in East Jerusalem and some of these sacred sites were vandalised by Muslims.

2. The Six Day War 1967

The refugees created as a result of the first Arab-Israeli war exacerbated the territorial dispute between Israel and the surrounding Arab nations. In the refugee camps, the Palestinians began to organise terrorist attacks against Israel. Fearful of an attack from the neighbouring Arab countries, Israel launched a pre-emptive strike against Egypt, Syria and Jordan in 1967. This war, known as the Six Day War, had far reaching consequences for Israel and the Palestinians. Israel defeated the Arab armies and annexed land from each of the defeated countries (Figure C28). The main gains to Israel were:

- the Gaza Strip and the Sinai Peninsula from Egypt.
- the Golan Heights from Syria.
- East Jerusalem and the West Bank (of the River Jordan) from Jordan.

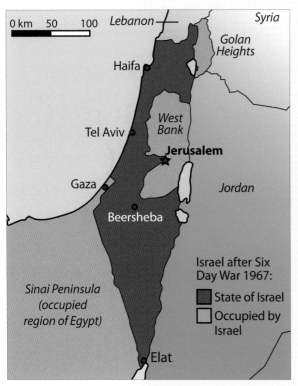

Figure C28: Map of Israel in 1967

As a result of these annexations, Israel had brought about a three-fold increase in the land area of the country, including East Jerusalem. Although there has been no international recognition of Israel's claim to these 'Occupied Territories', Israel still claims ownership of East Jerusalem and most of the West Bank (the Gaza Strip was granted autonomy in 1994). Israel had also succeeded in confining the Palestinians to two areas: the West Bank and the Gaza Strip. These two areas are 45 km apart. To cement their claim in the Occupied Territories, successive Israeli governments began building Jewish settlements. Over 800,000 Jews, equivalent to 13% of the total Israeli population, currently live in these heavily protected Israeli communities. These are often built on higher ground overlooking Palestinian towns and villages, and are clearly demarcated with flags and emblems of the Jewish Israeli state.

In 1973, in an attempt to regain the land lost in the Six Day War, Egypt and Syria attacked Israel in what became known as the Yom Kippur War. This war had a very high human cost for both sides, with no decisive conclusion reached.

Palestinian terrorism

The two wars mentioned created as many as 1.5 million refugees. According to international human rights law, civilian refugees should be allowed to return to their former homes once the conflict has ended. They should also be paid compensation for the loss of property and personal possessions. Many Palestinians fled to neighbouring Arab countries during the Six Day War but Israel has refused to allow them back into Israel or to pay them any compensation. The tents which were used initially for the refugees have been replaced by cheaply constructed concrete dwellings. According to the UNHCR (in 2016), the average amount of time spent as a refugee is 20 years. However, generations of Palestinians have lived as refugees since 1947 and many have regarded this as a human rights issue. There is a high level of overcrowding in the camps, with poor sanitation, poor health and high levels of unemployment. Increasing frustration and despair about their plight fomented animosity and led many Palestinians to resort to terrorism. They formed a number of paramilitary and political organisations under the umbrella name of the Palestine Liberation Organisation (PLO), led by Yasser Arafat. Initially, the PLO operated within Israel but was forced from Israel, first to Jordan and later to southern Lebanon. Its tactics included bomb attacks on Israeli civilians and international attacks, such as hi-jacking of aircraft and cruise liners and the massacre of 11 Israeli athletes at the Munich Olympics in 1972.

These terrorist attacks brought stiff retaliation from Israel, including air attacks on terrorist strongholds, which frequently caused civilian deaths, demolition of terrorists' housing, imprisonment, often without trial, and on occasions full scale war (see examples that follow).

Outcomes of the conflict
International intervention and peace processes

Following the Yom Kippur War, itself an example of international intervention, and the rise of the PLO, there was an increased drive from the international community for a long lasting solution to the Middle East crisis. There are four main areas of contention in this conflict:

- Israel's right to peaceful co-existence with her Arab neighbours.
- Palestinian demands for autonomy and statehood.
- The plight of the Palestinian refugees within Israel and in the surrounding Arab countries.
- The Occupied Territories and the status of Jerusalem.

1. Camp David peace deal 1979

The USA helped negotiate a cease-fire to the Yom Kippur War in 1974 and brokered a peace deal between Israel and Egypt, whereby Israel agreed to:

- return the Sinai Peninsula to Egypt.
- explore the possibility of granting autonomy to the West Bank and Gaza within 5 years.
- cease building settlements in the West Bank.

In return, Egypt agreed to:

- formally recognise the state of Israel.
- establish peaceful and diplomatic relations with Israel.
- a demilitarised zone in Sinai, 20 km from the Israeli border.
- allow Israel access to the Suez Canal.

Achievements of the Camp David Peace Deal 1979

The Camp David Agreement was controversial and did not receive backing from any other Arab nation in the Middle East or from the PLO. Nevertheless it was seen as laying the foundations for subsequent peace deals in the region. Among the achievements are:

- Israel and Egypt have maintained a 'cold peace' since 1979.
- Both countries have received generous investment from the USA.

However, it soon became clear that Israel was not going to allow full autonomy and set about a policy of increasing Jewish settlements in these Occupied Territories. In 1972, there were a total of 10,000 Jewish settlers in the Occupied Territories. By 1983, just 4 years after Camp David, there were 107,000. Palestinians regarded this as creeping annexation.

Israel had established peace with Egypt but there were still tensions with Syria. Throughout the remainder of the 1970s and early 80s, Israel was attacked by the PLO from southern Lebanon with support from Syria. To prevent further attacks from this source, Israel invaded southern Lebanon in 1982. The PLO was forced to leave Lebanon and Israel maintained a military occupation of southern Lebanon until 2000. The PLO no longer had a base close to the Israeli border but it continued its attacks on Israeli targets throughout the world.

The First Intifada and the formation of Hamas

Growing frustration among the Palestinians over the defeat of the PLO in Lebanon, along with lack of progress towards autonomy and the increasing Jewish settlement in the Occupied Territories, sparked an uprising of Palestinian youths, known as an Intifada, in 1987. The Intifada started as civil obedience, including a Palestinian boycott of Israeli shops, a general strike and public demonstrations against Israel. However, the Intifada soon became a violent uprising which lasted until 1993. An Islamic resistance movement, known as Hamas, formed in the Gaza Strip, with the objective of establishing an Islamic state in the region, marking a new dimension to this conflict. Hamas was essentially a terrorist organisation but its ideology revolved around Sharia Law, which has a close connection between state law and religious beliefs. Its objective of the creation of an Islamic state increased the potential for a major cultural conflict in this region. Hamas waged a Holy War against Israel, including suicide bomb attacks targeting the Jewish civilian population. Throughout the uprising, a number of committees were formed to lay the foundation for an independent state, in much the same way as the Jewish population had done so 50 years earlier.

The Intifada met with stiff Israeli retaliation and Israel was accused of human rights violations by some international pressure groups, including Amnesty International. There were mass arrests of Palestinians and claims of torture. Palestinians were subjected to curfews during periods of sustained unrest. Schools and universities in affected areas were closed. Arabic newspapers were censored and charities supporting the Palestinians were forced to close. Suspected key figures in the uprising were targeted and assassinated. Over 1,100 Palestinians and 160 Israelis were killed during the Intifada.

2. The Oslo Accords

A second major international attempt to secure a permanent solution to the Arab-Israeli conflict came in 1991. The USA helped secure the signing of A Declaration of Principles (the Oslo Accords) between Israel and the PLO in 1993. This set out a framework of a 'two state solution'. This meant each side agreeing to live in peaceful coexistence. To achieve this:

- Israel agreed to grant Palestinian autonomy in the West Bank and Gaza. Elections would be held in the West Bank to establish a Palestinian Council.
- the PLO agreed to give up its terrorist activities and to recognise the existence of Israel.

3. The Cairo Agreement in 1994

This furthered the proposals of the Oslo Accords by organising the actual transfer of authority to the Palestinians and a phased withdrawal of the Israeli army from the West Bank and Gaza. A peace treaty was also negotiated between Israel and Jordan. A number of amendments and redrafts of the peace deals took place but eventually, in 1995, the Israeli-Palestinian Interim Agreement was signed. It extended the powers of the Palestinian Council in the Gaza Strip and parts of the West Bank, and made some progress on the release of Palestinian prisoners held in Israeli jails but fell short of an independent state for Palestinians. Elections were held in the Occupied Territories to elect a Palestinian Council in 1996, with Yasser Arafat as the Prime Minister. This progress towards a lasting peace in the region was supported by the USA, the EU, Russia and Egypt. In return, the Palestinians recognised Israel and agreed to give up terrorism.

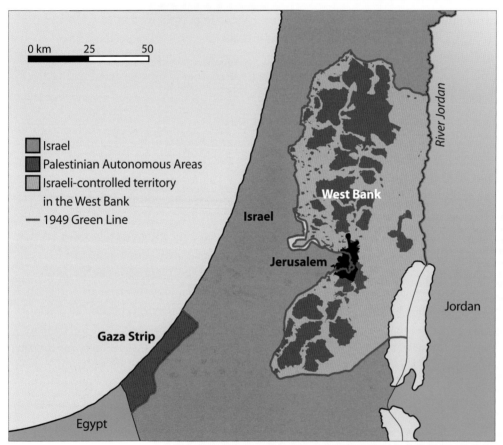

Key:
- Israel
- Palestinian Autonomous Areas
- Israeli-controlled territory in the West Bank
- 1949 Green Line

0 km   25   50

River Jordan

West Bank

Israel

Jerusalem

Jordan

Gaza Strip

Egypt

Figure C29: Map of the proposed plan for Palestinian autonomy in 1995

Achievements of the Oslo Accords and the Cairo Agreement

For the first time Palestinians had been given autonomy of some of their land. The Palestinian Authority did not have the support of the more extreme Islamist group, Hamas, which increased its suicide bomb attacks on Israel. Some right wing Israelis also opposed the deal and the Israeli Prime Minister was assassinated two months after the deal was signed. An election followed the assassination, which the right wing Likud party won. The peace process slowed down and there were renewed violent attacks on Israel from Hamas.

The Second Intifada 2000–2005

In addition, the Palestinians interpreted a visit to the Al Aqsa mosque by the Israeli government minister, Ariel Sharon, as proof that Israel was faltering on its agreement to withdraw from the Occupied Territories. Widespread rioting followed, marking the beginning of the Al Aqsa Intifada or Second Intifada, which resulted in the deaths of over 5000 Palestinians and 1000 Israelis.

In response to a number of suicide attacks, Ariel Sharon, by this stage Prime Minister of Israel, ordered the construction of a barrier around the Jewish settlements in the West Bank. This barrier is over 670 km long and varies in height from 5–8 metres. It has rolls of razor wire and is fitted with electronic sensors to detect attempts to breach the barrier. Israel claims this is necessary to protect Jewish settlements from suicide and sniper attacks. To the Palestinians this seemed to be further evidence that Israel intended to maintain control over much of the territory occupied by Jewish settlements in the West Bank. Barriers have also been built around the Gaza Strip.

Peace processes since 2000

Since 2000, several attempts have been made by the USA and others to work towards a two state solution to the conflict, including a Saudi Peace Plan in 2002 and a Roadmap for Peace in 2003 proposed by the USA, EU, UN and Russia but no real progress was made. Although Israel withdrew 8000 settlers from the Gaza Strip, despite strong opposition in 2005, there appears little willingness to remove them in the West Bank. For Israelis, Palestinian and Arab terrorism are the major obstacles to peace. In 2006, following attacks from Lebanese based terrorists, Israel fought a short war with Lebanon, and in response to daily rocket attacks from Gaza, first blockaded and then invaded Gaza in 2008.

The USA, under the direction of President Barack Obama, tried to restart peace talks on several occasions from 2008 with no real success. The major stumbling blocks remain the settlements in the West Bank and the issue of sovereignty over East Jerusalem. These two intractable problems remain just as prominent as they were in 1967. The continued blockade of Gaza increased hardship there and halted trade. In response, Gazans built a series of tunnels to smuggle goods but also used them to launch rocket attacks on Israel. Persistent attacks led Israel to the invasion of Gaza in 2008 (see above) and to the air attack in 2014, both of which had devastating consequences (Figure C32). In January 2017, the newly elected USA President, Donald Trump, voiced his support for Israel and, emboldened by this support, Israel announced its intention to build a further 3000 homes for Jewish settlers in the West Bank.

Social and economic impacts

Almost 70 years of conflict have cost many lives but in addition the economy has also been negatively affected. While all sections of the community are impacted, it is the plight of the Palestinians and the refugees that cause most concern. Since the creation of Israel and the annexation of the West Bank and Gaza, more than half the Arabs of pre-partition Palestine are thought to have been displaced. Following the violence of the Intifadas, Israel routinely demolished the homes of known terrorists and their families. As many as 600 homes were demolished between 2000 and 2005. Some observers have accused Israel of routine ethnic cleansing, a claim strenuously denied by Israel. Israeli restrictions on the movement of people and goods in Palestinian areas through checkpoints, road closures and curfews disrupt and frustrate everyday life. The blockade of Gaza has devastated the economy there (Figure C30). The Gaza population is heavily dependent on aid donations but the violence in the region has deterred some of this much needed aid. The two most recent wars, in 2008 and July 2014, have made the situation in Gaza much worse (Figures C31 and C32).

Figure C30: Social and economic characteristics in Gaza

Source: Data from 'Fast facts', UNDP report, August 2014, United Nations Development Report Office, UNDP

Facts

- Population: 1.8 million
- Total area: 365 km² (45 km long, 2.5 km wide)
- Gazan refugee population: 1.2 million
- Number of refugee camps: 8
- Unemployment: 47%
- Poverty rate: 60%
- 72% of Gazans are food insecure*
- 80% of Gazans are aid recipients
- Electricity supply reaches 2–4 hours a day

- 90% of Gaza water is unfit for human consumption

Since the July 2014 Crisis

- 1975 Palestinians killed (459 children, 239 women)
- 365,000 people displaced
- 10,690 housing units destroyed or severely damaged
- 1.2 million have no or limited access to water

* food insecure means not having access to or unable to afford sufficient food

Palestinians have been negatively affected by the building of the West Bank Barrier, which separates Jewish and Palestinian settlements in the West Bank. Parts of the Barrier are built on land confiscated from Palestinians. In the first two years of its construction, Palestinians lost over 100,000 olive and citrus trees, 75 hectares of green houses and 37 km of irrigation pipes. Many shops and houses were also demolished to allow for its construction. Healthcare is deemed totally inadequate. Because there are limited crossing points along the barrier, it is now more difficult for Palestinians to access medical care in Israel. Some estimates claim that almost one third of West Bank villages will have no access to healthcare in Israel. In towns near Jerusalem the average time for an ambulance to travel to the nearest hospital has increased from ten minutes to 110 minutes.

Figure C31: Contrasts in water availability between Israel and Palestinians

Source: Data from 'The Dry Facts', 'Discriminatory water supply', B'Tselem, Published: 10 Mar 2014, Updated: 27 September 2016

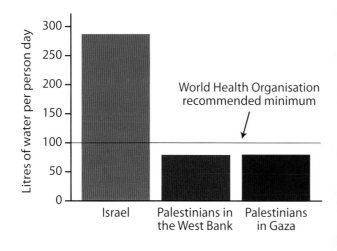

The issue of the allocation of water resources in the West Bank and Gaza is particularly serious. According to the World Bank, 90% of the West Bank's water is used by Israelis, despite them making up only a fraction of the total population. Palestinians also claim that their water supplies are frequently rationed, threatening not just their agriculture but health and sanitation.

Israelis, with their superior military prowess and higher level of development are nevertheless negatively impacted by this prolonged conflict. Surrounded by nations who have at times called for the destruction of Israel, they live under constant threat of attack (Figure C33). Palestinian suicide and rocket attacks from Gaza have caused many fatalities and injuries but also a significant increase in stress related illnesses. In addition, the financial cost of the many wars has put a strain on the economy. A permanent resolution of this conflict would serve both sides well but, given the support pledged for Israel's actions in the Occupied Territories by the USA President Trump, this seems a long way off.

Figure C32: Infographic of the impacts of the 2014 conflict in Gaza

Source: From 'The United Nations Independent Commission of Inquiry on the 2014 Gaza Conflict', by HRC, ©2014 United Nations, http://www.ohchr.org/ EN/HRBodies/HRC/ ColGazaConflict/Pages/ ReportColGaza.aspx, accessed 20.9.17. Reprinted with the permission of the United Nations

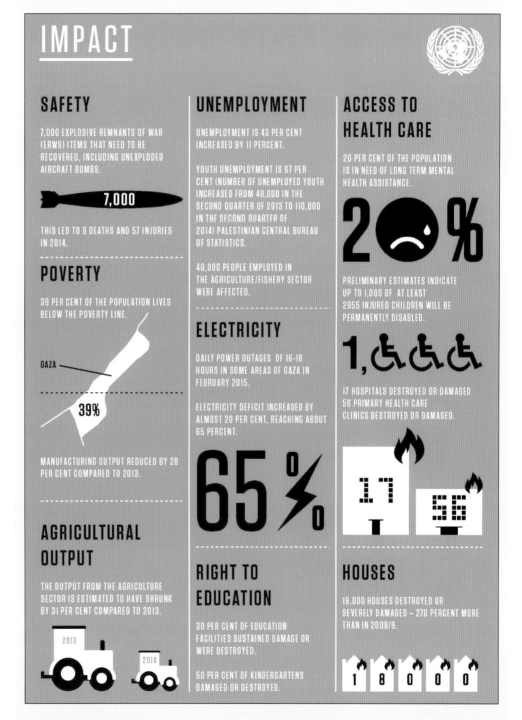

IMPACT

SAFETY

7,000 EXPLOSIVE REMNANTS OF WAR (ERWS) ITEMS THAT NEED TO BE RECOVERED, INCLUDING UNEXPLODED AIRCRAFT BOMBS.

7,000

THIS LED TO 8 DEATHS AND 57 INJURIES IN 2014.

POVERTY

39 PER CENT OF THE POPULATION LIVES BELOW THE POVERTY LINE.

GAZA

39%

MANUFACTURING OUTPUT REDUCED BY 28 PER CENT COMPARED TO 2013.

AGRICULTURAL OUTPUT

THE OUTPUT FROM THE AGRICULTURE SECTOR IS ESTIMATED TO HAVE SHRUNK BY 31 PER CENT COMPARED TO 2013.

2013
2014

UNEMPLOYMENT

UNEMPLOYMENT IS 43 PER CENT INCREASED BY 11 PERCENT.

YOUTH UNEMPLOYMENT IS 67 PER CENT (NUMBER OF UNEMPLOYED YOUTH INCREASED FROM 48,000 IN THE SECOND QUARTER OF 2013 TO 110,000 IN THE SECOND QUARTER OF 2014) PALESTINIAN CENTRAL BUREAU OF STATISTICS.

40,000 PEOPLE EMPLOYED IN THE AGRICULTURE/FISHERY SECTOR WERE AFFECTED.

ELECTRICITY

DAILY POWER OUTAGES OF 16-18 HOURS IN SOME AREAS OF GAZA IN FEBRUARY 2015.

ELECTRICITY DEFICIT INCREASED BY ALMOST 20 PER CENT, REACHING ABOUT 65 PERCENT.

65%

RIGHT TO EDUCATION

30 PER CENT OF EDUCATION FACILITIES SUSTAINED DAMAGE OR WERE DESTROYED.

50 PER CENT OF KINDERGARTENS DAMAGED OR DESTROYED.

ACCESS TO HEALTH CARE

20 PER CENT OF THE POPULATION IS IN NEED OF LONG TERM MENTAL HEALTH ASSISTANCE.

20%

PRELIMINARY ESTIMATES INDICATE UP TO 1,000 OF AT LEAST 2955 INJURED CHILDREN WILL BE PERMANENTLY DISABLED.

1,♿♿♿

17 HOSPITALS DESTROYED OR DAMAGED 56 PRIMARY HEALTH CARE CLINICS DESTROYED OR DAMAGED.

17   56

HOUSES

18,000 HOUSES DESTROYED OR SEVERELY DAMAGED – 270 PERCENT MORE THAN IN 2008/9.

1 8 0 0 0

Figure C33: Infographic of the attacks by Palestinian armed groups during the 2014 conflict in Gaza

Source: From 'The United Nations Independent Commission of Inquiry on the 2014 Gaza Conflict', by HRC, ©2014 United Nations, http://www.ohchr.org/EN/HRBodies/HRC/ColGazaConflict/Pages/ReportColGaza.aspx, accessed 20.9.17. Reprinted with the permission of the United Nations.

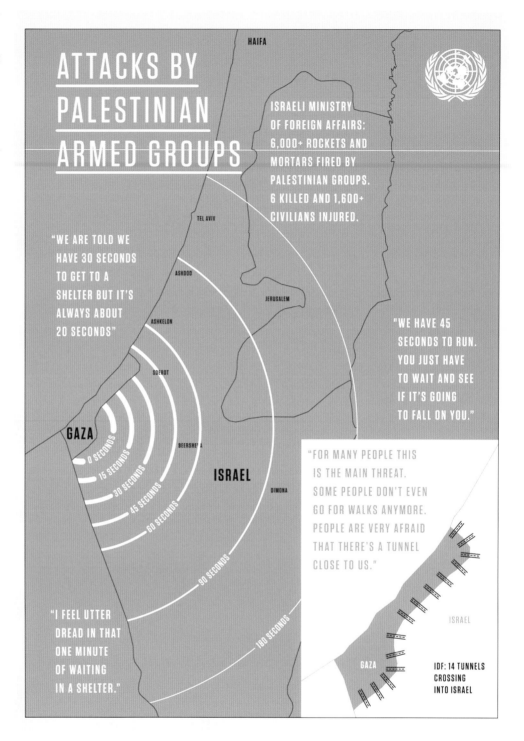

Exercise

1. Using the information in the two infographics in Figures C32 and C33, relating to the 2014 conflict between Gaza and Israel:

   (a) describe the impacts this conflict had on both Israelis and Palestinians.

   (b) explain why this conflict has been difficult to solve.

Exam Question

1. With reference to your national case study of ethnic conflict:

   - explain the causes of the conflict; and

   - describe the nature of the conflict. [18]

Question adapted from A2 1 Human Interactions and Global Issues,
January 2014, © CCEA 2017

References

A pictorial timeline of the Arab-Israeli conflict:
https://www.theguardian.com/world/gallery/2009/aug/17/israel-middleeast

Various news stories on Israel:
https://www.theguardian.com/world/israel

Gaza conflict 2014:
http://www.ps.undp.org/content/dam/papp/docs/Publications/UNDP-papp-focus-crisis-GazaFF082014.pdf
http://www.bbc.co.uk/news/world-middle-east-33223365
http://www.independent.co.uk/news/world/middle-east/israel-gaza-conflict-50-day-war-by-numbers-9693310.html
http://www.ohchr.org/EN/HRBodies/HRC/CoIGazaConflict/Pages/ReportCoIGaza.aspx

Terrorism in Israel:
http://www.johnstonsarchive.net/terrorism/terrisraelsum.html

Various news reports on Israel:
http://www.bbc.co.uk/news/world-middle-east-36100485
http://www.bbc.co.uk/news/world-middle-east-38856289
http://www.bbc.co.uk/news/world-middle-east-38458884
http://www.bbc.co.uk/news/world-middle-east-36682062
http://www.bbc.co.uk/news/world-middle-east-36197817

B'Tselem is an Israeli Human Rights Organisation. Its website contains many short articles and video clips relevant to this case study:
http://www.btselem.org/

1. THE CHANGING NATURE OF TOURISM

Case studies

General reference to places for illustration purposes only

Students should be able to:

(i) explain how mass tourism has developed into a global industry through developments in transport, increase in disposable incomes, package holidays and internet access

(ii) explain how tourism has brought positive social and economic impacts

(iii) explain how tourist demands and tourist resorts change over time – Pleasure Periphery and the Butler Model

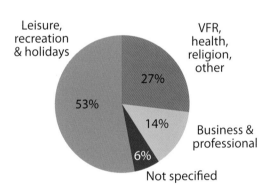

Figure D1: Inbound tourism by purpose of visit

Source: Data from 'UNWTO Tourism Highlights', 2016 Edition, World Tourism Organization (UNWTO)

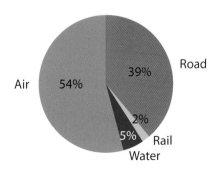

Figure D2: Inbound tourism by mode of transport, 2015

Source: Data from 'UNWTO Tourism Highlights', 2016 Edition, World Tourism Organization (UNWTO)

Tourism refers to travel for pleasure and the promotion and provision of services for tourists. Tourism operates at a local, regional and international scale. International tourists are referred to as arrivals or incoming tourists in their destination country and as outbound tourists from their home country. The duration of tourism visits ranges from one day, sometimes referred to as day trippers, to a maximum of one year, with the majority lasting 7–14 days. There are many types of tourism including recreation, visiting friends and relatives (VFR), religious pilgrimages, health, sport and business. Recreation is the main underlying reason for increases in tourism, accounting for over 50% of international tourism (Figure D1). Air and road transport are the main forms of transport used (Figure D2).

Modern tourism began in the nineteenth century but remained the privilege of the wealthy until the 1960s.

Since then, major social and economic changes occurred which enabled more people to avail of travel for leisure and many of these were international tourists. In 1950 there were approximately 25 million international tourists, rising gradually to 80 million in 1960. The growth in numbers has increased since 1960, with almost 1.2 billion tourist arrivals in 2015. This figure is predicted to continue to grow, reaching 1.8 billion by 2030. Figure D3 shows that the rate of growth has not been even over time. The increase in the 1960s marked the beginning of mass tourism. Mass tourism refers to large numbers of people visiting holiday destinations and visits usually confined to a few weeks in a year.

More than half of the 2015 arrivals went to a European destination (Figure D4). A further 16% went to North America. This emphasises the point that tourism is still dominated by MEDCs due to their greater levels of wealth and development. However, this pattern is changing and, increasingly, the LEDCs are developing their tourism potential. Since the 1990s, newly emerging tourist destinations in Africa, Asia/Pacific and the Middle East have all experienced rapid growth rates in the number of tourist arrivals.

Exercise

1. Describe the patterns and trends in international tourism numbers since 1960, as shown in Figure D3. Include figures and reference to places in your answer.

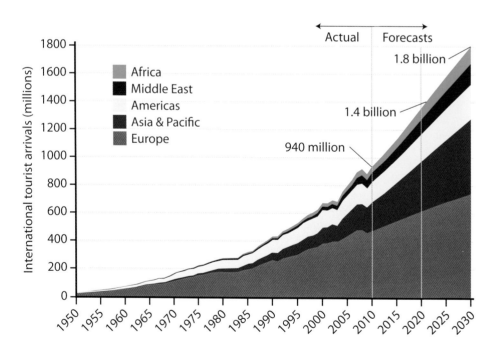

Figure D3: UNWTO Tourism towards 2020: actual trend and forecast 1950–2030

Source: Data from 'UNWTO Tourism Highlights', 2016 Edition, World Tourism Organization (UNWTO)

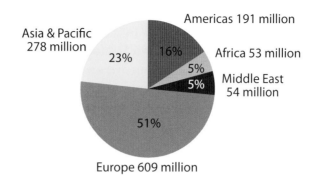

Figure D4: International tourist arrivals, 2015

Source: Data from 'UNWTO Annual Report 2015', World Tourism Organization (UNWTO)

The trends displayed in Figure D3 show that mass tourism has now become a global industry. There are many reasons for this, including:

Developments in transport

Efficient and affordable transportation is an essential requirement for mass tourism. Throughout the nineteenth century tourists largely relied on rail and sea transport. These methods of transport confined most tourists to local locations. In Northern Ireland, tourist resorts such as Bangor and Newcastle, Co Down, were linked by rail to Belfast. The developments in affordable air travel from the 1960s contributed to mass tourism in three ways.

1. The increase in affordable air travel meant many more people from a wider socio-economic base could travel abroad.
2. Mass tourism is concentrated on well developed and accessible destinations. The focus of these foreign trips was determined by the increased availability of airport facilities abroad.
3. The introduction of chartered flights associated with package holidays (see below) had a key role in providing affordable air travel and led to an increase in the numbers of international holidays. As stated earlier, the wealthier regions such as Europe and America together receive over 60% of all international tourists, in contrast to Africa which receives only 5% (Figure D4).

In the UK these developments in air travel coincided with increased disposable income and leisure time (see page 370). As a result, international trips from the UK more than doubled in the 1960s and 1970s. The main destinations included long haul flights to North America, encouraged by the opening of Disney World in Florida (1971), and increasingly to the Mediterranean seaside resorts in Spain.

The development of regional airports (such as Luton, Stansted, Belfast International and George Best Belfast City Airport) and budget airlines (such as Ryanair and EasyJet) offering cheap flights to popular tourist destinations brought about further increases in the numbers of international trips. For UK residents, visits abroad increased from 31.2 million in 1990 to 53.9 million in 1999, a 73% increase. Data from the Civil Aviation Authority shows that passenger traffic at regional airports doubled from 47 million passengers in 1995 to 95 million in 2005.

Other forms of transport contributed to increased foreign travel from the UK. Britain has several well developed ferry routes which provide easy access to continental Europe. The Channel Tunnel, which opened in 1994, provided an alternative form of transport to Europe for UK tourists. In its first full year of operation, the tunnel transported 1.8 million overseas residents home following a visit to the UK and 1.9 million UK residents back to the UK. By the end of the decade, nearly 9 million visits were completed through the tunnel, with the majority being by UK residents.

An increase in disposable income

Holidays are an expensive luxury. In 2016, a two week stay at a budget hotel in Spain for a UK family of four cost, on average, £4000, with additional spending required to cover living costs at the destination. In order to afford such a holiday, families need to have this amount of money as surplus to their everyday needs. This surplus is referred to as 'disposable income'. In the UK, disposable income is defined as income remaining after taxation and national insurance contributions have been deducted from a worker's wages. Income is wages earned plus any profits from investments, savings or private pensions. Figure D5 shows the trends in mean disposable income for the average UK household from 1977. Apart from fluctuations during periods of economic recession in the 1990s and 2008–2013, mean disposable income has more than doubled from 1977 levels. This means that families can better afford luxury items such as holidays. Credit card payments became increasingly popular from the late 1970s. They were seen as an easy way of obtaining a short term loan and boosted holiday sales. In addition, workers now have greatly improved working conditions. Government legislation guarantees workers paid holiday time off work and this has enabled most workers to have at least one annual break away from home. Higher income groups are able to afford several holidays away from home each year.

Exercise

1. Study Figures D5 and D6 relating to mean disposable income and international holidays from the UK.

   (a) Describe the trends in international trips between 1965 and 2015 as shown in Figure D6.

   (b) How do these trends reflect changing levels of disposable income as shown in Figure D5?

Figure D5: Growth of mean household disposable income* 1977–2015/2016

* mean disposable income adjusted for the average household

Source: 'Household disposable income and inequality in the UK: financial year ending 2016', release date 10 January 2017, Office for National Statistics licensed under the Open Government Licence v.3.0

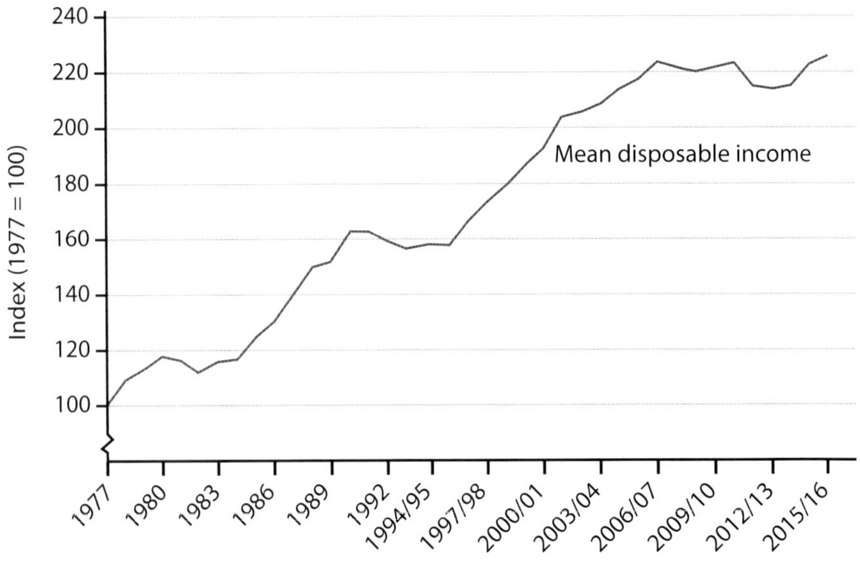

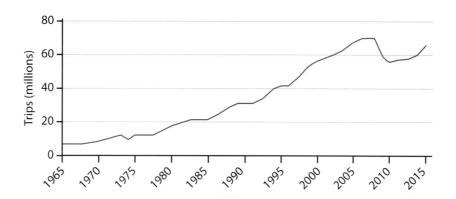

Figure D6: International trips by UK residents 1980–2015

Source: Data from 'Travel Trends', 3 July 2010 and 'Travel and Tourism', 20 May 2016, Office for National Statistics licensed under the Open Government Licence v.3.0

Package holidays

Package holidays offer a complete holiday deal including transport, accommodation and recreational activities organised by a tour operator and sold on the high street by a travel agent. In the UK in the late 1940s and 50s, a number of affordable domestic package holidays were provided by companies such as Butlins but it was the package holidays to the Mediterranean coastal resorts from the 1960s that became a key driving force of mass tourism. The introduction of the package holiday had a very significant impact on international tourism. Package holidays remove many of the obstacles to international tourism, such as language barriers. They provide an 'all in' deal for tourists, whereby a travel company arranges all aspects of the holiday from flights, accommodation, transport to and from the holiday airport, and offer tours and activities to the tourist.

Package holidays can be traced back to Thomas Cook, who organised what is considered to be the first package holiday from Leicester to Loughborough in 1841. Several years later he organised the first international package deal to Europe. The Thomas Cook organisation is one of the world's leading tour operators. In 2015, the company employed approximately 22,000 people in 17 countries, had over 20 million customers, a fleet of aircraft and a net income of £19 million. In the pre-Internet era, tour companies supplying these packages were the main source of foreign holidays. Travel agents and tour companies were able to offer holidays at competitive prices well within the reach of many. In the 1990s, 56% of all foreign holidays were purchased as a package deal but since then there has been an increase in alternative ways of booking holidays through the use of the Internet.

Internet access

The digital revolution in marketing through the Internet has had an important impact on tourism. In the UK, 89% of the population have Internet availability and nearly everyone has access to a computer, tablet or smart phone. According to figures released by the Association of British Travel Agents (ABTA), 76% of all holidays in 2016 were booked online. Through the use of online search engines (such as Trivago) and price comparison websites (such as Travel Supermarket), holidays become personalised to an individual's needs and preferences at the most competitive price.

Exercise

1. Define mass tourism and explain the factors that have contributed to its growth.

Positive social and economic impacts of tourism

Tourism is one of the world's most successful and resilient economic sectors. Since 1950, the number of international tourists has increased from 25 million to almost 1.2 billion in 2015. In the same period, international tourism receipts (money earned from tourism) increased from US$2 billion to US$1260 billion. In 2016, one in ten jobs globally was derived from tourism and in terms of export value, tourism ranked third after fuels and chemicals (Figure D7). Furthermore, as a result of improvements in transport, tourism is now operating in an increasing number of destinations in Africa and Asia. However, the benefits of tourism are not spread evenly across the world. America and Europe receive 60% of the total international tourism receipts while Africa receives only 3% (Figure D8). The United Nations World Tourism Organisation (UNWTO) views tourism as an important component of economic and social development, especially in LEDCs and tourism is included in three of the Global Goals for Sustainable Development, launched in 2015, but can contribute to all 17 goals.

Figure D7: Why tourism matters

Sources: World Tourism Organization (2016), "Why Tourism Matters", infographic (online), available at: www.unwto.org, © UNWTO, 92844/44/17

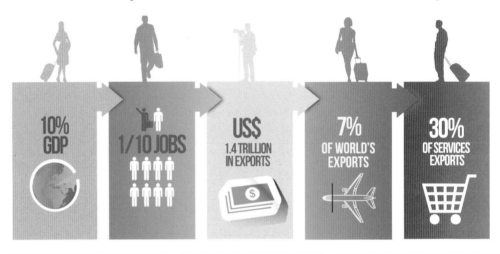

10% GDP

1/10 JOBS

US$ 1.4 TRILLION IN EXPORTS

7% OF WORLD'S EXPORTS

30% OF SERVICES EXPORTS

WHY TOURISM MATTERS

Figure D8: Global variations in tourist numbers and tourism receipts

Source: Data from World Tourism Organization (2016), "Why Tourism Matters", available at: www.unwto.org

ITA = International tourist arrivals
ITR = International tourist receipts in US$
m = million
bn = billion

Europe
ITA: 608m (51%)
ITR: $451bn (36%)

Americas
ITA: 193m (16%)
ITR: $304bn (24%)

Africa
ITA: 53m (5%)
ITR: $33bn (3%)

Asia Pacific
ITA: 279m (24%)
ITR: $418bn (33%)

Middle East
ITA: 53m (4%)
ITR: $54bn (4%)

Social impacts

The receipts from tourism create the potential for significant social impacts for the host country, provided the money remains in the country and is not 'leaked' or taken back to foreign tour companies. These benefits can be categorised as indirect and direct. Indirect benefits are those improvements designed for tourists but which also impact on local society. Examples of indirect benefits are improvements in basic infrastructure, including the supply of electricity, piped water and efficient sewage systems, which are installed to meet tourist demands but also benefit the local people. Similarly, improved transportation, such as road, rail and airport facilities, and an increase in service provision, such as shops and recreational amenities, enhance the quality of life of all.

Direct benefits include education and health programmes funded by tourism receipts, especially in poorer destinations. The Global Goals for Sustainable Development programme places great emphasis on the role that tourism has in delivering this aspect of social development. The UN has published a document outlining ways in which tourism can be delivered through each of the 17 goals. Programmes to provide education and health care systems are among the most obvious means of delivering social improvement in poorer regions and are often cited as examples of sustainable tourism. Tourism receipts have also been used to empower women by involving them in various aspects of the visitor experience. This has involved the preparation of craft and food products for sale to tourists.

Tourism inevitably results in contact between the local people and the visitors. This social interaction should lead to a mutual appreciation and understanding of each group's way of life.

Figure D9: Social impacts of ecotourism in Il N'Gwesi Group Ranch Kenya

Source: adapted from ilngwesi.com

Il N'Gwesi Group Ranch is a Maasai community of approximately 8,000 people living on the Grasslands of Mount Kenya in northern Kenya. The profits from a successful ecotourism project have been used to bring about considerable social improvements to the local community.

- Maasai children are now funded through primary and secondary education in an area with low levels of schooling. Some have continued their education at university or college.

- Health care provision has been enhanced through increased awareness of hygiene, safe waste disposal, disease transmission including HIV/AIDS, as well as the training of health care workers within the community.

- Many households have been given access to clean water by providing piped water to easy access points in local neighbourhoods and providing clean storage facilities for water in schools. Each household has been provided with toilet facilities. As a result of these improvements there has been a marked decrease in the incidence of water borne diseases.

- Women in Il N'Gwesi have been assisted in developing a craft industry making jewellery for sale to tourists. They have also been given loans to further develop their enterprise and training in managing their finances.

Economic impacts

The development of tourism can lead to economic prosperity in a number of ways. Job creation is the most obvious benefit with one in ten jobs worldwide associated with tourism (Figure D7). The jobs created fall into two categories:

- direct employment consists of jobs which involve face to face contact with tourists such as hotel staff.

- indirect employment consists of jobs which supply tourists' needs, such as food processing or hotel furnishings.

Tourism is a labour intensive service industry, with many of the jobs requiring only a minimum amount of training. Jobs in hotels, restaurants, shops and in other recreational amenities, as well as beach or poolside attendants fall into this category and are an invaluable source of income for those with low level skills. In the UK, 1.8 million people are employed directly in tourism and a further 2.4 million are employed indirectly. Many of these jobs are taken by people from the surrounding areas where there are limited opportunities for employment. Those in employment have increased spending power which generates increased consumer demand and leads to more spending in shops. In addition to the personal gain for those so employed, the taxation of their incomes provides additional funding for the government.

Figure D10: European tourist taxes, summer 2016

Source: Data from 'Taxing travel: How Europe's top destinations target tourists', *The Telegraph*, 25 April 2016

- Rome €196
- Florence €140
- Nice €100Paris €92.40
- Barcelona €69.44
- Bruges €59.36
- Balearic Islands €56
- Dubrovnik €25.76

Successful tourist destinations encourage foreign investment into hotel chains. For example, the Hilton hotel group has over 4800 hotels in more than 100 countries employing over 169,000 people. Tourist spending in hotels, bars, nightclubs and restaurants generates a large amount of income which can be invested in further development of the area. In addition, many tourist regions charge various types of 'tourist tax'. These taxes are used either to fund further development in the region or to contribute towards conservation practices. Figure D10 gives examples of some of the tourist taxes in Europe in 2016. They are based on a family group, with two teenaged children, staying for seven nights in a 5* hotel. In some cases additional taxes apply.

Figure D11: Economic impacts of tourism in Portugal

Source: Data from 'Travel and Tourism – Economic Impact Portugal 2015' The World Travel and Tourism Council, http://portugalcolombia.com/media/WTCCPortugal2015.pdf

Portugal is a small country, bordered to the west and south by the Atlantic Ocean and to the north and east by Spain. The country enjoys a Mediterranean type of climate and with its long Atlantic coastline and extensive beaches has developed a major tourist industry. The country has limited alternative sources of employment and tourism provides much needed employment and revenue. The World Travel and Tourism Council (WTTC), an organisation which collects and publishes data on international tourism, produced a report in 2015 of the economic impacts of tourism in Portugal. Among their findings were the following:

- Tourism contributed €27.3 billion, equivalent to 15.7% of the total GDP of Portugal and this is predicted to rise to 17% by 2025.

- Total employment in tourism amounted to 830,500 jobs or 18% of total employment. Direct employment alone provided jobs for 337,000 people or 7.4% of total employment.

- Foreign investment in hotels and golf courses was approximately €2.5 billion.

- Visitor exports (money spent by foreign tourists) reached €13.4 billion and, if the predicted increase in tourist numbers is realised, this figure should increase to €18 billion in 2025.

Exercise

1. Study Figures D12 and D13 relating to tourism in Portugal.

    (a) Describe the trends shown in each graph.

Figure D12: Foreign tourist arrivals, Portugal 2005–2015

Source: Data from 'Travel and Tourism – Economic Impact Portugal 2015' The World Travel and Tourism Council, http://portugalcolombia.com/media/WTCCPortugal2015.pdf

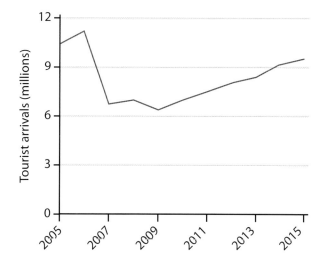

(b) The highest visitor exports did not occur when tourist numbers were at their highest. Suggest possible reasons that could explain this.

Figure D13: Foreign visitor exports, Portugal 2005–2015

Source: Data from 'Travel and Tourism – Economic Impact Portugal 2015' The World Travel and Tourism Council, http://portugalcolombia.com/media/WTCCPortugal2015.pdf

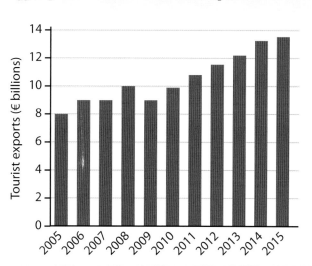

2. Explain how tourism can have positive social and economic impacts. You must make reference to places for illustration in your answer.

Tourist demands and tourist resorts change over time

Tourism is a constantly changing industry.

*   The increase in tourist numbers associated with mass tourism (see pages 368–371) is one of the most striking changes as it reflects changes in society and increasing levels of prosperity.

*   Although the richer MEDCs dominate tourism in terms of arrivals and receipts, there is a growing tourism industry in the emerging market countries such as India, China and Mexico (see 'Emerging markets', *Geography for CCEA AS Level*, Colourpoint Educational, pages 250–259). These countries have increased disposable incomes due to rapid economic growth and they are contributing to the rapid rise in tourism. They are also developing tourism destinations.

- Improvements in transport have also facilitated the growth of long haul flights and these are projected to double by 2020. Although it has been shown that the majority of tourists go on short haul flights, this development opens up the opportunity for a wider choice of holiday destinations.

- Tourism is driven by economic growth, with the strongest increases occurring in times of economic success and a slowing down in times of economic recession. Following the economic downturn in 2008, tourism continued to grow but at a slower rate for a number of years. Average annual growth in the years before 2008 was 6% but in the decade 2005–2015 average annual growth was 3.9%.

- Originally tourism and holidays were mostly confined to the summer season. Now there is a demand for holidays throughout the year. In addition to the traditional seaside summer holidays there are now winter holidays skiing or snowboarding and the warmer Mediterranean resorts are also popular during the off-peak season for some of the retired population from Northern Europe.

- With greater amounts of information available on the Internet and the media, other tourist opportunities are developing and there has been an increase in the range of holidays provided such as:

(i) Cultural and historical breaks – such as Florence, Athens and stately homes in Britain.

(ii) City breaks – such as New York, London and Paris.

(iii) Theme parks – such as Disney World Florida.

(iv) Skiing and snowboarding – such as Val D'Isere, French Alps.

(v) Ecotourism (environmentally friendly or green tourism) – such as Serengeti, Tanzania.

Figure D14: Cultural break, Florence Source: Ed Webster

Figure D15: City break, New York

Figure D17: Skiing and snowboarding, Val D'Isere

Figure D16: Theme park, Disney World Florida
Source: Alexandre Breveglieri

Figure D18: Ecotourism, The Serengeti plain, Tanzania

Tourism models

A number of models have been devised to explain these changes. Some of the models examine the changing demands of the tourist while others examine the evolution of the tourist resort.

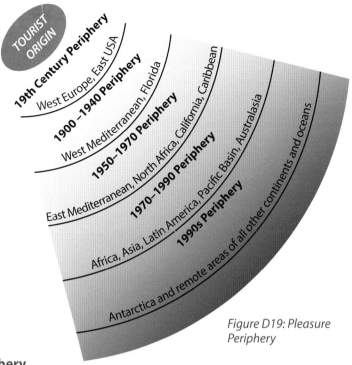

Figure D19: Pleasure Periphery

1. Pleasure Periphery

This model focuses on the behavioural demands of the tourist over time. With increased prosperity and improvements in transport technology, long distance travel has been made easier. Mass media and advertising play a large role in promoting new and more exotic tourist destinations. Expectations are increased and tourism is envisaged as a 'fashion industry' where tourists want to spend their holidays in the new and more fashionable resorts. The boundaries of tourism are seen as a tidal wave spreading outwards from the tourists' home area (Figure D19). The example of the changing pattern of British tourism illustrates this concept (Figure D20).

Exercise

1. Study Figure D20 below relating to changes in tourism in Britain.
   Explain these changes with reference to the concept of Pleasure Periphery.

   Figure D20: Changes in tourist demands in Britain

   - In the nineteenth century, wealthy British tourists spent their holidays at British seaside resorts.
   - In the 1950s and 60s, package holidays to specially developed holiday camps such as Butlins became popular.
   - From the 1960s, cheaper air travel and package holidays to the Spanish seaside resorts made travel abroad attractive.
   - In the 1980s and 90s, Florida and the Caribbean became more fashionable.
   - More recently, trips to Asia and Australia, as well as cruises to Antarctica and other remote areas are growing in demand.

2. Butler Model

The Butler Model, or Tourist Area Life Cycle (TALC), charts the life cycle of a tourist resort over time. A tourist destination is viewed as a product and tourists are the consumers. The tourist resort is dynamic and, in the same way as any product such as a computer or car, evolves over time. Consumer demand also changes over time – consider how often we upgrade mobile phones. In essence, the Butler Model describes the progression of the resort from its earliest time through to its peak. After this, a tourist resort will eventually go into decline unless management policies effect an upgrade which can prolong or revitalise the fortunes of a tourist destination. The Butler Model was devised in 1980 before the widespread use of the Internet, which has widened the choices available, but it is still an effective method of analysing the changing fortunes of tourist destinations.

Figure D21: Butler Model

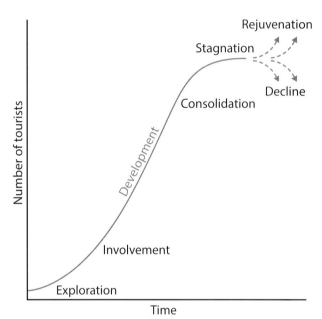

There are six stages in this process, which are shown below:

(i) Exploration

At the beginning of a resort's life cycle there are only a few tourists and minimum impact.

(ii) Involvement

In time the resort grows in popularity and the number of tourists increases. New developments including hotels, recreational facilities and general infrastructure are added. New employment opportunities for local people arise, although most of these are seasonal.

(iii) Development

Tourist numbers increase as a result of mass tourism through package holidays. A significant portion of the tourist trade and the wealth it generates may be controlled and managed by international organisations to the detriment of the local economy. Much of the work is seasonal, often employing people from surrounding rural areas.

(iv) Consolidation

Tourism is now a major industry in the region. Foreign companies continue to provide hotels etc but this leads to profits going abroad rather than being used in the resort. The local area does benefit from the developments such as infrastructure and seasonal employment but decisions over the allocation of resources often favour tourism over local needs (see case study of Mallorca, pages 390–395).

(v) Stagnation

The resort then becomes over crowded; the carrying capacity has been reached with increased pressure on resources. The resort is no longer fashionable and tourists seek newer resorts that better provide their demands. Eventually the resort suffers from over development or saturation.

(vi) Decline/rejuvenation

Saturation is followed by stagnation and decline, with loss of popularity for tourists and the international organisations. It is possible for a resort to recover from decline through a comprehensive management policy, a process known as rejuvenation.

Exercise

1. Study Resource A relating to Benidorm.

   (a) Draw a labelled diagram of the Butler Model.

   (b) Explain the changing nature of tourism in Benidorm with reference to the Butler Model.

Resource A: Development of tourism in Benidorm

Benidorm is a town on the eastern coast of Spain with a population of 69,000 in 2014. It is the centre of one of Spain's main tourist regions known

Benidorm has a high density of skyscraper hotels along the seafront

as the Costa Blanca. In the 1950s Benidorm's main economic activity centred on fishing, with only a limited tourist industry attracting local holiday makers. By 1959 the fishing industry had declined and the local mayor opened up the area for international tourism. Over the next 20 years Benidorm was transformed into a major tourism destination attracting tourists from Western Europe, especially the UK.

The package holiday industry provided the opportunity for low cost holidays from the UK and other west European countries. The weakness of the Spanish peseta relative to most European currencies made living costs in Spain affordable. Developers were given permission to build multi-storey hotel blocks and Benidorm still has the highest density of skyscrapers in Europe. Local infrastructure to cope with the growing number of tourists was provided including a new airport at Alicante, approximately 45 km from Benidorm, which opened in 1967.

Tourist numbers continued to rise, reaching a peak of 12 million in 1977. By this stage, tourism had transformed Benidorm. The building of multi-storey hotels had proceeded with limited planning control and practically all open space was used for building purposes. Water resources were over used, sewage treatment plants were inadequate with reports of raw sewage found in the sea and an outbreak of typhoid. In addition, Benidorm attracted a reputation of cheap holidays for British holiday makers associated with drunkenness and rowdy behaviour. Little of the original Spanish character of the resort remained; even food supply seemed to adjust to the stereotypical British tourist demands of 'chips with everything'. Families and Spanish tourists avoided the area and tourism began to decline.

From the 1990s, the local authorities have attempted to rebrand the resort by implementing a number of improvements including the upgrading of hotels and the installation of a new sewage system. A new theme park, which provided amenities for children, was built with the intention of attracting families to Benidorm. English speaking police were employed to improve communications with British tourists. The holiday season has been extended beyond the traditional peak summer months by diversifying into off-peak holidays for retired people and those with pre-school age children.

Tourism in Benidorm has improved as a result of these measures. The number of visitors has increased and although they have not returned to their peak of 12 million, the authorities have successfully rebranded the resort. It is now a more family friendly resort and increasingly attracting tourists from across Europe, including Spain.

Exam Questions

1. Explain how the concept of Pleasure Periphery helps our understanding of the changing nature of tourism. You must make reference to places in your answer. [8]

Question adapted from CCEA A21 Human Interactions and Global Issues paper, May 2014, © CCEA 2017

2. Study Resource A below relating to tourist developments along the Mediterranean coastline of Europe.

Draw a labelled diagram of the Butler Model. Briefly describe how this model can be applied to the tourism developments in regions such as the Mediterranean coastline of Europe. [8]

Question adapted from CCEA A22 Processes and Issues in Human Geography, Specimen Assessment Materials © CCEA 2017. For copyright reasons the text in Resource A has replaced the resource in the CCEA Specimen Assessment Materials.

Resource A: Tourist developments along the Mediterranean coastline

Over 220 million people visit the Mediterranean every year, making it the most popular holiday destination in the world. This figure is predicted to soar to 350 million by 2050, more than the population of the USA. The vast majority of these visitors come from Northern Europe.

On Spain's Costa del Sol today there is an almost unbroken line of development from Gibraltar to Malaga, and the picture is similar in France and Italy. The coast of the Mediterranean is 46,000 km long and it is forecast that by 2020 more than 50% of this will be built upon, largely by tourist developments.

Tourists require significant resources and produce large quantities of waste, rubbish and other forms of pollution, much of which ends up in the sea. In the middle of the summer waste is sometimes produced faster than it can be disposed of.

Tourism also requires large quantities of fresh water. While the average urban Spaniard uses about 250 litres per day, an average tourist consumes almost 500. Hundreds of millions of litres are used to provide swimming facilities, sometimes located within metres of the sea. Demand is highest during the summer, when rainfall is at its lowest. This particularly affects the Greek and Spanish islands, which have regions with small catchment areas and limited water storage facilities. Low rainfall also means that facilities such as golf courses need irrigation. It is estimated that golf courses across the Mediterranean use 2.3 million litres of water per day, and each year 5000 hectares of land is cleared to build more.

All of this comes at a significant cost to the environment. From Spain to the southern tip of Italy, 75% of sand dune habitats have already been destroyed, and the World Wildlife Fund estimates that over 500 plant species in the region are threatened with extinction. But there is some hope for the environment. There seems to be an increasing awareness amongst local governments and tourist operators that the natural environment needs support and they are seeking to revitalise resorts in a more sustainable manner.

Coastal development, Nice, French Rivera

References

UNWTO Tourism Highlights includes data on tourism:
http://mkt.unwto.org/publication/unwto-tourism-highlights-2016-edition

UNWTO Global Report on Women and Tourism:
http://ethics.unwto.org/en/publication/global-report-women-tourism-2010

Tourism issues in Spain:
https://www.theguardian.com/world/2016/dec/25/costa-little-more-spain-questions-its-tourism-strategy

2. CHALLENGES AND MANAGEMENT OF MASS TOURISM

Case studies

National tourism
management
policy: Mallorca

Students should be able to:

(i) demonstrate knowledge and understanding of the challenges that may arise from mass tourism – pollution, overcrowding, honeypot sites, social sustainability and competition for resources

(ii) evaluate strategies used to reduce the negative social and environmental impacts of mass tourism

The challenges that arise from mass tourism

The previous chapter dealt with the positive impacts that tourism can bring to a region. However, it has been shown that tourism, and in particular mass tourism, can also present challenges for a region. In the rush to meet the demands of mass tourism, planners often promoted short-term economic gain over potential long-term environmental issues. Currently, most tourist areas have adopted a more sustainable approach to tourism development including some form of management. Among the challenges resultant from mass tourism are:

Pollution

Anything that detracts from or causes actual harm to a tourist attraction is a major concern for tourist resorts. Pollution, in the form of damaged landscapes or habitats, increased noise levels, litter and waste disposal issues, is one of the main negative impacts of tourism.

Mass tourism in the Mediterranean resorts from the 1960s onwards paid little attention to the long-term impacts on these regions. The rapid influx of tourists in the summer season put extra demands on the waste disposal capacity of that area. There were many reports of raw sewage in the sea and in 1989 the Spanish tourist resorts of Salou and Benidorm reported outbreaks of typhoid (see Resource A, pages 379–380). The Mediterranean coastal region also experienced large-scale building of high-rise apartments and hotel blocks, resulting in overcrowded beaches and spoilt scenery. Further environmental damage was caused by the construction of artificial beaches, where sand was excavated from the seabed and transported to another area in order to extend beach facilities there. Such activities alter the natural balance between erosion and deposition and have a negative impact on the biodiversity of the area. Furthermore, budget airlines and low cost package holidays facilitated ever increasing numbers to visit the region. The main tourist areas also developed shops, restaurants, nightclubs, bars and other recreational activities for the growing number of tourists. Such developments caused noise pollution, litter and anti-social behaviour. These issues presented challenges, which prompted remedial action through management policies (see Mallorca case study, pages 390–395).

Cruises have become increasingly popular in the last 15 years as tourists seek new types of holidays (see Pleasure Periphery, page 377). Over 2 million British tourists are predicted to take a cruise holiday in 2017. This represents a 100% increase since 2007. Worldwide, approximately 25 million people chose a cruising holiday in 2016. In 2015, in the USA alone, cruise holidays earned over $36 billion and created over 330,000 jobs. Cruises have become more popular as a wider choice of destinations becomes available and more companies offer this type of holiday. Cruise ships have increased their passenger capacity, ranging from 3000 to 6000 passengers. They are essentially floating towns which are totally self-contained. The cruise ships require the dredging of deep water channels, which can cause damage to marine habitats. They frequently deliver thousands of tourists to environmentally sensitive areas, such as Antarctica (Figure D22) and coral reefs in the Caribbean. Fragile landscapes such as these are particularly vulnerable to environmental pollution from tourist developments. There are over 100 countries with coral reefs and about 25% of these reefs are damaged beyond repair, with a further 66% under serious threat. Tourism is said to have played a major part in this damage, with the commercial harvesting of coral for sale to tourists or tourists themselves breaking off chunks as souvenirs. Cruise ship anchors and sewage also damage the reefs. However, it is the environmental pollution associated with the running and maintenance of these large ships that is causing growing concern (Figure D23).

Figure D22: A cruise ship in Antarctica, which may pose a threat of pollution to this fragile environment

Figure D23: Cruise ship pollution

Cruise ships release high levels of harmful pollutants

- The largest ships burn approximately 170,000 litres of fuel daily to power their engines and to generate electricity.
- Ships use cheap, low-grade diesel that produces high levels of harmful emissions including nitrogen oxides, sulphur oxides, carbon dioxide and diesel particulate matter. These are damaging to air quality and respiratory health. According to a German environmental group, whose findings were reported in the *Guardian* online 21 May 2016, one medium cruise ship generates as many pollutants as 5 million cars going the same distance.
- The ships' engines are kept running while in port, often for several days, to maintain electricity supplies. In some ports, including Southampton on the south coast of England, there is a noticeable impact on air quality when cruise liners are in port.
- The waste produced on the cruise liners is treated on the ship but much of the equipment used is outdated and inefficient. Once treated the waste is dumped at sea. According to the environmental group, Friends of the Earth, a cruise ship with 7000 passengers, on a one week cruise produces 4.5 million litres of grey water (water from showers, washing, cleaning and galleys) and 1 million litres of sewage, containing high levels of nitrates and phosphates. High levels of phosphates and nitrates in water lead to the growth of algae, which is harmful to fish, coral and other marine life.
- Cruise ships also dump large amounts of toxic waste, including chemicals from dry cleaning products, batteries, photo processing waste and 450 million litres of waste petroleum into the oceans annually.

Tourism relies on efficient transport infrastructure, including airports and roads, and these have major potential for environmental pollution. High altitude skiing areas require cable cars, ski lifts and possibly funicular railways, resulting in extensive forest clearance. There are currently about 300 ski areas throughout the Alps, where 10,000 transport facilities serve more than 3,400 km² of ski areas. The laying of ski runs can lead to erosion and loss of biodiversity, causing irreparable damage to the landscape. The increasing use of snow canons to create artificial snow leads to additional problems as they use large amounts of water and energy, as well as chemical and biological additives. In Switzerland, ski resorts have also well developed mountaineering and hill walking tourist activities, which threaten the environment through trampling, footpath erosion and damage to wildlife habitats.

Overcrowding

Increased numbers of tourists visiting a resort put seasonal pressure on the resources of that area. In the case of rural tourism to country parks, the attraction is often the quiet, peaceful and scenic landscape. An influx of tourists will bring welcome revenue but the provision of amenities such as car parks, caravan sites and shops can damage the scenic attraction of the area, cause footpath erosion and threaten wildlife habitats.

Figure D24: A model of carrying capacity

Source: Adapted from a diagram by Kim Adams published in 'Recreation, Tourism and Carrying Capacity: A Case Study of the Impacts of VIsitors in a Rural/Wilderness area: Machu Picchu, Peru', *Geofile* online, January 2008, Nelson Thornes

The term 'carrying capacity' is often used in Geography to set an upper limit or threshold population that can be supported by an area. In relation to tourism, the carrying capacity of a resort refers to the maximum number of tourists that can be comfortably supported in that resort. An increase in tourist numbers would adversely affect the tourist potential of the area and lead to a decline in numbers.

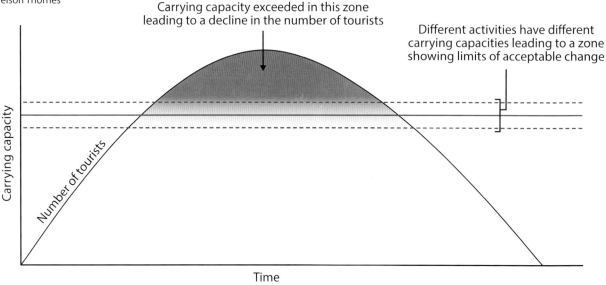

Note:

* While the specification does not include these terms, they are an important method of measuring overcrowding.

Essentially there are two components involved in assessing the carrying capacity of a tourist resort:

1. The maximum number of people that can be supported without causing adverse environmental impacts in the region, such as footpath erosion or vegetation trampling. This is sometimes referred to as the physical carrying capacity*.

2. The maximum number of people that can be supported without causing a decline in visitor enjoyment of an attraction, sometimes referred to as the quality of visitor experience*.

Physical carrying capacity is relatively easy to measure because the environmental outcomes (footpath erosion, damaged habitats) are obvious. However, setting a numerical limit on the numbers of people that can be supported without damaging the quality of visitor experience is much more subjective and will vary between types of tourist activity and the personality traits of the tourists themselves. Some tourist activities, such as hill walking, will typically have a lower carrying capacity than beach holidays. However, these are not absolute facts and there are many examples of large groups involved in hill walking. Furthermore, there are added difficulties or conflicts between different types of tourist activities in the same region. In the Peak District National Park, the National Park Authorities introduced a zoning plan whereby conflicting users of the Park were restricted to specific areas. More detail on National Parks is available in *Geography for CCEA AS Level*, Colourpoint Educational, pages 187–190.

Carrying capacity also refers to the supply/demand balance of amenities in an area. This might include the provision of car parks, hotels and general infrastructure. Some of the issues relating to problems in the Mediterranean resorts dealt with in the 'Pollution' section (pages 382–384) are also closely related to carrying capacity.

One measure of the effects that increased numbers of tourists have on the quality of visitor experience is known as Limits of Acceptable Change (LAC). This approach accepts that all tourism has impacts on a region and looks for ways to keep these impacts under control. In Arches National Park (Utah), a number of surveys were carried out to determine the number of visitors deemed acceptable in selected sites. Tourists were shown computer generated photographs of the sites occupied by different numbers of people, ranging from 2 to over 100 and asked to state which numbers they considered acceptable and unacceptable. The tourists rated the impact of the numbers of People At Any One Time (PAOT) on a scale of –4 to +4.

- A positive value meant the resort had not been adversely affected by the numbers of people.
- A negative value meant the resort had been adversely affected.
- A value of zero indicates the maximum number that can be tolerated in the resort without damaging the quality of visitor experience. This number of tourists represents the Limit of Acceptable Change. The results of the sample were averaged and presented in Figure D25.

Essentially, carrying capacity is a framework within which those in charge of tourism can monitor developments in a region and formulate management policies if necessary. In some cases conservation orders, which are legally binding, are placed on an area to protect it from excessive and damaging use. These can be at local level (such as Sites of Special Scientific Interest, SSSIs) or at regional level (such as National Parks). There are also conservation policies at a European level, Special Areas of Conservation (SACs), which deal with wildlife habitats and at international level, World Heritage Sites (sites which have global importance). Once carrying capacity has been reached, tourist management policies can be employed to increase the carrying capacity or at least correct the damage. However, in some cases this may not be possible and the resort will go into decline.

Exercise

1. Study Figure D25 which shows the results of a questionnaire about the carrying capacity of a National Park in Utah.

    (a) Comment on the patterns shown.

    (b) What factors would the researchers have needed to consider before carrying out the survey?

Figure D25: Acceptability ratings for numbers of people at any one time (PAOT) in Arches National Park, Utah (USA)

Source: Adapted from a graph published in 'Congestion, Crowding and Visitor Management in UK Country Parks', *Geofile* online, April 2002, Nelson Thornes

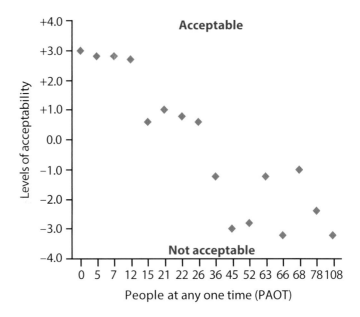

Honeypot sites

Areas that attract large numbers of tourists are known as honeypot sites. Such sites are frequently found in rural areas that have scenic, historic or other tourist attractions. The honeypot site is often created by rural planners to confine tourists to specific locations, while leaving the remainder of the region relatively free of tourists. These locations provide car parks, picnic and other tourist facilities, and therefore attract large numbers of visitors. The pressure of numbers can lead to overcrowding, which damages the tourism potential of the area. Overcrowding can also cause problems for local farmers.

The village of Castleton in the Peak District National Park had a population of 641 in the 2011 census but each year over 2 million tourists visit, the majority of whom come during the peak holiday season. The surrounding National Park has many attractions including geological sites, caves and caverns, hill walking opportunities, and cultural and historic sites. The area is remote and most people visit by car or as part of an organised coach tour. Congestion and inadequate tourist amenities have caused serious problems for Castleton. Concerns that a similar situation could develop in the Mournes were among the reasons for local objection to the Mournes being designated a National Park.

In the UK a number of management strategies have been devised to protect and manage the attractions of these rural areas. These strategies include the creation of Areas of Outstanding Natural Beauty (AONBs) and SSSIs/ASSIs. More details on these strategies are available from 'Planning for rural environments', *Geography for CCEA AS Level*, Colourpoint Educational, pages 183–191.

Social sustainability

Social sustainability refers to the ability of a community to function and adapt to changing situations without having their attitudes and ways of life altered in an adverse manner. Tourism can boost the economy of a region and young people in particular will leave traditional occupations in rural areas for higher paid employment in the service sector, such as in hotels and cafés. This can have a positive impact on the rural areas if money is sent back to the rural communities, in much the same way as migrants often send remittances back home. However, many of the jobs associated with tourism are seasonal and the tourism employee may have no income for part of the year. In addition, much of the work offers lower wages than other sectors of industry. Tour companies wish to keep costs low, particularly in the face of rising fuel prices in the early 2000s and the economic recession since 2008. This, combined with an abundant labour supply, results in the wages remaining low.

There are also limited opportunities for skills development or promotion. Workers often find that because of the seasonal nature of their employment they have to work long and anti-social hours for several months of the year. It has also been shown that this type of work can lead to the break-up of families. As much of the tourist trade is dominated by MNCs (Multi-National Companies), a lot of the money generated from tourism remains with the MNCs and does not benefit the local community. This process is referred to as leakage.

Tourists introduce an additional layer of cultural diversity to a region. In some ways this can be an enriching experience but on other occasions it can result in new challenges. Cultural conflicts can often arise from international tourism. This is especially the case where the more relaxed attitudes of modern tourists towards dress code and alcohol are at odds with more conservative local attitudes in the tourist destination. Potential cultural conflicts exist in some Middle Eastern countries and tourist resorts have even come under attack by those opposed to western cultures in Egypt. In Tunisia in 2014, a gunman from Islamic State shot 30 British tourists dead. In Kenya, much of the tourist trade is focused on the wildlife reserves and the Maasai tribes. The Maasai are tribal pastoralists viewed both as an asset and a threat to tourist development by the Kenyan government. Their traditional lifestyles and customs are regarded as a potential attraction for tourists but their nomadic lifestyle meant they once herded their animals on the protected wildlife reserves until the government resettled them outside these protected areas. This inevitably caused difficulties for the Maasai, leading many to abandon their traditional way of life and become involved in the provision of services such as craft centres. Tourism has brought increased wealth to these areas but overall the lifestyle of the Maasai has been changed and younger members are unlikely to keep up the traditional way of life. In many tourist destinations there is a lack of integration between tourists and the local population (see Mallorca case study, pags 390–395).

The display of wealth by international tourists often attracts numbers of unemployed people searching for employment. This can leave these people vulnerable to exploitation by unscrupulous individuals. On occasions where no work is available, some women and children end up in prostitution. There is a global child sex tourism industry, within which more than 1 million children are sexually abused by tourists every year. Although there are a number of organisations working on this issue, the numbers involved in child sex tourism are increasing. Thailand, Cambodia, India, Brazil and Mexico have been cited as having the largest numbers of child prostitutes. Management strategies to deal with some of the issues raised here usually rely on international agreements formulated by bodies such as the UN or through NGOs such as Tourism Concern (a UK based charity that campaigns for human rights in tourism).

The World Tourism Organisation has drawn up a code of ethics for tourism and although the code is not legally binding, countries are encouraged to comply with its recommendations. Tourism Concern has also produced documents relating to serious infringements on human rights, including child prostitution and human trafficking. The EU set up The European Trade Union Liaison Committee on Tourism (ETLC) in 1995 to represent workers in the tourism sector. This organisation is mainly concerned with the promotion of sustainable employment in the tourism industry.

Competition for resources

A tourist region requires investment in infrastructure (roads, airports) and amenities (hotels, entertainment). Such developments require vast amounts of money as well as land and water supplies. These things are often not in abundant supply and in such situations conflicts of interest can occur between the needs of the local community and the needs of the tourist industry. Tourism offers the potential of vast economic rewards and, as already stated, in some countries is a major export earner. It also offers the promise of foreign investment. In many cases, when it comes to allocating scarce resources, the needs of local people are sacrificed for the interests of the tourist industry. This competition for resources occurs worldwide but some of the most serious issues have been witnessed in the LEDCs or at least among poorer communities.

One of the significant tourist developments in the last 25 years has been golf tourism. The economic boom of the 1980s led to a worldwide growth in the number of golf courses. By the 1990s, 350 new golf courses were being built annually. Golf courses require large areas of land and there have been many reported cases of land being taken forcibly from local farmers who received little or no compensation. In addition, golf courses use vast amounts of water (see Figure D26).

Figure D26: Golf courses and water supplies

Source: information from 'Fact sheet #5: water & tourism', Centre for Responsible Travel, http://www.responsibletravel.org/

According to the Responsible Travel Organisation (a non-profit research institute which promotes sustainable tourism):

- the world's golf courses use 9.5 billion litres of water daily.
- an average golf course in Spain uses as much water as a town of 12,000 people.
- golf courses in Bali use 3 million litres of water every day, while over half the population (1.7 million of the island's 3.9 million residents) have inadequate access to clean water. Some villagers have to walk up to 3 km to collect water from a well and conflicts over water use are increasing.

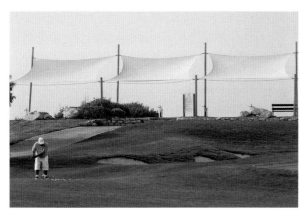

Figure D27: A golf course in Cyprus

Source: Anna Anichkova

In Cyprus, the government gave the go-ahead for 14 new golf courses in 2009, bringing the total number on the island to 17. Each golf course uses approximately 50 million litres of water each year. This is equivalent to the total water used annually by 1000 average households. Water supply is already a problem and reserves are said to be at their lowest for a century. In addition, large amounts of artificial fertiliser, pesticides and herbicides are used on golf courses. Much of these will get washed into ground water supplies, causing contamination of fresh water supplies.

Mass tourism and improvements in air travel have enabled tourists from wealthy countries to travel to exotic tropical locations, often in LEDCs. The contrast in the amounts of water used by the locals and the tourists are very stark. For example, the estimated daily domestic water consumption of local people on the island of Zanzibar, east of Tanzania, is just 30 litres per day. In contrast, luxury resorts in Zanzibar use up to 2000 litres of water per tourist per day. Some hotels even have guards patrolling their water pipelines to prevent locals from trying to tap into them.

Many indigenous groups have been forcibly displaced from their traditional lands in order to facilitate tourist developments. There are examples of governments and tourist developers moving tribal peoples from their lands in Kenya, Peru, Thailand and Honduras. Governments and developers have argued that much of this displacement was necessary in the interests of conservation and ecotourism but many of those displaced appear to have received little compensation.

It is obvious that the needs of local people have been overlooked in many cases. The problem is really a conflict between the potential wealth that tourist development can bring and fulfilling the everyday needs of the local community. There are a number of organisations that work to bring some of the worst examples to the public domain. By highlighting the most serious injustices that have occurred, these organisations hope to heighten people's moral consciousness against these developments. Tourism Concern successfully campaigned against a planned £2.8 billion tourist development in Zanzibar, with luxury hotels, golf courses and an airport. The development threatened the livelihood of some 20,000 local people, who feared they might be displaced and lose their valuable agricultural land. Tourism Concern also campaigned against forced displacements in various parts of East Africa. Further details are available on the Tourism Concern website (see 'Fighting displacement in East Africa', https://www.tourismconcern.org.uk/fighting-displacement-in-east-africa/).

The World Tourism Organisation, a United Nations Organisation, sets out to promote the sustainable development of tourism throughout the world and encourages the implementation of the aims and objectives of the Sustainable Development Goals in tourism development in LEDCs.

Exam Questions

1. With reference to places, explain how each of the following challenges may arise as a result of mass tourism in a region:

   - pollution
   - overcrowding
   - competition for resources [18]

References

General reference:
Tourism Concern – *https://www.tourismconcern.org.uk/*

Pollution:
Tourism threats in the Mediterranean – *http://www.monachus-guardian.org/library/wwftou01.pdf*

Mass tourism is ruining Barcelona and turning it into a 'theme park', claims controversial new documentary – *http://www.dailymail.co.uk/travel/article-2610312/Barcelona-ruined-mass-tourism-claims-documentary.html#ixzz4aU2yBoJA*

Overcrowding:
Six reasons why mass tourism is unsustainable – *https://www.theguardian.com/sustainable-business/six-reasons-mass-tourism-unsustainable*

Mass tourism can kill a city – just ask Barcelona's residents – *https://www.theguardian.com/commentisfree/2014/sep/02/mass-tourism-kill-city-barcelona*

Packed beaches and gridlock loom large as tourists swap terrorism hotspots for Spain – *https://www.theguardian.com/world/2016/may/14/gridlock-tourists-terrorism-spain-balearics*

The destinations under threat from tourism in pictures – *https://www.theguardian.com/environment/gallery/2012/may/30/destinations-under-threat-tourism-in-pictures*

Honeypot sites:
Castleton – *http://www.peakdistrict.gov.uk/visiting/visitor-centres/castleton*

Social sustainability:
Beauty of Bali under threat from pressures of mass tourism – *https://www.theguardian.com/world/2012/aug/07/bali-tourism-threatens-natural-beauty*

Competition for resources:
How does tourism affect the demand for water? *http://www.tourismconcern.org.uk/wp-content/uploads/2014/09/Unit2-Resource-A-1.pdf*

CASE STUDY: Mallorca, a study of a National tourism management policy

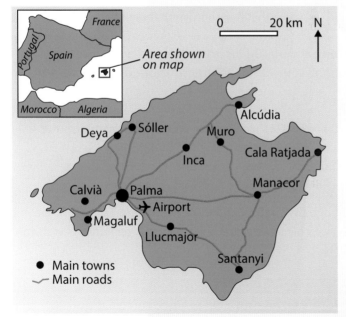

Figure D28: The main tourist resorts in Mallorca

Growth of tourism in Mallorca

The island of Mallorca is the largest of the Balearic Islands lying off the east coast of Spain. It was one of the earliest European destinations to experience mass tourism in the 1960s. It is an extremely popular tourist destination, especially with northern Europeans, millions of whom visit Mallorca every year and, during the most popular months, outnumber the resident population five to one. During the 1960s, improvements in living standards along with the introduction of paid holiday periods led to an increased demand for holidays away from home. Package holidays facilitated large numbers of people to consider a holiday outside their own country. The value of the Spanish currency (peseta) in the 1960s was low compared to other European currencies, making holidays to Spain in general relatively cheap. Mallorca, with its early experience in the tourist trade, therefore became a popular destination.

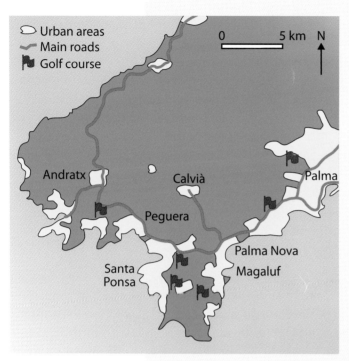

Figure D29: The main tourist resorts in Calvià

The numbers visiting the island grew rapidly. In 1960, 400,000 tourists arrived in Mallorca. By 1973, the figures had reached 3.5 million. In 2015, there were 12.5 million (the total resident population of the island in 2015 was 859,000). Most of this tourist development was, and still is, centred around the coastal areas, in particular in the region of Calvià in the south-west of the island. Calvià became one of the most important tourist regions in Mallorca, with approximately 1.7 million tourists visiting the resorts of Magaluf, Palma Nova, Santa Ponsa and Peguera annually. Calvià, with a local population of 44,000, was well suited to the development of mass tourism, with almost 60 km of beaches and close proximity to the international airport at Palma. In the traditional, low-income farming economy of Mallorca, the prospect of better paid jobs in the hotels and other tourist facilities was welcomed by most. There was a rapid increase in the number of hotels to cope with the growing numbers of tourists. Little regard was given to the long-term impact on the environment or indeed the quality of the tourist experience.

Consequences of tourism growth in Mallorca

Tourism brought an immediate boost to the economy of Mallorca, with almost two thirds of its population employed, either directly (in hotels and restaurants) or indirectly (services such as estate agents and food processing), in tourism. Overall, some 84% of Mallorca's Gross National Income (GNI) is connected to tourism. Practically all of the earliest tourist developments were on the coastal region and large numbers of the young, economically active population moved from the rural interior to find seasonal employment in the tourist areas. At the height of the mass tourism boom in Calvià, unemployment rates were typically about 4% lower than any other region in Spain and the average family income was 30% above the national average for all of Spain. A massive building programme, including hotels, roads and other tourist amenities provided further opportunities for employment.

Negative social impacts

Mass tourism did have some disadvantages for Mallorca. Some of the tourist developments were financed and designed by international tour operators, leaving only semi-skilled and manual job opportunities for the local Mallorcan population. In addition, the work in the service sector offered little opportunity for promotion or career advancement. Much of the work provided was seasonal and workers had to work long and anti-social hours to compensate for this seasonality of employment. However, in the early days of mass tourism these disadvantages seemed to be outweighed by the overall economic benefits tourism had brought to the island.

Mass tourism continued unabated well into the late 1970s, by which time the southern part of the island was almost completely transformed. The coastal area of

Figure D30: English café in Magaluf

Figure D31: Overcrowded built up area in Santa Ponsa

Calvià was densely packed with hotel and apartment complexes, numerous bars, restaurants and other leisure services. A number of English, Irish and German owned bars and restaurants were established to serve the large number of tourists from these countries. In the main tourist resorts most of the restaurants served either English or German food. English was spoken in practically all establishments and it was not necessary for the tourists to speak any Spanish while on holiday in Mallorca. By the late 1970s, there was very little traditional Mallorcan architecture or culture still remaining in this coastal region. There was little evidence of much social integration between local people and the masses of tourists. Throughout the 1970s and 1980s, the island continued to attract large numbers of young people staying in low priced accommodation. Mallorca had acquired a negative image of packed beaches, rowdy bars and nightclubs.

In addition, the traditional way of life in Mallorca was affected. Farmers often sold their land to developers who built villas which were out of character with the local rural surroundings. Many of these villas were sold as second homes to wealthy northern Europeans, mostly British and German. 'Second home' tourists did not integrate with local Mallorcans, leading to resentment.

Negative environmental impacts

There were also serious environmental problems associated with uncontrolled tourism. The seasonal influx of tourists placed heavy demands on scarce water resources. The landscaping of gardens within hotel complexes, the building of golf courses, swimming pools and the provision of showers meant that fresh water supplies were being over used. Mallorca had to undertake expensive desalinisation of seawater to meet the demand. In the late 1970s, much of the tap water was unfit for drinking. The situation was worse for local people, who found it difficult to compete for water supplies against the demands of tourism development. Local residents became increasingly resentful of the creation of golf courses, which used vast amounts of water. Furthermore, the pressure of numbers put undue stress on already inadequate waste disposal systems and the coastal waters were polluted.

The natural coastal landscape was altered dramatically. In Calvià, beaches were extended by up to 13% in a 20 year period and sand dunes removed to make way for more apartment blocks. Most of the natural dune vegetation was completely destroyed along with its wildlife habitats. Within the tourist centres, the landscape was completely altered to provide promenades and other tourist amenities. The increased number of tour buses and other vehicles resulted in an increase in air pollution.

Mallorca faced an impending crisis in the late 1980s. In the Calvià region, tourist numbers fell by almost 20% between 1988 and 1991. In part, this decrease was due to the increased popularity of other tourist destinations, such as Florida and the Caribbean. However, it was also due to the decline in the quality of the tourism product offered in Mallorca. These changes in tourism demand highlighted the lack of sustainability in the way tourism had developed in Mallorca. The over reliance on tourism as a major source of income and employment meant that local residents faced an increase in unemployment and a fall in living standards.

Tourism management in Mallorca

Strategies used to reduce the negative social and environmental impacts of mass tourism in Mallorca

A number of attempts to address the issues of pollution were made in the 1970s, such as the Mediterranean Action Plan (MAP), but these had only limited effect. Mallorca and the other Balearic islands gained autonomy from Spain in 1983, becoming the Balearic Autonomous Community (BAC). The BAC was given considerable power over the management of its own budget and planning. In the 1980s, concerns over environmental damage resulted in a number of areas with fragile ecosystems being given protected land status. Mallorca's first natural park was created in 1988, at Albufera close to Alcúdia in the north of the island (see Figure D28 for location). Further attempts to address the negative impacts of tourism were made throughout the 1980s but none proved successful.

Prompted in part by the United Nations Conference on Environment and Development (UNCED) in Rio 1992, which set out guidelines for incorporating sustainability into all aspects of development including tourism, and by the continued decline in tourism, the BAC formulated a new plan to address the challenges of mass tourism. This plan differed from earlier projects because it was based on the principles of sustainability – economic, social and environmental considerations. Its initiatives included:

- No new building was permitted on a belt of at least 100 m from the coast. Prior to this, hotels were often constructed on the site of former beach dunes.

- Extending the area of protected land. The Archipelago of Cabrera off the south-east coast became a National Park in 1993.

- Increased restrictions were introduced on the building of villas and second homes in rural areas.

- Measures were put in place to preserve the Mallorcan identity within rural towns and villages away from the coast. At the same time these inland areas were encouraged to engage in small rural tourism projects.

The UNCED concluded with the Earth Summit in Rio, which also emphasised the importance of implementing sustainable practices through local level projects, known as Local Agenda 21 (LA21). In Mallorca, the Calvià region formulated its own Local Agenda 21 programme for sustainable tourism. As one of the first areas to develop mass tourism in Mallorca, Calvià suffered most from over development. The main objectives of the project focussed on rebranding tourism in Calvià by delivering an upgraded tourism product that would be attractive to tourists and provide a sustainable economy for the local population. Strict regulations were laid down regarding new developments, including an environmental impact assessment on any new building programme. Developers were encouraged to use locally available resources where possible and to incorporate energy saving programmes in their design. These objectives were carried out through a series of 'lines of action' and initiatives. The following are some examples:

Figure D32: Redevelopment sites in Calvià

'Zona Verde' is a 'green zone'. The rest of the notice prohibits littering.

- A building clearance plan, which included the demolition of five sea front hotels and the compulsory purchase of land to prevent further construction.
- Upgrading the quality of tourist accommodation in order to attract a higher spending clientele.
  - Upgrading the physical environment in Magaluf and Palma Nova with pedestrian zones, green zones and tree planting.
  - Constructing 32 km of cycle paths and walkways to diversify the recreational opportunities in the area.
  - Imposing strict planning regulations on all new building projects regarding density of occupancy, waste disposal and energy conservation.
  - Launching a campaign to raise awareness of conservation of resources such as energy and water.
  - Introducing schemes to direct tourism away from the coast into activities such as hill walking, cycling and golfing.

Figure D33: Cycling in Sóller, western Mallorca (see Figure D28 for location)

- Implementing measures to minimise erosion of beaches, which in turn would reduce the need for beach nourishment. This unsustainable practice required off-shore dredging of sand, which was costly and damaging to marine ecosystems.
- Charging an eco-tax on hotel guests to generate income for environmental protection measures.
- Introducing a system of eco-labels for hotel and other tourist facilities. These were awarded to those establishments which adhered to energy conservation guidelines.
- Involving local communities in the plan through a Citizens' Forum.

Achievements of tourism management in Mallorca

There have been many positive outcomes from Mallorca's tourism management policy. The Calvià region has been modernised and the built environment has been enhanced and landscaped. Many hotels have been upgraded from 3 to 4 and 5 star in a drive to attract wealthier tourists. In 2005, the Balearic Islands recorded the third highest daily spend by tourists in all of Spain.

Tourist numbers increased following the modernisation programme and the tourist season has been extended beyond the peak summer months. There has been a marked increase in the range of activities available including golf courses, walking and cycling. A greater emphasis on recreational activities for children has encouraged more families to visit Mallorca. Environmental protection schemes, such as coastal defences and building regulations, have operated successfully in most cases.

In spite of these achievements, there have been setbacks. The eco-tax, which was to be used for environmental schemes, faced strong opposition and was dropped within a year of its introduction. In addition, Calvià, especially Magaluf, has retained some of its image as a destination for young English and German tourists seeking low-cost accommodation, alcohol, nightclubs and fast food. A number of incidents of anti-social behaviour and the deaths of three tourists in 2014 prompted the local authorities to take corrective action. The consumption of alcohol on the streets has been banned between 10 pm and 8 am. There are also restrictions on pub crawls. €240 million has been invested in Magaluf and adjoining Palma Nova to fund improvements in infrastructure and the construction of up-market restaurants and luxury bars. The persistence of the negative image of Magaluf has prompted the planners to avoid any reference to that resort, preferring to use Calvià instead. A new eco-tax of €2 per person was reinstated in 2016, with the aim of reducing the numbers coming to the island. A similar scheme has been put in place in Barcelona.

Mallorca aptly demonstrates the potential negative social and environmental impacts which can result from mass tourism. The management policies introduced have brought about environmental improvements and tourism has been extended across the entire island rather than being concentrated on the coastal region. In addition, most of the developments have been carried out by the Mallorcan Authorities and in the Calvià region there is considerable involvement of the local people in the decision making process. This stands in marked contrast to some of the earliest developments, which were largely associated with the international tour operators. Upgrading and rebranding schemes aimed at a higher spending tourist is an increasingly popular strategy and they have greatly improved the environment. However, there are still many English and German bars and restaurants and there is limited social integration between tourists and local people. Finally, it is important to realise that tourism is a dynamic industry and is affected by international events. Terrorist attacks in Sousse, Tunisia in 2015 and in Nice, France in 2016 have discouraged tourism to these destinations and redirected tourists to perceived 'safe' locations, such as mainland Spain and the Balearic Islands. An estimated 13 million tourists visited Mallorca in 2016, an increase of 2 million from the previous year. In addition, there has been an increase in the number of cruise ship visitors, with 524 ships docking in Palma in 2016. On one day alone, over 20,000 cruise ship passengers disembarked to spend a day in Palma and the surrounding area. These increased numbers of visitors bring short term economic gain but also present renewed challenges to the island and to those who are responsible for its management.

Figure D34: Cruise ships in Palma harbour

Source: Amic Hoteles Hotel Horizonte

Exam Questions

1. With reference to your regional/national case study of tourism management, evaluate the strategies put in place to reduce the negative social and environmental impacts of mass tourism. [18]

Question from CCEA A22 Processes and Issues in Human Geography, Specimen Assessment Materials © CCEA 2017

References

Calvià:
www.calvia.com/
Problems of mass tourism in Mallorca – *https://www.theguardian.com/travel/mallorca*

Magaluf regeneration 2015:
https://www.ft.com/content/192f02b0-f318-11e3-a3f8-00144feabdc0
http://www.travelweekly.co.uk/articles/58141/magaluf-targets-families-after-antisocial-crackdown
http://www.telegraph.co.uk/travel/destinations/europe/spain/majorca/news/Balconing-death-hotel-to-become-landmark-as-Magaluf-smartens-up/

Accommodation law, Barcelona:
https://www.theguardian.com/world/2017/jan/27/barcelona-cracks-down-on-tourist-numbers-with-accommodation-law

3. ECOTOURISM: OPPORTUNITIES, CHALLENGES AND REGULATION

Case studies

Small-scale case study of ecotourism: Costa Rica

Students should be able to:

(i) define ecotourism

(ii) demonstrate knowledge and understanding of how ecotourism can bring:

– social, economic and environmental benefits
– negative impacts:
social (displacement of local communities and threats to indigenous cultures)
economic (leakage)
environmental (greenwashing and damage to fragile environments)

(iii) discuss the challenges in establishing effective international regulation and explain how each of the following measures is used to regulate ecotourism:

– the Québec Declaration
– Global Ecotourism Conference 2007
– Green Globe Scheme
– UNESCO World Heritage Sites

The problems of mass tourism discussed in the case study of Mallorca (pages 390–395) clearly illustrate how tourism developments can be unsustainable. Since the late 1980s, as the traditional sun, sand and sea holiday became less popular for some, a new type of tourism developed, known as 'ecotourism'. Advances in information technology and transportation have changed the way in which people organise holidays with a move away from package deals and greater emphasis on personalised trips. Increased knowledge of the world has led people to visit areas for a specific interest – so-called 'niche tourism'. Ecotourism is one example of niche tourism and it represents a new level in the Pleasure Periphery model (page 377). Ecotourism involves visiting areas which have unique natural and often fragile environments, much of which may have some form of protected land status. Popular ecotourism destinations include tropical rainforests, tropical grasslands, wilderness areas (such as Alaska) and cultural heritage sites (such as Machu Picchu, an ancient Inca settlement in Peru). These areas are relatively undisturbed and provide few of the tourism amenities normally associated with mass tourism. There are no major hotel developments, nightclubs or theme parks. Indeed, this contrast with mass tourism is a key attraction of such sites.

Ecotourists seek to engage with the ecotourism destination by learning about the natural environment, the biodiversity, the cultural heritage and the local communities of the area. There is usually a high level of social integration between ecotourists and the local population. Ecotourism is widely referred to as 'responsible tourism', 'sustainable tourism' and 'green tourism', emphasising the environmental component of such developments. Typical ecotourism destinations are small-scale and low impact, focussing on environmental sustainability. In addition to conservation of the environment, energy conservation, recycling, water conservation and the use of biodegradable soaps are all an integral part of ecotourism. The number of ecotourism trips has been increasing at a rate of 20% annually since the early 1990s, almost three times faster than the tourist industry as a whole.

Ecotourism is a controversial issue and some environmentalists argue that any tourist development in the wilderness or fragile environments can never be regarded as sustainable. In support of their argument they cite examples of long distance flights to remote rainforest destinations or cruise ship visits to Alaska and Antarctica. Furthermore, some destinations are branded as 'ecotourism' even though they pay little attention to its guiding principles. Those in favour of ecotourism development emphasise the important economic contributions such developments can make towards conservation and the financial rewards to the local communities, many of which are in LEDCs. In reality, each side has valid points but, with careful regulation and constant monitoring of the ecotourism product, many believe the negative impacts can be minimised while the overall impact on conservation and the local communities is largely positive.

Exercise

1. Study Resource A regarding the definition of ecotourism. Use Resource A to help you discuss the problems with defining ecotourism.

Resource A: Definitions of ecotourism

A number of international organisations have proposed definitions of ecotourism including:

1. **The International Union for the Conservation of Nature (IUCN)** – a global authority on the natural world and the measures needed to protect it.

> Environmentally responsible travel to natural areas, in order to enjoy and appreciate nature (and accompanying cultural features, both past and present) that promote conservation, have low visitor impacts and provide for beneficially active socio-economic involvement of local populations.
>
> Source: Héctor Ceballos-Lascuráin, 'Tourism, ecotourism, and protected areas', IUNC, 1996, https://www.iucn.org/content/tourism-ecotourism-and-protected-areas-state-nature-based-tourism-around-world-and-guidelines-its-development

2. **The Nature Conservancy** – an international organisation working to protect ecologically sensitive environments.

> Ecotourism possesses the following characteristics:
> - conscientious, low-impact visitor behaviour.
> - sensitivity towards, and appreciation of, local cultures and biodiversity.
> - support for local conservation efforts.
> - sustainable benefits to local communities.
> - local participation in decision making.
> - educational components for both the traveller and local communities.
>
> Source: © The Nature Conservancy, https://www.nature.org/greenliving/what-is-ecotourism.xml

3. **The International Ecotourism Society** – a non-profit organisation working to promote ecotourism.

> Responsible travel to natural areas that conserves the environment, sustains the well-being of the local people and involves interpretation and education.
>
> Source: The International Ecotourism Society, http://www.ecotourism.org/what-is-ecotourism

Social, economic and environmental benefits of ecotourism

If ecotourism is carefully regulated and managed it can lead to a number of potential benefits to an area and its communities.

Social benefits

Many ecotourism destinations are in LEDCs where there are few job opportunities for young people. This frequently leads to out-migration of those in the economically active age groups. Over time this process results in an ageing population and has a detrimental effect on social sustainability. Potential job opportunities created by ecotourism can halt, or at least curtail this out-migration. Ecotourism projects are planned and managed at local level involving large numbers of the indigenous population working as guides, preparing food and providing accommodation. Engagement in such activities can help sustain a local community. In addition, many ecotourists are accommodated in eco lodges (groups of small wooden huts built in clearings in the forest) or in local people's houses. This creates the opportunity for interaction between the tourists and local people, helps sustain traditional cultures and increases mutual understanding.

The revenue from ecotourism can help fund projects that will lead to an increase in the standard of living. Examples include improved sanitation, water supply, health care, education, power supply and communications. Increased awareness of the needs of these communities can also encourage aid donations from tourists. The Sustainable Development Goals (SDGs) programme launched in 2015 highlighted sustainable tourism, including ecotourism as a means of empowering women. This can be achieved partly by involving women in producing and selling local craft products. It has been shown that women's rights have been strengthened in this way.

Figure D35: Goal 5

Source: World Tourism Organization (2015), *Tourism and the Sustainable Development Goals – Goal 5: Achieve gender equality and empower all women and girls*, UNWTO, Madrid

Achieve gender equality and empower all women and girls

Tourism can empower women in multiple ways, particularly through the provision of jobs and through income-generating opportunities in small and larger-scale tourism and hospitality related enterprises. As one of the sectors with the highest share of women employed and entrepreneurs, tourism can be a tool for women to unlock their potential, helping them to become fully engaged and lead in every aspect of society.

Economic benefits

As mentioned earlier, ecotourism creates employment opportunities and wealth that can be used to raise the standard of living in these destinations. Income is earned through the provision of essential services such as food, accommodation and entertainment for tourists. Education and training schemes enhance the level of skills of the local people who are then better equipped to gain higher paid jobs. In the best examples of ecotourism, all or most of the profit remains in the local area and is either invested into new projects or is paid in wages to the community. In turn this leads to a fall in poverty levels, an increase in disposable income and a greater demand for consumer goods.

Environmental benefits

The main focus of ecotourism is based around an appreciation of the natural environment and the need for sustainable use of resources. In the best examples of ecotourism the principles of sustainability are incorporated through the use of biodegradable soaps and packaging, green energy such as solar power, recycling and conservation of water resources. In addition, local products are used where possible to reduce the need for imports. By employing guides trained in ecosystem protection methods, damage to fragile environments is minimised. Information programmes designed to heighten awareness of the need to safeguard fragile environments have been shown to increase support for protected land status such as marine parks and wildlife reserves. Funding for conservation practices is gained from entrance fees charged at parks or for safari tours.

Negative impacts of ecotourism

As stated earlier, ecotourism is controversial and there are examples of destinations advertising holidays in remote fragile environments which do not comply with its essential criteria. Many of these destinations are adversely affected by the development of a tourism product which is not based on the principles of sustainability.

Negative social impacts
Displacement of local communities and threats to indigenous cultures

There are many reported incidents of local people being removed, sometimes forcibly, from their villages to make way for so-called ecotourism projects. Such practices also threaten traditional cultures. The Maasai people in East Africa are one example of a community displaced from their traditional grazing lands by the creation of one of the world's best-known wildlife parks, the Maasai Mara. The Maasai are a nomadic pastoralist community whose grazing lands extend across large parts of East Africa including the countries of Kenya and Tanzania. Approximately 70% of the national parks and game reserves in this area occupy land that was formerly used as grazing land by the Maasai. They have been denied access to grazing land in the protected areas, putting their only livelihood at risk. Most received no compensation and few have secured employment in the reserves, as most of the jobs go to more educated workers. Furthermore, tourism is not managed locally and the profits are not used for the benefit of the local community. In some cases game reserves were created without informing or consulting local people, who found out about the situation only when they received an eviction notice. Several thousand Maasai were removed from game reserves in Tanzania to make way for an exclusive game-hunting area. In 2009, a mass eviction left more than 200 homes burned and 3000 people homeless.

Figure D36: A tourist and two Maasai people

The Maasai traditional way of life is under threat from ecotourism in other ways. Attempts to relocate the Maasai in permanent settlements endangers their culture, which is based around a nomadic way of life. This has had a negative impact on some Maasai people, leading to an increase in alcoholism and prostitution. Mingling with tourists has brought the Maasai into contact with western diseases such as measles and chickenpox to which they have little immunity. The Maasai people are also viewed as a 'backdrop' to the ecotourist experience and many feel exploited as they are photographed by wealthy western visitors. The presence of affluent ecotourists has also encouraged the development of markets in wildlife souvenirs such as ivory. These practices are at odds with conservation policies and are happening in many other destinations worldwide.

In Botswana, the San people maintain a traditional hunting and gathering culture. They are known for their extensive knowledge of medicinal plants, spiritual healing and elaborate dance rituals. Between 1997 and 2005 the San were forcibly removed from their ancestral home in the Central Kalahari Game Reserve. Their homes were dismantled, schools and health services were shut down, their water supply was destroyed and lives were threatened.

In 2006, the San won a legal case that claimed their eviction from the reserve was unlawful and granted them the right to return home. However, they have been banned from hunting and must apply for permits to enter the reserve.

Negative economic impacts

Leakage

According to the UN Environment Programme (UNEP) only half of the tourist spending in LEDCs remains there. The remainder goes to foreign developers based in the wealthier MEDCs. This process is known as leakage. Leakage is not confined to ecotourism but its effects are particularly damaging in that sector because many ecotourism developments occur in LEDCs. Leakage can occur when the developments are owned by foreign companies such as major hotel chains. For example in Belize, a Central American country where ecotourism has developed, over 90% of recent developments are large-scale luxury hotels owned by international companies. Profits generated in these hotels return to the parent company. In these circumstances the only economic benefit to the local community is derived from employment opportunities. Many of these are low paid and seasonal. Better paid jobs, such as managers, are allocated to skilled workers from within the hotel network and are mainly from outside the local area. Leakage can also occur when products for the tourism development are imported rather than using local products. Partly this may be due to limited local availability but a desire to maximise profits in the developer's country is also significant. Whatever the reason, this leakage constitutes a loss of income to the country concerned.

Negative environmental impacts

Greenwashing and damage to fragile environments

Since there is no mechanism for imposing internationally agreed legal requirements on ecotourism developments there are incidences where these have been largely ignored. Ecotourism is a financially rewarding enterprise and some developers have sought to increase the range of holidays on offer by providing luxury holidays disguised as 'sustainable' or 'environmentally friendly'. For example, luxury hotels in fragile environments that claim to have an energy saving policy. Such activities are described as 'greenwashing'. Many of these hotels are foreign owned with little involvement with the local community apart from low-level skilled jobs. They are often located on prime natural sites with landscaped gardens and swimming pools. This leads to leakage of revenue back to the headquarters usually in richer MEDCs. Luxury hotels and their guests have limited social integration with the local community. They pose a threat to fragile environments because of their unsustainable use of scarce resources including water.

Figure D37: mini vans transport tourists in the Maasai Mara

Greenwashing can cause actual damage to fragile environments through increased pressure from tourists. In the Maasai Mara National Reserve in Kenya considerable damage has been caused to the natural vegetation by the large numbers of safari minibuses which transport tourists through the reserve. Once the natural vegetation is damaged the area becomes prone to invasion by secondary vegetation types. In addition, the increased number of vehicles poses a threat to the wildlife.

Coral reefs are especially vulnerable to tourist pressure. Reefs are damaged by boat anchors, tourists breaking off pieces of coral as souvenirs, and pollution. In Belize, so-called ecotourism developments have resulted in serious environmental degradation issues including:

- Mangrove swamps have been drained to make way for a landing strip, destroying important nesting grounds for birds.
- The coral reef has been damaged and there is over fishing, leading to a decline in lobster numbers.
- Unsupervised groups of tourists are permitted to visit nature reserves and they often fail to take sufficient care of the environment.

Fragile environments are also threatened by any form of development. The building of infrastructure, even for the most compliant of ecotourism developments, is potentially damaging. The clearance of forested land to build water treatment plants for eco lodges in Costa Rica reduced the habitat for squirrel monkeys. In other places, the inadequacy of sanitation facilities has resulted in waste and sewage being dumped in rivers.

Exercise

1. Using information from the websites listed below, discuss the extent to which you agree with the following statement:

    "The economic benefits from ecotourism outweigh the social and environmental issues which may arise from its development."

Negative impacts of ecotourism:

'They come, they photograph, but don't help': how ecotourism in the Amazon shortchanges the locals –
https://www.theguardian.com/environment/2015/mar/11/ecotourism-amazon-shortchanges-locals-ecuador

How eco is eco-tourism? –
https://www.theguardian.com/travel/2005/nov/12/ecotourism. guardiansaturdaytravelsection

Mara wildlife in serious decline –
http://news.bbc.co.uk/1/hi/world/africa/8008700.stm

The tribes paying the brutal price of conservation –
https://www.theguardian.com/global-development/2016/aug/28/exiles-human-cost-of-conservation-indigenous-peoples-eco-tourism

A rat, insects and litter: delights of mass tourism reach Galapagos –
https://www.theguardian.com/environment/2007/jan/10/frontpagenews. conservationandendangeredspecies

Economic benefits of ecotourism:

Ecotourism in Peru: community engagement and preserving biodiversity –
https://www.theguardian.com/sustainable-business/eco-tourism-peru-amazon-engaging-communities

Ecotourism Kenya: Basecamp Maasai Mara –
http://www.basecampexplorer.com/stories/kenya/empowering-staff-by-offering-opportunities/

CASE STUDY: Costa Rica, a small-scale study of the benefits and negative impacts of ecotourism

Figure D38: Map of Costa Rica

Costa Rica is a small country in Central America bordered by Nicaragua to the north and Panama to the south. With its tropical climate, and extensive beaches, Costa Rica has considerable potential for the traditional sun, sand and sea holiday. In addition, the country has a rich biodiversity with large areas of tropical rainforest and an estimated 10,000 plant species. These provide habitats for a wealth of wildlife, including over 850 species of birds, more than 200 reptiles and a similar number of mammals. There are also several active volcanoes and coral reefs off the Caribbean coast. It has been claimed that Costa Rica is the world's most ecologically diverse country, making it a prime location for ecotourism.

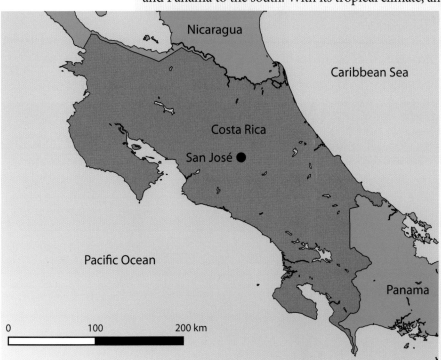

Figure D39: Costa Rica rainforest

Prior to 1970, Costa Rica's economy concentrated mainly on the growing of coffee and bananas, largely for the export market, and large areas of forest were cleared to provide additional land for this purpose. Competition from other countries led to a fall in demand for these products in the 1970s and Costa Rica was forced to restructure its economy. Tourism, and ecotourism in particular, became the main focus for development.

Several factors played a crucial role in establishing Costa Rica as one of the world's most important ecotourism destinations:

- A National Park Service was established in the 1970s to manage the diverse environments and over 25% of the country has some form of protected status. There are 30 national parks and several marine reserves.
- In common with some other countries in Central America, there have been periods of political unrest but there has been peace and stability since 1949. There is also a low crime rate.
- Government investment has financed effective sanitation measures and provided clean water. Many diseases associated with tropical climates have been eradicated.
- The people are well educated and social conditions are better than other countries in Central America (Figure D40).
- Costa Rica's location close to the USA provides easy access to major high-income populations. In terms of foreign tourists, 49% come from USA. A further 9% come from Canada and Mexico.

Exercise

Figure D40: Socio-economic data for selected countries in Central America

1. (a) Describe how the socio-economic characteristics of Costa Rica contrast with those for other countries in Central America as shown in Figure D40.

   (b) How might these contrasts affect the development of ecotourism in Costa Rica?

Country/ region	Birth rate per 1000	Death rate per 1000	Literacy rate %*	GNI per capita $US	Life expectancy in years m/f	Protected land %
Central America	19	5	No data	14,896	74/79	No data
Costa Rica	15	4	98	14880	77/82	27
Nicaragua	20	5	82	5,050	72/78	37
Panama	19	5	95	20,710	75/81	21

Source: Data from 2016 World Population Data Sheet, http://www.prb.org/ and

* United Nations Educational, Scientific, and Cultural Organization (UNESCO) Institute for Statistics, taken from the World Bank, http://data.worldbank.org/indicator/SE.ADT.LITR.ZS

The benefits of ecotourism in Costa Rica

Economic and social benefits

Costa Rica has benefitted enormously from developments in ecotourism. The economy had been stagnating in the 1970s with its over reliance on agricultural products. Ecotourism developments have diversified the economy and contributed to greater stability. The numbers of tourists has increased rapidly since the 1980s. In 1988, there were 325,000 visitors, increasing to 1 million in 1999 and to 2.9 million in 2016. The income generated by tourism reached US$2.4 billion in 2012. Tourism as a whole currently accounts for 12.5% of the total GNP. Approximately 247,500 people worked in tourism related jobs in 2014, many offering wages almost double the monthly income offered in non-tourist jobs.

Approximately 75% of ecotourism lodges and hotels are owned by Costa Ricans meaning that profits remain in the country rather than being leaked abroad. In addition, there has been a considerable 'trickle down' effect, as local Costa Ricans establish service industries for tourists such as restaurants, souvenir shops and transport firms. These services provide income for many local people. Ecotourists' demand for local food products including coffee has generated $16 million in recent years. All of this contributes to increasing living standards in the country and a growth in demand for consumer goods. Local communities have also benefitted from investments in schools and healthcare provision.

Environmental benefits

The increase in the area given protected land status is the most important environmental benefit from ecotourism, as it ensures the preservation of many important species of animals and vegetation. The protected land also contains rivers which have been used to generate hydro-electricity and sources of clean drinking water. Costa Rica is often regarded as a pioneer of ecotourism and has attracted many conservationists and academics to study its wealth of biodiversity. The government has also invested in environmental conservation schemes encouraging further research. A Tourist Board was established to monitor ecotourism impacts and with the help of government investment formulated an ecotourism regulation scheme known as Certification for Sustainable Tourism (CST). The CST has been used as a guideline for later ecotourism regulation schemes (see the section on 'Ecotourism Regulation', pages 408–410).

The first ecotourism developments involved eco lodges built in clearings in the forest using wood that had been discarded by loggers. The eco lodges are quite basic by western standards, with no electricity. Biodegradable soaps are used for washing and all glass and plastic is recycled. Water is purified by using naturally occurring enzymes and bacteria, and heated by solar energy. The owners of the eco lodges are Costa Rican and they have set up a charitable trust to educate people about the rainforest and provide activities such as bird watching.

Figure D41: Hanging bridge in the rainforest, Costa Rica. Tourists walk through the canopy rather than at ground level. This prevents damage to the forest floor vegetation.

Exercise

1. Study Figure D42 relating to an eco lodge in Costa Rica.

   The Figure states that El Remanso Lodge has received the highest level of certification for sustainability. Explain how this can be justified.

   Figure D42: El Remanso Lodge, Costa Rica

   Source: Adapted from 'El Remanso Lodge Achieves the Highest Level of Costa Rica's Sustainable Tourism Certification', TIES, The International Ecotourism Society, http://www.ecotourism.org

   El Remanso Lodge has been awarded with the 'Level 5' of the Certification for Sustainable Tourism (CST), a rigorous certification programme by the Costa Rican Tourist Board (ICT) that evaluates tourism companies' practices in natural, cultural and social resource management. CST is regulated by the Costa Rican National Accreditation Commission and consists of a scale of 5 levels of sustainable tourism achievements.

   This is the highest possible rating and El Remanso has achieved 100% of the points in the 4 areas of the evaluation. In addition to utilising renewable energy sources to power the lodge's operations, El Remanso Lodge implements various sustainability practices such as:

   - utilising local and sustainable construction materials including naturally fallen timber.
   - avoiding herbicides, pesticides or dangerous chemicals.
   - progressive waste management to avoid excess waste.
   - banning bottled water.
   - using fully biodegradable cleaning supplies.

   At El Remanso Lodge, 100% of its electricity is produced through a micro-hydroelectric system and a solar panel complements the system by activating the sand filter and ionisation system in the pool.

   ### Green adventure in a natural paradise

   Hidden in the jungle, El Remanso Lodge cradles both adventurers and travellers looking for a relaxing getaway in a natural paradise. A wide array of activities are available to suit every nature loving traveller, including waterfall rappelling, guided bird watching and exciting midnight hikes in the mysterious jungle. The lodge's 185 acres of private reserve offer unique opportunities to discover the magic of a tropical rainforest acting as a buffer zone to the famous Corcovado National Park, and to explore the wonders of one of the world's most bio-diverse regions.

   El Remanso Lodge actively contributes to the efforts to study and preserve the rainforest, by supporting local education programmes and by funding conservation projects – with the philosophy that "one of the most effective ways to protect the rainforest is by understanding how it works."

   The National Park of Corcovado, one of the most remote areas in the country, is home to the largest and most spectacular tropical primary rainforest in Costa Rica, as well as many rare species of endangered wildlife – including the beautiful tapirs, the biggest land mammal in Central and

South America, bull sharks and large crocodiles*. The park was created in 1975 in order to protect the land from gold mining and logging. Today it is renowned for being one of the most special ecotourism destinations in Central America.

* The American crocodile is a rare species not to be confused with the more widely occurring alligator.

The negative impacts of ecotourism in Costa Rica

At the start of ecotourism development it seemed that Costa Rica had achieved the correct balance between economic gain and environmental sustainability, as seen at El Remanso Lodge (Figure D42). However, there are also examples that show that ecotourism is having negative impacts.

Negative environmental impacts

Tourist overcapacity is one of the main areas of concern because it can damage fragile environments and wildlife. One of the principles of ecotourism was that it should be small-scale and low impact. The number of visitors to Costa Rica has been increasing and this has led to its fragile environments being exposed to more human pressure. In addition, dealing with the increased waste generated has created problems. Providing landfill sites uses up valuable land and there are reports of illegal dumping in rivers. In Manuel Antonio National Park, an average of 1000 tourists visit each day. Such numbers are difficult to manage and there are insufficient Park rangers. As a result, the Park is experiencing problems with tourists feeding animals and the dumping of litter. In addition, some of the luxury lodges have been accused of greenwashing and consequently endanger the local environment.

Competition from other ecotourism destinations has forced some providers to diversify into eco adventure activities. Examples include zip wires through the rainforest canopy, horse riding and rafting down some of the rivers. These activities have proved very popular but they are controversial, with many arguing they are contrary to the principles of ecotourism.

Figure D43: Horse riding in the rainforest

Negative economic and social impacts

When ecotourism was first established in Costa Rica the eco lodges offered few luxuries and, like El Remanso Lodge (Figure D42), were models of sustainability. Although many eco lodges still follow this model, there are also examples of expensive, luxurious lodges offering spa treatments and gourmet restaurants with international cuisine. These developments require considerable expenditure in infrastructure, such as roads and drainage, as well as a professional and skilled workforce. As an LEDC, Costa Rica has to depend on foreign investment and labour supply to meet these demands. Reliance on foreign investment and workers means that some of the wealth generated by ecotourism does not benefit Costa Rica. This leakage of income is a major concern. Local Costa Ricans are generally employed in the lower paid service jobs such as waiting and cleaning.

Ecotourism has undoubtedly had economic benefits in Costa Rica, which should lead to improved living standards for the local community. However, there is considerable inequality in the distribution of income. Costa Rica is ranked 66 on the Human Development Index (HDI) with a value of 0.776 and falls into the high human development band of countries. However, its Inequality Adjusted Human Development Index (IHDI) is 0.628 and the country is ranked 75. (For further details on these indices see *Geography for CCEA AS Level*, 2nd Edition, pages 221–223.) Ecotourism is also thought to underlie a social change in rural areas of Costa Rica. The potential financial gain from selling farmland for ecotourism ventures has led many rural dwellers to sell land to private developers. This has led to a decline in farming in some areas and Costa Rica now imports food.

It seems that Costa Rica has benefitted considerably from ecotourism but strict regulation is required to ensure that the negative impacts are minimised and the economic and social benefits are distributed across the community. The challenge for Costa Rica in the future is how to maintain the balance between economic gain and environmental conservation.

Exam Questions

1. With reference to your small-scale case study of ecotourism, discuss the benefits and negative impacts that have occurred. [18]

References

'Tourism and the Sustainable Development Goals', UNWTO:
http://www.e-unwto.org/doi/pdf/10.18111/9789284417254

'Eco-destinations, Botswana', TIES:
http://www.ecotourism.org/botswana

'Eco-destinations, Costa Rica', TIES:
http://www.ecotourism.org/costa-rica

'The World's most sustainable theme parks?', TIES:
http://www.ecotourism.org/news/worlds-most-sustainable-theme-parks

'Embracing the indigenous identity in Costa Rica through tourism', TIES:
http://www.ecotourism.org/news/embracing-indigenous-identity-costa-rica-through-tourism

'Shades of Green' *The Guardian*, 26 May 2007:
https://www.theguardian.com/travel/2007/may/26/saturday.costarica

Ecotourism regulation

Ecotourism has made a significant contribution to economic and social development in areas, especially LEDCs. It has also promoted and sustained conservation practices. However, as the previous section highlighted, there are many examples of ecotourism having had negative impacts including displacement of local communities, leakage, greenwashing and damage to fragile environments. In some areas attention has focussed on short-term economic gain without any real regard for the long-term impacts on local society or the environment. The term 'ecotourism' is frequently applied incorrectly to any form of tourism developments in remote or natural environments. Five star luxury 'eco lodges' in the Maasai Mara game reserves and in the rainforests of Costa Rica are just two examples of this practice. Transport improvements have made even the most remote areas accessible and as tourists seek new tourism opportunities there is a growing threat to environmentally sensitive areas such as Alaska. These areas generally have a low carrying capacity and require effective management policies to prevent serious damage. Ecotourism is relatively recent, developing since the 1980s, and it has taken time for management policies and regulation to become established. Although there is general agreement on the need for the management of ecotourism, establishing effective regulation has proved difficult. Some examples of these challenges are listed below:

- Ecotourism destinations cover a wide range of physical and cultural environments. Each presents a unique set of issues which have to be addressed.
- Establishing effective regulation across international boundaries is difficult and relies on agreements between tour operators and providers. Monitoring the level of compliance with regulation is also challenging.
- Ensuring that the criteria used to grant an ecotourism certificate or award is sufficiently rigorous.
- Raising awareness to ecotourism regulators that in some LEDC situations ecotourism is the main source of employment and income.
- Safeguarding the human rights of indigenous communities including their entitlement to shelter and livelihoods must be considered in all ecotourism projects. Local communities should be involved in these projects.
- Ensuring that the profits from ecotourism are shared with the indigenous population or used to fund social projects such as education and health care.

The emphasis on sustainability that emerged from the United Nations Conference on Environment and Development (UNCED) in Rio de Janeiro in 1992 was a landmark event promoting the inclusion of the principles of sustainability in all aspects of development. Several global initiatives emerged from the Rio Summit leading up to the new millennium. The United Nations also recognised the contribution of tourism, including ecotourism, in raising living standards in LEDCs through the Millennium Development Goals programme. The United Nations World Tourism Organisation (UNWTO) designated 2002 as the International Year of Ecotourism. The UNWTO organised a World Ecotourism Summit in Québec in May 2002.

The Québec Declaration 2002

In May 2002, over one thousand delegates from 132 countries attended the World Ecotourism Summit in Québec to discuss means of ecotourism regulation. The delegates at the summit recognised the growing interest in ecotourism and the economic potential it offered to indigenous communities especially in LEDCs. They also recognised that ecotourism could contribute significantly to conservation of environmentally sensitive areas. However, there was also a recognition that unregulated ecotourism could result in environmental damage, economic leakage and ultimately have serious negative impacts on local and indigenous communities. Their findings and recommendations were published in the Québec Declaration. Forty-eight recommendations were made to five main organisations and groups involved in the delivery of ecotourism:

1. National, regional and local governments
2. The private sector including tour operators
3. NGOs
4. International agencies
5. Local indigenous communities

The wide range of organisations and groups included in the Declaration emphasised the complexity in finding a sustainable approach to ecotourism. The recommendations in the Declaration focussed on two main aims:

1. To ensure the principles of economic, social and environmental sustainability are incorporated in all ecotourism destinations.
2. To encourage all ecotourism providers to conduct self-regulation schemes.

Self-regulation schemes involved the use of sustainability indicators and environmental impact assessments which would monitor the impact of ecotourism projects. The findings of these assessments were to be made public.

Many ecotourism destinations undertake self-regulation and gain membership of recognised ecotourism certification schemes. Examples include the Eco Warrior Awards (Kenya) and The Rainforest Alliance (an international scheme).

The Global Ecotourism Conference 2007 (GEC07)

Five years after the Québec Declaration, The Global Ecotourism Conference (GEC07) took place in Oslo (Norway). GEC07 had two main aims:

- To assess the achievements and challenges to ecotourism since 2002.
- To renew the commitment of national and regional ecotourism organisations to policies that would strengthen the industry's role in conservation and sustainable development.

Achievements from 2002–2007 include:

- An increasing number of countries and regions had developed ecotourism self-regulation strategies.
- Many ecotourism projects aimed to provide sustainable livelihoods to local people and contribute to conservation.
- Increased awareness of environmental issues such as climate change and their impacts on indigenous communities.
- The number of tourists visiting an ecotourism destination continued to grow.
- The wider travel and tourism industry had adopted some of the principles of sustainability that had been pioneered by ecotourism.
- Tourism in general and ecotourism in particular was recognised as a means of supporting the Millennium Development Goals programme target of poverty alleviation.

However, in spite of the achievements since the Quebec Declaration, a number of challenges still remained in 2007 including:

- Many of the world's natural areas remained under threat and there was a substantial loss of biodiversity in a number of areas. The increase in the number of tourists contributed to this increased pressure.
- The term ecotourism was still being applied loosely, leading to greenwashing.
- As many ecotourism destinations required long-distance flights the carbon footprint of the industry remained large and needed a concerted effort to reduce its emissions of greenhouse gases.
- Local communities were not fully involved in the delivery of ecotourism in their destination.

In response to these challenges GEC07 set out four themes and a number of actions that built upon the achievements of the Québec Declaration and addressed the outstanding challenges (Figure D44). In contrast to the Québec Declaration, which made recommendations specific to five main organisations or groups and focussed on self-regulation schemes, GEC07 applied their proposals to all involved in the delivery of ecotourism and set out strategies to be employed.

Figure D44: GEC07 Themes and selected actions

Source: adapted from 'Oslo Statement on Ecotourism', http://www.ecotourism. org/oslo-statement-on-ecotourism

1. Recognise the valuable role that ecotourism plays in local sustainable development.

Action: Develop strategies to engage and empower local indigenous communities in all aspects of ecotourism.

2. Maximise the potential of well-managed ecotourism as a key economic force for the conservation of natural and cultural heritage.

Action: Engage local communities and use local designs and materials in building ecotourism facilities in harmony with their surroundings. Developers should aim to combine creativity and new environmental technology with sustainable economic development strategies.

3. Support the viability and performance of ecotourism enterprises and activities through effective education, marketing and training.

Action: Make up-to-date information and research available about ecotourism markets and strengthen access to them through the most effective channels available including websites, online forums, mailing lists and radio broadcasts.

4. Address some of the critical issues facing ecotourism in strengthening its sustainability.

Action: Address tourism's impact on climate change by encouraging adapted travel patterns (for example, increase length of stay per trip), promoting more energy efficient means of transport, using reduced and zero-emission operation technologies and participating in reliable carbon offsetting schemes.

Exercise

1. Identify and describe two similarities and two differences between the Québec Declaration and GEC07.

2. Explain how the GEC07 builds upon the achievements of the Québec Declaration.

Green Globe Scheme

The emphasis on self-regulation schemes for ecotourism has often been criticised because it is difficult to have equal standards across such a wide range of destinations. Partly in response to this a number of global certification schemes have been developed. The Green Globe Scheme, developed in Los Angeles between 1992 and 1994 following the Rio Summit in 1992, is one of the best-known examples of a global certification scheme. It is a structured assessment of the sustainability of all aspects of a tourism product including travel to and from the destination, as well as hotel policies on energy use, recycling and building materials used. The scheme is wide ranging and is not restricted to ecotourism but can be applied to all components of tourism, including beach holidays and cruise ships.

The Green Globe Scheme assesses sustainability across 44 core criteria, grouped into four areas which are supported by 380 compliance indicators (Figure D45). These indicators are adapted to specific destinations and the entire scheme is reviewed and updated twice annually. To guarantee compliance, an independent auditor works with the tour companies on site. It is in use in over 90 countries. Three levels of certification are available:

1. Green Globe Standard – awarded to new members who have met all the required criteria.

2. Gold Member status – awarded to those who have held the standard award for five consecutive years.

3. Platinum status – may be awarded to those who have been members for at least ten years.

Figure D45: Green Globe Scheme, areas of assessment and selected criteria

Source: adapted from Green Globe, http://greenglobe.com/

1. Sustainable management
Criteria:

(i) Implement a sustainable management scheme.

(ii) Provide employee training in sustainable management.

2. Social and economic
Criteria:

(i) Actively support initiatives for social infrastructure and community development including education, health and sanitation.

(ii) Ensure local residents are employed, including in management roles. Training is offered as necessary.

3. Cultural heritage
Criteria:

(i) Follow established guidelines or codes of behaviour for visits to culturally or historically sensitive sites in order to minimise visitor impact and maximise enjoyment.

(ii) Contribute to the protection of local historically, archaeologically and spiritually important sites and do not impede access to them by local residents.

4. Environmental
Criteria:

(i) Ensure purchasing policy favours environmentally friendly products for building materials, capital goods, food and consumables.

(ii) Measure the purchase of disposable and consumable goods and that the business actively seeks ways to reduce their use.

Exercise

1. Study Figure D46 relating to Gaïa River Lodge, which has been awarded Green Globe Certification.

   Explain how economic, social and environmental principles of sustainability have been incorporated into this ecotourism destination.

Figure D46: Gaïa River Lodge Belize
Source: information from Green Globe, http://greenglobe.com/

Gaïa River Lodge is an eco lodge on the west coast of Belize. It has 16 eco lodges and has been awarded a Green Globe certification annually since 2014. The eco lodges are built in a rainforest location close to a river and waterfall. Its features include:

- Lodges are built from local building materials in a remote area with no paved roads.
- Local hydroelectricity schemes provide all the power for the lodges. Electricity is stored in long life photovoltaic batteries.
- Low voltage lighting is used on forest walkways. Compact fluorescent light bulbs are used in the lodges.
- The resort has been designed to manage storm water run-off and the collection of rainwater.
- An organic farm provides vegetables and herbs for the restaurant.
- The farm uses organically made pesticides and local farmers are engaged in a composting scheme to provide fertilisers.
- Local plants are used in landscaping the resort.
- Some of the resort's profits support biological research into a recently discovered species of sedge.
- A local women's group has received funding from the lodge to educate tourists on Mayan culture and to expand their craft industries.

UNESCO World Heritage Sites

The UN Education Scientific and Cultural Organisation (UNESCO) World Heritage Sites is a global strategy employed to protect sites that display some cultural, scientific or historical importance. Cultural and historical sites have been selected because they exhibit unique and remarkable human endeavour. Examples include the Italian cities of Florence and Venice, and the remains of ancient settlements and temples. Scientific sites are chosen for unique geological or ecological importance. Coral reefs, areas with rich biodiversity and volcanic areas are examples of such sites.

Figure D47: The Temple of Dendur reconstructed in New York Metropolitan Museum of Art

UNESCO World Heritage Site designation was introduced in 1972. It followed a petition to the USA and Europe from Egypt and Sudan in the late 1950s concerning possible threats posed by the building of the Aswan Dam to archaeological sites, including temples dating back to 15 BC. In return for financial and technological assistance in preserving these sites Egypt donated the remains of the three temples to Europe and the Temple of Dendur to the USA. The temple was removed and reconstructed in the Metropolitan Museum in New York (Figure D47). This incident raised awareness of the financial burden a country, especially an LEDC, incurred in protecting valuable sites. A special UN committee discussed this issue and proposed the designation of World Heritage Site status.

A UNESCO World Heritage designation aims to:

- encourage countries to sign the World Heritage Convention and to ensure the protection of their natural and cultural heritage.
- encourage member countries to set up management plans and reporting systems on the state of conservation of their World Heritage sites.
- help safeguard World Heritage properties by providing technical assistance and professional training.
- provide emergency assistance for World Heritage sites in immediate danger.
- support public awareness-building activities for World Heritage conservation.
- encourage participation of the local population in the preservation of their cultural and natural heritage.
- encourage international co-operation in the conservation of the world's cultural and natural heritage.

Source: adapted from UNESCO World Heritage Convention, http://whc.unesco.org

Countries wishing to avail of this designation must create a Tentative List of sites that could be potentially proposed for inscription on the World Heritage List. Once proposed, these sites are evaluated by one of UNESCO's advisory bodies. To be added to the List, each site must demonstrate it has Outstanding Universal Value (OUV), and meet at least one of ten criteria. Whether to add a site to the World Heritage List is decided by the World Heritage Committee, which meets once a year.

Figure D48: Examples of ecotourism destinations with UNESCO World Heritage Site status

Cocos Island National Park – Costa Rica

Cocos Island is the only island in the East Pacific with tropical rainforest vegetation. It has a unique marine habitat for sharks, tuna and dolphins.

Belize Barrier Reef

Belize Barrier Reef Reserve System

This is the largest coral reef in the northern hemisphere and provides a unique habitat for turtles, manatees and the rare American crocodile. The site is also listed as 'endangered' since 2009 due to mangrove cutting and over development.

There are a number of advantages from this designation including:

- funding and technical assistance in the formulation of management and conservation plans.
- World Heritage Site status raises public awareness of the significance of the location and increases its tourism potential.
- the use of 'endangered species' and 'endangered site' emphasises the urgent need for conservation.
- designated sites are legally protected by international treaties even in times of war. Therefore, having a UNESCO World Heritage designation provides excellent protection for a fragile environment.

Exam Questions

1. Discuss the challenges in establishing effective ecotourism regulation.
   Describe and evaluate **any two** of the following measures:

   - Québec Declaration
   - Global Ecotourism Conference (2007)
   - Green Globe Scheme
   - UNESCO World Heritage Sites [18]

Question from CCEA A22 Processes and Issues in Human Geography,
Specimen Assessment Materials © CCEA 2017

References

Québec Declaration:
https://www.gdrc.org/ucm/eco-tour/quebec-declaration.pdf

Global Ecotourism Conference 2007 (GEC07):
http://www.ecotourism.org/oslo-statement-on-ecotourism

Examples of self-certification schemes:
http://www.ecotourism.org/news/botswana-sustainability-camps-and-lodges-ecotourism-certified

'Greenloons Adds Alaska's Kenai Peninsula, Peru's Amazon Rainforest and Introductions to Maasai in Kenya', TIES:
http://www.ecotourism.org/news/greenloons-adds-alaskas-kenai-peninsula-perus-amazon-rainforest-and-introductions-maasai-kenya

Green Globe Scheme:
https://greenglobe.com/

UNESCO World Heritage Sites – this website has a number of links including an interactive map of all sites:
http://whc.unesco.org/en/globalstrategy/

Gaïa River Lodge Belize:
https://greenglobe.com/latest-news/gaia-riverlodge-protects-nature-and-culture-in-belize/2016

Glossary

Unit A2 1: Physical Processes, Landforms and Management

Option A: Plate Tectonics – Theory and Outcomes

Asthenosphere: The plastic layer of the upper mantle that lies below the solid lithosphere in which material flows, as convection currents, moving the plates above.

Collision margin: A plate boundary where two continental plates meet forming fold mountains, such as the Himalayas formed by the collision of the Indo-Australian and the Eurasian plates.

Conservative margin (transform): A plate boundary where two plates move past each other without the creation or destruction of plate material, such as the San Andreas fault line in California.

Constructive margin (divergence): a plate boundary where two plates are forced apart by convection currents in the plastic upper mantle (asthenosphere). Magma rises at the margin to form new, normally ocean, crust.

Continental crust: The less dense rock material that forms the land masses carried by tectonic plates.

Continental drift: A theory proposed by Alfred Wegener that the world's continents have changed their location over geological time. The theory is a forerunner of the modern concept of Plate Tectonics.

Continental shelf: A gently sloping and shallow underwater plain that surrounds many continents.

Convection: The vertical movement of warm air.

Convection current: The exchange of energy in the form of heat by flows of liquid. In the mantle deep hot spots cause upward flows of magma towards the crust, where they initiate circular currents that move the plates of the lithosphere.

Core: The central part of the Earth's structure. It consists of an inner solid core and a liquid outer core.

Crust: The outermost shell of the Earth's structure. It is composed of solid rocks and varies in thickness from thin ocean floor (average 7 km) to the continents (average 35 km).

Destructive margin (convergence): A plate boundary where one of two plates moving towards each other is forced downwards, subducted, into the upper mantle and subsequently destroyed.

Dilation theory: The concept that under tectonic stress, rocks strain and open up microscopic cracks in their structure. The theory has been used in the attempt to identify precursors of earthquake activity.

Elastic rebound: The return of rocks to their original position after stress is released by an earthquake.

Epicentre: The point on the Earth's surface directly above the origin or focus of an individual earthquake event.

Fault: A line of weakness in rocks along which vertical or lateral dislocation of the rocks has occurred.

Focus: The point of origin of an earthquake event in the Earth's crust.

Fold and **folding:** The bending of rocks caused by pressures from the Earth's crust.

Fold mountains: A range of mountains resulting from compressive tectonic forces crushing rocks upwards into folded forms, for example, the Alps of southern Europe. Often associated with collision margins.

Geographic Information Systems (GIS): Digitally stored and assessable geographic data, commonly as layers of mapped information.

Ground deformation: Changes in the shape of the ground surface as a consequence of an earthquake.

Hot spot (sub-lithospheric thermal anomaly): A point deep in the Earth's mantle where thermo-nuclear activity creates a hotter than average location. It is from these points that active plumes of magma (convection currents) rise to power the processes of plate tectonics.

Island arc: A curved line of volcanic islands associated with a destructive margin between two oceanic plates.

Land zoning: Where planning designates how areas may be used. An example is zoning to prevent building in an earthquake prone area or allocating a floodplain area to store water during a flood episode.

Liquefaction: The process by which loose and/or wet sediments lose their cohesion and strength when subjected to intense shaking, such as occurs in earthquakes.

Lithosphere: The solid outer layer of rocks of the Earth's structure. It includes the crust and the solid upper mantle which rests on the plastic material of the asthenosphere.

Magnetic stripping: The pattern of normal and reversed polarity magnetism recorded by rocks across the mid-ocean ridges of constructive plate margins.

Mantle: The bulk of the Earth's mass is formed by this layer, or sphere, that surrounds the core and lies beneath the crust.

Mid-Atlantic ridge: a series of narrow, parallel ridges that mark the creation zone of new oceanic plates along a constructive plate margin. They often contain a deep central rift valley. For example the mid-Atlantic ridge runs down the centre of the ocean rarely seen above sea level, only in places like Iceland.

Modified Mercalli scale: A scale measuring earthquake intensity based on earthquakes' effects on buildings and structures. It has now largely been replaced by the Richter scale.

Mohorovičić discontinuity (Moho): The line of change in the transfer speed of earthquake waves that marks the lower boundary of the crust where it meets the mantle.

Oceanic crust: The thinner but more dense plate material that forms the seafloor.

Ocean trench: A narrow but very deep section of the ocean floor, marking the point of subduction of one oceanic plate at a destructive plate margin.

Orogeny: A geological period marked by the formation of fold mountains. The current period is the Alpine orogeny associated with the formation of the Andes, Rockies, Atlas and Himalayan mountain ranges.

Paleomagnetism: The fossilised record of past magnetic patterns 'captured' as molten volcanic rocks harden and form, for example, along ocean ridges.

Pancaking: A process in which sections of tall buildings collapse onto lower floors as a result of earthquake events.

Plate: A section of rigid rock that forms part of the Earth's crust.

Plate tectonics: A theory that the Earth's crust is composed of irregularly shaped plates, some carry continents, and others form the ocean floor. These plates are moved by convection currents in the asthenosphere.

Precursor: An event or pattern of change that comes before an active earthquake episode.

Richter scale: A scale measuring earthquake magnitude based on amplitude. It is an open-ended scale with a magnitude 9.1 event the highest yet recorded.

Ridge-push (gravitational sliding): a suggested mechanism of plate motion. Mid-ocean ridges are higher than the adjacent ocean floor, so gravity causes the ridge to push away the lithosphere plate farther from the ridge.

Rift valley: Linear shaped lowland between highland areas, formed by tensional forces stretching a plate and causing faults and blocks to fall. Common at mid-ocean ridges, the East Africa Rift is a large land-based example.

Sea-floor spreading: The process by which new lithospheric plate material is formed at mid-ocean ridges.

Seamount: An isolated topographic feature rising from the sea floor, usually a submarine volcano.

Seismic gap theory: The concept that active seismic regions, that have had a long period without activity, are increasingly likely to be the location of a future earthquake event.

Seismic tomography: A technique to identify the Earth's internal structure using seismic waves produced by earthquakes or explosions. Seismic waves have been classified as **p** (primary/pressure, **s** (secondary/tranverse) and **l** (surface – Love and Rayleigh) waves.

Sial: The term to describe the less dense granitic rock that forms the bulk of the continents. They are dominated by the elements silica and aluminium.

Sima: the term to describe the more dense basaltic rock that forms the ocean floors. They are dominated by the elements silica and magnesium.

Slab-pull (dragging): A suggested mechanism for plate motion. As a subducting plate sinks into the mantle it pulls the rest of the plate behind it.

Subduction: The process by which plate material, generally oceanic, is forced down into the mantle and gradually destroyed by melting in a deep sea trench at a destructive plate margin.

Transverse fault: A line of weakness in rocks where the two sides slide past each other, in different directions or at different rates. These are very common along constructive plate margins on the ocean floor.

Tsunami: The Japanese term for a large sea wave created by earthquake or volcanic activity on the sea bed.

Wadati-Benioff Zone: A seismically active area below an ocean trench where subduction takes place.

Option B: Tropical Ecosystems – Nature and Sustainability

Afforestation: The planting of trees on land that is not currently forested.

Agroforestry: The use of land for a combination of agriculture and forestry.

Aridisol: The zonal soil for tropical semi-arid and desert regions.

Autotrophs: Self-feeding organisms such as plants.

Biomass: The total weight of living organisms in the area or ecosystem concerned. It is one of the three stores in the nutrient cycle model.

Biome: An ecosystem at a global scale, such as the tundra or mid-latitude grassland biomes.

Decomposers: Organisms that break down waste or dead organic material into simpler compounds.

Ecology: The study of the inter-relationships between living organisms and their environment.

Ecotourism: Tourism based on the natural attraction of an area and designed to safeguard the environment. It is a form of sustainable development.

Epiphyte: An organism (plant) that grows on the surface of another but is not parasitic.

Equator: An imaginary line that marks a plane at right angles to the Earth's axis. It divides the globe into the northern and southern hemispheres and it is the baseline for latitude ($0°$).

Equinox: The two annual dates when the Sun is directly over the Equator giving an equal 12 hours of day and night.

Hadley Cell: This is the model for the atmosphere's circulation in low latitudes (between 35° north and south of the Equator.

Herbivores: Plant eating organisms.

Heterotrophs: Organisms that depend on other organisms for their energy. They include herbivores, carnivores and omnivores.

Indigenous: Originating in or native to an area. The term is applied to plants, animals and people.

Interplanting: A system of farming where different crops are mixed in rows within one field or plot. This may include tree crops and annual plants.

Inter-Tropical Convergence Zone (ITCZ): This describes the area of the Earth's atmosphere where the north-east and south-east trade winds converge. It marks an area of low pressure (Doldrums) near the Equator associated with convectional uplift and heavy rainfall. Its location follows the annual migration of the overhead Sun.

Irrigation: The artificial and deliberate addition of water to the land to improve soil conditions for plant growth.

Karez (or qanat): A traditional irrigation system found across the Middle East and Pakistan.

Laterite: A layer of hardened sub-soil composed of iron and aluminium oxides found under certain conditions under tropical forests. It causes drainage problems and may limit the agricultural use of the soil.

Litter: The layer of organic material that gathers on the soil surface. It includes both waste products and dead plant and animal material. It is one of the three stores in the nutrient cycle model.

Non-Government Organisation (NGO): A voluntary body often with international membership. The term often refers to charities, especially in development issues.

Nutrients: Chemical 'foods' for plants.

Nutrient cycle: The transfer of organic and inorganic material into and through biotic systems.

Omnivores: Organisms whose normal diet consists of both plant and animal material.

Oxisol: The term for the zonal soil found under tropical forests.

Parent material: The underlying geology beneath a soil from which much of its inorganic material may be derived by weathering processes.

Primary Productivity Index: This is a measure of the rate at which an area of vegetation produces new plant material. It can be measured in tonnes/hectare/year or kg/m²/year.

Productivity (gross and net): The growth rate of new plant material in a given area over time. While gross productivity is the total rate, the net rate allows for the energy used by plants during their life processes.

Saline agriculture: The cultivation of plants that are salt tolerant.

Salinisation: The process of increasing salt content in soil that creates problems for plant development.

Savanna: The term used to describe the tropical grassland ecosystem of Africa. It is often used as a synonym for tropical grasslands.

Selva: The South American term for tropical rainforest. It refers to dry land forests as opposed to flooded varzea forests found near rivers that are regularly inundated.

Shifting Cultivation ('slash and burn'): This is the traditional form of agriculture in the tropical forests across the world. It consists of the clearance and short-term use of small plots of forest for crop production, followed by an extended period of abandonment for soil fertility regeneration.

Silviculture: The cultivation of trees, both forests grown for timber products, and groves and orchards for plant products, such as fruit, nuts and seeds.

Soil profile: A vertical section of a soil from the surface to the parent material, showing the pattern of horizons and characteristics.

Solstice: The two annual dates when the Sun reaches its most northerly or southerly position (the Tropic of Cancer around 21 June and the Tropic of Capricorn around 21 December).

Stratum specificity: In tropical forests the layered structure of the vegetation is matched by an assemblage of animal species that are associated with each layer.

Sustainability: The degree to which the use of a resource or resources impacts on its long-term use or availability.

Terre firme: This refers to dry land forests in the Amazon Basin as opposed to flooded varzea forests found near rivers that are regularly inundated.

Trade winds: The constant winds found around the equatorial region. They form the surface element of the Hadley Cell and their name reflects their importance in the era of sailing ships.

Tropics: The lines at 23½°N (Tropic of Cancer) and 23½°S (Tropic of Capricorn) of the Equator that mark the latitude of the overhead sun at mid-summer in each hemisphere.

Tropical: Strictly refers to the area between the tropics but more commonly to the whole region between 30°N and 30°S of the Equator.

Tropical desert: An arid biome associated with the high pressure zone around 30°N and 30°S of the Equator.

Tropical rain forest (TRF): A biome associated with the continuously hot and wet climate of the equatorial region of low pressure.

Tropical grassland: A biome associated with the wet and dry tropics between the equatorial forests and the tropical deserts.

Trophic: A term used in ecosystems to describe the transfer of energy between organisms through feeding.

Tropopause: The line marking the upper boundary of the lowest layer of the atmosphere. It lies around 6 km above the surface at the poles to a maximum of around 16 km at the Equator .

Troposphere: The lowest layer of the atmosphere in which most weather conditions are confined.

Tube wells: A water well with a metal tube drilled into the ground, commonly used to raise water for irrigation.

Varzea: A tropical forest area in the Amazon Basin that is subject to regular river floods. These tend to have more fertile soils than the rest of the basin.

Waterlogging: An environmental problem resulting from poorly managed irrigation, it inhibits healthy crop development and can promote the problem of salinisation.

Option C: Dynamic Coastal Environments

Abrasion: The process of breaking waves using sand and larger particles to erode the coast. Material is removed, resulting in undercutting and the possible collapse of unsupported cliffs.

Arch: A curved opening in a rock headland.

Attrition: Where sediment carried by waves is eroded: as particles are moved about by waves the impacts between particles and against the shore cause them to be broken up into smaller fragments.

Backshore: The area of shore above normal high tide.

Backwash: The return flow of a wave under gravity, after its breaks on the shore.

Beach: An accumulation of loose material, such as sand, shingle or pebbles, on a lake or sea shore.

Beach nourishment: A soft management scheme that adds sediment, sand or gravel to increase the coastal protection provided by a beach.

Berm: A flat topped ridge of sediment at the top edge of a beach near the high water mark.

Blowhole: A vertical crack in a sea cave that allows water from waves to blast into the air on a cliff top.

Cave: A hollow, normally at sea level, formed by wave action along a line of weakness in a coastal cliff.

Cliff: A steep or perpendicular slope commonly associated with high energy coastlines.

Cliff drainage and stabilisation: A hard engineering technique to remove rain water from rocks in a cliff to prevent it from slumping or sliding onto the shore.

Coast or **coastline:** This refers to the zone along a shore where the land meets the sea.

Constructive waves: These have a stronger swash than backwash and they often lead to the accumulation (aggradation) of sediment on the shore.

Continental shelf: A gently sloping and shallow underwater plain that surrounds many continents.

Coral bleaching: The breakdown of the symbiotic relationship between coral polyps and algae that will cause corals to starve. It is often caused by warming sea temperatures.

Coral reef: Underwater ecosystems bound together by calcium carbonate structures secreted by corals.

Cost Benefit Analysis (CBA): A process to determine if a management option on the coast is the best approach to achieve the required outcome in comparison to the expense required.

Cuspate foreland: A triangular-shaped coastal deposition landform. Created by longshore drift, it is composed of sand and shingle.

Destructive waves: High energy features in which the backwash is stronger than the swash, causing sediment to be removed or combed down from the shore into deeper water.

Dredging: The process of removing material from the bed of a river, lake or sea. It is a common process used to increase the carrying capacity or discharge of rivers.

Drift-aligned coast: A stretch of coast where waves normally break at an angle to the shore.

Dunes: Mounds of loose sediment formed by winds blowing onshore over wide sandy beaches.

Dune regeneration: A coastal management technique to create or restore dunes to help with coastal protection.

Dynamic equilibrium: This describes a situation where a balance is maintained despite continuous change. For example, the removal of material from a beach by longshore drift is balanced by new material carried in from the erosion of nearby cliffs.

Ecology: The study of the inter-relationships between living organisms and their environment.

Emergence: A process by which a new coastline is formed as relative sea level falls (actual sea fall or rising land).

Environmental Impact Assessment (EIA): A report on the likely impact of a project on the physical environment. Used in the decision-making process for coastal management.

Erosion: The wearing away and transport of the land surface by natural agents, including running water, wind, moving ice and wave action.

Estuary: The tidal mouth of a river where salt seawater and fresh river water meet.

Eustatic change (eustasy): The worldwide change in sea levels.

Fault: A line of weakness in rocks along which vertical or lateral dislocation of the rocks has occurred.

Fetch: The distance of open sea over which a wind can blow to create waves.

Fjord: A glacial U-shaped valley drowned by rising sea level and forming a steep-sided sea inlet.

Foreshore: The area of the shore that is uncovered at low tide.

Gabion: A device used to protect river banks or shorelines from erosion. It consists of pebbles or rocks contained in a wire cage.

Geo: A steep-sided narrow sea-inlet, usually formed along a vertical fault or line of weakness in the rock.

Groyne: Wooden, concrete or rock barriers built out perpendicular to the shore to trap sediment carried by longshore drift.

Hard engineering: The controlled disruption of natural processes by the use of artificial structures.

Headland: A narrow piece of land that projects out into the sea – also known as a cape.

High-energy coast: A shoreline that is subject to strong wave attack and dominated by erosion processes.

Hold the line: A UK government management option for coasts to retain the existing shoreline position.

Hydraulic action (wave pounding): An erosion process caused by the weight and energy of the water in waves.

Interdependence: The concept that places are mutually linked to each other through complex physical and social links. It suggests that any change in one part of a system inevitably has consequences, positive or negative, for other parts of that system.

Isostatic change: The alteration of the relationship between land and sea levels. For example, the gradual rise of land following an Ice Age.

Land zoning: When planning designates how areas may be used. Examples include zoning to prevent building in an earthquake prone area or allocating an area of floodplain to be available to store water during a flood episode.

Longshore drift (LSD): the process whereby waves approaching the coast at an angle move sediment laterally in a zig-zag motion.

Low-energy coast: A sheltered shoreline with constructive waves, where deposition is greater than erosion.

Managed retreat: A UK government coastal policy that allows the shoreline to erode in a controlled, managed way.

Offshore: The section of the shallow coastline that is always underwater.

Raised beach: A 'fossil' beach now above the present sea level.

Refraction: The change in direction of wave fronts moving onto a shore, caused by friction in shallow water.

Revetments: A coastal defence of armoured slopes designed to absorb wave energy and made of timber or concrete.

Ria: A drowned river valley forming a coastal inlet.

Rip-rap (rock armouring): Materials used to protect the coastline, such as large boulders or concrete blocks.

Salt marsh: A coastal ecosystem found in the intertidal zone and associated with deposition landforms such as spits.

Sediment cell: A section of coast in which material moves between sediment sources (supply) and sinks (losses).

Shore: Technically the land between the low water mark and the point where storm waves can reach – the area where the land reaches the sea.

Shoreline Management Plan (SMP): A document which sets out a strategy for coastal defence for a specified length of coast, the required UK government planning for all coastal regions.

Soft engineering: The use of ecological practices to reduce erosion and stabilise shorelines and river edges, while enhancing local habitats.

Solution (corrosion): Erosion by the dissolving of soluble minerals in rocks.

Spit: A narrow coastal land formation attached to the coast at one end. They often stretch across estuaries.

Stacks and **Stumps:** Isolated masses of rock near coastal cliffs and usually the remnant of a former arch. Stumps are worn stacks that may be covered at high tide.

Sub-aerial processes: Weathering and erosion processes caused by the atmosphere.

Submergence: A process by which a new coast is formed as relative sea level rises (actual sea rise or falling land).

Sustainability: The degree to which the use of a resource or resources impacts on its long-term use or availability.

Swash: The run of water onto a shore after a wave breaks.

Swash-aligned coast: A stretch of coast where waves normally break directly onto the shore.

Tombolo: A bar composed of sand or shingle that attaches an island to the shore.

Tide: The regular rise and fall of sea level resulting from the gravitational influence of the Moon and Sun.

Wave: The transfer of energy by moving water in the ocean generated by winds.

Wave-cut notch: An indentation cut by wave action into the base of the coastal shore or cliff.

Wave-cut platform (bench): A gently sloping erosional surface extending seaward from the base of coastal cliffs.

Wave length: The distance between the same part of two waves, for example, crest to crest.

Wave period: The time taken for a wave to pass.

Wave steepness: The height of a wave in relation to its length.

Option D: Climate Change – Past and Present

Ablation: The melting of ice from a glacier or ice sheet.

Adaptation: Adjusting natural or human systems in response to climate change, to moderate harm or exploit opportunities.

Afforestation: The planting of trees on land that is not currently forested.

Anthropocene Epoch: Suggested name for the recent geological period dominated by human activity.

Astronomic forcing: Climate change due to natural variation in the position of the Sun in relation to the Earth.

Calving: The process of icebergs forming by breaking away from the edge of ice sheets or glaciers.

Cenozoic Era: The present geology era which started around 66 million years ago.

Climate: The normal or average annual weather conditions for any given location.

Dendrochronology: The use of tree-rings data in dating wooden material and associated deposits.

Devensian/Midlandian: British/ Irish names for the last ice age period.

Drumlin: An oval-shaped hill formed by the streamlined movement of glacial ice sheets across glacial till.

Drumlin field or **swarm:** The collective terms used to describe an area dominated by drumlin scenery.

El Niño: A periodic climate pattern of unusual warming of surface waters in the equatorial Pacific Ocean.

Englacial: The sediment load collected and transported in the ice of a glacier or ice sheet.

Enhanced greenhouse effect: An increase in the natural

retention of atmospheric heat due to air pollution.

Era and epoch: Geology time intervals, these are: eon (the longest), through era and period to epoch.

Erratics: A piece of rock carried by glacial ice and deposited in or on a different type of local rock.

Esker: A sinuous ridge of sand and gravel sediment deposited by englacial or supraglacial streams.

Eustatic change (eustasy): The worldwide change in sea levels.

Feedback: (see also Interdependence) Negative feedback is when a system works to reduce the impact of an initial change, while positive feedback is when a system works to increase or build on the initial change.

Fluvioglacial: Processes, sediment and landforms associated with meltwater from glaciers.

Glacial till (boulder clay): Unsorted material carried and deposited by ice.

Glaciation: Covered by a glacier or ice sheet.

Glacier: A large mass of moving ice.

Greenhouse Gas (GHG): An atmospheric gas that retains longwave energy from the Earth's surface.

Heinrich event: A sudden shift in climate due to a massive release of ice into the north Atlantic.

Holocene Epoch: The current geological period that started with the end of the last glacial period 10,000 years ago.

Hummocky moraine: An undulating landscape where glacial ground moraine has been deposited.

Hydroelectric Power (HEP): Electric power generated by falling water.

Ice cores: Samples of ice drilled from glaciers or ice sheets that provide data on past climates and atmospheres.

Ice sheet/ice cap): A mass of glacier ice covering a large area, today found only in Antarctica and Greenland.

Interdependence: The concept that places are mutually linked to each other through complex physical and social links. It suggests that any change in one part of a system inevitably has consequences, positive or negative, for other parts of that system.

Interglacial: A warmer period between two cold glacial periods, for example, the current Holocene.

Interstadial: A short less cold period during a single glacial episode.

IPCC (Intergovernmental Panel on Climate Change): A body set up by the United Nations to provide an objective and scientific view of climate change and its political and economic impacts.

Isostatic change: A local or regional change in the relationship of land and sea levels. For example, the gradual rise of land following an Ice Age as the burden of ice is lifted from the land surface.

Isotopes: Variants of chemical elements, some of which change at a known rate.

Kame: An irregular mound or hill associated with sediment filled hollows of a retreating glacier.

Kettle hole: A sediment and water-filled fluvioglacial hollow left by retreating ice after isolated ice blocks melt.

Kyoto Protocol: From 1992 the legal commitment by most UN nations to reduce emissions of greenhouse gas.

Lacustrine: Sediments deposited in a lake bed environment.

La Niña: The opposite of El Niño. An abnormally large body of cold water forms in the central Pacific Ocean, causing cool sea surface temperatures.

Last Glacial Maximum (LGM): The period of greatest ice sheet extent in the last glacial period around 22,000 years ago.

Last Glacial Termination (LGT): The final ice advance before deglaciation, associated in Ireland with the Killard Point Stadial around 13,000 years ago.

Lidar (Light detection and ranging): a surveying system that uses laser light to record land surface and in 3D.

Lodgement: Glacial sediment spread by ice onto the basal rock surface beneath a glacier.

Loess: A fine grained, wind-blown deposit of glacial material found on the outer edge of outwash plains.

Milankovitch cycles: Cyclical variation in the Earth's position in relation to the Sun (eccentricity, axial tilt and precession of its orbit) that change the level of insolation reaching the Earth.

Moraine: Any unconsolidated sediment deposited by glacial processes.

Ocean-floor deposits: Sediments that can be examined and the results used to recreate past climatic and environmental conditions.

Outwash plain (sandur): A low-lying area formed of sediments deposited by meltwater outwash in front of a glacier.

Paleoclimatology: the scientific study of past climate changes on Earth.

Plate tectonics: A theory that suggests that the Earth's crust is composed of irregularly shaped sections or plates, some of which carry continents, while others form the ocean floor. These plates are moved slowly by convection currents in the asthenosphere.

Pleistocene: The 'Ice Age' Epoch from 2.6 million years ago to the start of the Holocene 11,700 years ago.

Pollen analysis: The study of plant pollen from lake bed or peat deposits that allow the recreation of past climatic conditions.

Push moraine: Small end moraines created by a short period of ice re-advance at the front of lowland ice sheets.

Radio-carbon dating: A method for finding the age of an organic object using radioactive isotopes of carbon.

Recessional moraine: A ridge of material deposited at the front of an ice sheet during a pause in its retreat.

Rogen (ribbed) moraine: Ridges of glacial till formed under a flowing ice sheet that run transverse to the direction of its flow.

Sandur: (see Outwash plain)

Solar forcing: The impact of variation in the level of solar insolation on climate change.

Stadial: A short, less than 1000 year, colder period during a single glacial episode.

Stratigraphy: The study of rock layers and the position and order of geological strata.

Subglacial: The environment beneath a glacier or ice sheet.

Supraglacial: The environment on the surface of a glacier or ice sheet.

Sustainability: The degree to which the use of a resource or resources impacts on its long-term use or availability.

Terminal (end) moraine: A ridge of material deposited at the front edge of an ice sheet at its maximum advance.

Tertiary Period: A name used for the geological period between 65 and 2.6 mya.

Tipping point: When gradual change becomes significant enough to cause a larger, more important change.

Unit A2 2: Processes and Issues in Human Geography

Option A: Cultural Geography

Cultural landscape: A landscape whose properties reflect the combined influence of nature and humankind.

Cultural nationalism: The shared culture of a nation based on matters such as history, tradition and language.

Culture: The beliefs, arts, achievements and social practices of a set of people.

Cyberbullying: Harassment or bullying over social media using computers, phones or other digital devices.

Cybercrime: Criminal offences using modern telecommunications networks.

Cyberspace: The virtual environment over which computer communications take place.

Digital divide: Inequalities between groups or regions regarding access to information and communications technology.

Discrimination: The unfair and unequal treatment of a particular group of people because of their ethnicity.

Forced migration: Coerced movement of a person or group away from the area in which they resided.

Ghetto: Part of a city in which members of minority groups are forced to live. Used initially for Jewish quarters of medieval European cities, now used more loosely.

Globalisation: A process which has seen the international spread of shared ideas, culture and goods across the globe.

Hybridity: A biological term referring to a mixture, now used widely in the social sciences for the mixing of peoples and cultures.

Internet: The electronic communications network.

Malware: Malicious computer software or programmes.

Nationalism: Social and political beliefs that further the identity and interests of a particular nation.

Race: A classification of people regarded as distinct because of their physical traits such as colour of skin, visible facial features or hair type.

Racism: Prejudice against a person or group because of their race.

Ransomware: Malicious software that demands the victim pay a ransom to regain control of their computer and/or data.

Religion: A cultural system of beliefs, related behaviours and practices.

Social class: The grouping of people into a position in a social hierarchy.

Social exclusion: The relegation of a person or group from the normal entitlements of society.

Social inequality: The result of the unequal distribution of resources and opportunities within a society.

Option B: Planning for Sustainable Settlements

Anthropocene: Proposed geological epoch reflecting recent human impact on the Earth's geology and ecosystems.

Apartheid: A system of racial segregation and discrimination imposed on South Africa from 1948–1991.

Biodiversity: The variety of plant and animal life present in any given area.

BRICS: Acronym for a collection of five emerging economies: **B**razil, **R**ussia, **I**ndia, **C**hina, **S**outh Africa.

Communal area: An area of a settlement belonging or relating to the community as a whole rather than individuals or households.

Congestion charge: A daily tax liable on vehicles entering a designated area of a city.

Counterurbanisation: The movement of people from urban areas to live in rural areas.

Cycle of poverty: Poverty passed down from one generation to the next.

Eco town: A settlement (usually planned and officially designated) where conscious efforts are made to maximise sustainability.

Greenbelt: A planning and land use policy that protects rural areas around urban settlements from development.

Greenfield site: Rural areas that have not been encroached upon by urban development

Pedestrianisation: A planning policy that reserves the use of (usually city centre) streets for pedestrians rather than vehicles.

Renewable energy: Energy from sources that are naturally replenished.

Residential concentration: People living in clusters usually for economic, social or safety reasons.

Rural-urban fringe: The outskirts of a city; the space between the city and the true rural area.

Suburbanisation: Population shift from the central urban areas to the edge of the city.

Sustainable development: The meeting of development objectives without damaging the long-term stability of natural ecosystems.

Option C: Ethnic Diversity

Annexation: Taking political control of a neighbouring country.

Asylum seekers: People who have come to a new country without the required legal documentation to gain entry. They ask permission to remain on the basis that they will face torture or death if they return home.

Autonomy: A region given some degree of political control while still remaining an integral part of the ruling country.

Civil disobedience: The active refusal to obey certain laws or commands of a government. It is a non-violent protest where the protesting group withdraws its participation in the working of the country.

Civil war: A situation where there are clearly identified armed forces within the country actively engaged in conflict with each other.

Colonisation: The setting-up of settlements in a new area, usually associated with the creation of empires.

Cultural conflicts: Conflict caused by fundamental differences in cultural expression, such as the conflict between Islamic fundamentalism and western culture.

Ethnic group: A group of people with a long, shared history and a distinct culture including some of the following characteristics: a common geographic origin or descent, a common language/literature, a common religion and being a minority within a larger community.

Discrimination: The unfair treatment of a particular group of people because of their ethnicity.

Ethnicity: The outward manifestation of belonging to an ethnic group.

Ethnic cleansing: The whole-scale violent removal of an ethnic group from an area.

Historical animosities: Distrust or hatred between ethnic groups deriving from past injustices.

Human rights abuses: The UN defines human rights as the "basic rights and freedoms to which all humans are entitled." Human rights abuses are when any of these rights or freedoms is denied. (In ethnic conflict situations this often affects one ethnic group.)

International intervention and peace processes: The involvement of outside countries or organisations such as the UN, and the formulation of a plan for a non-violent resolution to conflict.

Multiculturalism: A political ideology/policy aimed at recognising, celebrating and maintaining the different cultural identities within society.

Nationality: The feeling of belonging to a particular country or nation, such as being Greek or Italian.

Perceived ethnic and social identity: A subjective and complex process influencing the definition of ethnicity. It is affected by place of residence, age, gender, residential concentration and role in society.

Race: A classification of people regarded as distinct because of their physical traits such as colour of skin, visible facial features or hair type.

Racism: Prejudice against a person or group because of their race.

Refugees: A group of people unable to live safely in their home country for a number of reasons including ethnic conflict. A distinction is made between **Refugees,** who cross an international boundary and **Internally displaced people**, who flee to safety within their home country.

Residential concentration: People living in clusters (with people of similar ethnicity when applied to ethnic diversity) usually for economic, social or safety reasons.

Role: Refers to a person's occupation or position in society. (This has been shown to be a significant element in perceived ethnic identity.)

Sectarianism: Prejudice against a person or group because of their religion.

Segregation: The physical separation of groups of people (ethnic groups when applied to ethnic diversity).

Territorial disputes: Conflict between two or more groups (ethnic groups when applied to ethnic diversity) over control of territory and its people.

Terrorism: Armed conflict by an illegal guerrilla organisation which operates within the community. Terrorism operates in pursuit of an ideological goal, such as a Tamil homeland for the Tamil Tigers in Sri Lanka.

Territorial division: The division or partition of a former country into two or more separate political entities, such as the division of Ireland into Northern Ireland and the Republic of Ireland.

Option D: Tourism

Butler Model: Devised to examine the evolution of a tourist resort over time, there are six stages in this model: exploration, involvement, development, consolidation, stagnation and decline/ rejuvenation.

Carrying capacity: The maximum number of tourists that can be comfortably supported in a resort. If at this maximum, an increase in tourist numbers would adversely affect the tourist potential of the area.

Displacement of local communities: A negative social impact of ecotourism where local people are forced off their land to make way for ecotourism developments.

Disposable income: Income remaining after taxation and national insurance contributions have been deducted from a worker's wages.

Ecotourism: Environmentally friendly or green tourism.

Ecotourism regulation: Attempts to standardise the practice of ecotourism to promote positive outcomes and minimise potential negative outcomes.

Global Ecotourism Conference 2007 (GEC07): A conference held in Oslo 2007, to review the progress made in ecotourism regulation 5 years after the Quebec Declaration. Further recommendation and strategies were proposed to enhance the sustainability of ecotourism.

Green Globe Scheme: Developed in Los Angeles between 1992 and 1994, is a global sustainable tourism certification scheme. It is a structured assessment of the sustainability of all aspects of a tourism product and industry.

Greenwashing: International tour operators placing luxurious hotels in tropical areas, paying token attention to the ideals of ecotourism and claiming these resorts as eco-friendly.

Honeypot sites: Areas that attract large numbers of tourists, often leading to overcrowding.

Indigenous cultures: The local culture in an area such as the Maasai nomads in Kenya.

International tourist arrivals, incoming tourists or inbound tourists: International tourists in their destination country.

Leakage: This usually occurs in LEDCs, where foreign, usually MEDC companies, develop tourism and claim the profits. The profits are therefore of no benefit to the local community.

Limits of Acceptable Change (LAC): A method of assessing the effects of increased tourist numbers on the quality of visitor experience in a resort or tourist region.

Mass tourism: Where a large number of tourists are concentrated in a few well developed holiday resorts, usually confined to a short peak season.

Niche tourism: Visiting areas for a specific interest, such as observing wildlife in their natural surroundings.

Outbound tourists: Tourists leaving their home country to go abroad on holiday.

Package holiday: An 'all in' deal for tourists whereby a travel company arranges all aspects of the holiday from flights, accommodation, transport to and from the holiday airport, and offers tours and activities to the tourist.

Pleasure Periphery: A tourism model that focuses on the behavioural demands of the tourist over time. Tourism is envisaged as a 'fashion industry' where tourists want to spend their holidays in the new and more fashionable resorts. The boundaries of

tourism are seen as a tidal wave spreading outwards from the tourists' home area.

Pollution: The introduction of harmful substances into an environment. In the case of tourism this includes increased litter, waste and noise, disposal issues and damaged landscapes, all resulting from tourist developments. Pollution is one of the main negative impacts of tourism.

Québec Declaration: In May 2002, delegates attending the World Ecotourism Summit in Québec discussed means of ecotourism regulation. Their findings and recommendations were published in the Québec Declaration. It focused on sustainable ecotourism and encouraged self regulation by all ecotourism providers.

Social sustainability: The ability of a community to function and adapt to changing situations without having their attitudes and ways of life altered in an adverse manner.

Theme park: An amusement park or resort developed around a theme, with the buildings

and rides reflecting this. Examples include Euro Disney (Paris, France), Alton Towers (Staffordshire, England) and Six Flags (New Jersey, USA).

UNESCO World Heritage Sites: The UN Education Scientific and Cultural Organisation (UNESCO) World Heritage Sites is a global strategy employed to protect sites that display some cultural, scientific or historical importance. Cultural and historical sites have been selected because they exhibit unique and remarkable human endeavour. Examples of UNESCO sites include The Giant's Causeway (a unique volcanic landscape in Northern Ireland), the city of Florence (renaissance art and architecture in Italy) and the Great Barrier Reef (a coral reef off the Queensland coast, Australia).

Visiting Friends and Relatives (VFR): An important reason for tourism growth is individuals wishing to spend time with friends and family.

Copyright

Acknowledgements

Questions from CCEA Geography Past Papers, 2008–2016 and Specimen Assessment Materials are included with the permission of the Northern Ireland Council for the Curriculum, Examinations and Assessment, © CCEA 2017.

For the avoidance of doubt, the following permissions only apply to the figures stated. The rest of the book is ©Colourpoint Creative Ltd and is not released under the following licenses. The numbers denote page numbers.

The following images are licensed under the Creative Commons Attribution 2.0 Generic license. Permission is granted to share and adapt this work for any purpose, even commercially, provided you follow the conditions of this license, which can be viewed at https://creativecommons.org/licenses/by/2.0/

74 (top), 75 (bottom), 135, 221 (middle), 341 (left), 376 (top), 395

The following images are licensed under the Creative Commons Attribution-ShareAlike 2.0 Generic license. Permission is granted to share and adapt this work for any purpose, even commercially, provided you follow the conditions of this license, which can be viewed at https://creativecommons.org/licenses/by-sa/2.0/deed.en

75 (bottom)

The following images are licensed under the Creative Commons Attribution 3.0 Unported license. Permission is granted to share and adapt this work for any purpose, even commercially, provided you follow the conditions of this license, which can be viewed at https://creativecommons.org/licenses/by/3.0/

41 (right), 76 (bottom)

The following images are licensed under the Attribution-ShareAlike 3.0 Unported license. Permission is granted to share and adapt this work for any purpose, even commercially, provided you follow the conditions of this license, which can be viewed at https://creativecommons.org/licenses/by-sa/3.0/deed.en

59 (top), 74 (bottom), 341 (right), 389

The following image is licensed under the Creative Commons Attribution 3.0 IGO license. Permission is granted to share and adapt this work for any purpose, even commercially, provided you follow the conditions of this license, which can be viewed at https://creativecommons.org/licenses/by/3.0/igo/legalcode

274 (top)

Credits

Where information or data has been used, sources are cited next to the figures within the body of the book.

The following photographs, diagrams, maps, graphs and tables are all included with the kind permission of the copyright holders. The numbers denote page numbers.

663highland: 59 (top)

Alexandre Breveglieri: 376 (bottom left)

Amal: 341 (right)

Amic Hoteles Hotel Horizonte: 395

Anna Anichkova: 389

Archivo Museo Salesiano: 200 (top)

Author, Eileen Armstrong: 327 (bottom two), 331 (all), 376 (middle left), 413 (bottom)

Author, Martin Thom: 10 (bottom), 18 (top), 26 (all), 33 (bottom), 35 (all), 43, 72 (all), 73 (all), 76 (top three), 91, 96, 97 (left & bottom), 99 (top), 101 (top), 104 (top two), 110 (bottom three), 113 (all), 115 (all), 123 (bottom), 124 (bottom three), 125 (bottom three), 126 (all), 127 (all), 128 (top two), 129 (all), 132 (bottom two), 133 (middle four), 134 (top two), 137 (all), 140 (top), 144 (top), 147, 152, 153 (bottom two), 157, 158 (all), 159 (all), 160 (middle two), 161 (all), 162 (all), 163 (top two), 164, 176 (top), 179, 181 (both), 182 (all), 184 (top), 185 (top two), 189 (all), 190 (top), 191 (all), 193 (bottom two), 194, 196 (bottom), 201 (top), 208 (top two)

Author, Stephen Royle: 49 (top), 219 (all), 221 (top & bottom), 222 (all), 223 (bottom), 224, 225 (all), 227 (all), 230 (all), 231 (all),236 (all), 239 (top), 259 (top), 261 (all), 265, 275 (bottom), 276, 277, 278 (all), 291 (all), 293, 294, 298 (all), 299, 300 (all), 302, 303, 304, 305, 306 (all), 307, 310 (bottom two), 311 (top three), 312 (right & bottom), 313 (top), 314 (bottom), 351 (bottom), 381, 392 (all), 394 (all)

Baros: 145 (both)

Boaworm: 41 (right)

CAMTA: 108 (top two)

CCEA: 25, 240, 259 (bottom), 281, 333 (top), 351 (top), 352, 353, 354

David Rydevik: 52

Doc Searls: 221 (middle)

Dr L Proudfoot: 157 (top)

Ed Webster: 376 (top)

Ferdinand Reus: 75 (bottom)

GNS Science, New Zealand: 38

Greenpeace/Daniel Beltra: 200 (bottom)

H Adams and M Stanley: 100 (bottom)

iStockPhoto: 34 (top), 201 (bottom), 228 (bottom), 263 (right), 376 (right two), 379, 383 (all), 401, 402, 404 (top), 405, 407 (bottom), 414

Jim Linwood: 135

Justin McIntosh: 341 (left)

Kkonstan: 76 (bottom)

Lovelylight / Alamy Stock Photo: 247

Michael Taylor: 75 (top two)

Nevit Dilmen: 74 (bottom)

Nick Perrone: 223 (top)

NISRA, licensed under the Open Government Licence v.3.0: 323

Owen Glenn: 112 (all)

Raul Achahuanco / Explorer's Inn: 97 (right)

REUTERS / Alamy Stock Photo: 57

Rod Waddington: 74 (top)

Sarah MacKinnon: 242 (all), 243

United Nations:

Development Programme: 274 (top)

Human Rights Council: 363, 364

World Tourism Organization: 372 (top)

U.S. Department of Agriculture / NRCS Agricultural Water Enhancement Program (AWEP): 84 (left)

U.S. Department of Housing and Urban Development: 287 (top)

U.S. Geological Survey: 27 (right), 28 (top two), 41 (left), 48 (top two), 49 (bottom), 51 (bottom two), 55, 84 (right), 167

U.S. Navy: 62

Wesley Johnston: 34 (bottom)

Wonseob Song: 220